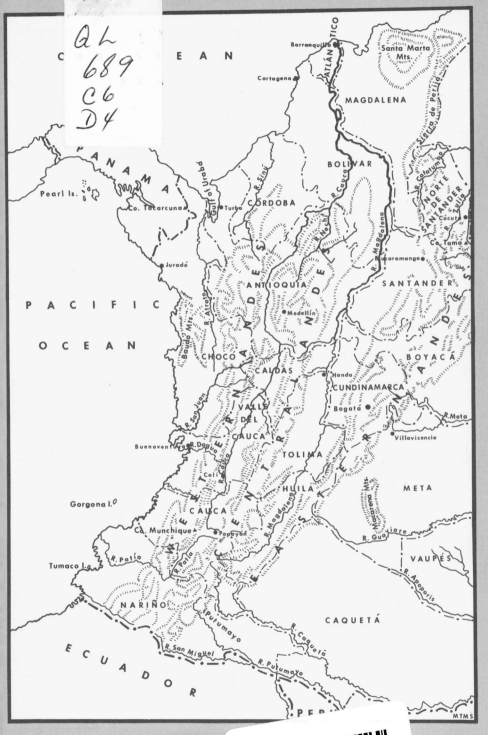

THE BIRDS OF
COLOMBIA

E. L. Poole

PLATE I

(All birds shown are males)

PARADISE TANAGER
(T. c. chilensis)
Page 358

**GLISTENING-GREEN
TANAGER**
(C. phoenicotis)
Page 357

**ORANGE-EARED
TANAGER**
(C. c. bourcieri)
Page 357

**YELLOW-BELLIED
TANAGER**
(T. x. xanthogastra)
Page 359

SPECKLED TANAGER
(T. c. bogotensis)
Page 358

**OPAL-RUMPED
TANAGER**
(T. v. iridina)
Page 356

**OPAL-BROWED
TANAGER**
(T. callophrys)
Page 357

**MULTICOLORED
TANAGER**
(C. nitidissima)
Page 357

THE BIRDS OF
COLOMBIA

*and adjacent areas of South
and Central America*

BY

R. MEYER DE SCHAUENSEE

Illustrated by
Earl L. Poole and
George Miksch Sutton

LIVINGSTON PUBLISHING COMPANY
Narberth, Pennsylvania

Published for
the Academy of Natural Sciences of Philadelphia

PRINTED IN THE UNITED STATES OF AMERICA

TO WILLIE

FOREWORD

The increasing interest in neotropical birds has emphasized the need for modern reference books in the English language. "The Birds of Colombia" is published to fill one of the larger gaps.

The convenience of jet travel and the spread of good hotels have opened wide new areas to the amateur birdwatcher and professional ornithologist alike. Field guides are now available for the West Indies, Mexico, Trinidad and Tobago; the present work is intended to assist the traveller in Central America and northern South America.

The author, R. Meyer de Schauensee often recalls his early interest in and fascination with birds, first as a boy in Switzerland, then after coming to Philadelphia with his family prior to World War I. He tells of his thrill at starting out at dawn to see and hear the seemingly endless variety of bird life. Continuing his interest he became associated with the Academy of Natural Sciences of Philadelphia. His first two ventures afield were expeditions to the Amazon and rio Negro, Brazil, where he obtained important collections for the museum and gained a firsthand knowledge of tropical bird life. He soon expanded his horizon of interest to many exotic parts of the world. He undertook major expeditions to the southern Shan States of Burma, northern Siam, Indonesia, and to the Kalahari Desert in South Africa where he obtained important collections of birds as well as fish, insects and small mammals. In 1935 he collected birds in the highlands and lowlands of Guatemala. For a number of years he directed and sponsored the bird collecting of K. Von Sneidern in Colombia; the results of Von Sneidern's field work and collections add considerably to our knowledge of the geographical distribution of Colombia birds and enabled the author to compile a checklist of the birds of Colombia which includes keys for identification, and distributional records. It was published by the University of Bogotá in 1948-1952. The present work is the culmination of his long interest in Colombian birds.

Mr. de Schauensee has published some hundred scientific papers on birds from various parts of the world, including China, Tibet, the Philippines, Indonesia, Oceania and the countries already mentioned. He is a

vii

Fellow of the American Ornithologists' Union, curator and chairman of the Department of Ornithology of the Academy of Natural Sciences, a member and Vice-President of its Board of Trustees.

H. Radclyffe Roberts
Director, Academy of Natural Sciences of Philadelphia

PREFACE

Probably no single country in the world is inhabited by so many different kinds of birds as is Colombia. Within its boundaries live 1567 different species which divide themselves into 2654 subspecies. These represent 56% of all the species of birds found in South America, and 80% of the species of birds found in Central America from Nicaragua southward.

Colombia's extraordinary ornithological richness is due to the fact that it enjoys certain geographical and topographical features not shared by any other South American republic. It is the only country in South America which has an Atlantic and Pacific coast line. It is the only country which from north to south stretches from Central America to the Amazon River. In the west the surface of the land is broken up by lofty mountain ranges whose feet are clothed with steaming, tropical jungle and whose summits are crowned with glistening, perpetual snow. East of the mountains stretches a vast, flat country of llanos in the north, and dense primeval forest in the south. Along the eastern Caribbean coast the country is dry, gradually turning into sandy desert sparsely covered with xerophytic vegetation and brush on the Guajira Peninsula.

It is due to the wide diversity of physical features that so many different kinds of birds inhabit Colombia, for there they are able to find almost any environment suitable to their needs.

An effective demonstration of the unbelievable richness of the Colombian avifauna is to compare it with that of all of North America north of Mexico: In the 439,000 square miles of Colombian territory there live 1556 species of birds as against the 691 species in the 7,200,000 square miles of the North American continent from the Rio Grande to the Arctic Circle.

No modern book exists in English on tropical birds of continental South America, therefore it is hoped that this book, describing as it does so many species, will help to fill an obvious need.

I am sure that the twenty splendid plates from the paintings of Dr. Earl L. Poole and the fine drawings by Dr. George Miksch Sutton will be found to add immeasurably to the value of "The Birds of Colombia", for no matter how carefully or minutely a bird is described, a drawing or painting conveys far more. Poole's paintings and Sutton's drawings not only accurately depict the birds, but they do so in a pleasing and lifelike manner. Most unfortunately Dr. Sutton sustained an injury to his hand which prevented him from doing the final two drawings (those heading the families Albatrosses and Shrike-Vireos) and they have been done by Dr. Poole.

This is a fitting place for me to acknowledge the deep dept of gratitude which I owe to Eugene M. Eisenmann of the American Museum of Natural History, New York. Because of his splendid work in furthering the standardization of English names for Neotropical birds I asked his advice on common names for Colombian birds. Not only did he give me his advice on that subject, but he carefully read the proofs as well and made very many valuable suggestions which have added greatly to the value of this book.

Most generous have been Dr. H. R. Roberts and James Bond of the Academy of Natural Sciences of Philadelphia in giving their advice on numerous questions concerning the preparation of this book. Dr. Ernst Mayr of Harvard University read the chapter on swallows and offered some valuable suggestions. Edwin O. Willis of Berkeley, California, who has done ornithological field research in Colombia, read part of the proofs and suggested a number of changes. Miss Maude Meyer de Schauensee prepared the carefully drawn maps and the diagram of a bird which contribute greatly to the usefulness of this work.

Acknowledgment is also made of the permission granted by Dr. Sutton and his publisher, John Wiley and Sons, Inc., for permission to reproduce a number of drawings from "Fundamentals of Ornithology."

Philadelphia
December 6, 1963   Rodolphe Meyer de Schauensee

TABLE OF CONTENTS

LIST OF PLATES

xiii

tailed Star-Frontlet *(Coeligena phalerata)*. Tawny-bellied Hermit *(Phaethornis syrmatophorus)*. Bearded Helmet-Crest *(Oxypogon guerinii)*. Empress Brilliant *(Heliodoxa imperatrix)*. Fork-tailed Woodnymph *(Thalurania furcata)*. Red-billed Emerald *(Chlorostilbon gibsoni)*. Sparkling Violet-Ear *(Colibri coruscans)*.

creeper *(Dendrocolaptes certhia)*. Gray-throated Leafscraper *(Sclerurus albigularis)*. Slaty Spinetail *(Synallaxis brachyura)*. Andean Cinclodes *(Cinclodes fuscus)*.

INTRODUCTION

ORNITHOLOGICAL HISTORY

The first collections from Colombia were made by native plume hunters who secured birds for the millinery trade. These collections began to arrive in Europe early in the last century. The skins were made up in a certain manner and can be recognized even today as "Bogotá trade skins." The hunters ranged widely in search of specimens but no indication was ever given as to where they got them. It is only comparatively recently that the ranges of many Colombian birds have become known—indeed, a few are still known only from "Bogotá."

The first birds to be recorded from definite localities in Colombia were a few specimens secured by the Frenchman Delattre in 1846 on a voyage from Buenaventura on the Pacific coast to Pasto in Nariño. An expedition headed by Lieut. Michler, U. S. A., collected specimens on the lower Atrato in 1860 while surveying a canal route from the Caribbean to the Pacific via the Atrato lowlands. In 1870 Claude Wyatt collected in Santander and secured a few interesting birds. The first really large collection was that made by T. K. Salmon, an Englishman employed by the Colombian government, who resided at Medellín. He collected in Antioquia and sent 3,500 specimens belonging to 468 species to the British Museum and a report on them was published in 1879.

In the same year Eugène Simon, the hummingbird specialist, made the first collections in the Sierra Nevada de Santa Marta and ascended the mountains to snow line. Later on, in 1897-98, W. W. Brown made large collections in the same region for the Museum of Comparative Zoology at Harvard and in 1899 Herbert Smith secured 3,000 Santa Marta specimens for the American Museum of Natural History. M. A. Carriker, Jr. also secured large collections from there, most of which went to the Carnegie Museum and which formed the basis for the important work by W. E. Clyde Todd and M. A. Carriker, Jr. "The Birds of the Santa Marta Region" published in 1922. A good part of this collection was purchased by the Academy of Natural Sciences.

The first comprehensive collection from many regions of Colombia was made for the American Museum of Natural History. The work com-

1

menced in 1910 and culminated in F. M. Chapman's classic "The Distribution of Bird Life in Colombia," published in 1917. In this work 1285 species and subspecies were listed, and for the first time the range of many species became known.

In 1938 Mr. Kjell von Sneidern of Popayán began collecting Colombian birds for the Academy of Natural Sciences of Philadelphia. He continued this work until 1952, amassing large collections from many regions of Colombia. Additional specimens were secured in southeastern Colombia by the Mena brothers of Quito, Ecuador. These collections formed the basis for the author's "Birds of the Republic of Colombia" published in "Caldasia," the bulletin of the Universidad Nacional de Colombia at Bogotá, under the inestimably helpful editorship of Prof. Armando Dugand. In this work a total of about 2,400 species and subspecies were listed as occurring in the country. It appeared serially from 1948 to 1952.

Active students of ornithology at the present time in Colombia are Prof. Armando Dugand, Brother Nicéforo — María, Brother Antonio Olivares, Ignacio Borrero, F. C. Lehmann, K. von Sneidern and M. A. Carriker, Jr.

THE GEOGRAPHY OF COLOMBIA

THE MOUNTAINS

Colombia occupies the northwestern corner of South America. It is bounded on the north by the Caribbean Sea and Panama, on the west by the Pacific, on the east by Venezuela and Brazil and on the south by Ecuador, Peru and Brazil.

The western part of the country is broken up by massive mountain ranges, while the eastern part is flat, the northern half of it a land of llanos and patches of forest, the southern half clothed with a rolling, green sea of forest which stretches virtually unbroken to the Amazon.

In the northeast corner of Colombia, in the department of Magdalena, rises the isolated Sierra Nevada de Santa Marta. Their feet bathed in the warm waters of the Caribbean, the mountains leap upward to snow line, reaching their climax on the Pico Cristóbal Colón, 19,000 ft. (5,800 m.), the highest peak in Colombia.

The Sierra Nevada does not form part of the main Andean system, which is composed of three parallel chains, the Eastern, Central and Western Andes. The Eastern Andes rise at the base of the Guajira Peninsula, across the valley of the río Cesar from the Sierra Nevada where the range is called the Sierra de Perijá. The highest point of the Eastern Andes is reached in Boyacá where the Nevado de Ritacuva rises to 18,000 ft. (5,493 m.). The Central Andes running southward between the Magdalena and Cauca Rivers reach their highest point on the Nevado del Huila, 18,900 ft. (5,750 m.). The Western Andes separating the Cauca Valley from the Pacific watershed are lower, but still reach the respectable altitude of 13,800 ft. (4,200 m.) on the Cerro Tamaná. These three ranges join in a massive knot north of Pasto in northern Nariño and continue southward rising to an altitude of 15,600 ft. (4,764 m.) on the volcano of Cumbal near the boundary of Ecuador. Thence they continue southward uninterruptedly to the Straits of Magellan.

Snow line on these high peaks is found as low as 14,800 ft. (4,500 m.) in the rainy season but at the close of the dry season is about 1,000 ft. higher.

In addition to the main ranges there are three minor ones. The most interesting are the mountains along the Panamanian border. Although only reaching a height of about 6,000 ft., they are known to support an interesting montane fauna in Panama. The Colombian slope is as yet very little known.

The Baudó Mountains separating the Atrato Valley from the Pacific coast rises to about 5,500 ft., but so far nothing of particular interest has been recorded from their higher slopes.

Finally the Macarena Mountains, a range rising, isolated, just east of the Eastern Andes in southern Meta has been disappointing ornithologically, for nothing of particular interest has been discovered on them although they rise to a height of about 7,000 ft.

Eastern Colombia

East of the Eastern Andes flat grassy plains broken here and there by patches of woods and stands of palms extend north of the río Guaviare from the base of the mountains to the Orinoco River. South of the Guaviare, the flat country is broken here and there by low ridges and in contrast to the open plain north of the river, a vast green sea of primeval forest stretches unbroken to the río Negro and the Amazon. The average height above sea level of these eastern lowlands is about 800 ft., the highest ridges not rising above 2500 ft.

The Rivers

Many great rivers drain the country, some flowing into the Caribbean, others into the Pacific, but the largest form part of the Orinoco and Amazon systems.

West of the Andes the most important is the Magdalena which rises at the head of the valley between the Eastern and Central Andes and flows due north, emptying into the Caribbean at Barranquilla. Its great affluent, the río Cauca rises at the head of the valley between the Central and Western Andes and joins the Magdalena at 8°55′ N.

The largest river in western Colombia is the Atrato, which flows northward through Chocó into the Caribbean at the Gulf of Urabá.

No rivers of importance run into the Pacific. The two largest are the río San Juan flowing southward in southern Chocó and reaching the Pacific just north of Buenaventura and the río Patía rising in the Central

Andes south of Popayán, near the source of the Cauca but flowing in the opposite direction, southwestward through southern Cauca and northwestern Nariño to the Pacific.

East of the Andes the Meta, Vichada, and Guaviare rise at the base of the Eastern Andes and flow into the Orinoco. Forming part of the vast Amazonian drainage are the Guainía, actually the upper course of the río Negro, the Vaupés known in Brazil as the Uaupés, the Apaporis, the Caquetá known in Brazil as the Japurá and the Putumayo known in Brazil as the Içá. This last forms the boundary between Colombia and Peru for over 400 miles. At Leticia, in Amazonas, the Amazon itself forms Colombia's southernmost boundary.

A map of all of Colombia and another, more detailed map showing the part from the Eastern Andes westward to the Pacific Ocean, are printed on the inside covers of this book.

ZOOGEOGRAPHY OF COLOMBIA

Colombia faunistically is divided in two: the vast, almost uninhabited, flat lowlands east of the Andes occupying slightly less than one-third of the country, and the wildly mountainous area west of the Eastern Andes. These two main divisions split up into well-marked faunal areas.

THE AMAZONIAN REGION

South of the río Guaviare the vast forests support birds widespread through upper Amazonia, some ranging northward along the forested lower slopes of the Eastern Andes as far as Meta.

THE ORINOCO REGION

This land of llanos, palm groves and patches of woods lying north of the río Guaviare stretches eastward to the Orinoco and an avifauna typical of that of the open country encountered from the Guianas westward across Venezuela to the base of the East Colombian Andes is found there.

THE CATATUMBO REGION

This region of heavy forest at the eastern base of the Eastern Andes in Norte de Santander is drained by the río Catatumbo which flows eastward into Lake Maracaibo, Venezuela. It is inhabited by a number of birds found nowhere else in Colombia, among which are the Pygmy Swift and the Red Siskin.

THE SIERRA NEVADA DE SANTA MARTA

Springing from the warm Caribbean Sea, these isolated mountains rise rapidly to the frigid glaciers and snows which crown their summits. They do not form part of the Andean system and are indeed almost island-like: many birds are found upon their upper slopes which occur nowhere else. Among them are a parakeet, several hummingbirds, flycatchers and

4

many others. Unaccountably certain families commonly found in other parts of Colombia do not appear to exist in the Santa Marta region. They are the Sun-Grebe, Sun-Bittern, Barn Owl, potoos, barbets, gnateaters and pipits.

THE CARIBBEAN REGION

The Caribbean coast of Colombia from the río Sinú eastward across the swampy lower Magdalena Valley and eastward along the coast, except the northern foothills of the Santa Marta Mountains, to the Guajira Peninsula is for the most part a semi-arid region, becoming desert-like on the almost bare Guajira plains. The birds of this region are closely related to those of Venezuela. The Bare-eyed Pigeon, Scaled Dove, Troupial, Vermilion Cardinal and a few others are restricted in Colombia to the Guajira Peninsula.

THE CENTRAL COLOMBIAN MOUNTAIN REGION

Central Colombia from the west slope of the Eastern Andes to the west slope of the Western Andes is the heartland of the Colombian avifauna, for on the slopes of these three great chains of mountains live a large number of birds found nowhere else, such as the Tolima Dove, the Rufous-fronted Parakeet, the strange Recurve-billed Bushbird and many others.

THE COLOMBIA–PACIFIC REGION

Stretching from eastern Panama southward, west of the Western Andes to northwestern Ecuador, is a region of dense forest and torrential rainfall, the rain in some places reaching well over 400 inches a year. It may be subdivided into two sections: a northern area extending from the Panama border to the headwaters of the río Atrato, and a southern section extending from the headwaters of the río San Juan to the Ecuador border.

In this unhealthy region strong endemism exists and in it are found some of the most interesting Colombian birds. Among the most notable are the Tooth-billed Hummingbird, the Empress Brilliant, barbets, puff-birds, the White Cotinga, the Club-winged Manakin, the Finch-like Tanager and the Chestnut-mantled Oropendola. A few birds typical of the Pacific fauna have found their way from western Antioquia to the humid, heavily forested lower Cauca Valley and even to the lower Magdalena, and further collecting may disclose more. Most species are, however, confined to their inordinately wet Pacific habitat by the dry zone of Panama to the north, and the even drier, almost arid region to the south commencing at 1°30′ S. in western Ecuador. To the west the lofty Western Andes shuts them off from the rest of Colombia.

THE ALTITUDINAL ZONES

The faunal regions are not the only limiting factor in the distributional pattern of Colombia's birds. Just as important are the altitudinal zones in restricting ranges. Both temperature and vegetation change rad-

5

ically as one ascends the mountains. Between 2° and 6° north latitude the mean temperature at sea level is 82.4° Fahr., at 8,000 ft. it is 57.2°, and at 16,400 ft. it drops to 30.2°.

The various zones occur at the following altitudes:

Tropical Zone	sea level to 4500-5500 ft.
Subtropical Zone	4500-5500 to 7500-8500 ft.
Temperate Zone	7500-8500 to 9500-11,500 ft.
Páramo Zone	9500-11,500 ft. to snow line.

Glaciers and snow fields cover the higher peaks above 15,500 ft. (4,700 m.). During the rains the snow line may drop three or four hundred feet and during the dry season ascend to 15,800 ft. (4,800 m.).

Below the snows the inhospitable Páramo Zone, swept by icy winds, sleet and fog alternating with brilliant sunshine, is a land of open rolling plateaus and valleys. It is bleak and rocky at its upper limits, but covered with scrubby growth, composites, and coarse grasses at its lower limits. Here and there small ponds and sphagnum bogs are found in the depressions.

The Páramo Zone gradually merges, through a zone of mixed páramo vegetation and stunted, moss-covered trees, into the Temperate Zone, a variable region of semi-arid, bushy or sparsely wooded country; parts of it are humid and mist-covered, supporting forest composed of small trees overgrown with moss and epiphytes. Near the lower elevations of the Temperate Zone feathery tree ferns, and stately groves of towering Wax Palms in which Yellow-eared Parrots nest, are occasionally found, especially in the Central Andes. Tree line is found near the upper limits of this zone.

The Temperate Zone gradually gives way to the Subtropical Zone, a region of luxuriant rain forest, the trees covered with epiphytes and mosses, the branches often laced together with lianas. Where the rainfall is insufficient to support this type of vegetation the arid Temperate Zone reaches downward into it or the arid Tropical Zone invades it from beneath. Due to varying altitudes of the mountainous terrain of central Colombia and the wind currents modified by them, rainfall can vary widely within the space of a few miles or even from one valley to the next, where one can receive 100 inches of rain a year compared to 20 inches for its neighbor.

Below the lower limits of the Subtropical Zone lies the hot Tropical Zone which occupies three-fifths of the country. It is a region which presents many contrasts, from the dense rain forest of the Pacific coast, almost drowned by an incredibly heavy rainfall, to the bare desert plains of the Guajira Peninsula. Humid tropical forest is found in northern and northwestern Antioquia, the Caribbean coast west of the río Sinú, the upper Sinú Valley and the lower Cauca Valley south to about 7°N. eastward to the middle Magdalena Valley between 9° and 5°30′ N. From there forest continues eastward to Santander and the foothills of the Sierra de Perijá.

Somewhat isolated is the rather narrow strip of humid forest covering the northern slopes of the Santa Marta Mts. In central Colombia the extent of the forests is continuously being modified by lumbering and clearing operations. Of course, south of the río Guaviare a sea of forest extends to the Amazon.

Semi-arid conditions exist from the lower río Sinú eastward becoming progressively drier until desert conditions prevail on the Guajira Peninsula, this progression only interrupted by the forest on the north slope of the Santa Marta Mts. which extends to the shore of the Caribbean.

Semi-arid conditions also prevail elsewhere in Colombia; the upper Magdalena Valley, the Cúcuta lowlands, and the region about Ocaña all supporting only semi-arid and transitional vegetation. Farther westward the upper Cauca Valley is also a semi-arid region and small pockets even are found on the west slope of the Western Andes in the upper Dagua and upper Patía Valleys. Rather surprisingly the summits of a few isolated hills rising above the humid forest of the Amazonian region are covered with scrubby xerophytic vegetation.

These many environments support a birdlife which is adapted to particular conditions, and the mountains, vegetation and temperature form effective barriers separating one species from another. For example, a species living in the dry, hot, upper Magdalena Valley is cut off from the rest of Colombia by the humid forest to the north and south. Similarly, a species such as the Rufous-fronted Parakeet inhabiting the cold upper slopes of the Central Andes would not descend into the hot Cauca of Magdalena Valley to reach either of the other two ranges. Within a few miles of Bogotá three different subspecies of Crested Bobwhite exist, one in the Subtropical Zone of the western slope, another in the Subtropical Zone of the eastern slope, and a third on the Bogotá savanna in the Temperate Zone, the two Subtropical Zone forms effectively cut off from each other by the cold of the intervening Temperate Zone.

All species, however, do not invariably adhere to their particular life zones and sometimes are found below or above their usual limits. These movements are probably seasonal, but for the most part birds do not stray far from their preferred zonal habitat.

MIGRANTS

Considerable numbers of birds, particularly warblers, migrate from North America to Colombia in winter, many arriving there as early as August and a few remaining as late as May.

A few migrate to Colombia from the West Indies and more from southern South America are found there during the northern summer months, the austral winter. No bird breeding in Colombia is known to migrate, but local movements take place, either due to weather conditions or in search of ripening fruit.

7

Chart of a Bird

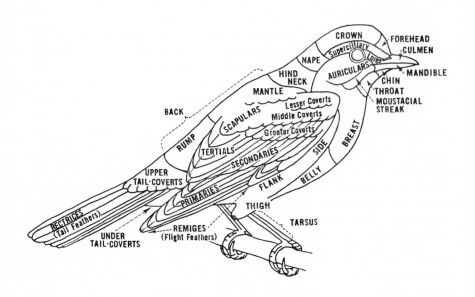

Terms used in this book to describe the plumage and external features of a bird are shown above. Although this drawing is of a thrush-like songbird, the terms used are applicable to all birds regardless of family.

8

HOW TO USE THIS BOOK

All the species which are found in Colombia, and many of the sub-species, are described. Included are those on Gorgona Island, but not those on the Caribbean islands of San Andrés and Providencia.

The arrangement is as follows:

First the name of the family is given, accompanied by a drawing of a typical member. Then a short account of the family is provided describing the habitat, habits, nesting or any other pertinent information.

This account is followed by a series of four numbers in parentheses. The first, followed by "Col." indicates the number of species found in Colombia; the second followed by "S.A.", the number of species found in continental South America; the third followed by "N. & S.A.", the number of species found in North, Central and South America, and the last followed by "wld.", the number of species found in the world. This allows a comparison of the Colombian avifauna with that of the rest of the world.

Next, an "Aid to Identification" is given. Although not a key leading to a specific bird, it is an elimination key leading to a group of birds which have certain characters in common such as "all black," "with red in plumage," "tail unusually long" permitting one to discard birds not having the character mentioned. These categories are followed by numbers which refer to those assigned to each species in the family. In some cases this number is followed by an E which denotes the fact that the species in question is found only east of the Eastern Andes and therefore need not be looked up if one is west of them.

Many Colombian bird families contain well over 50 species and five over 100, the flycatchers being the most numerous with 150. A key leading to individual species in families of this size would be too cumbersome and slow and it is felt the present type of key can be used to much better advantage. In cases where families contain five species or less no "aid" is given, nor are the species numbered. In the case of nighthawks and night-jars, although there are many more than five species, no aid is given and the species are not numbered, as the birds are nocturnal and a key would be of little use.

The English and scientific names of the species are given, then the

9

description preceded by the total length in inches. In the case of hummingbirds, of which there are 135 species of varied aspect, the bill length is given separately.

The English names used in this book are regarded as applicable to a species as a whole, not merely to the bird found in Colombia. Wherever possible, the name selected suggests something characteristic of the bird to which it is applied and which may help in distinguishing it from its relatives. Heretofore English names have been used in a haphazard manner, different authors using different names for the same bird. Through the pioneering efforts of Eugene M. Eisenmann in his attempts to standardize English names, uniformity is gradually being attained. The names herein used are for the most part the ones used by him in his "The Species of Middle American Birds," or suggested by him for recently or soon to be published books on Neotropical birds. Thus it is hoped, for example, that *Zonotrichia capensis,* will be known as the Rufous-collared Sparrow from Mexico to the Straits of Magellan, with obvious advantages to the bird student.

The range of the species outside of Colombia is given next, followed by the range in Colombia. A general idea of the habitat is provided, and in addition the altitudinal zone which the bird inhabits is indicated. In cases where a species breaks up into subspecies, the range of each is given; when two subspecies differ from each other in a more or less obvious way, their name will be preceded by a number which corresponds to the number in the description when a choice is given as "wing with wing bar (or without bar, 1) ." The main description always applies to the birds whose name is not preceded by a number.

As yet the complete distribution of many Colombian birds is not known and the range given will undoubtedly be amplified when the study of the avifauna is more complete. However, by using the range outside of Colombia, one can often infer what the complete distribution is. For example, if a species is known from eastern Panama and northwestern Ecuador, but in Colombia has been taken only in northern Chocó, the chances are that it occurs southward down the Pacific coast to Nariño.

The range given outside of Colombia permits the use of this book in both Central America and other parts of South America because all the countries in which the birds occur are listed.

All recorded species are based on specimens which have actually been collected. Note should be taken of the following three which have recently been seen in Caquetá: White-eyed Antwren *(Myrmotherula leucophthalma,* probably *spodionota),* Sclater's Fruiteater *(Pipreola,* probably *sclateri)* and the Spotted Tody-Tyrant *(Todirostrum maculatum,* probably *signatum).* None is unexpected as all are known from eastern Ecuador.

THE BIRDS OF
COLOMBIA

TINAMOUS (Tinamidae)

Fig. 1. White-throated Tinamou
(Tinamus guttatus) p. 14

Tinamous are found from southern Mexico to Argentina and Chile. Although somewhat resembling partridges in appearance, they are related to rheas and ostriches. In size they vary from that of a quail to a guinea-hen. Their legs are rather short, the wings rounded, and the tail usually hidden by the tail-coverts. Clothed in shades of brown, they live on the ground, feeding on fruits, seeds, and insects.

Most species inhabit the forest and brush of the tropical zone but a few live in grasslands and in the mountains as high as the temperate zone. Shy and secretive birds, their melodious whistling notes are more often heard than the birds are seen.

Tinamous nest on the ground, and their eggs are remarkable for their glossy, enamel-like surface and bright shades of reddish purple, blue, olive green, and other colors. (16 Col.; 39 S.A.; 40 N.&S.A.; 40 wld.)

AID TO IDENTIFICATION

Back uniform brown 8, 9, 10, 13, 14, 15, 16.
Back slaty or black 2, 7.
Back with broken bars 1, 3.
Back conspicuously banded 11E, 12E, 13, 14, 15.
Wings and upper parts spotted: 4E, 5, 6.

1. GRAY TINAMOU
(Tinamus tao)

Description. 16 - 18". Crown and neck black, the latter spotted white; throat white. Above grayish olive more or less speckled and barred blackish. Below light grayish, flanks barred; under tail-coverts cinnamon.

Range. Northern Venezuela and British Guiana, eastern and southern Brazil, eastern Bolivia, Peru and Ecuador.

Colombia. Forest. Upper tropical and subtropical zones. Northern part of the Sierra de Perijá *(septentrionalis)*; east of the Eastern Andes in Meta, possibly eastward to the Cauca Valley *(larensis)*.

13

2. BLACK TINAMOU
(Tinamus osgoodi)

Description. 16 - 17". Uniform slaty black, throat gray. Under tail-coverts cinnamon.

Range. The Urubamba Valley in central Peru.

Colombia. Forest. Upper tropical zone at the head of the Magdalena Valley *(hershkovitzi)*.

3. GREAT TINAMOU
(Tinamus major)

Description. 16 - 18". Crown rufous (or slaty, 1); neck rufous; throat white. Upper parts light (or dark, 1) olivaceous brown more or less barred with black. Lower parts grayish brown, freckled darker; under tail-coverts cinnamon.

Range. Southern Mexico, southward through Central America and the forested regions of tropical South America.

Colombia. Forest. Tropical zone. Northwest Colombia, south to the middle Atrato *(saturatus)*, thence southward through Nariño (1, *latifrons*.) The Santa Marta region and Santander *(zuliensis)*. Southeastern Colombia *(ruficeps)*.

4. WHITE-THROATED TINAMOU
(Tinamus guttatus) Fig. 1

Description. 12 - 13". Crown slaty; throat white. Back uniform chocolate brown, wings lighter with pale spots. Under surface dull pinkish brown.

Range. Southern Venezuela to northern Bolivia and eastward down to the Amazon Valley to Pará.

Colombia. Forest. Tropical zone. East of the Andes in Putumayo and Caquetá.

5. HIGHLAND TINAMOU
(Nothocercus bonapartei)

Description. 14-15". Crown blackish gray; throat pale rusty. Back dark brown freckled with black. Lower surface pale brown with wavy, thin black bars. Wings and abdomen pale spotted.

Range. Costa Rica southward to western Venezuela and eastern Ecuador.

Colombia. Forest. Subtropical zone of the Eastern and Central Andes and the Perijá Mts. *(bonapartei)*. The tropical zone at the base of the Eastern Andes in Meta and Tolima *(discrepans)*. Upper tropical and subtropical zones of the Western Andes *(intercedens)*.

6. TAWNY-BREASTED TINAMOU
(Nothocercus julius)

Description. 14 - 15". Forecrown rufous; throat white. Upper surface olivaceous brown crossed by obscure, narrow, wavy black lines; wings spotted with pale buff. Lower breast and abdomen bright cinnamon-rufous.

Range. Western Venezuela and Ecuador.

Colombia. Forest. Subtropical and temperate zones of the Eastern, Central, and Western Andes.

7. CINEREOUS TINAMOU
(Crypturellus cinereus)

Description. 10½ - 11½". Crown and hindneck dull reddish brown. Uniform ashy brown to slaty gray above. Uniform ashy gray below (or entirely brownish black, 1).

Range. Venezuela, the Guianas, and northeastern Brazil. Ecuador southward to Bolivia.

Colombia. Forest. Tropical zone. East of the Andes from Meta southward *(cinereus)*. Western Colombia from the Gulf of Urabá southward west of the Western Andes (1, *berlepschi*).

8. LITTLE TINAMOU
(Crypturellus soui)

Description. 8½ - 9". Above uniform rich brown, crown darker. Throat white, rest of under surface rich rufous (♂) or ochraceous (♀). The smallest tinamou found in Colombia.

Range. From central Mexico, southward through Central America to Venezuela, the Guianas, southern Brazil, and Bolivia. Trinidad and the Pearl Islands.

Colombia. Forest and scrub. Tropical and lower subtropical zones of the middle Magdalena, Sinú and Cauca Valleys up to about 6000 ft. *(caucae)*; western shore of the Gulf of Urabá southward down the Pacific coast *(harterti)*; northeastern Colombia southward to Boyacá *(mustelinus)*. East of the Eastern Andes, in Meta and Vaupés *(soui)*, in Caquetá and Putumayo *(caquetae)*.

9. BROWN TINAMOU
(Crypturellus obsoletus)

Description. 10½ - 11½". Top of head black, sides of head and throat gray. Upper parts bright chestnut (♂), tinged gray (♀); below rufous, lighter than back.

Range. Northern Venezuela, northern and southern Brazil, Paraguay, Bolivia, northeast Argentina, Peru, and Ecuador.

Colombia. Tropical and undoubtedly subtropical zone east of the Andes. At present known in Colombia only from "Bogotá" *(castaneus)*.

10. UNDULATED TINAMOU
(Crypturellus undulatus)

Description. 11 - 12". Crown blackish brown, throat white. Back dark brown vermiculated with black, wings paler. Breast pale gray, abdomen browner, flanks barred pale buff.

Range. Southern Venezuela, British Guiana south to Argentina, Paraguay, and Bolivia.

Colombia. Forest. Tropical zone east of the Andes from Meta southward *(yapura)*.

11. VARIEGATED TINAMOU
(Crypturellus variegatus)

Description. 11 - 12". Top and sides of head dark gray, throat white. Upper mantle bright rufous, back ochraceous broadly banded with black. Breast bright ferruginous; flanks barred olive brown and buff.

Range. British and French Guiana, Venezuela, eastern Ecuador southward to central and southeastern Brazil.

Colombia. Forest. Tropical zone east of the Eastern Andes *(variegatus)*.

12. BARRED TINAMOU
(Crypturellus casiquiare)

Description. 10 - 10½". Head and neck bright chestnut, throat white. Upper back brown, rest of back boldly banded black and ochraceous. Breast light gray, belly white; flanks barred with black.

Range. Extreme southwestern Venezuela.

Colombia. Forest. Extreme southeastern Colombia along the río Guainía and río Vaupés.

13. RED-FOOTED TINAMOU
(Crypturellus noctivagus)

Description. 11 - 12". ♂: Top of head rufous-brown, turning to rufous on neck and sides of head. Mantle vinaceous-brown; feathers of lower back with a subterminal black bar. Inner remiges mottled black and pale buff. Tail and upper tail-coverts barred black and whitish buff. Throat white; upper breast grayish; rest of underparts pale cinnamon-buff, barred on flanks with black. ♀ similar to ♂ but shoulders, inner remiges, lower back, upper tail-coverts, and tail regularly barred black and pale buff.

Range. Venezuela, the Guianas, Brazil, Peru, and northern Bolivia.

Colombia. Forest and scrub. Northeastern Colombia from Atlántico to the Perijá Mts. *(idoneus)*. East of the Andes in Meta *(duidae)*, in Arauca *(cursitans)*.

14. SLATY-BREASTED TINAMOU
(Crypturellus boucardi)

Description. 10 - 11". Generally similar to No. 13. Differs by being somewhat darker, but principally by having the lower back in females barred dark brown and black instead of pale buff and black; also, the gray wash on the breast in both sexes is more pronounced.

Range. Mexico to northern Costa Rica.

Colombia. Forest. Tropical zone in Córdoba and northern Antioquia *(columbianus)*.

15. MAGDALENA TINAMOU
(Crypturellus saltuarius)

Description. 10 - 11". Front of crown dark gray. Throat white, gray on the lower neck; breast cinnamon-buff; center of abdomen dull white. Upperparts rich brown changing to sepia on the lower back. Lower mandible yellowish white.

Range. Colombia.

Colombia. Forest. Tropical zone in the hills around Ayacucho in Magdalena.

PLATE II

WHITE HAWK
(*Leucopternis albi-*
collis williaminae)
Page 52

PLUMBEOUS KITE
(*Ictinia plumbea*)
Page 48

LAUGHING FALCON
(*Herpetotheres*
c. cachinnans)
Page 56

BAT FALCON
(*Falco r. rufigularis*)
Page 58

ORNATE HAWK-EAGLE
(*Spizaëtus ornatus vicarius*)
Page 54

WHITE-TAILED HAWK
(*Buteo albicaudatus colonus*)
Page 50

PEARL KITE
(*Gampsonyx*
swainsoni leonae)
Page 58

CRANE HAWK
(*Geranospiza caerul-*
escens balzarensis)
Page 54

BARRED
FOREST-FALCON
(*Micrastur rufi-*
collis interstes)
Page 16

E.L.Poole

16. CHOCO TINAMOU
(Crypturellus kerriae)

Description. 11½ - 12½". ♂ : Top and sides of head black; throat gray. General plumage dark chestnut brown, paler below, indistinctly banded black on lower back. Flanks and under tail-coverts black and buff. Legs light red, toes darker. ♀ similar to ♂ but shoulders barred black and rufous.

Range. Colombia.

Colombia. Forest. The tropical zone of Pacific Colombia in the Baudó Mts.

GREBES (Podicipedidae)

Fig. 2. Pied-billed Grebe
(*Podilymbus podiceps*)

Colombian grebes are found in lakes and ponds from the tropical to the temperate zone. Their lobed toes distinguish them from most other swimming birds. Their bills, unlike those of ducks, are narrow and pointed.

They feed on fish, insects, and other small animals, and are expert divers. Their nest is made of reeds and floats on the water. (4 Col.; 8 S.A..; 12 N.&S. A.; 19 wld.)

PIED-BILLED GREBE
(*Podilymbus podiceps*)

Description. 12″. Breeding plumage: Bill thick, yellow with a conspicuous black band. Above dark grayish brown. Chin and throat black; under surface white blotched with dusky. Winter plumage similar but no band on bill and throat white like rest of underparts.

Range. From Canada southward to Chile and Argentina. The West Indies, Trinidad and Tobago.

Colombia. Lakes and ponds from the tropical to the temperate zone (*antarcticus*).

LEAST GREBE
(*Podiceps dominicus*)

Description. 9″. Breeding plumage: Top of head and hindneck dark bluish gray; throat black, rest of neck and upper parts brownish gray. Lower parts white; wing-feathers largely white (only seen in flight). Bill thin, black, tip white. In winter, throat and foreneck white.

Range. From Texas and Lower California, southward through most of tropical South America to Argentina. The West Indies.

Colombia. Tropical to lower temperate zones throughout Colombia where there are fresh-water ponds and lakes (*speciosus*).

CRESTED GREBE
(*Podiceps occipitalis*)

Description. 11″. Breeding plumage: Occipital crest and hindneck black; sides of crown and entire back gray. Silky, plume-like feathers behind the eye grayish brown. Entire under surface and inner webs of secondaries white. In winter, gray above, white below.

Range. The mountains of western South America from Ecuador southward to Tierra del Fuego and the Falkland Islands.

Colombia. Temperate and lower páramo zones. Mountain lakes of Nariño and southern Cauca (*juninensis*).

18

EARED GREBE
(Podiceps caspicus) Plate III

Description. 11 - 13″. Breeding plumage: Forecrown grayish, becoming glossy black on hindcrown and nape; hindneck and back ashy blackish with a greenish gloss. Wings grayish, inner remiges white. Long silky plumes springing from behind eye golden buff on upper portion, becoming chestnut on lower portion. Throat black, front of neck rich chestnut, sides of body chestnut mixed with silvery gray. Under parts silky white. In winter, grayish black above, patch at sides of head, throat and front of neck white. Bill black, slightly upturned.

Range. Breeds in western North America southward to northwestern Mexico. Northwestern South America. North American birds winter southward to Guatemala. The species breeds also in Europe, Asia, and Africa.

Colombia. Resident on the lakes of the Eastern Andes in the temperate zone from Bogotá northward *(andinus)*.

ALBATROSSES (Diomedeidae)

Fig. 3. Galápagos Albatross
(*Diomedea irrorata*)

Albatrosses are very large, web-footed seabirds characterized by pointed, long and exceptionally narrow wings. They are essentially birds of the open ocean and rarely approach land except at their breeding grounds, usually on remote islands.

They feed on cuttlefish and other marine animals. (1 Col.; 8 S.A.; 12 N.&S. A.; 14 wld.)

GALAPAGOS ALBATROSS
(Diomedea irrorata)

Description. 35″. A very large seabird with a wing spread of 6 to 8 feet. Head and neck white. Upper parts smoky brown with wavy white lines. Lower parts dusky. Bill yellow.

Range. Breeds in the Galápagos Islands from April to July. Wanders to the coast of South America from the gulf of Panama to Peru in the non-breeding season.

Colombia. Wanders to the Pacific coast, where it has been seen off Octavia Bay, Chocó.

20

SHEARWATERS (Procellariidae)

Fig. 4. Sooty Shearwater
(Puffinus griseus)

These medium-sized seabirds, like albatrosses, live far out at sea where they glide rapidly on fixed, narrow wings over the waves, just skimming the water. They are gregarious in habits. Their food consists of small marine life. They nest in burrows or rock crevices, many species emerging only at night to feed. They breed usually on remote islands, wandering widely after the breeding season. (2 Col.; 2 S.A.; 37 N.&S.A.; 56 wld.)

WEDGE-TAILED SHEARWATER
(Puffinus pacificus)

Description. 15 - 16". Chocolate brown above; grayish brown (or white, light phase) below. Face and throat brownish gray. Wings and tail blackish, tail wedge-shaped. Bill reddish; feet flesh color.

Range. Breeds in the warmer portions of the Pacific and Indian Oceans. In the non-breeding season wanders as far north as Japan and Mexico.

Colombia. Recorded from the northwest coast (*chlororhynchus*).

SOOTY SHEARWATER
(Puffinus griseus)

Description. 16 - 19". Uniform dark sooty gray, under surface of wings paler. The tail is wedge-shaped.

Range. Breeds in the Falkland Islands, the islands off Cape Horn, and the Andes of Chile; also on many islands of the southern Pacific. In summer migrates to the North Atlantic, Greenland and the Faroe Is. In the non-breeding season occurs in the North Atlantic and North Pacific oceans as far as the Arctic Circle.

Colombia. Recorded off the Chocó coast in May.

STORM PETRELS (Hydrobatidae)

Fig. 5. Least Petrel
(*Halocyptena microsoma*)

Storm Petrels are closely related to shearwaters and do not differ from them in habits. Their flight, however, is very different, for they do not sail but use their wings in a rapid, fluttering action, sometimes touching the surface of the water with their outstretched feet. They are the smallest of all seabirds. (4 Col.; 4 S.A.; 18 N.&S.A.; 18 wld.)

WHITE-VENTED PETREL
(Oceanites gracilis)
Description. 5¾ - 6″. Sooty black. Upper and under tail-coverts and center of abdomen white. A pale band on wings. Tail square.

Range. Breeds in the Galápagos Islands and probably the Pacific coast of South America.

Colombia. Recorded as common off the coast of Nariño in September (*gracilis*).

WEDGE-RUMPED PETREL
(Oceanodroma tethys)
Description. 6¼ - 6½″. General color dark, smoky grayish brown; rump white. Tail forked.

Range. Breeds in the Galápagos Islands, the Pescadores, and off the coast of Peru on the San Gallán Islands in May and June.

Colombia. Recorded from the Pacific coast in March (*kelsalli*).

BLACK PETREL
(Loomelania melania)
Description. 9″. Sooty black above; browner below. Greater wing-coverts paler, forming a wing band. Tail deeply forked.

Range. Breeds off Lower California from May to September. Migrates southward to Peru.

Colombia. The Pacific coast.

LEAST PETREL
(Halocyptena microsoma)
Description. 5 - 6″. General color sooty black, grayer below. Secondaries pale-edged, forming a wing-band. Tail wedge-shaped.

Range. Breeds off the coast of Lower California from July to September. Southward in winter to Ecuador.

Colombia. The Pacific coast (March).

22

TROPICBIRDS (Phaëthontidae)

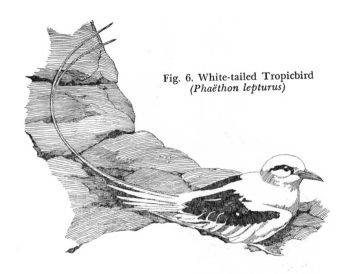

Fig. 6. White-tailed Tropicbird
(Phaëthon lepturus)

Essentially marine in habits, tropicbirds are swift on the wing, somewhat resembling pigeons in their manner of flight. They usually fly, with quick wingbeats, high above the water, and dive from a considerable height after fish. They are often seen far from land. Adult birds have enormously long central tail feathers. (2 Col.; 3 S.A.; 3 N.&S.A.; 3 wld.)

RED-BILLED TROPICBIRD
(Phaëthon aethereus)

Description. 19″ excluding quill-like lengthened tail feathers. Lores, stripe through the eye joining on the nape, black. Upper surface white, barred with black; entire lower surface white tinged pink. Lengthened tail feathers up to 28 inches, white. Bill red, or orange.

Range. Tropical Atlantic and Pacific Oceans, off the American coasts. Cape Verde Islands. Northern Indian Ocean. **Colombia.** Recorded from Malpelo Island, and probably occurs off the coast of Colombia *(mesonauta)*.

WHITE-TAILED TROPICBIRD
(Phaëthon lepturus)

Description. 16″ excluding lengthened tail feathers. The adult differs from *P. aethereus* by smaller size and white, unmarked back. The young have the back banded, but more coarsely than in *aethereus*. The bill is yellow and the flanks are marked with sooty black. The adult bird has a red bill. Lengthened tail feathers up to 20″.

Range. The tropical Atlantic, Pacific, and Indian Oceans.

Colombia. The Caribbean coast *(catesbyi)*.

23

PELICANS (Pelecanidae)

Fig. 7. Brown Pelican
(*Pelecanus occidentalis*)

Pelicans inhabit coastal waters, and may often be seen plunging, head downwards, with a splash after fish. They fly with head retracted, with slow, majestic wing beats. Gregarious, they nest in colonies, building their nests in low trees and bushes near the coast line. (1 Col; 1 S.A.; 2 N.&S.A.; 6 wld.)

BROWN PELICAN

(Pelecanus occidentalis)

Description. 50″. Bill long (18 - 20″). Top of head and sides of neck white, rest of neck chestnut. Upper parts mostly silvery gray, the feathers with dark borders. Underparts grayish brown.

Range. The Pacific and southern Atlantic coasts of the United States, southward through the Caribbean to Venezuela, British Guiana, and in the Pacific south to Chile. The Galápagos Islands.

Colombia. The Caribbean coast, occasionally on the lower Magdalena R. (*carolinensis*). The Pacific coast (*murphyii*).

BOOBIES (Sulidae)

Fig. 8. Masked Booby
(Sula dactylatra)

These large seabirds are recognizable by their long pointed wings, wedge-shaped tails, and stout, sharply pointed bills. Gregarious, flocks are often seen flying in straggling lines close to the water. Most species inhabit tropical seas. Boobies are frequently seen plunging head first into the sea after fish which they pursue and capture under the surface. Most species do not wander far from land. They nest in colonies and are the source of much of the guano used for fertilizer, which is collected on the islands off the Peruvian coast. (4 Col.; 5 S.A.; 6 N.&S.A.; 9 wld.)

BLUE-FOOTED BOOBY
(Sula nebouxii)

Description. 34". Front of head and throat white, rest of head and neck dull cinnamon brown. Back brown, feathers pale tipped; rump white. Wings and tail silvery brown. Under parts white. Feet bright blue; face and gular sack slaty; bill dull greenish blue.

Range. Mexico to Peru.

Colombia. The Pacific coast.

PERUVIAN BOOBY
(Sula variegata)

Description. 29". Head, neck and under parts white. Back brown, feathers edged white. Wings brown; tail largely white. Bill purplish blue; legs bluish gray.

Range. Breeds on the islands off the coast of Peru and Chile.

Colombia. Casual on the Pacific coast.

MASKED BOOBY
(Sula dactylatra)

Description. 31". Entire body plumage white. Wings and tail chocolate brown. Face black; bill orange yellow with dark tip, pink or light red in females; legs olive to blackish.

Range. Warmer parts of the Atlantic, Pacific and Indian Oceans.

Colombia. The Pacific coast *(granti)*.

BROWN BOOBY
(Sula leucogaster)

Description. 30". Entirely chocolate brown except for white lower breast and belly. Face and gular sack yellow; bill yellow with dark tip; legs chrome-yellow. In the Pacific coast form the ♂ has the head and neck paler and much grayer, and in the ♀ the back and wings as well as the head and neck are grayish. Gular sack and base of bill pea green. Legs yellowish to light pea green.

Range. Warmer parts of the Atlantic, Pacific and Indian Oceans.

Colombia. Caribbean coast *(leucogaster)*. Pacific coast *(etesiaca)*.

25

CORMORANTS (Phalacrocoracidae)

Fig. 9. Neotropic Cormorant
(Phalacrocorax olivaceus)

Cormorants are found along the seacoast and do not wander far from land; some inhabit inland waters. They are gregarious and some species are important producers of guano. Their plumage is mostly glossy, greenish black and their bills are strongly hooked. They live on fish which they capture by pursuing them under water. (2 Col.; 6 S.A.; 11 N.&S.A.; 30 wld.)

NEOTROPIC CORMORANT
(Phalacrocorax olivaceus)

Description. 28″. Shiny greenish black. Sides of face and throat white with a tuft of white feathers on each side of head in breeding plumage. Facial skin and gular sack dull yellow; legs black.

Range. Southern United States south to Tierra del Fuego.

Colombia. Coasts and rivers throughout the country, mostly in the tropical zone, but occasionally to the temperate *(olivaceus)*.

GUANAY CORMORANT
(Phalacrocorax bougainvillii)

Description. Head, neck and upper parts glossy greenish black. Throat and under parts white. Facial skin red, gular sack brown; bill dusky; legs red.

Range. Breeds on islands off the coast of Peru and Chile.

Colombia. A marine species found casually on the Pacific coast, so far recorded from Gorgona Island and Buenaventura Bay in February.

DARTERS OR ANHINGAS (Anhingidae)

Fig. 10. Anhinga
(Anhinga anhinga)

Anhingas or darters rather resemble cormorants, but the very small head, long, thin neck and sharply pointed bill serve to distinguish them. They are usually found singly or in pairs in fresh-water lakes and rivers, and frequently may be seen swimming with only the head and neck above water. When perching over the water they often sit with their wings half extended and drooping. They feed on fish. (1 Col.; 1 S. A.; 1 N.&S.A.; 2 wld.)

ANHINGA
(Anhinga anhinga)

Description. 28-36". ♂: Mainly glossy greenish black. Greater wing-coverts broadly silvery white, lesser wing-coverts spotted with silvery white; innermost remiges and scapulars streaked black and silvery white. Tail-feathers crimped, pale tipped, tail fan-shaped, carried spread in flight. ♀: Generally similar to ♂ but head, neck and breast grayish buff, separated from the black on the breast by a chestnut band. *Immature:* Mainly brownish with little or no white on the wings.

Range. Southern United States to Argentina. The West Indies, Trinidad and Tobago.

Colombia. Tropical zone east of the Eastern Andes *(anhinga)*; west of the Eastern Andes *(leucogaster)*.

27

FRIGATEBIRDS (Fregatidae)

Fig. 11. Magnificent Frigatebird
(Fregata magnificens)

Although almost never seen far from land frigatebirds are the only completely marine birds which never settle on the water. They spend much of their time sailing on narrow, pointed wings, high above the sea, diving after terns and other seabirds, forcing them to disgorge their food which they seize before it reaches the water. They also pick up food from the surface of the sea. Their tails are long and pointed, and can be opened to form a deep fork; this forms a good mark of recognition even at a distance.

At night they roost in trees near the seacoast, where they also build their nest. In some Pacific islands frigatebirds, like carrier pigeons, carry messages from island to island. (1 Col.; 3 S.A.; 3 N.&S.A.; 5 wld.)

MAGNIFICENT FRIGATEBIRD
(Fregata magnificens)

Description. 40″. ♂ : Entirely black. Inflatable pouch, orange or red. ♀ similar but breast and upper abdomen white (head white, imm.).

Range. From the Bahamas southward through the Caribbean to the coasts of Venezuela and Panama, Ecuador, Peru, the Galápagos Islands. On the Atlantic coast of South America southward to southern Brazil. The Cape Verde Islands and the west coast of Africa. Strays both north and south of its usual range.

Colombia. Caribbean and Pacific coasts, accidental inland, (Cauca Valley).

28

HERONS (Ardeidae)

Fig. 12. Great Blue Heron
(Ardea herodias)

Many species of heron inhabit the rivers and marshes of Colombia. In habits they of course do not differ from herons found in other parts of the world. (21 Col.; 21 S.A.; 24 N.&S.A.; 58 wld.)

AID TO IDENTIFICATION

Back gray 1, 2, 6, 10.
Back white 3, 6, 7, 8, 9.
Back green or black 4, 12, 13.
Back brown 15, 16, 20.
Back mottled, streaked or banded 5, 11ᴱ, 14, 15, 16, 17, 18, 19, 21.

1. GREAT BLUE HERON
(Ardea herodias)

Description. 42-50″. Crown white widely bordered with black (ad.), or all black (imm.) ; neck buffy white, central line mixed rufous and black. Back blue-gray. Under parts white streaked with black. Thighs rufous.
Range. Breeds in Alaska, Canada, the United States and Mexico. Winters in the southern United States to northern South America. The Galápagos Islands.
Colombia. Winter visitor, October-December. Northern Colombia southward to the upper Cauca Valley *(herodias)*.

2. WHITE-NECKED HERON
(Ardea cocoi)

Description. 45 - 54″. Entire crown blue-black; neck white, central line blue-black.

Back blue-gray. Under parts streaked black and white. Thighs white.
Range. Eastern Panama southward to the Straits of Magellan.
Colombia. Rivers and marshes of the tropical zone.

3. CAPPED HERON
(Pilherodius pileatus)

Description. 20 - 24″. Entire plumage white except for black cap. Two long, narrow, white nuchal plumes. Upper mandible and legs bluish gray, lower mandible with livid purple streak. Orbital skin cobalt blue.
Range. Panama south to Brazil and Bolivia.
Colombia. Rivers and marshes of the tropical zone.

4. GREEN HERON
(Butorides virescens)

Description. 16 - 20". Crown and occipital crest blackish green; sides of head, the neck, sides of breast and the upper back purplish chestnut; throat, front of neck and center of breast white streaked and spotted with blackish. Lower breast and belly grayish brown. Feathers of mantle, elongated in breeding season, bronzy green margined with ashy. Wing-coverts bronzy green edged with buff; primaries slaty gray and rectrices bronzy green. *Immature*: Cap brownish black, pale streaked. Sides of head, the neck, sides of breast and the back brownish, throat, front of neck, sides of breast white streaked and spotted with grayish brown. Wing-coverts bronzy brown the feathers edged and spotted with buff. Wings and tail slaty.

Range. Southern Canada south to northern South America. Caribbean islands. The Pearl Islands.

Colombia. Marshes and mangroves. Winter resident in northeastern Colombia *(virescens)*.

5. STRIATED HERON
(Butorides striatus)

Description. 13 - 18". Generally similar to No. 4 but readily distinguishable by having the sides of head, sides of neck and sides of breast gray; further, the lower breast and belly are paler and purer gray. *Immature*: Very similar to No. 4 and only distinguishable by having the sides of the head and neck grayer with little or no brown tinge.

Range. South America, Asia, Africa, Australia, the East Indies and the Pacific islands.

Colombia. Rivers and coasts in the tropical to lower temperate zones *(striatus)*.

6. LITTLE BLUE HERON
(Florida caerulea)

Description. 20 - 26". Whole head and neck maroon, rest of plumage dark blue-gray. *Immature*: Entirely white, occasionally piebald. Dark bill, feet and legs in any plumage.

Range. Southern United States to Argentina. The West Indies.

Colombia. Tropical to temperate zones, on lakes, rivers and in mangrove swamps *(caerulescens)*. The North American form has been recorded from western Colombia. A specimen banded in Oklahoma in June was recovered at Quibdó, Chocó in October of the same year *(caerulea)*.

7. CATTLE EGRET
(Bubulcus ibis)

Description. 14 - 20". Mostly white. Back, head, neck and plumes springing from the back orange-cinnamon in breeding season only. Bill, feet and legs yellow.

Range. Northern South America to the United States. West Indies. The Iberian Peninsula, Africa, Madagascar, Asia, the East Indies.

Colombia. Tropical zone; usually seen in small flocks in pastures near cattle *(ibis)*.

8. COMMON EGRET
(Casmerodius albus)

Description. 35 - 40". All white. Bill yellow; feet and legs black.

Range. Warmer parts of the continents of the world. New Zealand. In the Americas from southern Canada to Patagonia. The West Indies.

Colombia. Tropical, occasionally temperate, zones in marshy lands *(egretta)*.

9. SNOWY EGRET
(Leucophoyx thula)

Description. 19 - 25". All white. Bill and legs black, toes yellow.

Range. United States south to Chile, Argentina and Bolivia. The West Indies.

Colombia. Salt and fresh water marshes, rivers and lagoons of the tropical zone *(thula)*.

10. TRICOLORED HERON
(Hydranassa tricolor)

Description. 22 - 26". Crown, neck, wings, upper back slaty gray; rump white. Throat buffy, streak down front of neck and base of neck maroon. Plumes of back sandy, occipital crest white in breeding season. Breast and belly white. *Immature:* Throat white; neck chestnut; back gray; belly white.

Range. Southern United States, south to eastern Brazil and western Ecuador. The West Indies, Trinidad.

Colombia. Tropical zone on tidal flats, coastal swamps, marshlands, and mangroves (*ruficollis*).

11. WHISTLING HERON
(Syrigma sibilatrix)

Description. 20 - 22″. Crown black; throat whitish, neck and breast buffy; belly white. Back and wings slaty gray; wing coverts dark buff with black streaks. Face blue; bill short, thick, flesh colored with black tip.

Range. Western Venezuela. Southern Brazil, Paraguay, Uruguay, northern Argentina, eastern Bolivia.

Colombia. Rivers, swamps and marshes. Northeastern Colombia east of the Andes south to Meta (*fostersmithi*).

12. CHESTNUT-BELLIED HERON
(Agamia agami)

Description. 26 - 30″. Front of crown blackish, hind crown and long crest slaty blue, throat white. Above mostly deep, shiny green. Shoulders and underparts mainly chestnut. Breast slaty, the feathers of the lower neck recurved with pale central streaks. Young birds are brownish above, creamy white below.

Range. Mexico to Brazil and Bolivia.

Colombia. Inland rivers; usually tropical, occasionally to lower temperate, zones.

13. BLACK-CROWNED NIGHT-HERON
(Nycticorax nycticorax)

Description. 23 - 27″. Forehead white, crown, crest and back greenish blue-black. Throat and foreneck white, rest of under parts very pale grayish white. Sides of neck, wings, lower back, rump and tail pale brownish gray. Bill black, short, thick. *Immature:* Top of head dusky; neck and breast streaked buffy and gray. Wings,

back and tail grayish brown. Wing-coverts spotted white.

Range. North and South America. Europe, Asia.

Colombia. Fresh and saltwater marshes. Tropical to lower temperate zones (*hoactli*).

14. YELLOW-CROWNED NIGHT-HERON
(Nyctanassa violacea)

Description. 26 - 30″. Crown and streak under eye white with strong buff wash, rest of head black. Neck and under parts gray, belly mixed with white. Upper surface blackish, the feathers widely edged with gray giving a streaked appearance; rump and upper tail-coverts gray. *Immature:* Head, neck, under parts streaked brown and white; upper parts brown spotted with white.

Range. Southern and central United States, Mexico, Central America southward to Argentina and Bolivia.

Colombia. Swampy forest; mangroves and swamps. Tropical zone, except the west coast (*cayennensis*). West coast (*caliginis*). The Guajira Peninsula (*bancrofti*).

15. RUFESCENT TIGER-HERON
(Tigrisoma lineatum)

Description. 26 - 30″. Head, neck and upper breast chestnut; front of neck and upper breast mixed with white, belly pale grayish brown. Back black, finely banded with buff. Wing-feathers slate-gray. *Juvenal:* Entire upper surface broadly banded black and rufous-buff; lower surface buffy white, spotted with black.

Range. Honduras, south to Argentina and Bolivia.

Colombia. Tropical zone throughout on the banks of forest streams (*lineatum*).

16. FASCIATED TIGER-HERON
(Tigrisoma fasciatum)

Description. 25 - 28″. Crown black, sides of head slaty, neck blackish with fine buffy bars, stripe down front of neck white mixed with black; belly gray to ochraceous; flanks slate gray unbanded (except in young birds); back blackish with fine buff bars. *Immature:* Head with buff bars, barring above coarser. *Juvenal:*

PLATE III

EARED GREBE
(*Podiceps
caspicus andinus*)
Page 19

CRESTED SCREAMER
(*Chauna chavaria*)
Page 39

SPOT-FLANKED
GALLINULE
(*Porphyriops
melanops bogotensis*)
Page 73

CRESTED BOBWHITE
(*Colinus cristatus decoratus*)
Page 65

HELMETED CURASSOW
(*Pauxi p. pauxi*)
Page 61

SLATE-COLORED
COOT
(*Fulica ardesiaca*)
Page 74

TAWNY-FACED
QUAIL
(*Rhynchortyx c. cinctus*)
Page 66

SALVIN'S
RAZOR-BILLED
CURASSOW
(*Mitu salvini*)
Page 60

PIED PLOVER
(*Hoploxypterus cayanus*)
Page 79

RUFOUS-SIDED CRAKE
(*Laterallus
melanophaius oenops*)
Page 72

CRESTED GUAN
(*Penelope
purpurascens aequatorialis*)
Page 62

GREATER ANI
(*Crotophaga major*)
Page 113

BROWN-BACKED
WOOD-RAIL
(*Aramides wolfi*)
Page 71

COLOMBIAN
CHACHALACA
(*Ortalis columbiana*)
Page 63

BANDED
GROUND-CUCKOO
(*Neomorphus radiolosus*)
Page 114

Like that of No. 15, but bill shorter and stouter, whiter below with fewer bars.

Range. Costa Rica and Panama. Northern Venezuela, through western South America, south to Peru and Argentina.

Colombia. Mountain streams from the tropical to the lower subtropical zone, west and east of the Andes (*salmoni*).

17. BARE-THROATED TIGER-HERON
(*Tigrisoma mexicanum*)

Description. 29 - 31″. Very similar to No. 16, but larger with much longer bill, throat wholly bare, sides of head light bluish gray, abdomen deeper cinnamon. In any plumage separable from Nos. 15 and 16 by wholly bare throat; younger birds have white bars across terminal third of primaries.

Range. Mexico southward to extreme northwestern South America.

Colombia. Fresh water and brackish marshes. Known only from the lower Atrato Valley (*mexicanum*).

18. ZIGZAG HERON
(*Zebrilus undulatus*)

Description. 12 - 13″. Above slaty black with indistinct wavy dark buffy bands on mantle and wing-coverts. Ample crest black. Sides of head, foreneck, chest and sides of body sandy buff vermiculated with fine black lines; center of abdomen and under tail-coverts white. *Rufous phase:* Differs from the dark phase in being more coarsely banded on the upper surface; forehead rufous instead of black, sides of head and neck chestnut, foreneck and under parts rufous, whitish on center of abdomen and under tail-coverts.

Range. Venezuela southward to the Amazon and Mato Grosso.

Colombia. Swamps east of the Andes in Arauca and Vaupés.

19. STRIPE-BACKED BITTERN
(*Ixobrychus involucris*)

Description. 12 - 14″. Coronal streak black. Top and sides of head, back and sides of neck fawn. Back striped black and cinnamon buff. Below white broadly striped with fawn. Wing-coverts and tips of primaries chestnut, rest of primaries dark brown.

Range. Trinidad, northern Venezuela, and British Guiana. Southern Brazil to northern Patagonia.

Colombia. Tropical zone. The Santa Marta region and Atlántico. The occurrence of this species in Colombia has been doubted but as it is found in Venezuela there is every probability that it does occur in Colombia.

20. LEAST BITTERN
(*Ixobrychus exilis*)

Description. 10 - 11″. (or 13 - 14″, 1) ♂: Crown and nape, back, tail and innermost remiges glossy greenish black. Sides of head, back of neck, greater wing-coverts and outer webs of secondaries chestnut. Throat white, rest of underparts buffy white. ♀ like ♂ but back chocolate brown.

Range. Canada southward to Paraguay. **Colombia.** Marshes and ponds. Tropical zone. Migrant to the Cauca Valley (*exilis*). The Cauca Valley and the Santa Marta region (*erythromelas*). Temperate zone of the Eastern Andes (1, *bogotensis*).

21. PINNATED BITTERN
(*Botaurus pinnatus*)

Description. 23-26″. Crown black; back and sides of neck banded black and buff, front of neck and underparts striped rufous and buff. Back mottled, rufous, buff and black.

Range. Mexico, southward to northern Argentina.

Colombia. Marshes. Tropical to temperate zones.

BOAT-BILLED HERONS (Cochleariidae)

Fig. 13. Boat-billed Heron
(Cochlearius cochlearius)

Except for their curious bills, boatbills do not differ in appearance from other herons. They are more or less solitary and live chiefly in forest near fresh water lagoons and rivers. (1 Col.; 1 S.A.; 1 N.&S.A.; 1 wld.)

BOAT-BILLED HERON
(Cochlearius cochlearius)

Description. 23-25″. Bill blunt, very broad, as wide as head. Crown, long, ample crest and upper back black; rest of back gray. Forehead and throat white; sides of neck gray (or pinkish buff, 1). *Immature*: Crown black, back and neck rufous brown.

Range. From Mexico to Brazil, northern Argentina and Peru. Trinidad.

Colombia. Swampy woods and marshes. Tropical, rarely to lower temperate zone, except west coast *(cochlearius)*. Western shore of the Gulf of Urabá and probably down the west coast (1, *panamensis*).

34

STORKS (Ciconiidae)

Fig. 14. Jabirú
(*Jabiru mycteria*)

Storks are not so dependent on water as herons are. They are usually seen on grassy plains. They are distinguishable from herons in flight by carrying the neck extended. (3 Col.; 3 S.A.; 3 N.&S.A.; 17 wld.)

WOOD IBIS
(*Mycteria americana*)

Description. 40". White; remiges and tail black. Bare head and neck slaty. Bill black, decurved at tip; legs black.

Range. Southern United States to Peru and Argentina. Greater Antilles, Trinidad.

Colombia. Swamps and lagoons. Tropical zone of northern Colombia southward up the Cauca Valley. Eastern Colombia.

MAGUARI STORK
(*Euxenura galeata*)

Description. 38". White; wings and tail black. Bill straight, orange-red; legs orange-red.

Range. Venezuela, British Guiana southward to Chile.

Colombia. The llanos east of the Andes.

JABIRU
(*Jabiru mycteria*)

Description. 52". White; head and neck bare, black, red at base. Bill very heavy, black. Legs black.

Range. Mexico to Argentina and Bolivia.

Colombia. Open marshy areas from the lower Cauca and lower Magdalena to the eastern llanos and Vaupés.

IBISES AND SPOONBILLS (Threskiornithidae)

Fig. 15. White Ibis
(*Eudocimus albus*) p. 37

Ibises are distinguishable from herons and most storks by their curved bills. Like storks, they fly with extended necks. Young ibises are grayish brown, all more or less alike and hard to tell apart in the field. They live on fish, crustaceans and vegetable matter and nest in trees or on the ground in marshes. (9 Col.; 11 S.A.; 11 N.&S.A.; 28 wld.)

AID TO IDENTIFICATION
Head and neck buffy white or all white 1, 5.
Mostly dark green or bronzy 2ᴱ, 3, 4, 7, 8.
Red or pink 6, 9.

1. BUFF-NECKED IBIS
(Theristicus caudatus)

Description. 29-31″. Head, neck and upper breast buffy white, strongly shaded orange-rufous on head and breast. Back and under surface dark gray; rump green. Wing-coverts and tertials white. Flight-feathers and tail greenish black.

Range. South America generally southward to Argentina.

Colombia. Tropical zone, except the west coast, generally in open rather dry, savanna country *(caudatus)*.

2. SHARP-TAILED IBIS
(Cercibis oxycerca)

Description. 28-30″. Entire plumage glossy greenish black with purplish reflections. Bill, bare patch around eye, feet and legs red; throat yellow.

Range. Orinocan Venezuela, the Guianas and adjacent Brazil.

Colombia. The llanos east of the Andes in marshy areas, and on banks of streams.

3. GREEN IBIS
(Mesembrinibis cayennensis)

Description. 22-24″. General color shiny bronzy green, duller and darker below. Head gray, hind neck and sides of neck shining emerald green. Bill greenish; feet and legs jade green.

Range. Panama to Argentina and Bolivia.

Colombia. Swampy forest in the tropical zone, except the southwest. /

4. WHISPERING IBIS
(Phimosus infuscatus)

Description. 18-20″, General color blackish green. Bill pale flesh, bare face some-

36

what darker. Feet and legs whitish flesh.
Range. South America generally to Brazil
and Argentina.

Colombia. Small wooded streams and
rivers, lagoons and tidal flats. Northern
half of Colombia from the mouth of the
río Sinú eastward *(berlepschi).*

5. WHITE IBIS
(Eudocimus albus) Fig. 15

Description. 24". All white, tips of primaries blue-black. Bill curved. Skin of
face, bill and legs scarlet.

Range. Southern United States to northern South America.

Colombia. Mangroves, lagoons and
swamps. Tropical zone of northern Colombia from the mouth of the Sinú to the
eastern llanos and Macarena Mts.

6. SCARLET IBIS
(Eudocimus ruber)

Description. 22". Entirely scarlet except
for blue-black wing tips. Skin of face, bill
and legs scarlet.

Range. Tropical South America, occasionally West Indies and Central America.
Trinidad.

Colombia. Lagoons in the lower Magdalena and marshes in the llanos east of
the Andes in Arauca and Meta.

7. GLOSSY IBIS
(Plegadis falcinellus)

Description. 20-22". Head and neck,
upper back, under parts chestnut-maroon.
Rest of plumage glossy green and purple.
Bill and bare facial skin slate gray, in
breeding season with white border; feet
and legs dark gray.

Range. Of virtual world-wide distribution
in the temperate and tropical zones.

Colombia. Caribbean coast *(falcinellus).*

8. WHITE-FACED IBIS
(Plegadis chihi)

Description. 18 - 21". Very similar to No. 7
but smaller, and differing further in
having the bare skin of the face red, outlined with white feathers.

Range. Breeds in North America southward to Mexico and Florida. Also in
Venezuela and southern South America.

Colombia. Recorded from Colombia without precise locality.

9. ROSEATE SPOONBILL
(Ajaia ajaja)

Description. 28-32". Bill flat, very wide,
broadening at tip. Whole head bare,
black and greenish yellow. Neck white,
rest of plumage rosy pink. Wing-coverts
and tail-coverts crimson. Tail straw
yellow.

Range. Southern United States, the Bahamas, Greater Antilles, Trinidad southward to Argentina and Chile.

Colombia. Coastal marshes, inland ponds
and swamps. Tropical zone of northern
Colombia and up the Cauca Valley to the
vicinity of Cali.

FLAMINGOS (Phoenicopteridae)

Fig. 16. American Flamingo
(Phoenicopterus ruber)

Flamingos live in large colonies near salt or brackish waters where they feed on small crustaceans. Their nests, closely spaced, are made of mud and rise a few inches above the water. They are recognizable from the heron-like birds by their short, sharply decurved bills and very long necks and legs. They fly with them outstretched. Some species live on lakes high in the Andes of Peru southward. (1 Col.; 3 S.A.; 3 N.&S.A.; 6 wld.)

AMERICAN FLAMINGO
(Phoenicopterus ruber)

Description. 40-48″. General plumage rosy pink, wings black-tipped. Bill pink with black tip, short, thick and sharply curved downward.

Range. The Bahamas and West Indies. Southern Mexico, locally southward to the mouth of the Amazon. Peru and southern Brazil southward, to the Straits of Magellan and the Falkland Islands. The Galápagos Islands.

Colombia. Marshes and sea coast near the mouth of the Magdalena river *(ruber)*.

38

SCREAMERS (Anhimidae)

Fig. 17. Horned Screamer
(Anhima cornuta)

These large, ungainly birds, probably related to geese, are found on open grasslands and marshy areas. They are characterized by their large feet, and by sharp spurs found on the bends of their wings. They often fly to great heights, where they sail in circles, sometimes almost out of sight. On the ground they walk slowly in a stately fashion. Their loud cries can be heard for a great distance. The nest, made of reeds, is placed upon the ground. Their food consists of plants and roots. (2 Col.; 3 S.A.; 3 N.&S.A.; 3 wld.)

HORNED SCREAMER
(Anhima cornuta)

Description. 34-38″. General plumage glossy greenish black. Shoulders, mottling on head and neck, under wing-coverts and belly white. A horn-like quill on top of head. Bill and legs black.

Range. Tropical South America. Formerly Trinidad.

Colombia. Grasslands and the marshes in the tropical zone, virtually throughout. Not recorded from western Nariño.

CRESTED SCREAMER
(Chauna chavaria) Plate III

Description. 30-36″. Crown and crest gray, rest of head white: neck black. Rest of plumage gray, paler below. Under wing-coverts white. Bill grayish, legs rosy.

Range. Northern Venezuela.

Colombia. Tropical zone. Grasslands and marshes of the Sinú and lower Magdalena Valleys.

DUCKS AND GEESE (Anatidae)

Fig. 18. Torrent Duck
(Merganetta armata) p. 44

Colombian ducks generally resemble ducks found in other parts of the world in habits. They live on fresh and salt water marshes, mountain lakes, rivers and mangroves. The males of some species in winter assume an eclipse plumage in which they resemble the female.

The most distinctive among Colombian ducks are the little Torrent Ducks. They inhabit fast-flowing mountain streams, their long and stiff tails probably helping to fend them off the rocks when swimming and diving in the swirling waters of their mountain habitat. Their bills are narrow, and are suited to feeding on water insects and larvae. Their whistling notes are loud enough to be heard over the roar of the torrents. (21 Col.; 43 S.A.; 82 N.&S.A.; 145 wld.)

AID TO IDENTIFICATION

Facial plumage variegated in contrast to rest of plumage 3, 5, 7, 9, 10, 11, 13, 19, 20, 21.

Facial plumage not variegated, back mostly brown 1, 2, 6, 7, 8, 9, 10, 11, 12, 13, 14, 15.

Back or wings mostly green 4E, 16E.

Back blackish or blackish green 14, 15, 17, 18.

Back striped or banded 2, 19, 21.

1. BLACK-BELLIED TREE-DUCK
(Dendrocygna autumnalis)

Description. 20- 22". Crown brown turning blackish on hind crown and hind neck; sides of head and neck grayish, throat white. Breast russet brown, turning grayish brown on lower breast; entire abdomen and tail black. Back rufous-brown; wing-coverts white. Bill bright pinkish red; legs flesh colored. In the Tree-ducks the sexes are similar. In flight their long legs protrude beyond the tail.

Range. Texas to Argentina.
Colombia. Rivers, marshes and tidal flats. Tropical, occasionally to the temperate zone *(discolor)*.

2. FULVOUS TREE-DUCK
(Dendrocygna bicolor)

Description. 18 - 20". General color fulvous-brown. Hind neck black; upper back barred black and rufous, lower back black. Elongated feathers at sides cream color, edged black. Bill and legs gray.

Range. California and the southern United States, Mexico. Eastern Panama to the Guianas and Trinidad. Eastern Brazil and northern Argentina. Eastern Africa, Madagascar, India, Burma and Ceylon.

Colombia. Rivers and lakes. Tropical, occasionally lower temperate zones. The Magdalena Valley, Cauca Valley and the Eastern Andes.

3. WHITE-FACED TREE-DUCK
(Dendrocygna viduata)

Description. 16 - 18″. Face and foreneck white, back of head and neck and band across throat black. Lower breast, center of abdomen and lower back black. Extreme upper back, breast and shoulders chestnut, mantle brown, feathers buff-edged. Sides of body finely barred black and white. Bill slate gray with pale band; legs blue-gray.

Range. Costa Rica southward over tropical South America, Trinidad, Africa, Madagascar and the Comoro Islands.

Colombia. Tropical, occasionally temperate zones of northern and eastern Colombia.

4. ORINOCO GOOSE
(Neochen jubatus)

Description. 24 - 30″. Whole head, neck, upper breast whitish, tinged ashy-buff, slightly mottled. Lower breast, abdomen, and upper back reddish cinnamon, turning blackish brown in center. Rest of back, wings and tail shiny dark green, patch on wing white. Upper mandible mostly black, lower red. Legs light red.

Range. Venezuela, south to Argentina and Bolivia.

Colombia. Wooded rivers and fresh water marshes, generally in pairs, in the llanos east of the Eastern Andes.

5. WHITE-CHEEKED PINTAIL
(Anas bahamensis)

Description. 15 - 17″. Top of head brown, from below eye white, very sharply defined. Back of neck brown, freckled with black; throat and foreneck white. Upper back and whole under surface fulvous, spotted dusky; lower back dusky brown. Wing speculum emerald green, edged

above and below with cinnamon, tertials edged cinnamon. Tail pointed, pale buff. Bill blue-gray, orange-red at base.

Range. Bahama Islands and West Indies, Curaçao. South America south to Argentina and Chile. The Galápagos Islands.

Colombia. Coastal lagoons, mangroves and fresh water marshes. Tropical zone of the lower Magdalena Valley *(bahamensis).*

6. YELLOW-BILLED PINTAIL
(Anas georgica)

Description. 24 - 28″ (or 21 - 24″, 1). Top of head rufescent-brown, (or blackish, 1) sides of head and neck finely (or coarsely, 1) freckled dusky. Upper parts of plumage brown, feathers with dark centers; under surface whitish. Wing speculum blackish with slight green reflections, edged above and below with cinnamon-buff. Tail rather long (or short, 1) and pointed. Bill yellow, ridge black.

Range. Cooler parts and mountains of southern and western South America from Colombia to Tierra del Fuego. The Falkland Islands and South Georgia.

Colombia. Lakes and ponds. Temperate zone. The Andes of Nariño *(spinicauda).* The central portion of the Eastern Andes and the upper Cauca Valley *(1, niceforoi).*

7. COMMON PINTAIL
(Anas acuta)

Description. 23 - 29″. ♂ : Whole head and upper neck brown, hindneck blackish, lower neck, and a line extending up side of upper neck white. Underparts white. Back finely lined black and white. Wing-coverts gray, innermost remiges elongated, black edged buff, wing speculum bronze-green, edged above cinnamon, below white. Tail black, long, pointed. ♀ : Top of head rufous streaked black, sides of head and neck fawn speckled dusky. Whole back brown variegated with white and buff. Tail dark brown, barred white. Under surface white. Bill blue-gray.

Range. Europe, Asia and North America. Kerguelen I. Winters in North Africa, tropical Asia, the Pacific islands, the West Indies and northern South America.

Colombia. Lagoons, ponds and marshes.

Winter resident, October-April. Tropical to temperate zones.

8. ANDEAN TEAL
(Anas flavirostris)

Description. 14½ - 16″. Head somewhat crested, freckled buffy and blackish. Back blackish brown, feathers pale-edged. Below buffy-white, feathers with dark centers giving a coarsely spotted appearance. Wings grayish brown, speculum black with purplish green reflections, margined above with rufous, below with buff. Bill bluish gray.

Range. The Andes of western South America, southward to southern Brazil, Bolivia and Tierra del Fuego. The Falkland Islands.

Colombia. Ponds in the temperate and páramo zones. The Central and Eastern Andes, northward to about Bogotá (andium): Bogotá northward (altipetens).

9. AMERICAN WIDGEON
(Anas americana)

Description. 17 - 22″. ♂ : Crown, large patch on shoulders, lower breast and under parts white. Broad bronze-green streak from behind the eye meeting on back of neck; rest of head freckled black and white. Upper breast pinkish, upper back pinkish gray, vermiculated black, lower back black, vermiculated white. Tail gray. Wing speculum black with bronze-green reflections. Bill gray with black tip. ♀ : Whole head and neck freckled, white and black. Back dark brown, feathers edged pale. Sides of body and upper breast pinkish brown. Wing speculum dull black.

Range. Breeds in western North America. Winters southward to the West Indies and Panama, and some Pacific islands.

Colombia. Winter resident October-April. Tropical to temperate zones. Recorded from Eastern Andes and the Cauca Valley.

10. BLUE-WINGED TEAL
(Anas discors)

Description. 15 - 16″. ♂ : Crown and chin black, large white crescentic mark in front of eye, rest of head gray. Back dark brown, feathers edged paler. Shoulders sky blue, wing speculum green, margined white above. Underparts purplish brown spotted and barred with black. Bill black, legs yellow, feet dusky. ♀ : Head and neck and body plumage mostly brown, feathers edged paler. Shoulder blue, speculum emerald green, edged above with white.

Range. Breeds in northeastern (1), central and western North America. South in winter to the northern half of South America. Bermuda and the West Indies.

Colombia. Fresh and salt water marshes. Winter resident, Sept.-April. Tropical to temperate zones (discors). The subspecies (1, orphna) has been recorded from Cali.

11. GREEN-WINGED TEAL
(Anas crecca)

Description. 13 - 16″. ♂ : Head chestnut brown, broad streak behind eye bronze-green outlined in white. Upper back and sides of body finely vermiculated black and white; lower back gray. Below mostly white; round black spots on breast. Wing speculum emerald green, bordered buff above, white below. ♀ similar to Blue-winged Teal but no blue on shoulder. Bill, legs and feet dark gray in both sexes.

Range. Breeds throughout the Northern Hemisphere. Winters southward to Central America, Africa, and Asia.

Colombia. Inland ponds and marshes. Casual. Recorded from the Eastern Andes in January (carolinensis).

12. CINNAMON TEAL
(Anas cyanoptera)

Description. 15-17″. ♂ : Crown blackish, rest of head, neck, breast, sides of body reddish chestnut dotted dusky (or plain 1). Back blackish with paler mottling. Shoulders blue, wing speculum bronze-green, broadly bordered white above. ♀ : Like Blue-winged Teal, but wing speculum brown only slightly glossed bronze-green. Bill black, legs and feet yellow in both sexes.

Range. Breeds in northwestern North America and southward in western South America to Bolivia.

Colombia. Ponds, rivers and marshes. Occasional winter visitor to northern Colombia, recorded in October and April, (1, *septentrionalium*). Resident in the temperate zone of the Eastern Andes, south to Nariño (*borreroi*). Resident in the tropical zone of the Cauca Valley below 3600 ft. and possibly the lower Magdalena Valley (*tropicus*).

13. NORTHERN SHOVELER
(Anas clypeata)

Description: 17-20". ♂: Bill very wide. Head and neck mostly metallic green. Breast and sides of back white. Upper back dark brown, lower back and upper tail-coverts deep green. Shoulder blue, speculum emerald green, bordered white above. Lower breast and belly chestnut. Tail black and white. ♀: Mostly brown above; shoulder blue, speculum dull bronze-green, bordered white above. Rather like a Blue-winged Teal but much larger. Bill black, feet orange in both sexes.

Range. Breeds in the Northern Hemisphere. South in winter to northen South America, Africa and Asia. Hawaiian Islands.

Colombia. Winter resident, October to March. Eastern Andes, temperate zone, and the Cauca Valley.

14. SOUTHERN POCHARD
(Netta erythrophthalma)

Description. 20". ♂: Head mostly very dark brown; sides of body paler brown. Rest of plumage almost uniform brownish black, slightly vermiculated with brown on back. Wing speculum and inner part of secondaries white. Bill blue-gray with black tip. No eclipse plumage. ♀: More or less uniform brown, throat, front and sides of neck and area at base of bill whitish. Wing speculum white.

Range. Venezuela to southern Peru. Eastern Brazil. Southern and eastern Africa.

Colombia. Coastal lagoons, mountain lakes and river marshes. Resident. Locally distributed on open waters from the tropical to the temperate zones.

15. LESSER SCAUP
(Aythia affinis)

Description. 15 - 18". ♂: Head and neck black, glossed with purple (dull brownish black in winter). Breast, upper back, rump and upper tail-coverts black. Center of back and sides white, with narrow wavy black lines. Lower breast and belly and patch on wing white. Bill blue-gray. ♀: Irregular white patch around base of bill. Rest of head, neck, breast, back dark brown. Lower breast and abdomen white.

Range. Breeds in western North America. Winters southward to northern South America and Trinidad.

Colombia. Winter resident in the lakes of the Eastern Andes and in the middle Cauca Valley. Recorded during January and February, and in June. Birds found in late spring and summer are probably wounded birds.

16. BRAZILIAN TEAL
(Amazonetta brasiliensis)

Description. 14-16". Crown and back of neck, lower back and rump black. Wing-coverts and outer secondaries brilliant metallic green, turning purplish on inner secondaries; wing speculum white, bordered above by black. Bill and feet orange-yellow. ♀ similar to ♂ but duller, with white marks in front of eye. Bill olive, feet dull yellow.

Range. The Orinoco, Amazon and Paraguay river basins.

Colombia. Wooded streams and marshes east of the Eastern Andes.

17. COMB DUCK
(Sarkidiornis melanotos)

Description. ♂ 30" — ♀ 22". ♂: Crown black, rest of head and neck white dotted with black. Upper back and lower surface white, rest of back black glossed with oily green and purple. Bill surmounted by a bony black comb. No eclipse plumage. ♀ similar, but smaller and without comb.

Range. Eastern Panama, northern and eastern South America. Trinidad. Tropical Africa and Asia.

Colombia. Swampy woods and savanna. Arboreal. Upper tropical to temperate zones of the Eastern, Central and Western Andes *(sylvatica)*.

18. MUSCOVY DUCK
(Cairina moschata)

Description. ♂ 33″ — ♀ 26″. ♂: A very large blackish green duck with a big white patch on the wing. Face bare, with red, warty protuberances. Bill black with a livid pale bluish band. No eclipse plumage. ♀ similar, but much smaller.

Range. Mexico, southward to Peru and Argentina. Trinidad.

Colombia. Tropical, rarely temperate zones, on thickly forested streams and ponds. Arboreal.

19. MASKED DUCK
(Oxyura dominica)

Description. 15″. ♂: Face black, neck and breast bright chestnut, the back heavily mottled with black. Wing speculum white. Tail black, stiff, erect, fanshaped. ♀: Top of head, stripe through eye and another below it black. Face and throat buffy white. Above barred black and white; or black and buff, below ochraceous, breast spotted black. Wing speculum white.

Range. Mexico and the West Indies. Trinidad southward to Chile and Argentina.

Colombia. Ponds with dense water vegetation. Tropical zone of northwestern Colombia and the temperate zone of the Eastern Andes.

20. RUDDY DUCK
(Oxyura jamaicensis)

Description. 15″. ♂: Crown black, sides of head and cheeks white, more or less speckled black, neck black (or head and neck black, chin white, 1). Rest of plumage bright chestnut, except for whitish belly. Tail, black fan-shaped, erect, stiff. ♀: Crown and stripe below eye brown, sides of head fawn, rest of upper parts grayish brown. Sides buffy brown narrowly barred blackish.

Range. Canada southward to the Bahamas, West Indies and Mexico thence through Central America and western South America to Tierra del Fuego.

Colombia. Lakes and ponds near reed beds and water vegetation. Temperate and páramo zones of the Eastern and Central Andes *(andina)*. Andes of Nariño (1, *ferruginea*).

21. TORRENT DUCK
(Merganetta armata) Fig. 18

Description. 14½ - 16″. ♂: Crown and back of neck, stripe through eye continued down side of neck black, sides of head and rest of neck white. Above sandy brown, striped black. Under surface white, streaked gray. Rump vermiculated gray and black, wing speculum green bordered white above and below. Bill narrow, rosy red. Tail gray, long and stiff. ♀: Crown and back of neck gray vermiculated black. Back like ♂. Entire underparts orangerufous.

Range. Suitable localities, throughout western South America.

Colombia. Mountain torrents of the upper tropical to páramo zones of the Andes, including Santa Marta *(colombiana)*.

AMERICAN VULTURES (Cathartidae)

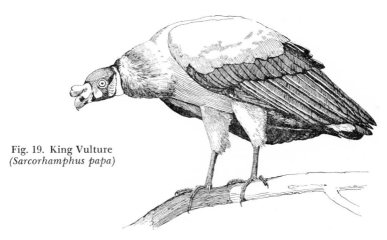

Fig. 19. King Vulture
(Sarcorhamphus papa)

American Vultures are all or chiefly black except for the King Vulture. They live on offal and the Black Vulture in particular serves a very useful purpose in keeping towns and villages in more primitive areas in a sanitary condition. Their soaring flight is very graceful and just before rain storms in the tropics Black Vultures are carried almost out of sight by the upward air currents. That species is one of the most familiar sights in towns and villages in South America.

Vultures are found in heavy tropical forest, open savanna, swamps, arid lands and mountains. (6 Col.; 6 S.A.; 7 N.&S.A.; 7 wld.)

ANDEAN CONDOR
(Vultur gryphus)

Description. 38 - 44"; wing span about 10 ft. Head bare, purplish flesh, with comb on top of head. Ruff of white down around neck. A large patch of silvery white on wing. Rest of plumage black. The young are brown.

Range. From the Straits of Magellan northward in the Andes to Venezuela.

Colombia. Temperate and páramo zones of the Andes and Santa Marta Mts.

KING VULTURE
(Sarcorhamphus papa)

Description. 28 - 32"; wing spread about 6½ ft. Head bare, orange, red and blue. Plumage mainly creamy white; rump, wings and tail black. Ruff slate gray, almost black on hind neck. Immature birds are dark brown but often show white on under parts.

Range. Mexico to Argentina. Trinidad.

Colombia. Tropical, occasionally to temperate zone in both open and forested country. Not reported from the southwest and not found any longer in the upper Cauca Valley.

BLACK VULTURE
(Coragyps atratus)

Description. 22 - 26"; wing spread 4½ ft. Head bare, grayish black. Plumage black. Patch on underside of wing, white. Tail short and square. Flapping flight interrupted by short sailings.

Range. Central and southern United States, southward to Chile and southern Brazil and Argentina. Margarita Island.

Colombia. Tropical to temperate zones, throughout the country, frequently in towns and villages *(brasiliensis)*. It is possible that in the Andes of Nariño a large form *(foetens)* is found for it has been recorded as far north as Quito.

45

TURKEY VULTURE
(Cathartes aura)

Description. 28 - 30"; wing spread about 6 ft. Head bare, purplish red (black in young birds). Plumage brownish black. Tail long, slender. Flight almost uninterrupted sailing, showing silvery under surface of remiges.

Range. From Canada to the Straits of Magellan. Trinidad, the West Indies.

Colombia. Tropical to lower temperate zone throughout the country. Less of a town bird than the Black Vulture. The forms in Colombia have not been worked out, but probably three occur: *septentrionalis* from North America as a migrant, *ruficollis* in the Amazonian and Orinocan regions and *jota* in the rest of the country. They differ from each other only in size.

YELLOW-HEADED VULTURE
(Cathartes burrovianus)

Description. 22 - 25"; wing spread 4 ft. (or 28 - 32", wing spread about 6 ft., 1). Head bare, yellow, red and bluish. Above dull black, feathers prominently tipped and edged with dull grayish brown; below brownish black. Whitish patch on under side of wing. Remiges silvery gray beneath.

Range. From Mexico southward to Panama. Venezuela, British Guiana and Surinam southward through Brazil to Paraguay, Uruguay and northern Argentina.

Colombia. Tropical zone, often in swampy places. The Cauca and upper Patía Valleys eastward through the Magdalena Valley to the Guajira Peninsula, and east of the Andes south to Meta.

GREATER YELLOW-HEADED VULTURE
(Cathartes melambrotos)

Description. 30 - 33". Very like the Yellow-headed Vulture but larger, the plumage entirely deep black with a greenish or bluish sheen and no admixture of brownish tones. Under surface of wings dull, dark brownish gray.

Range. Southern and eastern Venezuela, British Guiana, Surinam. Northern Brazil, eastern Peru.

Colombia. Tropical zone in Caquetá and Vaupés.

EAGLES AND HAWKS (Accipitridae)

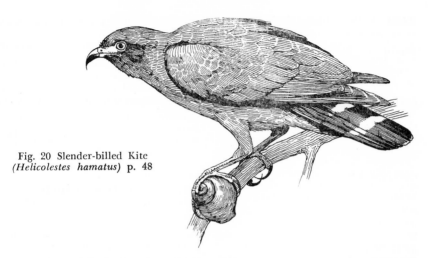

Fig. 20 Slender-billed Kite
(Helicolestes hamatus) p. 48

Eagles and hawks are distinguishable from falcons by more rounded and broader wings, the more frequent sailings in flight and by shorter and thicker toes. In habits they are similar to hawks found elsewhere. Females are usually much larger than males.

Immature plumages have not been described, but most species are streaked or spotted below and are difficult to distinguish in the field. Not infrequently two color phases, a dark and a light, are found in adult birds. (47 Col.; 51 S.A.; 66 N.&S.A.; 203 wld.)

AID TO IDENTIFICATION OF ADULTS

Black, brown or gray above, white below 1, 2, 3, 14, 17, 18, 19, 20, 26, 30E, 31, 40, 41, 44, 46, 47.
Barred below 4, 5, 10, 12, 13, 14, 15, 16, 18, 22, 23, 27, 33, 45, 47.
Dark above, moderately to heavily streaked below 5, 25, 44, 46.
Body plumage white, or gray or black 4, 6, 7, 8, 9, 13, 17, 19, 24, 28, 29, 32, 34, 35, 37.
Band across chest 13, 21, 36.
Crested 13, 38, 39, 40, 42, 43.

1. WHITE-TAILED KITE
(Elanus caeruleus)

Description. 15 - 16″. Forehead, sides of head, entire under parts and tail white. Back pale gray. Wing-coverts and patch on under side of wing black. Bill black, feet yellow.

Range. Southern United States to Nicaragua. Venezuela, Argentina and Chile. Trinidad.

Colombia. Usually seen flying over open savannas and marshy areas. Tropical, rarely temperate zone, virtually throughout *(leucurus)*.

2. SWALLOW-TAILED KITE
(Elanoïdes forficatus)

Description. 24 - 25″. Whole head, neck and underparts white. Back and tail bronzy black; tail very long, deeply forked. Bill black, feet blue-gray.

47

Range. Southern United States, south to Venezuela, Argentina, and Bolivia. Greater Antilles, Trinidad.

Colombia. Swampy forests. Tropical to temperate zone. Not recorded from the Santa Marta region (yetapa).

3. GRAY-HEADED KITE
(Leptodon cayanensis)

Description. 18 - 20". Head gray, all of under parts white. Back black; tail black with two white bands. Under side of wings and tail banded black and white. Bill black, feet blue-gray.

Range. Mexico to Venezuela, Bolivia and southern Brazil. Trinidad.

Colombia. Forest. Tropical northern Colombia from the Pacific coast to the Santa Marta region. On the Pacific coast south to the Baudó Mts.

4. HOOK-BILLED KITE
(Chondrohierax uncinatus)

Description. 15 - 17". ♂ : Bill very heavy, roundly hooked. Above slaty, below rather paler, either uniform or narrowly banded with white, cinnamon or buff. Tail black with two white bands. Bill yellowish green; legs orange-yellow. *Dark phase:* All black, tail with one broad white bar. Bill blackish, legs dusky yellow. ♀ : Above dark gray, a rufous nuchal collar. Below broadly banded white and rufous-brown. Tail blackish with two bands of white, brown or gray.

Range. Mexico to Venezuela and Argentina. The Greater and Lesser Antilles. Trinidad.

Colombia. Swampy forests and marshes. Feeds on toads and snails. Tropical rarely to the lower temperate zone throughout the country, but not recorded from the Pacific coast (uncinatus).

5. DOUBLE-TOOTHED KITE
(Harpagus bidentatus)

Description. 12 - 14". ♂ : Top and sides of head blackish gray, back dark gray. Throat white with a central black line. Under parts mostly cinnamon-rufous barred with gray and white. Tail banded with black. ♀ similar to ♂, but lower parts more extensively cinnamon. Legs orange yellow.

Range. Mexico southward to western Ecuador, Venezuela, Bolivia and Brazil. Trinidad.

Colombia. Forest. Feeds on large insects and lizards. Tropical zone west of the Andes (fasciatus), east of the Andes (bidentatus).

6. PLUMBEOUS KITE
(Ictinia plumbea) Plate II

Description. 13 - 15". Entirely bluish gray, darker on center of back. Primaries rufous on inner web. Tail black, square. Wings long, pointed, protruding well beyond tail when perched.

Range. Mexico (summer only) southward to Venezuela, Argentina, Bolivia. Trinidad.

Colombia. Forest. Tropical and subtropical zone. Not recorded from Nariño.

7. EVERGLADE KITE
(Rostrhamus sociabilis)

Description. 15 - 17". ♂ : Slaty black; upper and under tail-coverts white. Tail rather long, slightly forked, white at base and tip. Bill black, very slender; base of bill, bare orbital region and legs bright red. ♀ : Dark brown, streaked white or buff below. Eyebrow white. Tail white at base. Base of bill, orbital region and legs bright orange.

Range. Florida, southward through Central America, and east of the Andes to Venezuela, Argentina and Bolivia. Cuba.

Colombia. Marshes and llanos of the tropical, rarely to the lower temperate zones (sociabilis). Feeds on snails.

8. SLENDER-BILLED KITE
(Helicolestes hamatus) Fig. 20

Description. 14 - 15". Blue-gray including upper and under tail-coverts. Tail black (with two white bands, imm.). Bill very slender; base of bill, orbital region, legs orange yellow.

Range. Dutch Guiana and Venezuela. The Amazon valley to eastern Peru. Panama.

Colombia. Swampy forests. Northern Colombia from the west shores of the Gulf of Urabá undoubtedly eastward locally, to Amazonian Colombia. Feeds on snails.

9. BICOLORED HAWK
(Accipiter bicolor)

Description. 14 - 17". Above dark gray, below light gray. Wings and tail sooty brown, the latter with 3 or 4 indistinct black bars. Thighs chestnut-rufous. Sexes alike. Bill black, orbital skin and legs yellow.

Range. Mexico southward to Venezuela, Argentina and Chile.

Colombia. Forested areas of the tropical zone. Northwestern and northern Colombia, the Cauca and Magdalena Valley and east of the Andes southward to Caquetá (bicolor).

10. COOPER'S HAWK
(Accipiter cooperi)

Description. 15 - 20". Above dark bluish gray, darkest on crown. Under parts cinnamon buff, spotted and barred with white. Tail rather long, rounded, brownish gray with three or four black bars and tipped white. Sexes alike. Legs deep lemon yellow.

Range. Breeds in temperate North America. Winters from the central United States to Costa Rica.

Colombia. Straggler in winter. Recorded once from Cundinamarca in February. (Specimen banded at Charleswood, Manitoba, Canada).

11. TINY HAWK
(Accipiter superciliosus)

Description. 8 - 11". Above slaty gray. Throat white, rest of under parts white very narrowly banded grayish brown. Tail ashy brown with four dark brown bars.

Range. Costa Rica southward to Venezuela, Paraguay and Argentina.

Colombia. Tropical forested zone west of the Andes and Santa Marta (fontanieri). East of the Andes (superciliosus).

12. SEMICOLLARED HAWK
(Accipiter collaris)

Description. 12 -14". Head blackish, cheeks white. Upper parts sooty brown, with an ill-defined white collar on hind neck. Below white broadly barred with brown. Tail ashy brown with five darker bars.

Range. Western Venezuela, and western Ecuador; the Santa Marta Mts.

Colombia. Tropical zone of the Pacific coast; Tolima and "Bogotá."

13. GRAY-BELLIED HAWK
(Accipiter poliogaster)

Description. 17 - 20". Crown, sides of head and neck black. Upper surface dark leaden gray; under surface pale gray with dark hair-like shaft streaks; throat paler. Tail black with three obscure ashy gray bars. Sexes alike. Bill black, legs yellow. *Immature*: Head crested. Crown and nape black, sides of head, collar on hindneck and sides of neck and band across lower breast rufous. Throat white, streaked black, rest of under parts white broadly banded black. Back blackish brown, the feathers edged white. Tail with four dark bands and white tip. Looks much like No. 42 but is considerably smaller. Until recently the immature bird of this species was thought to represent a distinct species (*A. pectoralis*).

Range. Spottily distributed in Venezuela, British Guiana, Brazil, Bolivia, Paraguay and Argentina.

Colombia. Dense forest. Tropical zone. Recorded only from the Santa Marta region and the Macarena Mts., but undoubtedly more widely spread.

14. SHARP-SHINNED HAWK
(Accipiter striatus)

Description. 11 - 13". Upper surface including ear-coverts slaty gray. Cheeks and under surface white with some dusky streaking or more or less uniform bright chestnut, barred grayish white. Thighs bright chestnut. Tail ashy brown with dusky bars. Legs yellow.

Range. North America. Guatemala to Nicaragua. Western Venezuela and western South America to Bolivia, southern Brazil and Argentina. The West Indies. North American birds winter as far south as western Panama.

Colombia. Upper tropical to temperate zone of the Santa Marta region and the Eastern, Central and Western Andes; the Macarena Mts. (ventralis).

15. SAVANNA HAWK
(Heterospizias meridionalis)

Description. 20 - 25". Whole head, neck, shoulders, parts of remiges and all the under parts rufous, the latter inconspicu-

ously and narrowly barred with black. Back slaty, rump, and upper tail-coverts and tail black, the latter with white bar and tip. Legs yellow.
Range. Panama southward to Venezuela, Bolivia and Argentina. Trinidad.
Colombia. Savanna and swamp. The Caribbean coastal area, lower Magdalena Valley, the Cauca Valley and the eastern llanos *(meridionalis)*. A large form migrating from the south has been recorded from the Guajira Peninsula.

16. BLACK-CHESTED HAWK
(Buteo fuscescens)
Description. 24 - 27". Above slaty black; wing-coverts ashy gray barred black. Chest slaty black, rest of underparts white finely (to coarsely, imm.) barred with black. Tail black, tipped white.
Range. Venezuela, southward through western South America to southern Brazil and Tierra del Fuego.
Colombia. Open country. Subtropical and temperate zones of the eastern Andes and the southern portion of the central Andes *(australis)*.

17. WHITE-TAILED HAWK
(Buteo albicaudatus) Plate II
Description. 20 - 24". Crown, sides of head and upper parts slaty; lesser wing-coverts rufous. Under parts and rump white. Tail white with fine black crossbars, and wide black subterminal bar. In the dark phase almost entirely blackish brown, tail silvery gray obscurely barred.
Range. Southwestern United States, southward to Venezuela, Ecuador, Peru, Chile and Argentina. Trinidad and the Dutch West Indies.
Colombia. Forest. Upper tropical and subtropical zones west of the Andes *(hypospodius)*, east of the Andes and Santa Marta and the Guajira Peninsula *(colonus)*.

18. VARIABLE HAWK
(Buteo poecilochrous)
Description. 22 - 24". Dark slate both above and below, barred with white on belly and thighs. Tail white with about twelve dark bars and a black subterminal band. ♀ similar but mantle rufous and gray of breast mixed with rufous. In the

light phase both sexes have the under parts white.
Range. The Andes southward to northern Chile and northwestern Argentina.
Colombia. Upper tropical and subtropical zones. Upper Cauca and upper Patía Valleys.

19. RED-BACKED HAWK
(Buteo polyosoma)
Description. 20 - 22". ♂: Above and below bluish slate; tail white with about nine dark crossbars and a subterminal black band. In the light phase underparts white. Mantle occasionally rufous. ♀: Head, neck, upper breast and thighs slate; mantle and belly rufous. In the light phase like ♂ but mantle rufous.
Very similar to No. 18 but slightly smaller. Probably not distinguishable in the field.
Range. Temperate zone of the Andes and southern South America in Argentina and Tierra del Fuego. Falkland Islands and Juan Fernandez.
Colombia. Temperate zone on the west slope of the central Andes and subtropical zone in the upper Cauca Valley *(polyosoma)*.

20. ZONE-TAILED HAWK
(Buteo albonotatus)
Description. 18 - 22". Slaty black, tail with three white bars, the basal one partly concealed. Bill black with whitish base; legs yellow.
Range. Southwestern United States south to Nicaragua, and scattered records southward through South America to Paraguay and Bolivia. Trinidad, the Pearl Islands.
Colombia. Tropical zone of the Santa Marta region, and east of the Andes in Meta and Caquetá.

21. SWAINSON'S HAWK
(Buteo swainsoni)
Description. 19-22". Above dark brown; throat white, a broad band across chest dull chestnut; rest of underparts white, tinged buff and lightly barred on sides with rufous. Tail dark brown with a pale patch at base and with numerous grayish bars. Base of bill, and legs yellow.
Range. Breeds from Alaska southward

through the western United States to northern Mexico. South in winter to Venezuela, Ecuador, Argentina and Chile. **Colombia.** Dry, open country. Winter resident. Recorded from November to February in the subtropical and temperate zones of the Eastern Andes and the Cauca Valley.

22. BROAD-WINGED HAWK
(Buteo platypterus)
Description. 14-19". Above dark brown. Throat white, rest of under surface including thighs regularly banded cinnamon-rufous and white. Tail black with two broad white bands. Base of bill and legs yellow.
Range. Breeds in southern Canada and the United States east of the plains, southward to Texas; the West Indies, Tobago. South in winter to Venezuela, Brazil, Ecuador and Chile.
Colombia. Winter resident from October to April mostly in the tropical and subtropical zone (platypterus). Large flocks during migration.

23. ROADSIDE HAWK
(Buteo magnirostris)
Description. 13-15". Above brownish gray (to pale ashy gray, 1.) tip and inner web of remiges barred with rufous. Throat and breast grayish brown (or pale gray, 1), rest of under surface regularly and narrowly barred cinnamon brown (or pale cinnamon, 1) and white. Tail brown with four or five gray (or cinnamon brown, 2) bars.
Range. Mexico, southward through Central America to Venezuela, the Guianas, southern Brazil, Argentina and Bolivia. Cozumel Island. Bay Islands, Pearl Islands.
Colombia. Savanna and pasturelands. Tropical and subtropical zone of the Eastern Andes and the upper Magdalena Valley and east of the Andes from Boyacá, southward (magnirostris). The middle Magdalena Valley and the Caribbean coast southward down the Pacific coast to the Baudó river (1, insidiatrix). Nariño, northward to the middle Cauca Valley and the Pacific coast as far as the río San Juan (2, ecuadoriensis).

24. WHITE-RUMPED HAWK
(Buteo leucorrhous)
Description. 14-16". Uniform black; tibial feathers rufous. Tail black, white at base and crossed by a single ashy bar. Under tail-coverts and under wing-coverts creamy white.
Range. Venezuela, eastern and western Ecuador south to Peru, southern Brazil, Paraguay and Argentina.
Colombia. Subtropical zone of the Santa Marta Mts., the Central and Western Andes.

25 WHITE-THROATED HAWK
(Buteo albigula)
Description. 15 - 17". Above blackish brown. Throat, breast, abdomen white, breast and abdomen streaked blackish. Sides of neck, sides of breast and body ferruginous. Thighs barred rufous. Tail blackish brown with numerous, inconspicuous darker bars.
Range. Western South America in Chile, Peru, Ecuador, Venezuela.
Colombia. Subtropical and temperate zones. Recorded only from "Bogotá" and the Western Andes.

26. SHORT-TAILED HAWK
(Buteo brachyurus)
Description. 14-16". Forehead white. Crown, sides of head and back black. Below white including wing lining. Tail black, whitish below. Occasionally all black or sooty brown with the under sides of remiges whitish, barred dusky (dark phase).
Range. Florida, Mexico, Central America, southward to western Venezuela, and western South America to Peru, Bolivia, thence eastward to western Paraguay, Argentina and southern Brazil.
Colombia. Wet or swampy forest. Tropical rarely to temperate zone of the Santa Marta Mts. and the three Andean ranges (brachyurus).

27. GRAY HAWK
(Buteo nitidus)
Description. 15-17". Above pale slaty gray; pale gray on throat and upper breast. Lower breast and belly barred gray and white. Tail black with three conspicuous white bars.

Range. From the southwestern United States, southward to Venezuela, the Guianas, Bolivia and Argentina. Trinidad. Colombia. More or less open country of the Caribbean coast, the lower Magdalena Valley and the eastern llanos (*nitidus*). West side of the Gulf of Urabá (*blakei*).

28. BAY-WINGED HAWK
(Parabuteo unicinctus)
Description. 18-22". Uniform brownish black (or slightly streaked with white below, 1). Shoulders and thighs rufous-chestnut. Tail white with wide black subterminal band.Upper tail-coverts white. Range. Southern United States, southward to western Ecuador and Peru. East of the Andes from northern Venezuela southward to Paraguay, Argentina and Bolivia. Margarita Island. Colombia. Open savanna country. Tropical zone of the Cauca and Patía Valley (*harrisi*). The Caribbean coast on the Guajira Peninsula and in Atlántico (1, *unicinctus*).

29. WHITE HAWK
(Leucopternis albicollis) Plate II
Description. 18 - 22". Mostly white, primaries and subterminal tail band black (or, similar but crown spangled with black, 1; or similar but interscapular region white spotted with black; wings black, tail black with a broad white subterminal band, 2). Range. Southern Mexico to Venezuela, Peru and central and western Brazil. Trinidad. Colombia. Forest. Western Colombia from the Panama border to the lower río Anchicayá (*costaricensis*). Dry forest. Caribbean coast and lower Magdalena Valley to the east slope of the Andes in Boyacá and possibly Meta (1, *williaminae*); east of the Andes from the río Guayabero south to the Amazon (2, *albicollis*).

30. BLACK-FACED HAWK
(Leucopternis melanops)
Description. 15-16". ♂ : Head, neck, and underparts white; crown and nape streaked with black. Back and inner remiges black spotted white. Primaries and tail black, the latter with one broad

white band. ♀ similar but head white except for black lores, orbital region and ear-coverts. Range. Venezuela, the Guianas and Amazonia. Colombia. Forest. Tropical zone of Caquetá.

31. SEMIPLUMBEOUS HAWK
(Leucopternis semiplumbea)
Description. 13-14". Above uniform leaden gray. Wings and tail black, the remiges edged gray, the tail with one or two white bars. Entire underparts white with a few black streaks on sides of throat and breast. Legs orange. Range. Nicaragua to northwest Ecuador. Colombia. Forest. Tropical zone. Pacific coast eastward to the Magdalena Valley.

32. SLATE-COLORED HAWK
(Leucopternis schistacea)
Description. 15-17". Uniform bluish slate color. Tail black with a median white band and tip (or no white tip, 1). Under wing-coverts slate (or white, 1). Feet and legs orange. Range. Panama to western Ecuador. East of the Andes in southwestern Venezuela, Peru and the lower Amazon. Colombia. Forest. Tropical zone. West of the Western Andes (1, *plumbea*) ; east of the Andes (*schistacea*).

33. BARRED HAWK
(Leucopternis princeps)
Description. 18-20". Head, and upper parts, throat and foreneck slaty black; rest of under parts white narrowly barred with black. Tail black with a median white bar. Legs yellow. Range. Costa Rica to western Ecuador. Colombia. Forest, tropical zone. West slope of the Eastern Andes in Santander, Chocó and Nariño (*zimmeri*).

34. GREAT BLACK HAWK
(Buteogallus urubitinga)
Description. 24 - 26". Black. Rump, upper tail-coverts, one narrow, one broad tail band, white. Cere, orbital skin and legs pale yellow. Range. Mexico, southward to Venezuela, Argentina and Chile. Trinidad. Tobago. Colombia. Swampy woods and marshes in the tropical zone (*urubitinga*).

35. COMMON BLACK HAWK
(Buteogallus anthracinus)
Description. 18-22″. Black. One broad white band across middle of tail. Base of bill and legs orange.
Range. Southwestern United States to northern Venezuela, British Guiana, Ecuador and Peru. Trinidad.
Colombia. Caribbean coast in mangroves and swamps and semi-arid woods; east of the Andes south to the Macarena Mts. *(anthracinus)*. Pacific coast; Gorgona Island *(subtilis)*.

36. BLACK-COLLARED HAWK
(Busarellus nigricollis)
Description. 18-20″. Whole head white, nape streaked dusky. An extensive black patch on foreneck; rest of plumage bright chestnut-rufous. Primaries and distal end of tail black.
Range. Mexico southward to Venezuela, Argentina and Bolivia.
Colombia. Rivers and marshes of the tropical zone but not recorded from the southwest *(nigricollis)*.

37. SOLITARY EAGLE
(Urubitornis solitaria)
Description. 26 - 28″. Dark slaty gray, darkest on head which is slightly crested. Tail rather short, black with a white or grayish median band and white tip. Base of bill and legs yellow.
Range. Mexico, southward to Venezuela and in western South America to Peru.
Colombia. Tropical and subtropical zone in the Santa Marta region and the Western Andes *(solitaria)*.

38. CRESTED EAGLE
(Morphnus guianensis)
Description. 32-34″. Head with long brown crest, white at base, with black terminal spots. Above brownish black, feathers with brownish edges. Upper tail-coverts and wing-coverts with ashy white edges. Tail black, tipped white with three or four ashy brown bars. Neck and chest grayish brown to blackish brown. Lower breast and rest of underparts white, barred with pale rufous to black. Bill black, legs yellow.
Range. Honduras southward to Venezuela, Paraguay and Argentina.

Colombia. Forest. Tropical zone, but not recorded from the southwest.

39. HARPY EAGLE
(Harpia harpyja)
Description. 34 - 37″. Sides of head and throat gray, the head with a long and broad crest and ruff darker gray. Upper surface and chest blackish gray, rest of underparts white, the thighs barred with black. Tail black crossed by several ashy bars. Bill blue-gray, legs yellow.
Range. Mexico southward to Venezuela, Bolivia and Argentina in heavy forest.
Colombia. Tall forest of the tropical zone both east and west of the Andes.

40. BLACK-AND-CHESTNUT EAGLE
(Oroaëtus isidori)
Description. 23 - 25″. Head with long thin black crest. Above black including sides of head and throat. Under surface entirely chestnut-rufous with some narrow black streaks on breast. Thighs black. Tarsus feathered. Tail ashy gray, the terminal third black. *Immature*: Head and neck white with dark streaks. Upperparts brown, feathers edged pale. White below. Tail marbled gray and brown with three black bands.
Range. Northern Venezuela, southward to Ecuador, Peru, Bolivia and western Argentina.
Colombia. Dense mountain forest. Sea level to temperate zone. Not recorded from Nariño. A sight record from the arid Guajira Peninsula.

41. BLACK-AND-WHITE HAWK-EAGLE
(Spizastur melanoleucus)
Description. 22 - 24″. Head, neck and underparts white. Lores, orbital region and patch on crown black. Back black, wings brownish black. Tarsus feathered. Tail evenly barred black and grayish brown.
Range. Mexico southward to Venezuela, the Guianas, Bolivia and Argentina.
Colombia. Forest. Tropical and subtropical zone. Meta. The Perijá Mts. westward into the Magdalena Valley, and the west slope of the Western Andes.

42. ORNATE HAWK-EAGLE
(Spizaëtus ornatus) Plate II

Description. 23 - 25″. Top of head and long crest black. Throat white bordered laterally by a broad black band. Hind neck, sides of head and sides of breast tawny buff; lower breast, belly and flanks and feathered legs barred black and white. Above mostly black, the upper tail-coverts margined white. Tail long, conspicuously and evenly barred grayish brown and black.

Range. Mexico southward to Venezuela, Peru, Paraguay and Argentina. Trinidad.

Colombia. Tropical forest west of the Eastern Andes *(vicarius)*, east of the Andes *(ornatus)*.

43. BLACK HAWK-EAGLE
(Spizaëtus tyrannus)

Description. 25 - 28″. Black. Base of long crest feathers, bars on thighs, spots on belly white. Tail long, with four or five equal bars of black and grayish brown.

Range. Mexico to Venezuela southeastern Brazil, eastern Peru and eastern Bolivia. Trinidad.

Colombia. Tropical zone. In forested areas probably throughout *(serus)*.

44. MARSH HAWK
(Circus cyaneus)

Description. 18 - 24″. ♂ : Head, neck, chest, upperparts and central tail feathers pale gray; wing-feathers tipped dusky. Rump and underparts white, the latter lightly spotted and barred rufous. Outer tail-feathers barred black. ♀ : Sides of head and upper parts dark brown, streaked paler. Below tawny buff, the throat and breast streaked brown. Rump white, tail feathers grayish brown with four or five darker bars.

Range. Breeds in the Northern Hemisphere. Winters in south to north Africa and eastern Asia, and in America in the southern states, the West Indies, Central America and Colombia.

Colombia. Winter resident November to March. Grassy or marshy areas west of the Eastern Andes *(hudsonius)*.

45. CINEREOUS HARRIER
(Circus cinereus)

Description. 17 - 22″. ♂ : Above ashy gray, primaries black. Upper tail-coverts white; tail ashy with dark subterminal band. Throat and chest gray barred white. Below, including thighs narrowly barred orange-rufous and white. ♀ : Above brown; rump white, barred with pale rufous. Below barred orange-rufous and white. Wings and tail ashy gray barred with brown.

Range. Western South America from Colombia to Tierra del Fuego and the Falkland Islands.

Colombia. Marshes and grasslands. Subtropical and temperate zone of the Eastern Andes, both slopes southward into Nariño.

46. LONG-WINGED HARRIER
(Circus brasiliensis)

Description. 18 - 24″. ♂ : Head, throat and upper surface black. Forehead, eyebrow, chin, rump and underparts white; flanks barred with rufous brown. Tail ashy gray tipped with white, with six black bars. ♀ : Forehead, cheeks and throat whitish. Above brown, upper tail-coverts white. Underparts dark brown streaked paler. Tail ashy with four black bars.

Range. Mostly eastern South America from Venezuela to Patagonia. Trinidad.

Colombia. Tropical zone. Marshes and grasslands, east of the Andes and the upper Cauca Valley.

47. CRANE HAWK
(Geranospiza caerulescens) Plate II

Description. 17 - 20″. Blue-gray. Tail black with two rather narrow white bands. Legs long, yellow to reddish orange.

Range. Mexico southward through Central America southward to northwestern Peru. East of the Andes from Venezuela and the Guianas southward to Bolivia, Paraguay, and Argentina.

Colombia. Usually near marshy river banks. Tropical zone. The Santa Marta region, the Magdalena Valley and Meta *(caerulescens)*. Tropical Pacific coast of Colombia *(balzarensis)*.

OSPREYS (Pandionidae)

Fig 21. Osprey
(Pandion haliaetus)

Ospreys feed on fish which they catch by plunging after them, feet first. They are always found near water. Their white underparts and dark wings, which are more bent backward when sailing than in other hawks, help to identify them. (1 Col.; 1 S.A.; 1 N.&S.A.; 1 wld.)

OSPREY
(Pandion haliaetus)
Description. 21 - 24". Whole head, neck and underparts white. Crown, hind neck, eye-stripe, back, wings and tail dark brown, the latter with five to seven dark bars on under side.

Range. Seacoasts, large rivers and lakes in the temperate and tropical regions of the world.

Colombia. Coasts and large rivers throughout the country. Occasionally over mountain lakes as high as 10,500 ft. *(carolinensis).*

FALCONS AND CARACARAS (Falconidae)

Fig. 22. Peregrine Falcon
(Falco peregrinus) p. 58

Falcons differ from hawks in usually having narrower and much more pointed wings and more slender toes. In flight they soar much less, and often hover while looking for their prey. They feed on birds, mammals and reptiles and are found virtually everywhere except the oceanic islands and the Antarctic. (17 Col.; 21 S.A.; 24 N.&S.A.; 58 wld.)

AID TO IDENTIFICATION

Dark above, white to buff below 1, 2, 3, 8, 11.
Banded below 2, 4, 5, 10, 12.
Streaked below 12, 16, 17.
All or partially black, bare skin of throat and face red or yellow 6E, 7, 9, 10.
Black and white or gray, white and chestnut 11, 13, 14, 15, 17.

1. LAUGHING FALCON
(Herpetotheres cachinnans) Plate II

Description. 18 - 22″. Crown to extreme upper mantle and underparts creamy white to pale buff, crown narrowly streaked black. Sides of head, continued as collar around hindneck, black. Back and wings chocolate brown. Tail conspicuously banded black and white.

Range. Southern Mexico to Venezuela, Peru, Brazil, Bolivia and Argentina.

Colombia. Rivers and marshes of the tropical and subtropical zone *(cachinnans).*

2. COLLARED FOREST-FALCON
(Micrastur semitorquatus)

Description. 18 - 24″. Above black. Collar around hind neck, throat, spot on auriculars and entire underparts white (occasionally tawny). Tail long, rounded, conspicuously barred black and white.

Range. Mexico southward to Venezuela, the Guianas, southward to Peru, Bolivia, Paraguay and Argentina.

Colombia. Tropical forests, often near palm trees, of northern and northwestern Colombia down the west coast to Buenaventura *(naso).* The Santa Marta region and Boyacá *(semitorquatus).*

56

3. SLATY-BACKED FOREST-FALCON
(Micrastur mirandollei)

Description. 14 - 16". Above slate gray, darker on head. Below white. Tail black tipped white and crossed by three white (or ashy, 1) bars. Young birds have the breast feathers edged pale grayish.

Range. Costa Rica to Venezuela, the Guianas, Brazil and Peru.

Colombia. Forest. Tropical western coast down to Buenaventura *(1, extimus)*. East of the Andes *(mirandollei)*.

4. BARRED FOREST-FALCON
(Micrastur ruficollis) Plate II

Description. 13 - 15". Above blackish brown, collar on hindneck buffy white. Throat white, underparts thickly barred blackish brown and white. Tail long, blackish with three (or five, 1) narrow white bars and white tip.

Range. Mexico to western Ecuador and southward east of the Andes to Argentina.

Colombia. Forest. Tropical to subtropical zone of the Santa Marta region *(zonothorax)*, the west coast and the Cauca Valley *(1, interstes)*.

5. LINED FOREST-FALCON
(Micrastur gilvicollis)

Description. 12 - 14". Above slaty gray (or blue-gray, 1), throat pale gray, underparts white, barred on chest with thin, wavy black lines (or more regularly with gray lines, 1). Tail short, black with three (or one, 1) white bars.

Range. Western Ecuador and tropical South America east of the Andes, from Venezuela, the Guianas and Ecuador south to Brazil, Bolivia and Argentina.

Colombia. Forest. Tropical zone east of the Andes *(gilvicollis)*. Southwestern Colombia west of the Andes from Cauca southward *(1, plumbeus)*.

6. YELLOW-THROATED CARACARA
(Daptrius ater)

Description. 17 - 19". Entirely black with greenish reflections except for white band at base of tail. Orbital skin orange, throat bright yellow. Legs yellow.

Range. Southern Venezuela, the Guianas southward to eastern and western Brazil and Bolivia.

Colombia. Forests and clearings of the tropical zone east of the Andes.

7. RED-THROATED CARACARA
(Daptrius americanus)

Description. 19 - 22". Glossy black. Belly, thighs and under tail-coverts white. Orbital skin, throat and legs vermillion.

Range. Mexico southward to Venezuela, central Peru and southern Brazil.

Colombia. Forests of the tropical zone *(americanus)*.

8. YELLOW-HEADED CARACARA
(Milvago chimachima)

Description. 16 - 18". Head and neck buff, streaked with brown; a black stripe behind eye; below pale to deep buff. Upper parts dark brown, feathers edged paler. Tail buffy white with seven narrow dark bars.

Range. Panama southward over the greater part of tropical South America from Venezuela and the Guianas to Bolivia and Argentina. Curaçao.

Colombia. Tropical and subtropical zones. More or less open grasslands, often accompanying cattle. Generally throughout the country except for the Amazonian region *(cordatus)*. On the Amazon at Leticia *(chimachima)*.

9. MOUNTAIN CARACARA
(Phalcoboenus megalopterus)

Description. 20 - 22". Head crested; head, neck and back black. Under surface striped black and white. Remiges tipped white. Bend of wing, belly, thighs, upper and under tail-coverts, under wing-coverts white. Tail black, with white terminal band. Bare skin of face, throat, and legs orange-red. Young birds are brown with a buff rump; outer tail-feathers deep buff.

Range. Western and southern South America.

Colombia. Temperate and páramo zone of Nariño and southern portion of the Central Andes *(carunculatus)*.

10. CRESTED CARACARA
(Caracara plancus)

Description. 20 - 24". Crown, crest, back, thighs black, mantle barred with wavy buff bars. Throat whitish, foreneck and chest buff, latter barred black. Upper and under tail-coverts white; tail buff with many narrow black bars and wide black subterminal band. Bare face red; bill bluish gray; legs yellow.

Range. Florida southward to Central America, Venezuela and Tierra del Fuego. Margarita and Blanquilla Islands. Cuba.

Colombia. Tropical to temperate zone in dry, open country of the Andes (cheriway).

11. PEARL KITE
(Gampsonyx swainsoni) Plate II

Description. 8 - 10". Forehead and sides of head orange-buff; throat, sides of neck, collar around hindneck, wing-coverts and underparts white. Above slaty gray, except for chestnut interscapular patch; patch on sides of chest black. Thighs pale rufous. Secondaries broadly tipped white. Tail black.

Range. Nicaragua. Venezuela, the Guianas, Argentina and Bolivia. Trinidad.

Colombia. Semi-arid and humid regions. Open woodlands in the tropical zone of the Caribbean coast and forests west of the Gulf of Urabá and the middle Magdalena Valley (leonae).

Recently, this species has been placed in the Accipitridae next to the White-tailed Kite. Anatomical studies tend to confirm this classification.

12. PEREGRINE FALCON
(Falco peregrinus) Fig. 22

Description. 15 - 20". Above dark bluish slate, darker on head and wings. Throat, patch on ear-coverts (or no patch on ear-coverts, 1) and upper breast white. A conspicuous blackish moustacial streak. Rest of underparts banded buffy white and black. Tail bluish slate with five or six dark bars and white tip.

Range. Virtually cosmopolitan.

Colombia. Winter resident, migrating from the north, October to March (anatum). Summer resident migrating from the south (June, July) to southwestern Colombia (1, cassini).

13. ORANGE-BREASTED FALCON
(Falco deiroleucus)

Description. 13 - 15". Above black, feathers bordered by slate gray. Side of head black, throat buffy white, chest, thighs and under tail-coverts chestnut, belly black barred and spotted rufous buff. Tail black with three grayish white bars.

Range. Mexico southward to western Venezuela, Peru and Argentina. Trinidad.

Colombia. Tropical and subtropical zone of the Magdalena Valley west to the west slope of the Western Andes in Cauca. East of the Andes in Boyacá.

14. BAT FALCON
(Falco rufigularis) Plate II

Description. 9 - 12". Side of head and upper parts black, shading to bluish slate posteriorly. Tail black banded narrowly by three or four slaty bands. Throat and upper breast white; thighs, abdomen and under tail-coverts deep chestnut.

Range. Mexico southward to Venezuela, Peru, Bolivia and Argentina. Trinidad.

Colombia. Open and savanna country. Feeds on bats. Tropical zone. West of the Andes (petoensis). East of the Andes (rufigularis).

15. APLOMADO FALCON
(Falco femoralis)

Description. 15 - 18". Crown blackish slate surrounded by a tawny buff band. Space behind eye and moustacial streak black. Upper parts slaty black, the tail conspicuously banded by six or seven white bands. Sides of neck, throat and underparts tawny buff, the belly crossed by a broad black band, the feathers edged white.

Range. Southwestern United States to Venezuela, British Guiana and Tierra del Fuego. Trinidad.

Colombia. Subtropical and temperate zones. Drier portions of northern Colombia southward in the middle Cauca and

Magdalena Valleys, east of the Andes in Meta *(femoralis)*. Extreme southern Cauca Valley and Nariño *(pichinchae)*.

16. MERLIN
(Falco columbarius)

Description. 10 - 13″. ♂ : Above dark slaty blue, sides of head paler. Below white to buffy streaked brown or rufous brown. Tail blue-gray with a broad subterminal band and three or four narrower black bars, tipped white. ♀ similar but above dark brown.

Range. Breeds in North America, northern Europe and northern Asia. Winters in northern South America, to Venezuela and Peru, the West Indies, Trinidad, Tobago, Aruba, Bonaire, Curaçao. Northern Africa, northern India, and southern China.

Colombia. Winter resident October to May. Tropical to temperate zone west of the Andes *(columbarius)*. A paler race breeding in northwestern North America has been recorded once from Santa Marta, February *(bendirei)*.

17. AMERICAN KESTREL
(Falco sparverius)

Description. 9-11″. ♂ : Center of crown chestnut surrounded by gray. Throat and sides of head white, the latter with two vertical black stripes and a black spot on ear-coverts. Hind neck and back chestnut rufous, barred black. Tail rufous tipped white, with a broad subterminal black bar. Wings blue-gray. Under surface buffy white to cinnamon spotted black on sides. ♀ similar but wings like back, tail barred black.

Range. From Arctic America to Tierra del Fuego. Trinidad. Birds breeding in North America migrate southward as far as eastern Panama.

Colombia. Savannas and open country. Tropical to temperate zone. Santa Marta eastward to the Orinoco *(isabellinus)*. The llanos del Meta southward to Caquetá, and the Eastern Andes and Magdalena Valley *(intermedius)*. The Cúcuta region and along the Venezuelan boundary *(ochraceus)*. The Cauca Valley, the Pacific coast and Nariño *(caucae)*. Extreme northern Antioquia *(subsp.?)*.

CURASSOWS, GUANS AND CHACHALACAS (Cracidae)

Fig. 23. Great Curassow
(*Crax rubra*) p. 62

These large gregarious game birds, varying in size from that of a turkey to a pheasant, inhabit the forests and thickets of tropical America. Curassows feed on the ground but resort to trees when disturbed and perch there at night; guans are more arboreal and frequently feed on fruit and berries high up in the tree-tops. Their nests of sticks are built in branches of forest trees. They lay two or three very large, rough-shelled eggs. Some of the species, particularly the chachalacas, are noisy and reveal their presence by their cackling notes. Curassows emit a low grunting sound, guans a piping note. (24 Col.; 34 S.A.; 39 N.&S.A.; 39 wld.)

AID TO IDENTIFICATION

Black and white (tail tipped white) 2E, 4, 7, 8E, 9, (tail all black) 5E, 6E, 10.
Chestnut and black or buff and black 1E, 3E, 4, 6E, 7, 9.
Bronzy olive above (back pale streaked) 12E, 13, 14E, 17, (not streaked) 11, 15, 16, 22.
Outer tail feathers chestnut or olive tipped white 18E, 19, 20, 21.
Generally deep glossy blackish green 23E, 24.

1. NOCTURNAL CURASSOW
(Nothocrax urumutum)

Description. 26". Crown and long flat crest black. Neck and underparts orange-rufous, paler on belly. Back and tail vermiculated brown and black. Tail tipped pale. Legs red.

Range. Southern Venezuela, eastern Ecuador, southward to Peru and western Brazil.

Colombia. Forest. Tropical zone east of the Andes from Caquetá southward and eastward.

2. SALVIN'S RAZOR-BILLED CURASSOW
(Mitu salvini) Plate III

Description. 35". Entirely blue-black, except for white belly, flanks, under tail-coverts and tip of tail. Bill red, highly arched, narrow and sharply curved. Legs red.

Range. Eastern Ecuador and northeastern Peru.

Colombia. Tropical forested zone along the eastern base of the Eastern Andes.

60

3. LESSER RAZOR-BILLED CURASSOW
(Mitu tomentosa)

Description. 33″. Similar to *M. salvini* but belly, flanks, under tail-coverts chestnut.

Range. British Guiana and Venezuela eastward to Colombia.

Colombia. Forested regions and wooded river banks east of the Eastern Andes.

4. HELMETED CURASSOW
(Pauxi pauxi) Plate III

Description. 36″. Black with a green gloss. Belly, flanks, under tail-coverts and tip of tail white. A large bony fig-shaped casque from one to three inches in height springing from the forehead. Legs red. *Rufous phase:* Head and neck black; upper parts buffy brown, the feathers with sub-terminal black bars, wing-coverts margined whitish. Flight feathers and tail buffy brown, vermiculated black. Lower surface paler the feathers edged dusky. Belly and under tail-coverts buffy white.

Range. Western Venezuela. Bolivia.

Colombia. Forest. Upper tropical and subtropical zone. Northern Norte de Santander *(pauxi)*. Extreme northeastern Colombia in the Perijà Mts. *(gilliardi)*.

5. BLACK CURASSOW
(Crax alector)

Description. 38″. ♂: Head crested, the crest feathers curled forward at tips. Entirely glossy black except for white belly, flanks and under tail-coverts. Tail all black. ♀ like ♂ but crest feathers barred white. Bill blackish, yellow to light red at base. Legs blue-gray.

(As all male Curassows look alike and differ only in the color and shape of the wattles at the base of the bill, color of the legs, and the presence or absence of a white tip to the tail, only these distinctive characters will be given for the next five species.)

Range. The Guianas, southern Venezuela, and north Brazil west to the río Negro.

Colombia. Forest. Tropical to lower subtropical zone east of the Andes from Meta southward.

6. WATTLED CURASSOW
(Crax globulosa)

Description. 36″. ♂: (See No. 5.) Tail black. Red or yellow wattles at the base of the bill. Legs gray. ♀ differs from the ♂ in having the belly, flanks and under tail-coverts chestnut rufous, and no wattles.

Range. Upper Amazon from eastern Ecuador south to northeastern Bolivia.

Colombia. Forests east of the Andes from Caquetá southward to the Amazon.

7. BLUE-KNOBBED CURASSOW
(Crax alberti)

Description. 36″. ♂: (See No. 5.) Tail tipped white. Bill greenish, swollen bony knobs at base of lower mandible blue. Legs flesh. ♀: Head, neck and upper breast black. Upperparts, wings and tail black narrowly banded with white. Outer primaries, wing-coverts and lower breast rufous-chestnut, paling to cinnamon on belly and sides of body, the latter barred with black.

Range. Colombia.

Colombia. Forest. Tropical zone of northern Colombia west of the Andes from the Santa Marta region to the upper Sinú Valley.

8. YELLOW-KNOBBED CURASSOW
(Crax daubentoni)

Description. 33″. ♂: (See No. 5.) Tail tipped white. Knobs at base of lower mandible yellow; legs gray. ♀ like ♂ but crest, wing-coverts, breast and sides of body barred with white. Bill black.

Range. Northwestern Venezuela.

Colombia. Forest. Tropical zone east of the Andes in Arauca, eastern Magdalena and the Montes de Oca in the Guajira Peninsula.

9. ANNULATED CURASSOW
(Crax annulata)

Description. 30″. ♂: (See No. 5.) Tail tipped white. Base of bill yellow, legs flesh. No wattle. ♀: Black, barred on wing-coverts and conspicuously from chin to lower breast with buffy white. Crest feathers extensively white, black only for terminal quarter. Not well known, possibly a subspecies of *C. daubentoni*.

Range. Colombia.

Colombia. Forest. Humid tropical zone of the Santa Marta region.

10. GREAT CURASSOW
(Crax rubra) Fig. 23

Description. 36″. ♂: (See No. 5.) Tail all black. Bill black; knob at base of upper mandible, and the base of lower mandible yellow. Legs pale gray. ♀: Head and neck black, spotted with white, crest broadly barred with white. Rest of plumage chestnut, paler on belly. Tail banded broadly black and buff.

Range. Mexico southward to western Ecuador.

Colombia. Forest. Tropical zone of Pacific Colombia, eastward to the upper río Sinú and the Gulf of Urabá *(rubra)*.

11. CRESTED GUAN
(Penelope purpurascens) Plate III

Description. 36″. Bare skin of face blue, of front of neck red. Head, hindneck, upper back, wings, almost uniform bronzy olive. Chest streaked white; lower back, belly, rump and under tail-coverts chestnut. Tail coppery olive. Head crested.

Range. Mexico to Venezuela and western Ecuador.

Colombia. Forest. Tropical zone. Northern Colombia in the Perijá Mts., the Santa Marta region and the Magdalena Valley *(brunnescens)*. The Pacific coast and eastward across northern Colombia to Boyacá and Arauca *(aequatorialis)*.

12. RUFOUS-BREASTED GUAN
(Penelope jacquaçu)

Description. 30″. Differs from the Crested Guan in having the lower back and upper tail-coverts olive brown. The tail and wings much greener; the lower breast rufescent-chestnut, feathers edged white, belly rufous. In size it is smaller.

Range. Western South America, south to Bolivia.

Colombia. Forested zone east of the Andes *(jacquaçu)*.

13. CAUCA GUAN
(Penelope perspicax)

Description. 30″. Face blue-black, foreneck red, bare. Legs red. Crown, hindneck, upper mantle bronzy olive, each feather narrowly edged with gray. Entire breast olive, each feather rather broadly edged white. Wings and tail coppery olive. Lower back, belly, upper and under tail-coverts chestnut.

Range. Colombia.

Colombia. Forest. Known only from the upper tropical and subtropical zone at the southern end of the Western Andes and the west slope of the Central Andes. (Perhaps a race of the Rufous-Breasted Guan.)

14. GREEN-BACKED GUAN
(Penelope granti)

Description. 34″. Similar to No. 12, but larger and with the entire back olive green; lower breast and belly darker and less rufescent.

Range. British Guiana, Venezuela, and northern Brazil.

Colombia. Forest. Southeastern Colombia in the río Guainía region *(orienticola)*.

15. BRONZY GUAN
(Penelope ortoni)

Description. 26″. Face blue-black, foreneck red, bare. Uniform bronzy olive above, lower back and upper tail-coverts browner. Breast and upper belly brown, feathers edged white, lower belly uniform olive brown. Distinguishable from other guans by complete absence of rufescent tones below.

Range. Western Ecuador.

Colombia. Forest. Subtropical zones of Pacific Colombia from the Baudó Mts. southward.

16. ANDEAN GUAN
(Penelope montagnii)

Description. 24″. Region around the eye bare, throat feathered. Crown, hindneck dark olive, feathers edged with gray. Mantle, wings and tail bronzy; lower back, upper and under tail-coverts chestnut, obscurely banded with black. Throat and breast olive, feathers broadly edged with pale gray; abdomen pale brown. Bill brown with yellow tip; legs salmon pink.

Range. Western Venezuela, southward through the Andes to Bolivia.

Colombia. Forest. Upper subtropical to temperate zones of the Eastern and Central Andes, southward into Nariño on the west slope of the mountains *(montagnii)*. East slope of the Andes of Nariño *(brooki)*.

17. BAND-TAILED GUAN
(Penelope argyrotis)

Description. 27″. Crest of long, narrow (or broad, rounded, 1) feathers dark olive, edged with gray. Upper back, wings and breast bronzy brown (or olive green, 2), feathers white edged; rest of underparts and lower back brown. Primaries edged with olive gray; tail bronzy with broad, diffused rufous (or buffy white, 1) terminal band.

Range. Northern Venezuela. Southwestern Ecuador and northwestern Peru.

Colombia. Forest. Upper tropical and subtropical zones of the Santa Marta Mts. *(colombiana)*. Subtropical zone of the Perijá Mts. (1, *albicauda)*. Subtropical zone of the northern part of the Eastern Andes (1, 2, *mesaeus)*.

18. SPECKLED CHACHALACA
(Ortalis guttata)

Description. 20″. Crown dark brown, superciliaries gray. Upper back bronzy brown; wings and central tail-feathers somewhat greener; outer tail-feathers mostly chestnut; lower back and under tail-coverts chestnut. Throat black; feathers of neck bronzy brown, streaked with gray, breast bronzy brown spotted with white; lower breast gray; flanks rufescent. Legs grayish brown.

Range. Eastern Ecuador southward to eastern Brazil and Bolivia.

Colombia. Forest. Tropical zone, east of the Eastern Andes *(guttata)*.

19. COLOMBIAN CHACHALACA
(Ortalis columbiana) Plate III

Description. 23″. Forehead whitish, rest of head and neck gray (or forehead same color as rest of head, 1). Back, wings and central tail-feathers bronzy olive green. Breast blackish, feathers margined white giving a scaly appearance; rest of under parts grayish (or tinged rufescent, 1); under tail-coverts brown; outer tail-feathers mostly chestnut. Legs dark red.

Range. Colombia.

Colombia. Forest. Tropical and upper subtropical zones of the middle and upper Magdalena Valley *(columbiana)*. Middle and upper Cauca Valley (1, *caucae)*.

This species is often considered as a subspecies of *guttata*. Both differ from all other chachalacas found in their region by having light chestnut outer tail-feathers.

20. RUFOUS-VENTED CHACHALACA
(Ortalis ruficauda)

Description. 23″. Forehead and malar region black, crown and side of head gray. Upper parts and chest olive green, lower back somewhat browner; lower breast and belly grayish brown; flanks light rufous; crissum rufous chestnut. Tail bronzy green broadly tipped white (or rufous, 1).

Range. Northern Venezuela, Tobago.

Colombia. Forest. Tropical zone of the Santa Marta region to the east and south of the mountains *(ruficrissa)*. Mountains above Nazaret in the Guajira Peninsula *(lamprophonia)*. Cúcuta region *(baliolus)*. Arauca (1, *ruficauda)*.

21. CHESTNUT-WINGED CHACHALACA
(Ortalis garrula)

Description. 20″ (or 19″, 1): Head and neck rufous brown (or crown blackish gray, cheeks olive, 1), upper surface bronzy green to bronzy brown. Primaries rufous chestnut; tail bronze green, all but central feathers tipped white (or buff, 1). Breast brownish olive. Rest of under parts whitish (or buff, 1).

Range. Nicaragua to northern Colombia.

Colombia. Thickets and scrub. Tropical zone of northern Colombia to the upper Sinú Valley (*garrula*). Pacific coast near the Panama border eastward to the Gulf of Urabá where intermediate with *mira* of eastern Darién (1, *chocoensis*).

22. SICKLE-WINGED GUAN
(*Chamaepetes goudotii*)

Description. 25″. ♂: Whole head, neck, upper surface, wings and tail bronze green (or front of neck rufescent, 1). Rest of underparts rufous chestnut. Outermost primaries attenuated. Facial skin light blue; legs pinkish red. ♀ similar but front of neck brownish, back paler.

Range. Colombia, southward to Peru.

Colombia. Forest. Subtropical zone of the Santa Marta Mts. (1, *sanctaemarthae*). Upper tropical to temperate zone of the Eastern, Central and Western Andes (*goudotii*). Nariño east of the Andes (1, *tschudii*), west of them (*fagani*).

23. WHITE-HEADED PIPING GUAN
(*Pipile cumanensis*)

Description. 27″. Entire plumage glossy greenish black, except for white crown and crest, streaks on breast and wing-coverts, and patch on wing. Bare skin of face blue, legs red.

Range. Venezuela south of the Orinoco, the Guianas southward to Ecuador, Peru and central and southern Brazil, Paraguay, Bolivia and northern Argentina.

Colombia. Forest. Tropical zone east of the Eastern Andes (*cumanensis*).

24. WATTLED GUAN
(*Aburria aburri*)

Description. 28″. Black, glossed bronze-green. Bare patch of skin and wattle hanging from neck yellowish white, legs pale yellow.

Range. Western Venezuela to eastern Ecuador and Peru.

Colombia. Forest. Upper tropical and subtropical zones of the Eastern, Central and Western Andes. The Macarena Mts.

QUAILS AND PARTRIDGES (Phasianidae)

Fig. 24. Black-fronted Wood-Quail
(Odontophorus atrifrons) p. 66

Quails and partridges belong to the large family of pheasants. Poorly represented in the Americas they reach their highest development in Asia where such well-known species as Ring-necked and Golden Pheasants and peacocks occur.

Essentially ground birds, all are excellent for the table and are hunted wherever they are found. In Colombia all except the bobwhite are inhabitants of heavy forest and thick scrub and are very difficult to shoot as they fly off swiftly through the dense vegetation. Their food consists of seeds, fruit and insects. They are gregarious; nest on the ground. (7 Col.; 12 S.A.; 30 N.&S.A.; 165 wld.)

AID TO IDENTIFICATION

Breast spotted 1, 4, 6.
Lower parts barred or scalloped 2, 7.
Under parts plain 3, 5, 7

1. CRESTED BOBWHITE
(Colinus cristatus) Plate III
Description. 8½ - 9½ ". ♂ : Long crest sandy. Eyebrow, cheeks and throat plain chestnut; forehead, space above and below eye, ear-coverts and chin white. Hindneck and extreme upper back black, spotted with white, rest of back brown spotted with black. Breast and sides of body chestnut spotted with white (or breast plain chestnut, 1). ♀ : Crest barred brown and buff. Throat white to rusty, spotted black. Hindneck, breast, sides of body variegated white, black and buff giving a spotted effect. Back dark to pale brown, barred and spotted black.
Range. From Guatemala southward to Venezuela and eastward to the Guianas and northeastern Brazil.

Colombia. Scrub, pastures, open woods. Humid tropical zone of the Caribbean coast west to the southwest base of the Santa Marta Mts. *(decoratus)*. Semi-arid country at the northern base of the Santa Marta Mts. *(littoralis)*. Arid plains of the Guajira Peninsula and the eastern base of the Santa Marta Mts. *(cristatus)*. Tropical and subtropical zones of the Cauca Valley to the west slope of the Western Andes *(badius)*. Tropical and subtropical zones of the upper and middle Magdalena Valley, up to about 6500 ft. and the middle Sinú Valley *(leucotis)*. Temperate zone of the Eastern Andes in Cundinamarca and Boyacá above 7500 ft. *(bogotensis)*. Tropical and subtropical zones of the east slope of the Eastern Andes (1, *parvicristatus*).

65

2. MARBLED WOOD-QUAIL
(Odontophorus gujanensis)
Description. 10 - 11". General appearance plain dark brown; actually obscurely barred and marbled below with black, buff and a little white. Wings variegated black, buff and brown. Upper back gray, finely barred and speckled with black, lower back browner.
Range. Costa Rica, south to Venezuela, the Guianas, Brazil and Bolivia.
Colombia. Forest and second growth. Tropical zone. Northern Colombia, from the Pacific coast eastward to the Perijá Mts. (marmoratus). Meta southward to Caquetá and Vaupés (buckleyi).

3. RUFOUS-FRONTED WOOD-QUAIL
(Odontophorus erythrops)
Description. 10 - 10½". Crest uniform blackish brown. Forehead, above and below the eye, ear-coverts and under parts chestnut. Throat black, gorget white, bordered below by a black and white band. Back dark brown, vermiculated buffy. Wings dark brown, mottled with black and spotted with buff.
Range. Honduras to western Ecuador.
Colombia. Forest and second growth. Tropical zone. The Pacific slope south to Nariño. Eastward to the west slope of the Central Andes in Antioquia (parambae).

4. BLACK-FRONTED WOOD-QUAIL
(Odontophorus atrifrons) Fig. 24
Description. 11 - 12". ♂ : Crest chestnut-brown. Forehead, narrow eyebrow, chin, throat and ear-coverts black. Upper back grayish brown, vermiculated with black, lower back spotted with black. Wings variegated grayish, chestnut and black, spotted with buff. Breast grayish brown spotted with buff; lower breast and belly ochraceous, streaked with black. Tail longer than in other Colombian species. ♀ similar but more rufescent below.
Range. Western Venezuela.
Colombia. Forest. Santa Marta Mts. between 3600-7000 ft. (atrifrons). Subtropical zone of the northern end of the Eastern Andes (variegatus).

5. CHESTNUT WOOD-QUAIL
(Odontophorus hyperythrus)
Description. 10 - 11". ♂ : Feathers around eye and ear-coverts white; crown, sides of head, throat and underparts orange-rufous. Back brown, vermiculated with black, feathers streaked gray on hindneck. Wings similar, but mottled with black and spotted with buff. ♀ : Crown blackish brown, feathers around eye and ear-coverts white. Chin, throat and upper breast chestnut; rest of underparts gray.
Range. Colombia.
Colombia. Humid cloud forest. Subtropical zones of the Eastern, Central and Western Andes.

6. GORGETED WOOD-QUAIL
(Odontophorus strophium)
Description. 10". ♂ : Crown and ear-coverts blackish brown, sides of head white speckled with black; chin white, throat black, crossed by a crescentic white mark; rest of underparts reddish chestnut with large white spots on breast. Above dark brown, variegated with black, chestnut and buff. ♀ or immature: slaty below.
Range. Colombia.
Colombia. Known only from near Bogotá.

7. TAWNY-FACED QUAIL
(Rhynchortyx cinctus) Plate III
Description. 7 - 8". ♂ : Lores, eyebrow and cheeks bright orange-rufous; entire crown reddish brown, slightly spotted with black; upper part of ear-coverts black, forming a streak behind the eye. Chin white, throat and breast pearl gray; lower breast tawny buff; belly white, flanks barred buff and black. Back dark gray, feathers of mantle edged with maroon. Lower back and rump variegated pinkish buff and black. Wings variegated maroon, black and buff. ♀ : Crown and mantle dark chestnut, lower back and upper tail-coverts dark ochraceous tawny, vermiculated and spotted with black. Streak behind eye and throat white. Broad band across breast reddish brown; underparts white coarsely barred with black. Wings like the ♂.
Range. Honduras to western Ecuador.
Colombia. Forest. Tropical zone of Pacific Colombia, eastward to the Sinú Valley (cinctus). The west coast from the Baudó Mts. southward (australis).

HOATZINS (Opisthocomidae)

Fig. 25. Hoatzin
(Opisthocomus hoazin)

The Hoatzin is one of the most peculiar of all living birds, and its relationship to other families is obscure.

In appearance it somewhat resembles a pheasant. It is also reminiscent of the African turacos, relatives of the cuckoos, particularly in its awkward movements and clumsy flight. Gregarious, they frequent low trees and bushes over or near banks of woodland streams and rivers and live exclusively on water plants. Their voice consists of a hoarse, grunting croak, often heard at night.

Nestling Hoatzins have extraordinary powers. When alarmed they dive from the flimsy nest of sticks into the water below and can swim swiftly both above and below the surface. They are able to climb out of the water to the overhanging branches of the low trees, aided by claws on the first and second finger of their wings. (1 Col.; 1 S.A.; 1 N.&S.A.; 1 wld.)

HOATZIN
(Opisthocomus hoazin)

Description. 24 - 26″. Long, fan-shaped crest rufous darkening to black at the tip. The upper surface bronzy olive, the hindneck and mantle streaked buff, the lower back dark ashy brown. Shoulder pale buff, lesser wing-coverts edged white, greater coverts edged buff; outer wing-feathers chestnut. Tail bronze green with a broad buff terminal band. Throat and breast buff, rest of under parts chestnut. Facial skin blue, legs grayish, eye red.

Range. The Guianas and the basins of the Orinoco and Amazon rivers.

Colombia. Banks of swampy, wooded rivers in the tropical zone east of the Andes.

67

LIMPKINS (Aramidae)

Fig. 26. Limpkin
(*Aramus guarauna*)

Limpkins in size and appearance look like ibises, and like them fly with neck and legs outstretched, but differ radically in habits. Actually they are related to rails and cranes. Their name is probably derived from their somewhat limping gait.

They live on fresh-water snails and mussels which are found in marshes and swampy woods. Solitary in habits, their nest is placed either on the ground or in low bushes near the water.

Their oft-repeated wailing notes can often be heard at night. The name *carau* given by Vieillot to the Paraguayan subspecies is descriptive of its cry. (1 Col.; 1 S.A.; 1 N.&S.A.; 1 wld.)

LIMPKIN
(*Aramus guarauna*)

Description. 23 - 28". Top of head, front of neck and entire under surface brown; throat whitish streaked with brown. Upper surface dark bronzy brown, hindneck and upper mantle heavily streaked with white. Lower parts with concealed white streaks.

Range. From southern Georgia south to Venezuela, the Guianas, Brazil, Ecuador, Peru, Bolivia and Argentina. The Greater Antilles. Trinidad.

Colombia. Tropical zone of northern Colombia and the Pacific coast southward to Nariño (*guarauna*).

68

TRUMPETERS (Psophiidae)

Fig. 27. Common Trumpeter
(Psophia crepitans)

Trumpeters are a small family of birds found only in tropical South America. About 20 inches high, in shape they resemble a miniature rhea. They inhabit moist forests and live on small reptiles, insects and vegetable matter. They go about in flocks and nest in holes in trees or in the tops of palms. They are terrestrial, do not fly readily, preferring to run from danger. Although their feet are not webbed they are able to swim.

They have a variety of notes, but their most characteristic one is a series of booming, grunting sounds which carries for a considerable distance.

Trumpeters are easily tamed and may often be seen in villages wandering about in complete liberty. They are reputed to keep gardens and yards free from snakes. (1 Col.; 3 S.A.; 3 N.&S.A.; 3 wld.)

COMMON TRUMPETER
(Psophia crepitans)

Description. 20 - 22". General color black; feathers of upper breast edged metallic blue. Feathers springing from center of back elongated and turning to ochre color, the webs much decomposed. Feathers of head dense, plush-like. Bill olive yellow. Legs long, bluish gray.

Range. Venezuela, the Guianas, northern Brazil, Ecuador and northeastern Peru.

Colombia. Dense forest. Tropical zone east of the Andes. In Meta *(crepitans)*; from the Macarena Mts. southward to Caquetá and Vaupés *(napensis)*.

69

RAILS (Rallidae)

Fig. 28. Bogotá Rail
(*Rallus semiplumbeus*) p. 71

Rails are found almost throughout the world and are absent only in polar regions. They feed on animal and vegetable matter. Northern species migrate southward in winter and in spite of their weak flight many cover long distances.

Rails in Colombia are found mostly in the tropical zone and inhabit coastal marshes and mangroves as well as inland swamps, moist forest and river banks. A few, however, inhabit the marshes and lake shores high in the Andes.

The paucity of records for the rails is of course due to their secretive habits. They are undoubtedly much more widespread than the known ranges in Colombia would indicate. (27 Col.; 43 S.A.; 46 N.&S.A.; 132 wld.)

AID TO IDENTIFICATION

Spotted or barred above 5, 15, 19E, 20E.
Mostly uniform dark gray 23, 26, 27.
Streaked above (below buff) 2, 3, (below gray) 4, 12.
With blue in plumage 24, 25E.
Uniform above (below gray) 1, 11, 14, 21, 22, (below buffy white to chestnut)
6, 7, 8, 9, 10E, 13, 16, 17E, 18.

1. BLACKISH RAIL
(*Rallus nigricans*)

Description. 9½ - 11½". Top and sides of head and entire underparts ashy gray, throat white. Upper parts olive, tail black. Bill yellowish green, legs brick-red.

Range. From eastern Ecuador southward to eastern Peru, eastern Brazil, Paraguay and northern Argentina.

Colombia. The upper Cauca Valley from the vicinity of Medellín, southward to Nariño (*caucae*).

2. CLAPPER RAIL
(*Rallus longirostris*)

Description. 12½ - 13½". Crown and hindneck brown; sides of head gray; throat and streak from bill to above eye white. Upperparts olive brown, feathers edged gray giving a streaked appearance. Front of neck and underparts pale buff; sides of body olive brown, banded white.

Range. A coastal species. The United States, southward through Central America to Venezuela, the Guianas, eastern Brazil, western Ecuador and Peru. The West Indies and Trinidad.

Colombia. The Guajira Peninsula and perhaps westward along the northern coast in mangrove swamps (*phelpsi*).

3. VIRGINIA RAIL
(*Rallus limicola*)

Description. 8½ - 9½". Entire upperparts broadly streaked brown and black; wing-coverts chestnut. Sides of head gray, throat white. Lower neck, breast and sides of body pinkish buff, center of abdomen whitish. Flanks black banded white.

Range. From southern Canada, southward to Guatemala. Mountains of Ecuador. Argentina and Chile.

Colombia. Marshy places in the subtropical zone on both slopes of the mountains of Nariño (*aequatorialis*).

4. BOGOTA RAIL
(*Rallus semiplumbeus*) Fig. 28

Description. 9 - 10". Entire upperparts streaked olive brown and black, wing-coverts chestnut. Sides of head and neck and entire underparts blue-gray; throat white. Flanks black with narrow white bars; under tail-coverts white. Bill red, culmen and tip black.

Range. Colombia.

Colombia. Marshy places in the temperate zone of the Eastern Andes in Boyacá and Cundinamarca.

5. SPOTTED RAIL
(*Rallus maculatus*)

Description. 10 - 11". Top and sides of head, hindneck, upper mantle and chest black, boldly spotted with white; throat white. Rest of underparts banded black and white. Back and wings olive-brown, streaked black and white. Under tail-coverts white. Bill yellowish, red at base.

Range. Cuba. Mexico. British Honduras. Venezuela southward to Argentina and Peru. Trinidad and Tobago.

Colombia. "Bogotá" and swampy places in the upper Cauca Valley (*maculatus*).

6. UNIFORM CRAKE
(*Amaurolimnas concolor*)

Description. 9 - 10". Entire upperparts olivaceous brown. Entire under surface rufous-chestnut; throat buff.

Range. Jamaica. Mexico, southward to Ecuador, British Guiana, eastern and southern Brazil and Bolivia.

Colombia. West of the Andes in Cauca and Nariño and east of them in Meta (*castaneus*).

7. RUFOUS-NECKED WOOD-RAIL
(*Aramides axillaris*)

Description. 12". Head, neck, breast, sides of body, flight feathers rufous-chestnut, center of throat whitish. Mantle blue-gray; closed wings olive. Lower back, upper and under tail-coverts and tail black. Under wing-coverts barred black and white. Bill yellowish green. Legs coral.

Range. Mexico, south to western Ecuador, Venezuela, and British Guiana. Trinidad. The Bay Islands.

Colombia. Mangroves and thickets. Recorded from Cartagena eastward to the Santa Marta region and the Pacific coast in Chocó.

8. GRAY-NECKED WOOD-RAIL
(*Aramides cajanea*)

Description. 14 - 15". Head, neck and thighs gray; throat white. Breast and sides of body rufous-buff; center of abdomen, upper and under tail-coverts, lower back and tail black. Mantle and closed wings olive. Flight-feathers chestnut. Bill yellow. Legs coral.

Range. Mexico to Argentina and Bolivia.

Colombia. Forest and second growth. Tropical zone, virtually throughout the entire country (*cajanea*).

9. BROWN-BACKED WOOD-RAIL
(*Aramides wolfi*) Plate III

Description. 12 - 13". Top and sides of head, neck ashy gray. Throat extensively white; mantle, breast, sides of body and flight-feathers dull chestnut brown. Closed wing olive. Belly, lower back, upper and under tail-coverts and tail black. Bill yellowish green. Legs light red.

Range. Western Ecuador.

Colombia. Forest and second growth. Tropical zone of the Pacific coast, from the upper Atrato southward.

10. CHESTNUT-HEADED CRAKE
(Anurolimnas castaneiceps)

Description. 7½ - 8½". Forecrown, sides of head, front and sides of neck and entire breast orange-rufous. Rest of plumage olive brown. Legs orange-red.

Range. Eastern Ecuador.

Colombia. Banks of forest streams. Caquetá southward.

11. SORA
(Porzana carolina)

Description. 8 - 9½". Center of crown, area around base of bill, throat and center of neck black. Eyebrow, sides of head and neck, chest blue gray; flanks barred black and white. Upper parts olive brown mottled black, streaked white.

Range. Breeds in Canada and United States. South in winter to Peru and eastern Brazil.

Colombia. Fresh and salt water marshes. Winter resident, October to May. Santa Marta region; temperate zone of the Eastern Andes; middle Cauca Valley.

12. ASH-THROATED CRAKE
(Porzana albicollis)

Description. 8 - 9". Entire upper parts mottled olive and black. Throat white; sides of head, neck and rest of under parts blue-gray. Flanks barred black and white. Bill green, ridge blackish. Legs horn.

Range. Tropical South America from Venezuela and the Guianas to southern Brazil and Argentina. Trinidad.

Colombia. Swamps of the lower Magdalena Valley and east of the Andes in Arauca and Meta (typhoeca).

13. YELLOW-BREASTED CRAKE
(Porzana flaviventer)

Description. 5 - 5½". Eyebrow yellowish white. Crown and stripe through eye, black. Throat and breast buffy yellow; abdomen white, flanks barred black and white. Back black, streaked white; closed wing brownish yellow mottled and barred with black and white. Maxilla black, mandible greenish gray; legs dull yellow.

Range. The Greater Antilles. El Salvador. Venezuela, the Guianas, eastern Brazil, Paraguay and northern Argentina.

Colombia. Swamp and scrub. The llanos of Meta, northward to Santa Marta and the lower Magdalena Valley (bangsi). Northwestern Colombia, southward into the middle Cauca Valley (flaviventer).

14. GRAY-BREASTED CRAKE
(Laterallus exilis)

Description. 5½ - 6". Crown, sides of head, neck and breast gray, throat white. Nape and upper mantle chestnut; back and wings olive brown; rump, upper tail-coverts and wing-coverts and flanks barred black and white. Bill greenish black; legs horn.

Range. Honduras and Nicaragua. Venezuela, the Guianas southward to the Amazon Valley and eastward to Peru. Western Ecuador. Trinidad.

Colombia. Tropical zone. The Cauca Valley, and across northern Colombia to the Magdalena Valley. East of the Andes southward to Putumayo.

15. BLACK CRAKE
(Laterallus jamaicensis)

Description. 5½ - 6". Head, neck and breast dark gray; throat whitish. Hind-neck and upper mantle chestnut, rest of upper parts, belly, flanks and flight-feathers dusky brown spotted with white, flanks barred with white.

Range. North America. Jamaica. Coast of Peru. Central Chile.

Colombia. Known only from "Bogotá" trade skins (subsp?).

16. RUFOUS-SIDED CRAKE
(Laterallus melanophaius) Plate III

Description. 6½ - 7". Entire upper parts olive brown, tail black. Sides of neck, breast and under tail-coverts rufous; throat, foreneck and center of breast white; flanks barred black and white.

Range. Nicaragua southward to western Ecuador. Venezuela and British Guiana southward to Uruguay, Paraguay, Argentina and Bolivia.

Colombia. Tropical zone west of the Western Andes (albigularis); east of the Andes (oenops). Córdoba to Santa Marta (cerdaleus).

17. BLACK-BANDED CRAKE
(Laterallus fasciatus)

Description. 7½ - 8". Head, neck and under surface chestnut, barred on belly, flanks and under tail-coverts with black; rest of plumage olive brown.

Range. Eastern Ecuador to northwest Brazil and northeast Peru.

Colombia. Tropical zone east of the Andes from Meta southward.

18 RUSSET-CROWNED CRAKE
(Laterallus viridis)

Description. 6½ - 7". Top of head, entire under surface rufous chestnut; sides of head grayish; rest of plumage olive brown. Legs salmon.

Range. Venezuela and the Guianas southward over Brazil, eastern Ecuador and Peru.

Colombia. Swamps. Tropical zone of the middle Magdalena Valley (brunnescens). East of the Andes (viridis).

19. DOTTED CRAKE
(Micropygia schomburgkii)

Description. 5½ - 6". General color sepia brown, spotted on nape, back and sides of breast with white, the spots surrounded by a black border. Spots on wings pale rufous. Crown light chestnut; forehead, sides of head and underside pale rufous. Center of throat and abdomen white. Legs red.

Range. Venezuela, British and French Guiana, eastern and central Brazil.

Colombia. Marshy grassland. Tropical zone. Recorded only from the río Guayabero near the base of the Macarena Mts. in Meta (schomburgkii).

20. SPECKLED CRAKE
(Coturnicops notata)

Description. 5 - 5¼". Blackish, the upper surface tinged olive brown. Head and neck finely dotted with white, the back with narrow broken white bars. Throat white; feathers of breast edged with and flanks barred with white. Iris red; bill and legs black.

Range. Venezuela, British Guiana, Uruguay, Argentina.

Colombia. Marshy grassland. Tropical zone. Recorded only from the río Guayabero at the base of the Macarena Mts. in Meta.

21. PAINT-BILLED CRAKE
(Neocrex erythrops)

Description. 7½ - 8½". Forecrown, sides of head, neck and underparts blue-gray; under tail-coverts barred black and white. Entire upper parts olive. Bill yellow, orange basally.

Range. Venezuela south to Brazil, Paraguay and Argentina. Western Ecuador, western Peru.

Colombia. Swamps and marshy fields. Tropical and subtropical zone. West of the Eastern Andes and the Santa Marta region (colombianus). Temperate zone of the Eastern Andes and in the tropical zone in Vaupés (olivascens).

22. SPOT-FLANKED GALLINULE
(Porphyriops melanops) Plate III

Description. 10 - 10½". Crown and front of face black; sides of head, the neck and upper mantle gray; center of belly white; flanks olive brown with round white spots. Center of back olive brown. Shoulders rich chestnut. Bill greenish yellow with a broad dusky median band.

Range. Eastern Brazil, Argentina, Paraguay, Uruguay, Bolivia and Chile. Eastern Peru.

Colombia. Marshy ponds and fields. Temperate zone of the Eastern Andes (bogotensis).

23. COMMON GALLINULE
(Gallinula chloropus)

Description. 13 - 14″. Mostly slaty gray, darkest on head and neck. Back and wings dark olive brown. Stripes on flanks, center of belly and under tail-coverts white. Bill scarlet, tip olive green. Legs and long toes pale green, base of tibia scarlet.

Range. From southern Canada, southward to Venezuela, Brazil, Bolivia, Paraguay, Uruguay, Argentina and Chile. The West Indies, Bahamas and Trinidad.

Colombia. Lakes and swamps. Tropical zone of the Cauca and lower Magdalena Valleys. Occasionally in the temperate zone in the Eastern Andes *(pauxilla)*.

24. PURPLE GALLINULE
(Porphyrula martinica)

Description. 12 - 13″. Head and hindneck dark blue; foreneck, breast and upper belly violet blue. Upper mantle, sides of breast, wing-coverts verditer blue; rest of back olive. Belly and flanks black; under tail-coverts white. Bill red with yellow tip, frontal plate blue. Legs and long toes, yellow.

Range. Southern United States south to Venezuela, Ecuador, Peru, Paraguay, Argentina and Bolivia. The West Indies. Trinidad and Tobago.

Colombia. River banks, swamps and lakes. Throughout the tropical zone, occasionally to the temperate zone. Gorgona Island.

25. LITTLE GALLINULE
(Porphyrula flavirostris)

Description. 9-10″. Top of head, hindneck and mantle olive; lower back blackish. Sides of head, neck and breast and wing-coverts turquoise blue. Throat, front of neck, center of breast, and rest of underparts white. Bill yellowish green. Legs and long toes yellow.

Range. Venezuela. The Guianas, southward in eastern Brazil to Paraguay and eastern Bolivia.

Colombia. Swamps. Tropical zone east of the Andes in Caquetá.

26. AMERICAN COOT
(Fulica americana)

Description. 14 - 15″. Head and neck slaty black; back grayish brown; under surface ashy gray. Bend of wing, tips of secondaries and under tail-coverts white. Bill white, frontal shield rounded posteriorly (or pointed, 2); legs olive with a red band on tibia (or without it, 1).

Range. Canada south to Panama and in the Andes southward to Chile and western Argentina. The West Indies.

Colombia. Lakes and ponds. Temperate zone of the Eastern Andes *(colombiana)*. Temperate zone of the Andes of Nariño and Cauca (1, *peruviana*). Birds recorded in winter from the Cauca Valley are possibly North American migrants (2, *americana*).

27. SLATE-COLORED COOT
(Fulica ardesiaca) Plate III

Description. 17 - 18″. Head and neck black, rest of plumage slate gray except white under tail-coverts. Bill white, frontal shield yellow. Legs pale bluish.

Range. Andes of Ecuador and Peru.

Colombia. Ponds in the temperate zone of the Andes of Nariño.

SUN-GREBES (Heliornithidae)

Fig. 29. Sun-Grebe
(Heliornis fulica)

Sun-Grebes are related to rails. They have webbed toes and swim and dive expertly, often swimming half submerged. They live on quiet forest streams where they catch small fish, crustaceans and insects. Their note is said to resemble a dog's bark. In addition to the American species there is one in Africa and another in Asia. (1 Col.; 1 S.A.; 1 N.&S.A.; 3 wld.)

SUN-GREBE
(Heliornis fulica)

Description. 11 - 12″. Top of head, hind-neck, broad stripe behind eye and spot at base of bill blue-black. Spot below eye and conspicuous eyebrow white. Cheeks cinnamon or white. Sides of neck with a white stripe, bordered below by a broad blue-black stripe. Underparts white, breast shaded with clay color; flanks olive. Entire upper surface olive brown. Tail broad, dark brown with white tip. Lower mandible pink; feet yellow, banded with black. Toes webbed.

Range. Mexico south to Venezuela, Bolivia and Argentina. Trinidad.

Colombia. Spottily distributed in the tropical zone. Recorded from Norte de Santander, Antioquia, Chocó, Nariño and Meta.

75

SUN-BITTERNS (Eurypygidae)

Fig. 30. Sun-Bittern
(Eurypyga helias)

Sun-Bitterns superficially resemble herons but are at once distinguishable from them by their short legs and long tails. Cousins of the rails they live on the banks of forest streams and feed on insects which they catch by a lightning-fast thrust of their long, straight and sharply pointed bill. Their wings and tail show a striking pattern of bars and spots. They build a large round nest of leaves and sticks with an entrance on the side. It is placed in a low tree or shrub. (1 Col.; 1 S.A.; 1 N.&S.A.; 1 wld.)

SUN-BITTERN
(Eurypyga helias)

Description. 17 - 20". Top and sides of head black. Stripe above and another below the eye and throat white. Back and sides of neck very finely barred black and fulvous brown. Stripe down front of neck plain fulvous. Breast mottled and barred black and buff, abdomen whitish. Mantle barred black and buff (♂) or slaty and black (♀). Lower back and upper tail-coverts barred black and white. Wing-coverts with large round white spots. Primaries broadly and conspicuously banded with chestnut, olive, black, gray and white. Tail narrowly barred gray and white and crossed by two broad bands of black and chestnut. Lower mandible and legs yellow.

Range. Southern Mexico to western Ecuador. Venezuela and the Guianas southward to Brazil, Ecuador, Peru and Bolivia.

Colombia. Forested streams in the tropical zone west of the Andes *(major)*; Amazonian Colombia *(helias)*.

JACANAS (Jacanidae)

Fig. 31. Wattled Jacana
(Jacana jacana)

These small long-legged inhabitants of marshy shores of streams and ponds are recognizable by their exceedingly long toes and nails which enables them to run over floating vegetation. Sharp spurs are found on the wing joint. The forehead is bare and red lappets adorn the base of the bill. Jacanas swim easily and dive readily. Their food consists of small snails, fish, seeds and vegetable matter. They occur in tropical parts of Africa, Asia and Australia. (1 Col.; 1 S.A.; 2 N.&S.A.; 8 wld.)

WATTLED JACANA
(Jacana jacana)

Description. 9½ - 10½ " Head, neck, upper mantle, breast, center of belly and under tail-coverts black. Primaries and secondaries pale yellow, dark tipped. Back purple maroon (or chestnut maroon, 1; or chestnut 2; or greenish black, 3). Bill yellow, bare forehead and wattles red; feet and legs blue-gray.
Young birds are bronzy above, white below with a broad buffy eye stripe.

Range. Panama southward to Bolivia.

Colombia. Marshy woods and swamps. Tropical zone east of the Andes (1, *intermedia*). North bank of the Amazon (2, *peruviana*). Northern Colombia from the lower Atrato eastward to Santa Marta and the Magdalena Valley (3, *hypomelaena*). The middle and upper Cauca Valley. East of the Andes in Arauca *(melanopygia)*.

77

OYSTERCATCHERS (Haematopodidae)

Fig. 32. American Oystercatcher
(Haematopus palliatus)

These large shore birds are easily distinguishable from other species by their coral-colored, chisel-like bills and their blackish brown and white plumage. Heavy-set and short legged, they frequent rocky shores and open beaches and feed on limpets which they pry off rocks. Their chisel-shaped bills are used to open mussels, clams and oysters.

They nest on shingle beaches and lay two to four eggs. Their call notes consist of loud shrill whistles.

Oystercatchers occur everywhere except in polar regions and oceanic islands. (1 Col.; 3 S.A.; 4 N.&S.A.; 6 wld.)

AMERICAN OYSTERCATCHER
(Haematopus palliatus)

Description. 16 - 18″. Head, neck, upper breast black. Upper parts brown. Under parts, upper tail-coverts, secondaries white. Iris yellow.

Range. From northern Lower California southward along the shores of the Pacific to southern Chile. From New Jersey southward to the Gulf of Mexico and along the Atlantic coast of South America to Argentina. The Bahamas and West Indies. The Galápagos Islands.

Colombia. Shores, preferably rocky, of the Caribbean and Pacific coasts *(palliatus)*.

78

PLOVERS (Charadriidae)

Fig. 33. Southern Lapwing
(Belonopterus cayennensis)

Although plovers are often seen on the seashore they are not so dependent on the sea as are most of the sandpipers. Many species inhabit plains country, sometimes arid regions, as well as mountain grasslands. They run swiftly, feed on insects and other animal matter. Some have crests, others have spurs on their wings or lappets or wattles on their faces: features not shared by the sandpipers and their allies. In some species of plover the winter plumage differs from the summer garb. Plovers are widely distributed throughout the world. (9 Col.; 15 S.A.; 17 N.&S.A.; 63 wld.)

AID TO IDENTIFICATION

Back uniform, tail white with a broad black band 1, 2ᴱ, 3; tail partly rufous 8; central tail feathers like back, outer ones white 6, 7, 9.
Back mottled, tail conspicuously barred black and white 4, tail obscurely barred 5.

1. SOUTHERN LAPWING
(Belonopterus cayennensis)

Description. 12 - 14″. Forehead, long narrow occipital crest, and center of throat black. Crown, sides of head, neck, upper breast buffy gray, lower breast black. Back bronzy grayish green. Lesser wing-coverts black, median wing-coverts shining green glossed with purple, remiges black. Greater wing-coverts, upper tail-coverts and belly white. Tail black, basally white with narrow white tip.
Range. Panama southward in South America east of the Andes from Venezuela and the Guianas to Tierra del Fuego.
Colombia. Pastures, open plains, occasionally to the temperate zone. Not recorded in Caquetá or Nariño *(cayennensis).*

2. PIED PLOVER
(Hoploxypterus cayanus) Plate III

Description. 8½ - 9½″. Forecrown, sides of head, upper mantle, scapulars forming a V on back and broad band across breast black. Center of crown sandy gray encircled by white. Center of back, wing-coverts and innermost remiges sandy grayish, middle remiges white, primaries black. Throat, underparts and rump white. Outer tail-feathers white with black terminal band, rest basally white, terminally black.
Range. South America east of the Andes from Venezuela to southern Brazil, Bolivia and Argentina.
Colombia. Banks of rivers and ponds. Tropical zone east of the Eastern Andes.

79

3. ANDEAN LAPWING
(Ptiloscelys resplendens)

Description. 12 - 13". Head, throat and upper mantle whitish; breast gray, rest of under surface, and basal half and tip of tail, greater wing-coverts and outer webs of secondaries white. Lesser and median wing-coverts shining purple. Entire back bronze green with purple reflections. Primaries and distal half of tail purple-black.

Range. Temperate and páramo zone of the Andes from Ecuador southward to northern Chile and northwestern Argentina.

Colombia. Temperate zone of the Andes in Nariño; accidental in the Eastern Andes as far north as Bogotá.

4. BLACK-BELLIED PLOVER
(Squatarola squatarola)

Description. 10 - 13". *Winter:* Above brown, speckled and spotted with white. Underparts dirty white, somewhat streaked dusky. Tail barred black and white. *Summer:* Forehead and sides of neck white, sides of head and underparts black; belly and under tail-coverts white. Upper parts blackish brown boldly mottled with white.

Range. Breeds in the circumpolar regions. South in winter to the southern hemisphere, southward to southern Brazil, Asia, Africa, Australia and New Zealand.

Colombia. Seashore and pastures. Winter resident, September-March. Caribbean and Pacific coast, Cauca Valley and the temperate zone of the Eastern Andes.

5. AMERICAN GOLDEN PLOVER
(Pluvialis dominica)

Description. 9 - 11". Very similar to the Black-bellied Plover, but considerably smaller and spotted with yellow above. Tail grayish brown, unbarred; lower abdomen black.

Range. Breeds in Arctic America and Siberia. Winters southward to Brazil, Bolivia and Argentina. India, China, Hawaii southward to Australia, Tasmania and New Zealand.

Colombia. Seashore and pastures. Winter resident, September - December. Tropical to temperate zone *(dominica)*.

6. SEMIPALMATED PLOVER
(Charadrius semipalmatus)

Description. 7 - 8". *Winter:* Forehead, collar on hindneck and under parts white. Back and chest-band brown. Bill and legs yellow, tip of bill black. *Breeding plumage:* Similar, but bar on forecrown and chest-band continued around hindneck black.

Range. Breeds in northern North America, winters from the southern United States to Patagonia.

Colombia. Sandy beaches. Winter resident, July - March. Both coasts; occasionally in the upper Cauca Valley.

7. COLLARED PLOVER
(Charadrius collaris)

Description. 6 - 6½" Rather like No. 6 but much paler above, collar on hindneck pale rufous instead of white. Bill longer, all black.

Range. Mexico southward to western Ecuador, Peru, Bolivia, Argentina, Brazil, Venezuela and the Guianas. The Lesser Antilles, islands in the southern Caribbean. Trinidad.

Colombia. Rivers, ponds and salt lagoons throughout in the tropical zone.

8. KILLDEER
(Charadrius vociferus)

Description. 8 - 11". Underparts white with two black bands on chest. Back brown; rump tawny rufous. Outer tail-feathers barred black and white, next pair tawny, the succeeding feathers becoming more olivaceous, all but central pair with a black subterminal bar and white tip.

Range. Breeds in North America south to Mexico. Winters southward to Venezuela and Ecuador, the West Indies, Aruba, Curaçao and Bonaire. Resident races in the West Indies, western Peru and Chile.

Colombia. Stubble fields and pastureland. Winter resident, December - March. Tropical to temperate zone *(vociferus)*.

9. THICK-BILLED PLOVER
(Charadrius wilsonia)

Description. 7 - 8". *Winter:* Forehead white. Above grayish brown (or rufescent brown, 1); below white, a brownish band across chest. *Summer:* Similar, but band across chest, and another across fore-crown black. Bill black, long, heavy.

Range. Southern United States southward to Venezuela, Brazil, Peru and Chile. Resident races in the West Indies and the coast of Peru.

Colombia. Sandy beaches, sand flats. Resident on the Pacific coast *(beldingi)* and on the Caribbean coast (1, *cinnamominus).*

CURLEWS, SNIPES AND SANDPIPERS (Scolopacidae)

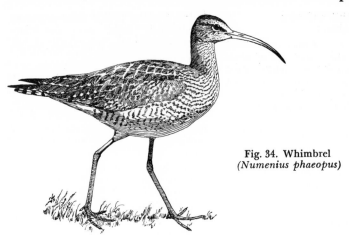

Fig. 34. Whimbrel
(Numenius phaeopus)

More northern in distribution than plovers, all the species found in Colombia, with the exception of some of the snipes, are only transients or winter visitors.

Most of the species are more dependent on water than the plovers and are found on the seashore, or along river courses, in marshlands and tidal mud flats. The marine species are usually seen in flocks. (24 Col.; 32 S.A.; 44 N.&S.A.; 82 wld.)

AID TO IDENTIFICATION

Primaries barred 1, 2, 13^E, 23, 24, or with a large white patch 7.
Primaries unbarred rump or upper tail-coverts plain white or barred black 3, 4, 8, 9, 10, 16, 22; rump not white, bill very long and straight 11, 12, 14, 15; bill not conspicuously long, tail barred 5, 6, unbarred 17, 18, 19, 20, 21.

1. UPLAND SANDPIPER
(Bartramia longicauda)

Description. 11 - 12". Crown blackish, median stripe and superciliaries buff. Back dark brown, streaked buff. Throat and abdomen white, lower neck and breast buffy, dark streaked. Tail long, central feathers dusky, outer ones orange-buff and all barred black. Bill yellowish with dark tip and ridge; legs yellowish. Has the habit of lifting its wings after landing.

Range. Breeds in North America. Winters in southern Brazil, Argentina and Uruguay.

Colombia. Transient, September - October and April. Pasturelands and grassy hillsides from the tropical to temperate zones.

2. WHIMBREL
(Numenius phaeopus)

Description. 15 - 18". Bill arched, 2½ - 4". Crown and stripe through eye blackish, median stripe and superciliaries buffy white, streaked. Upper parts brownish gray mottled and streaked with whitish. Under parts white streaked on lower neck and chest and sides of body. Tail barred with white. Legs gray.

Range. Breeds in the Arctic. Winters in South America to eastern Brazil and Chile. Also Europe, Asia and Africa.

Colombia. Winter resident from early August to early April on both coasts, and occasionally in the upper Cauca Valley *(hudsonicus)*.

3. LESSER YELLOWLEGS
(Tringa flavipes)

Description. 9 - 11". Upper parts dark brown spotted and barred with white. Rump and tail white, latter lightly barred. Below white streaked on breast and sides of neck. No wing stripe. Legs yellow.

Range. Breeds in North America. Winters from the southern United States southward to Argentina and Chile. The West Indies, Trinidad.

Colombia. Winter resident, end of July to mid-April on both coasts and inland marshes up to the temperate zone.

4. GREATER YELLOWLEGS
(Tringa melanoleuca)

Description. 12½ - 15". Similar to No. 3 but much larger. In winter, both are less spotted above and less streaked below.

Range. Breeds in North America. Winters from the southern United States southward to the Straits of Magellan. The West Indies, Trinidad.

Colombia. Winter resident, end of July to early May on coasts and inland swamps up to the temperate zone.

5. SOLITARY SANDPIPER
(Tringa solitaria)

Description. 7 - 8½". *Summer:* Above dark olive brown, streaked on head and neck and speckled on back with white. Tail dark, the outer feathers barred black and white. Below white, neck and breast narrowly streaked. No wing stripe. *Winter:* Grayer and less spotted above, less streaked below. Legs olive greenish.

Range. Breeds in North America; winters from the southern United States to western Ecuador and Argentina. The West Indies and Trinidad.

Colombia. Winter resident, August to April on inland waters from the tropical to the temperate zone *(solitaria)*. A larger form *(cinnamomea)* breeding in northwestern North America undoubtedly also occurs as it is known in winter from Ecuador to Argentina.

6. SPOTTED SANDPIPER
(Actitis macularia)

Description. 7 - 8". *Summer:* Above olive brown obscurely streaked and barred. Eyebrow and under surface white, the latter with conspicuous round black spots. Tail dark, outer feathers barred with white. White stripe on wing. *Winter:* Plain white below, more or less plain grayish brown above. Bill flesh, tip black. Legs pinkish. Has habit of bobbing up and down.

Range. Breeds in North America. Winters from the United States to Brazil and Chile. The West Indies, Trinidad.

Colombia. Winter resident, August to May. Coasts and inland waters up to the temperate zone.

7. WILLET
(Catoptrophorus semipalmatus)

Description. 14 - 17". *Summer:* Above pale grayish brown, streaked dusky on head and neck and barred on back. Below white spotted and barred dusky. Wings black with a broad white band. Rump white, tail pale gray. *Winter:* Pale gray above, plain white below. Legs blue-gray. The large size and conspicuous white wing-patch are diagnostic.

Range. Breeds in North America, the Bahamas and West Indies. Winters from California southward to Peru and the Amazon. The Galápagos Islands. Trinidad.

Colombia. Winter resident, September to April on both coasts on beaches and grassy coastal flats *(inornatus)*. The nominate form *(semipalmatus)* probably occurs in Colombia in winter for it has been taken in Ecuador. It differs from *inornatus* by being smaller.

8. RUDDY TURNSTONE
(Arenaria interpres)

Description. 8 - 9½". *Summer:* Strikingly patterned in black, white and chestnut. Head and underparts mostly white. Stripe through eye continuing down sides of neck to form a large patch on breast black. Back bright chestnut with broad black bands. Lower back white, upper tail-coverts black; tail white with broad black subterminal band. Broad white wing-stripe. Legs orange red. *Winter:* Pattern more or less similar but everywhere duller: chestnut replaced by brown, white of head replaced by grayish brown.

Range. Breeds in the Arctic; winters from the southern United States southward to Brazil and Chile. Trinidad. Europe, Africa, Asia, New Zealand and tropical Pacific islands.

Colombia. Winter resident, September-May. On stony beaches of the Caribbean coast *(morinella).*

9. COMMON DOWITCHER
(Limnodromus griseus)

Description. 10 - 11″. Snipe-like. Bill long, straight, up to 2½″. *Summer:* Above dull cinnamon-buff streaked and spotted with black. Lower back white, upper tail-coverts white barred blackish. Sides of head, neck and underparts pinkish cinnamon, more or less spotted blackish. *Winter:* Head and upper back nearly uniform gray; rump white, tail barred. Eyebrow and under-parts grayish white. Secondaries broadly edged white. Legs olive green.

Range. Breeds in Arctic America. Winters from the southern United States south-ward to northern Peru and eastern Brazil. The West Indies. Trinidad.

Colombia. Winter resident on mud flats, fresh water marshes of both coasts *(griseus).*

10. LONG-BILLED DOWITCHER
(Limnodromus scolopaceus)

Description. 11 - 12″. Similar to No. 9 but larger.

Range. Breeds in northeastern Siberia and northwestern Alaska. Winters south to Guatemala and casually to Argentina.

Colombia. Casual. One record from the Cauca Valley. A doubtful record.

11. COMMON SNIPE
(Gallinago gallinago)

Description. 10 - 11″. Crown sepia brown with a pale median and eyebrow stripe. Above mottled black and various shades

of buff forming four stripes. Throat and abdomen white, sides barred black. Neck and breast yellowish buff narrowly streaked. Bill long, up to 2¾″, legs short.

Range. Breeds in northern Europe, Asia, North America and South America from the base of the Andes eastward. Northern birds winter from the southern United States southward to Venezuela and eastern Brazil. The West Indies, Trinidad. Asia, Indonesia and the Philippines.

Colombia. Winter resident, July - March. Marshy meadows and moist woods from the tropical to páramo zone *(delicata).* Resident, tropical zone of the eastern llanos and the Orinoco region *(paraguaiae).*

12. NOBLE SNIPE
(Gallinago nobilis)

Description. 12 - 13″. Resembles No. 11 but bill longer, and fore-neck and chest much more heavily streaked with black.

Range. Andes of western Venezuela and Ecuador.

Colombia. Subtropical but usually tem-perate to páramo zones in moist meadows. The Eastern and Central Andes and the mountains of Nariño.

13. GIANT SNIPE
(Gallinago undulata)

Description. 14″. Best identified by very large size and by having the primaries and secondaries barred, not uniform as in other snipes.

Range. Locally distributed in Venezuela, the Guianas and northern Brazil, Argen-tina, Paraguay and southern Brazil.

Colombia. Marshy savannas of the eastern llanos *(undulata).*

14. BOGOTA SNIPE
(Chubbia imperialis)

Description. 11″. Above rufous chestnut, streaked on neck and banded on back with black. Sides of head, the neck and chest rufous chestnut, spotted on neck and banded on breast with black. Rest of underparts broadly banded black and white.

Range. Colombia.

Colombia. Temperate zone in the region about Bogotá. Known from few specimens.

15. ANDEAN SNIPE
(Chubbia jamesoni)

Description. 12". Above much like No. 11. Below whitish narrowly banded with dusky.

Range. The Andes of western Venezuela, Ecuador, Peru and Bolivia.

Colombia. Swampy places in the temperate and páramo zones of the Santa Marta Mts. and the Eastern Andes (jamesoni); the Central Andes (chapmani).

16. SANDERLING
(Crocethia alba)

Description. 7 - 8½". Summer: Cinnamon rufous above streaked and spotted with black. Throat and belly white, neck and breast buffy, streaked darker. Primaries blackish, prominent wing-stripe white. Sides of rump white. Tail black. Legs black. Bill black, short and rather stout. Winter: Very "white"; pale gray above, white below.

Range. Virtually world-wide. Breeds in Arctic regions. Winters from the temperate to the tropical zone.

Colombia. Probably winter resident on sandy beaches on both coasts; rarely recorded inland (Cauca Valley). Recorded in September and October.

17. SEMIPALMATED SANDPIPER
(Calidris pusilla)

Description. 5½-6½". Above dark brown, streaked with gray and buff. Primaries blackish, narrow white wing-stripe. Sides of rump white. Eyebrow and underparts white, streaked on sides of neck and on breast. Winter plumage more uniform. Bill, rather short, and legs black.

Range. Breeds in Arctic America and eastern Siberia. Winters from the southern United States southward to Peru and Brazil. The West Indies. Trinidad.

Colombia. Winter resident, September to May, on sandy beaches on both coasts.

18. WESTERN SANDPIPER
(Calidris mauri)

Description. 6 - 7". Rather similar to No. 17 but scapulars rufous and with a longer bill. Winter, more grayish above. Legs black.

Range. Breeds in Alaska. Winters from the southern United States southward to Venezuela, Ecuador and Peru. The West Indies, Trinidad.

Colombia. Winter resident on sandy beaches of the Caribbean coast. Recorded from September to January.

19. LEAST SANDPIPER
(Calidris minutilla)

Description. 5 - 6½". Best distinguished from No. 17 by yellowish green legs.

Range. Breeds in Arctic America. Winters from the United States southward to Peru and central Brazil. The West Indies, Trinidad, the Galápagos Islands.

Colombia. Winter resident, July - April, on mud flats, salt marshes and beaches of both coasts, and inland in the Atrato and Cauca Valleys.

20. BAIRD'S SANDPIPER
(Calidris bairdii)

Description. 7 - 7½". Best distinguished from No. 19 by its larger size, buffy brown head and well-marked buff breast band. White wing-stripe narrow. Feathers of back pale-edged giving a scaly appearance. Legs dusky green.

Range. Breeds in Arctic America and eastern Siberia. Winters in the Andes of Ecuador southward to Bolivia, Chile and Argentina.

Colombia. Transient, recorded only in the autumn. The Cauca Valley and the temperate zone of the Eastern Andes.

21. PECTORAL SANDPIPER
(Calidris melanotos)

Description. 8 - 9½". Distinguishable from No. 20 by larger size, streaked back, more sharply marked breast band, no wing stripe, and by greenish yellow legs and base of bill.

Range. Breeds in eastern Siberia and Arctic America. Winters from Peru and Bolivia southward to Patagonia. Casually to Australia and New Zealand.

Colombia. Transient in autumn (August-November) on both coasts and in the interior up to temperate zone in marshy areas.

22. STILT SANDPIPER
(Micropalama himantopus)

Description. 7½ - 9". *Summer:* Above dark brown streaked and barred buffy white. Ear patch rusty chestnut. Lower parts barred, rump white barred black. *Winter:* Grayish brown above, superciliary whitish, white below. Rump white, no wing-stripe. Legs long, greenish. Rather like Lesser Yellowlegs (No. 3), but bill longer somewhat decurved at tip, legs differently colored.

Range. Breeds in Arctic America. Winters in central Brazil, Bolivia, Paraguay, Uruguay and Argentina.

Colombia. Transient, recorded from both coasts in the autumn (September). A few may winter.

23. BUFF-BREASTED SANDPIPER
(Tryngites subruficollis)

Description. 7 - 8½". Looks like a miniature Upland Plover. Above tawny buff, streaked and spotted with black. Throat white, rest of underparts pinkish buff, paler in winter. Central tail feathers black, lateral feathers brown with black subterminal bar and white tip. Bill short, black; legs yellow.

Range. Breeds in Arctic America. Winters in central Argentina.

Colombia. A species which prefers grassy meadows to the ocean front. It has been recorded up to the temperate zone as well as from the Caribbean coast. Transient, September-December, April.

24. RUFF
(Philomachus pugnax)

Description. 10 - 12½" *Summer:* In breeding plumage recognizable from any Sandpiper by conspicuous ruff and ear tufts, of any shade of brown, or black, or white, or combinations thereof. *Winter:* Somewhat resembles an Upland Plover, but head without stripes, tail with black central stripe and oval white patch on each side; bill longer. Legs dull yellow or olive green.

Range. Breeds in northern Europe and Asia. Winters in Africa, India and Burma. Occasional on the east coast of the United States and West Indies.

Colombia. Accidental winter visitor. Recorded from "Bogotá." Prefers marshes and fields.

AVOCETS AND STILTS (Recurvirostridae)

Fig. 35. Common Stilt
(Himantopus himantopus)

Stilts inhabit both fresh- and salt-water lagoons. They can be told from any other shore birds by their exceedingly long coral-pink legs (8"). Gregarious, they nest in colonies, the nest being a depression scraped out in the sand or mud. Stilts swim easily and feed on insects and crustaceans as well as small frogs and fish. (1 Col.; 2 S.A.; 3 N.&S.A.; 7 wld.)

COMMON STILT
(Himantopus himantopus)

Description. 14". ♂: Forehead and large spot above and behind eye white. Crown, back of neck, back and wings black with a bluish green gloss. Rump and entire underparts white, the chest sometimes tinged with pink in the breeding season. Tail pale gray. Bill black, iris red, legs coral pink. ♀ similar to ♂ but black of upper parts duller and browner especially on the back.

Range. Virtually world-wide in the temperate and tropical zones. Birds breeding in the northern part of the range are migratory.

Colombia. Caribbean coast. The Cauca and Magdalena Valleys and the eastern llanos *(mexicanus)*.

PHALAROPES (Phalaropodidae)

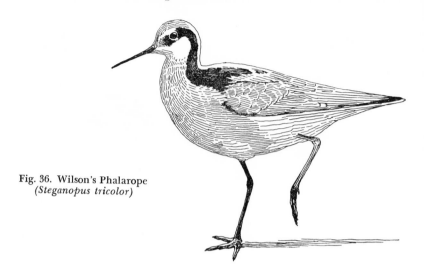

Fig. 36. Wilson's Phalarope
(Steganopus tricolor)

Phalaropes resemble sandpipers, but differ from them in having lobed toes, and in having different habits. Of the three species, two nest in the Arctic tundra, while the third breeds on the plains of western North America. The latter winters in the Andes, the other two spend the winter far out at sea. Phalaropes fly swiftly but erratically in dense flocks near the surface of the water, alternately flashing their white underparts and dark upperparts as they turn in unison with almost military precision. They swim in vast "rafts" in their main wintering quarters off the Pacific coast of South America, West Africa, Arabia, the Red Sea and Indian Ocean.

Phalaropes are peculiar in that females are much larger and more brightly colored than males. The dull-colored males incubate the eggs and rear the young. (2 Col.; 3 S.A.; 3 N.&S.A.; 3 wld.)

RED PHALAROPE

(Phalaropus fulicarius)

Description. 8 - 9". Top of head black, cheeks white. Lower parts cinnamon. Back streaked yellowish buff and black. Winter plumage blue-gray above, forehead and lower surface white. Wings with white stripe.

Range. Breeds in the Arctic regions. Winters at sea southward to Chile, the coast of Africa and Arabia.

Colombia. The Pacific coast (one record).

WILSON'S PHALAROPE

(Steganopus tricolor)

Description. 8 - 9". Crown, center of back gray, the latter mixed chestnut. Stripe from base of bill through eye and down sides of neck black, turning chestnut. Underparts white. Winter plumage very similar to the Red Phalarope but with no white stripe on wing.

Range. Breeds on the plains of western North America. Winters in highlands of Peru and Bolivia, southward to Chile.

Colombia. Recorded in September on the Pacific coast, in the upper Cauca Valley in October.

THICK-KNEES (Burhinidae)

Fig. 37. Double-striped Thick-Knee
(Burhinus bistriatus)

Thick-Knees resemble enormous plovers with short, thick bills. In habits they are largely nocturnal, as evidenced by their very large eyes. They run swiftly on their long legs and are found in stony, open, brush country. They nest on the bare ground. They inhabit Europe, Africa, Asia, and Australia in addition to tropical America. (1 Col.; 2 S.A.; 2 N.&S.A.; 9 wld.)

DOUBLE-STRIPED THICK-KNEE
(Burhinus bistriatus)

Description. 17 - 19". A white stripe above the eye followed by a dark one. Top of head, back, wings, breast streaked dark brown and fulvous. Belly and broad wing-bar white. Tail with a subterminal white bar and black tip.

Range. Southeastern Texas (Kleberg County, accidental). Mexico southward to British Guiana and northwestern Brazil. The island of Hispaniola.

Colombia. Caribbean coast. The upper Magdalena Valley and the eastern llanos *(pediacus)* .

89

JAEGERS AND SKUAS (Stercorariidae)

Fig. 38. Pomarine Jaeger
(Stercorarius pomarinus)

Jaegers might be called marine hawks. Powerful fliers, they prey on other birds, rob nests of their eggs, and birds of their food. They breed on the cold coasts and islands of the Arctic and Antarctic, and winter to the north or south of their breeding grounds. They are distinguishable from gull-like birds by their protruding central tail-feathers. In the non-breeding season they range far out to sea. (1 Col.; 2 S.A.; 4 N.&S.A.; 4 wld.)

POMARINE JAEGER
(Stercorarius pomarinus)

Description. 20 - 23". Dark grayish brown above, cap darker. Base of primaries white, forming a wing patch. Sides of neck and breast straw yellow. Below mostly white, abdomen grayish brown (light phase); on underparts dark like back (dark phase). Tail wedge-shaped with twisted central tail feathers protruding one to three inches.

Range. Breeds in Arctic America, Asia and Europe. Winters south to Peru, South Africa, India and Australia.

Colombia. In winter occasionally off the Pacific coast.

GULLS AND TERNS (Laridae)

Fig. 39. Large-billed Tern
(*Phaetusa simplex*) p. 92

Gulls and terns are not usually seen far from land. The latter virtually replace gulls in tropical seas, gulls being partial to cooler regions. Terns can usually be distinguished from gulls by their sharply pointed bills, narrower and more pointed wings and forked rather than square tails. They dive into the water after fish, a habit not shared by gulls. Most species are marine but a few are found only on inland waters. (14 Col.; 29 S.A.; 45 N.&S.A.; 82 wld.)

AID TO IDENTIFICATION

Above dark (tail virtually square) 1, (tail deeply forked) 5, 9.
Above pale, head black, or mottled 2, 3, 4.
Above pale, crown only black or streaked (bill yellow or orange) 6, 10E, 11, 13, (bill red) 7, 8, 12, (bill black) 8, 9, 14.

1. GRAY GULL
(Larus modestus)

Description. 16 - 18″. *Summer:* Head white, body plumage mouse gray. Wings black with a white band; tail gray with a wide black terminal band. *Winter:* Similar, but head brown. Bill and feet black.

Range. Breeds in the deserts of Peru and Chile; at sea peculiar to the cold Humboldt current, from Ecuador southward.

Colombia. Strays to the coast of southwest Colombia.

2. LAUGHING GULL
(Larus atricilla)

Description. 15 - 17″. *Summer:* Head grayish black with a white bar above and below the eye. Bill red, feet brown. *Winter:* Head white mottled with brownish gray. Underparts white, mantle dark gray. Five outer primaries black. Bill black.

Range. Breeds on the Atlantic coast of North America southward to Central America, the West Indies and Trinidad. Winters southward to Peru and Bolivia.

Colombia. Winter visitor from September to May on both coasts, occasionally in the upper Cauca Valley. Birds in breeding plumage have been observed in May on the Caribbean coast.

3. FRANKLIN'S GULL
(Larus pipixcan)

Description. 13½ - 14″. *Summer:* Head black with a white bar above and below the eye. Mantle and wings light bluegray. Wing-feathers with white tip, and a black subterminal bar on the five outer primaries. Hindneck and upperparts white. Bill dark red. *Winter:* Similar but head mostly white except for dusky area about eye, on ear-coverts and hindneck. Bill blackish.

91

Range. Breeds in the interior of Canada and the western United States. Winters from the Gulf states southward to western South America as far as Chile.
Colombia. Winter visitor. Recorded from the Pacific coast (Octavia Rocks, May).

4. SABINE'S GULL
(Xema sabini)
Description. 12 - 14". Head and throat white with dusky patches (slate-colored in summer). Neck, underparts and forked tail white. Mantle pearl gray. First four primaries black, all except first with white tip. Bill and feet black, the bill with a yellow tip. In the immature, the tail is forked as in the adult, but has a wide terminal black band.
Range. Breeds in the Arctic. Winters off the west coast of Africa and South America, south to Chile.
Colombia. Winter resident off the Pacific coast *(sabini)*.

5. BLACK TERN
(Chlidonias niger)
Description. 9 - 10". Head, neck and underparts black. Back, wings and short slightly forked tail, slate gray. In winter the head, neck and underparts are white, the head mottled with gray. Bill black, feet dusky.
Range. Breeds on inland lakes and marshes of North America and Europe. Winters south to Chile and Dutch Guiana; Africa, and northwestern India.
Colombia. Winter resident, both coasts *(surinamensis)*.

6. LARGE-BILLED TERN
(Phaetusa simplex) Fig. 39
Description. 15". Crown glossy black. Mantle and tail slate gray. Underparts white. Primaries dark brown; upper wing-coverts and secondaries edged white. Tail short, nearly square. Bill very thick, orange-yellow.
Range. Large rivers and estuaries of the Atlantic drainage of tropical South America. Trinidad.
Colombia. Chiefly the larger rivers and

estuaries of the Caribbean and Atlantic drainage. Sometimes found on lakes in the temperate zone of the Eastern Andes up to 11,500 ft. *(simplex)*.

7. CASPIAN TERN
(Hydroprogne caspia)
Description. 18 - 22". Crown and nape black (streaked white in winter). Mantle ashy gray; underparts white. Tail slightly forked, grayish white. Bill very thick, red; feet black.
Range. Breeds in North America, chiefly in the interior from Canada south to the Gulf of Mexico. Also in Europe, Asia, Africa, Australia and New Zealand. Winters south to northern South America, Asia, Africa, and Indonesia.
Colombia. Winter resident recorded from December to May on the Caribbean coast and the lower Magdalena river.

8. COMMON TERN
(Sterna hirundo)
Description. 12 - 15". Top of head black (streaked white in winter). Mantle dark pearl gray, rump white. Outer web of outer primaries black. Throat white, breast and belly pale gray. Tail white, deeply forked. Bill red with black tip; black in winter.
Range. Breeds in North America, the Caribbean, Europe and Asia. South in winter to Peru and Argentina, Trinidad. Southern Asia and South Africa.
Colombia. Winter resident on both coasts *(hirundo)*.

9. BRIDLED TERN
(Sterna anaethetus)
Description. 13 - 15". Forehead white; top of head and line through eye black. Upperparts, wings and deeply forked tail dark grayish brown. Underparts white. Bill and feet black.
Range. Often seen far from land. Tropical and subtropical seas and oceans.
Colombia. The Pacific coast *(nelsoni)*.

10. YELLOW-BILLED TERN
(Sterna superciliaris)

Description. 9 - 11″. Forehead white; crown, nape and line through eye to bill black. Upperparts gray, lowerparts white. Four outer primaries blackish. Tail forked, gray. Bill and feet dull yellow.

Range. Estuaries and rivers from the Orinoco to the Río de la Plata, Argentina.

Colombia. A fresh-water species found on the larger rivers in the Amazonian and Orinocan drainage.

11. LEAST TERN
(Sterna albifrons)

Description. 8 - 10″. Very similar to the Yellow-billed Tern but paler above with the bill and feet brighter yellow, and tail somewhat longer.

Range. Breeds in North America south to the West Indies and Margarita Island. Europe, Asia and Africa. Birds breeding in North America winter as far south as Brazil and Peru.

Colombia. Transient (?), recorded in April and May from the Caribbean coast (antillarum).

12. ROYAL TERN
(Thalasseus maximus)

Description. 19 - 21″. Summer: Crown and crest black, forehead often white. Neck, underparts and deeply forked tail white; mantle gray. Bill orange, feet black. Winter: The forecrown is white, hindcrown and crest mixed with white.

Range. Breeds on the coasts of the southern United States and in the West Indies. South in winter to Peru and Argentina. The west coast of Africa.

Colombia. Winter resident, October to April, on both coasts (maximus).

13. CAYENNE TERN
(Thalasseus eurygnathus)

Description. 16 - 17″. Very similar to the Royal Tern but smaller, and bill lemon yellow.

Range. Southern Caribbean southward on the east coast of South America to Patagonia.

Colombia. The Caribbean coast.

14. SANDWICH TERN
(Thalasseus sandvicensis)

Description. 14 - 16″. Very similar to the Royal Tern but smaller and with a black yellow-tipped bill.

Range. Breeds in Europe, North Africa, western Asia, the southern United States and Central America. Winters southward to Brazil, Argentina, southern Africa and western India.

Colombia. The Caribbean coast (acuflavidus).

SKIMMERS (Rynchopidae)

Fig. 40. Black Skimmer
(Rynchops nigra)

Distinguishable from other gull- and tern-like birds by their habits of flying, with rapid wing-beats, just above the surface of the seas, skimming the water with their knife-like bills while feeding on small fish and crustaceans. They are gregarious and partially nocturnal and nest in colonies on sandbanks.

In addition to the Black Skimmer of American waters, another species is found in Africa and a third in India and Burma. (1 Col.; 1 S.A.; 1 N.&S.A.; 3 wld.)

BLACK SKIMMER
(Rynchops nigra)

Description. 16 - 18″. *Summer:* Upperparts and wings black, secondaries edged white. Tail forked, grayish white. Forehead, sides of head and underparts white. Bill half black, half orange, lower mandible long-est. *Winter:* A white collar across hind-neck.

Range. Eastern and southern United States and northwestern Mexico southward to the Straits of Magellan.

Colombia. Caribbean coast and larger rivers *(cinerascens).*

94

PIGEONS AND DOVES (Columbidae)

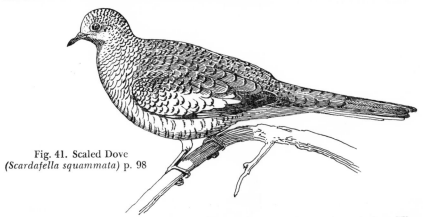

Fig. 41. Scaled Dove
(Scardafella squammata) p. 98

Pigeons in Colombia are numerous both in quantity and varieties. They exhibit a wider range of colors than is generally associated with this family, but none is as brilliantly colored as the fruit pigeons of Malaysia. While well represented in South America, the Oriental region supports almost two-thirds of all the species of pigeons, and there they reach the heights of diversification and brilliance of color.

Found from sea level to the temperate zone, in desert regions and tropical rain forest, this adaptable group feeds on fruits and seeds. Some are largely terrestial while others are almost never seen on the ground. The sexes are usually alike in plumage but females are duller. (29 Col.; 46 S.A.; 60 N.&S.A.; 289 wld.)

AID TO IDENTIFICATION

Tail banded or contrastingly tipped (underparts buff to vinous or chestnut) 3, 8, 9, 12, 13, 14, 16, 18, 19, 20, 21, 22ᴱ, (underparts gray or white) 10, 17, 23.

Tail uniform (underparts buff to chestnut) 1, 2, 4, 6, 7, 11, 15, 24, 26, 28, 29, (underparts gray or white) 5, 25, 27.

1. SCALED PIGEON
(Columba speciosa)

Description. 11 - 13″. ♂ : Head purplish brown, throat pale pinkish. Neck and breast metallic purplish black, conspicuously spotted with white; the upper back similar but spotted cinnamon, giving a scale-like appearance; rest of upperparts chestnut. Wings and tail black. Lower breast vinaceous cinnamon, white on crissum. Bill bright red. ♀ duller, back dull brown.

Range. Mexico south to Venezuela, Peru, Bolivia and Paraguay. Trinidad.

Colombia. Tall forest trees of the humid tropical zone.

2. BARE-EYED PIGEON
(Columba corensis)

Description. 12 - 13″. Entire head, neck and underparts vinous pink, under tail-coverts white. A band of feathers at base of hindneck edged with silvery gray and fringed with black; feathers of extreme upper mantle edged with pinkish brown, shot with violet reflections and fringed with black. Back pale brown, rump and upper tail-coverts gray. Tail, pale sandy grayish. Wing-coverts like back, the greater ones broadly edged with white, forming a conspicuous band. Primaries dark brown, under wing-coverts gray. Large bare patch about eye blue; bill yellow, basally reddish.

Range. Coast of Venezuela. Margarita

PLATE IV

SPECTACLED
PARROTLET
*(Forpus conspic-
illatus caucae)*
Page 106

YELLOW-EARED
PARAKEET
(Ognorhynchus icterotis)
Page 104

GOLDEN-PLUMED
PARAKEET
(Leptosittaca branickii)
Page 104

ORANGE-CHINNED
PARAKEET
(Brotogeris j. jugularis)
Page 106

BLUE-HEADED PARROT
*(Pionus menstruus
rubrigularis)*
Page 108

PAINTED PARAKEET
(Pyrrhura picta subandina)
Page 105

IVORY-BILLED ARAÇARI
(Pteroglossus f. flavirostris)
Page 184

GRAY-BREASTED
MOUNTAIN TOUCAN
(Andigena h. hypoglauca)
Page 183

EMERALD TOUCANET
*(Aulacorhynchus
prasinus phaeolaemus)*
Page 185

PLAIN-BREASTED
GROUND-DOVE
(Columbigallina m. minuta)
Page 99

SAPPHIRE QUAIL-DOVE
*(Osculatia saph-
irina purpurata)*
Page 100

OLIVE-BACKED
QUAIL-DOVE
(Geotrygon veraguensis)
Page 101

E.L.Poole

Island, Aruba, Curaçao and Bonaire.

Colombia. Arid coastal regions of the Santa Marta region and the Guajira Peninsula.

3. BAND-TAILED PIGEON
(Columba fasciata)

Description. 13 - 15″. Head and underparts vinaceous gray, white band on the nape. Upper mantle bronze green, feathers dark-edged; rest of upperparts brownish gray, bluish gray on wing-coverts. Crissum white. Tail dark gray with a broad, dark subterminal band. Bill and legs yellow.

Range. Southwestern Canada to Venezuela, Peru and northwestern Argentina. Trinidad.

Colombia. Forest in the subtropical to temperate (rarely tropical) zone of the Andes and the Santa Marta region *(albilinea).*

4. PALE-VENTED PIGEON
(Columba cayennensis)

Description. 12 - 13″. Mostly rich vinaceous; hindcrown and nape shot with metallic purplish green. Rump and upper tail-coverts bluish slate. Abdomen and under tail-coverts whitish. Tail dull brown. Bill black, legs red.

Range. Southern Mexico southward to western Ecuador, Venezuela, Brazil, Bolivia and Argentina. Trinidad and Tobago.

Colombia. Humid lowland forests, plains and ranchlands. The Santa Marta region, the lower Magdalena and Cauca Valleys westward to the Atrato River *(pallidicrissa).* The upper Atrato Valley southward along the coast *(occidentalis).* The upper Cauca and upper Patía Valleys *(tamboensis).* Forests east of the Andes *(cayennensis).*

5. DUSKY PIGEON
(Columba goodsoni)

Description. 10 - 11″. Crown, sides of head and underparts plumbeous gray, abdomen brownish. Hindneck metallic purplish brown, rest of upperparts and tail dark purplish brown. Under tail-coverts pale chestnut. Under side of wings cinnamon.

Bill black, legs red.

Range. Western Ecuador.

Colombia. Rain forests of the Pacific coast from the headwaters of the Atrato southward.

6. RUDDY PIGEON
(Columba subvinacea)

Description. 12 - 13½″. Head, neck and underparts light vinaceous purple, paler on throat. Upper surface brownish cinnamon. Wings and tail chocolate; under wing-coverts vinaceous. Bill black, legs red.

Range. Costa Rica to western Ecuador. Venezuela southward to Brazil and Bolivia.

Colombia. Open forest and clearings. Tropical forests of western Colombia from Nariño north to the headwaters of the río San Juan *(berlepschi).* Northwestern Colombia in the Sinú Valley *(ruberrima).* Tropical and subtropical zones of the Magdalena and Cauca Valleys south of 9° N. Lat. *(anolaimae)* Norte de Santander in the Catatumbo region *(zuliae).* Southeastern Colombia from Caquetá southward *(ogilvie-granti).* Orinoco and probably the Vaupés region *(purpureotincta).*

7. PLUMBEOUS PIGEON
(Columba plumbea)

Description. 11 - 13″. Head, neck and underparts purplish vinaceous. Upper surface and tail dark sepia brown with an olive sheen. Wings bronzy brown; under wing-coverts dark grayish vinaceous. Bill black, legs red.

Range. Western Ecuador. The Guianas, Brazil, Peru, Venezuela southward to Bolivia and Paraguay.

Colombia. Forest. Tropical and subtropical zones. The Central and Eastern Andes and the Caquetá region *(bogotensis).* West of the Western Andes from the headwaters of the río San Juan southward *(chapmani).*

8. MOURNING DOVE
(Zenaida macroura)

Description. 11 - 13″. Forehead fawn, back of head mouse gray, a black spot on ear-coverts. Upperparts grayish brown, glossed with shining bronzy purple on nape, rump slaty gray. Below mostly pinkish buff. Tail long, graduated and pointed, middle pair of feathers like back, rest basally gray with a narrow black subterminal bar and broad white tips. Wing-coverts spotted with black.

Range. Breeds in North America southward to the Bahamas and Mexico. In winter, south to Panama.

Colombia. The only record is that of a bird shot at Cartago, Valle, in May. It was banded as a nestling in western Iowa (marginella).

9. EARED DOVE
(Zenaida auriculata)

Description. 9 - 11". Top of head gray; forehead, sides of head, and breast vinous (or cinnamon, 1). A black spot behind the eye and a larger one below ear-coverts black; sides of neck metallic purple with golden reflections. Above olive brown, the wing-coverts spotted with black. Flanks and under wing-coverts light blue-gray. Central tail feathers brownish gray, the rest gray with a subterminal black band and whitish (or deep rusty buff, 1) tip.

Range. From Venezuela southward to Chile and northern Argentina. The West Indies; Curaçao, Aruba and Bonaire. Trinidad and Tobago.

Colombia. Savanna and sparsely wooded lands. Temperate zone of the Eastern Andes (1, pentheria). Tropical zone of the Magdalena Vàlley, the Caribbean coast and the llanos east of the Andes (1, stenura). The subtropical and temperate zone of the upper Cauca Valley, upper Patía and Dagua Valleys and the tropical zone of Nariño (caucae). Temperate zone of the Andes in Nariño (vulcania).

10. SCALED DOVE
(Scardafella squammata) Fig. 41

Description. 8 - 9". Above pale sandy brown, below pinkish white, each feather terminating in a crescentic black bar. Inner webs of primaries rufous. Central tail-feathers sandy brown, rest mostly black with broad white tips. Tail long, pointed.

Range. Arizona and Texas, southward to Costa Rica. Venezuela, French Guiana. Tableland of Brazil from Maranhão, southward to Mato Grosso. Paraguay. Trinidad, Margarita Island.

Colombia. Arid tropical Caribbean coast, and the llanos in Arauca and Meta (ridgwayi).

11. BLACK-WINGED DOVE
(Metriopelia melanoptera)

Description. 8 - 9". Upperparts grayish brown; lower parts pale vinaceous. Wing-coverts and flanks gray. Throat and bend of wing white. Remiges and tail black, the latter basally gray. Under wing-coverts black and white.

Range. Ecuador to Peru, Bolivia, Chile and western Argentina.

Colombia. The mountains of Nariño in the subtropical and temperate zones (saturatior).

12. COMMON GROUND-DOVE
(Columbigallina passerina)

Description. 6 - 6½". ♂ : Forehead, sides of head, neck, breast and abdomen pinkish vinous, feathers edged or centered with dusky on neck and breast giving a scaled appearance. Top of head and nape pale gray. Upperparts and central tail-feathers grayish or olive brown. Wings with conspicuous blue-black spots; under wing-coverts and primaries cinnamon. Tail-feathers except central ones basally gray, then black, the outer ones tipped white. ♀ similar but without pinkish vinous tones.

Range. Southern United States southward through Central America and the West Indies to Venezuela, Ecuador and northern Brazil. Trinidad. Margarita Island, Aruba.

Colombia. Arid littoral, open woodland, savanna. The Caribbean coast and the northern end of the Eastern Andes on the east slope (albivitta). Extreme eastern Colombia in Vaupés (griseola). The middle Magdalena Valley (parvula). The dry parts of the upper Dagua and Patía Valleys (nana).

13. PLAIN-BREASTED GROUND-DOVE
(Columbigallina minuta) Plate IV

Description. 5 - 6". ♂ : Crown gray, upperparts pale grayish brown, wings spotted with metallic blue-black. Underparts plain vinaceous. Inner webs of flight-feathers chestnut. Tail dusky, outer feathers tipped white. ♀ like ♂ but underparts grayish olive with white throat and belly.

Range. Mexico southward through Central America to Venezuela, Brazil, Bolivia and Paraguay. Trinidad.

Colombia. Drier open and scrubby parts of northern Colombia eastward to Meta (elaeodes). From Meta southward (minuta).

14. RUDDY GROUND-DOVE
(Columbigallina talpacoti)

Description. 6 - 7". ♂ : Top of head gray, palest on forehead. Upperparts cinnamon, wings black spotted. Underparts vinaceous, crissum chestnut. Remiges chestnut, tipped black. The outer tail feathers black, tipped cinnamon. ♀ : Grayish brown above, paler below.

Range. Mexico southward to Venezuela, Bolivia and Argentina. Trinidad, Tobago, and Margarita Island. The Guianas.

Colombia. Virtually throughout the drier parts of tropical and subtropical Colombia except the west coast, and in areas not occupied by next two subspecies (rufipennis). Upper Cauca and Patía Valleys (caucae). Extreme southeastern Colombia on the Amazon (talpacoti).

15. BLUE GROUND-DOVE
(Claravis pretiosa)

Description. 8 - 9". ♂ : Head and underparts pale blue-gray, paler on forehead, sides of head and underparts; black spots on wings. Outer tail-feathers black. ♀ : Mainly olive or tawny brown. Rump and middle tail-feathers rufous, outer tail-feathers black. Wing-coverts spotted and barred purple-chestnut; abdomen pale gray.

Range. From southern Mexico southward through Central America and western South America from western Venezuela to northern Bolivia.

Colombia. Tropical zone throughout the country in forested regions.

16. MAROON-CHESTED GROUND-DOVE
(Claravis mondetoura)

Description. 8 - 9". ♂ : Above slate gray, forehead whitish; wings spotted with metallic violet-black. Throat white, neck and chest deep purplish chestnut; abdomen gray fading to white on under tail-coverts. Tail grayish, outer feathers broadly tipped white. ♀ : Mainly olive brown. Wings spotted and banded with metallic purple. Forehead and tail-coverts cinnamon, throat and belly white. Outer tail-feathers tipped white.

Range. Mexico to Venezuela and southward through western South America to Bolivia.

Colombia. Forest. Tropical to temperate zone. Recorded from the Eastern and Western Andes (mondetoura).

17. GRAY-CHESTED DOVE
(Leptotila cassinii)

Description. 10 - 11". Forehead, throat and belly whitish; neck and breast gray tinged vinaceous on breast. Upperparts and sides of body dark olive brown. Outer tail-feathers blackish, tipped white.

Range. Mexico southward to Colombia.

Colombia. Tropical lowland forests in western Colombia south to the upper Atrato and eastward to the middle Magdalena Valley (cassinii).

18. TOLIMA DOVE
(Leptotila conoveri)

Description. 9 - 10". Crown dark gray, throat white; hindneck vinaceous brown glossed violet. Upper mantle vinaceous gray, shot with shining violet; rest of upperparts dark brown with a purple sheen. Chest vinaceous pink, in sharp contrast to buff lower breast and abdomen; crissum white. Wing-lining cinnamon-rufous. Tail slaty, outer feathers tipped white.

Range. Colombia.

Colombia. The subtropical zone of the east slope of the Central Andes, from Tolima south to Huila.

19. WHITE-TIPPED DOVE
(Leptotila verreauxi)

Description. 11 - 13". Head vinaceous, palest on forehead; hindneck strongly shot with metallic violet green. Upperparts olive brown; below vinaceous. Outer tail-feathers dusky conspicuously tipped with white. Wing-lining cinnamon. Skin about eye red (or blue, I).

Range. Mexico southward through Venezuela to southern Brazil, Paraguay, Argentina and Bolivia. The Dutch West Indies, Trinidad, Tobago. The Trés Marías Islands.

Colombia. Semi-arid region, forest and clearings. Tropical to lower temperate zones of northern Colombia and the Magdalena Valley (1, verreauxi). The Cauca Valley, eastern and western Nariño (decolor).

20. GRAY-HEADED DOVE
(Leptotila plumbeiceps)

Description. 10 - 11". Forecrown pale gray, hindcrown and nape blue-gray; sides of head and neck buffy; center of throat, abdomen and under tail-coverts white. Breast pinkish vinaceous. Upperparts olive brown. Lateral tail-feathers black, tipped white.

Range. Mexico to Colombia. Coiba Island.

Colombia. Forests. Upper tropical and subtropical zones of western Colombia, south to the río Dagua and eastward to the middle and upper Cauca Valley.

21. PALLID DOVE
(Leptotila pallida)

Description. 9 - 10". Forecrown white, rest of crown bluish gray, nape and hindneck purplish gray. Throat white, sides of head, neck and the breast pale vinaceous, rest of underparts white. Upperparts rufous brown, tinged purplish on upper back. Outer tail-feathers rufous brown, darker distally, tip white.

Range. Western Ecuador.

Colombia. Tropical Pacific Colombia from the upper río San Juan southward.

22. GRAY-FRONTED DOVE
(Leptotila rufaxilla)

Description. 10½ - 11½". Forehead grayish white, crown blue-gray, nape dull purplish, hindneck shining purple violet. Center of throat white, sides of head and neck rufescent. Upperparts and sides of body olive brown. Breast and belly white, under tail-coverts brown and white. Wing-lining cinnamon. Outer tail-feathers blackish, two outermost tipped white.

Range. From Venezuela and the Guianas southward to Brazil, Uruguay, Paraguay and Bolivia. Trinidad.

Colombia. Humid forest. Tropical zone east of the Andes from Meta northward (pallidipectus); from Meta southward (dubusi).

23. SAPPHIRE QUAIL-DOVE
(Osculatia saphirina) Plate IV

Description. 10 - 11". ♂ : Forehead and cheeks white, the latter bordered below by a blackish purple band. Crown gray, darkening posteriorly to deep purple-blue, nape golden green, changing to bronze green with metallic purple reflections on hindneck and mantle. Lower parts white, the breast tinged gray; under tail-coverts buffy. Back rich purple, purple-blue on upper tail-coverts. Tail short, slaty black, outer feathers with a gray terminal band, the outermost with a white spot at tip. ♀ similar but duller and upperparts tinged olive. Quail-doves all have very short tails.

Range. Western South America, east and west of the Andes from Colombia to Peru.

Colombia. Undergrowth and floor of tropical forests of Pacific Colombia from the upper Atrato southward into Nariño (purpurata).

24. RUDDY QUAIL-DOVE
(Geotrygon montana)

Description. 8½ - 9½" ♂ : Bright chestnut above, hindneck and back strongly shaded reddish purple. Throat pinkish cinnamon, becoming vinous on breast; abdomen and crissum pale cinnamon. ♀ much duller. Upperparts and breast brownish olive, buffy cinnamon in center and on belly.

Range. Mexico and the West Indies, southward to Venezuela, Brazil, Paraguay and Bolivia.

Colombia. Tropical occasionally to temperate zone. Undergrowth and forest floor in heavy forest throughout *(montana)*.

25. VIOLACEOUS QUAIL-DOVE
(Geotrygon violacea)

Description. 9 - 10″. Forehead white, a purple gold patch on nape; sides of head buffy pink. Throat white; foreneck and breast vinous; rest of underparts white. Hindneck and mantle metallic purple, lower back olive, feathers edged purple; dull cinnamon on rump. Tail cinnamon purple; primaries chestnut.

Range. Nicaragua to western and northern Venezuela. Dutch Guiana. Northeastern Brazil southward to Bolivia and Paraguay.

Colombia. Heavy forest in the tropical zone of northern Colombia and east of the Andes southward to the Macarena Mts. *(albiventer)*.

26. OLIVE-BACKED QUAIL-DOVE
(Geotrygon veraguensis) Plate IV

Description.. 9- -10″. Forehead and line below the eye white, the latter bordered above and below by a black line. Hindcrown, back and sides of neck, upper back and upper breast dull violet purple shot with gold on occiput and hindneck. Throat, center of belly and under tail-coverts white tinged rufescent. Lower breast and sides rufescent brown. Lower back, wings and tail olive.

Range. Costa Rica to western Ecuador.

Colombia. Humid forests of the tropical zone of Pacific Colombia and eastward into the middle Cauca Valley.

27. RUSSET-CROWNED QUAIL-DOVE
(Geotrygon goldmani)

Description. 10 - 11″. Forehead fawn, crown and nape russet brown, hindneck grayish brown glossed with purple-bronze;

interscapular region purplish brown, rest of upperparts olive brown. A broad pinkish buff malar stripe bordered below by a black line; throat white turning into bluish gray on neck and breast; abdomen whitish buff. Wings and tail olive brown.

Range. Eastern Panama.

Colombia. Forest. Known only from the Pacific coast near the Panama border *(goldmani)*.

28. LINED QUAIL-DOVE
(Geotrygon linearis)

Description. 11 - 13″. Forehead rufous changing into vinous on crown and into gray with a green lustre on occiput, bounded behind by a grayish white band. Sides of head and the throat whitish, rufous at base of lower mandible; a black malar streak. Hindneck purple-brown, mantle purplish blue, rest of underparts rufous brown. Breast vinous, rest of lower parts reddish brown, whitish in middle of abdomen. Wings and tail rufous brown.

Range. Mexico southward to Venezuela. Trinidad and Tobago.

Colombia. Forest. Tropical and subtropical zone of the Santa Marta region *(infusca)*. East of the Andes from the Macarena Mts. northward and west of them to the middle Magdalena and the middle Cauca Valleys *(linearis)*.

29. WHITE-THROATED QUAIL-DOVE
(Geotrygon frenata)

Description. 13 - 14″. Forehead and cheeks vinous, changing into dark gray on crown. A black malar streak, throat white, neck gray, breast grayish brown, abdomen white. Mantle purple with a greenish luster, rest of upperparts and wings rufous brown. Tail brown.

Range. Western South America south through Ecuador to Bolivia.

Colombia. Upper tropical and subtropical forests. Pacific Colombia east to the Central Andes and on the east slope in Nariño *(bourcieri)*.

MACAWS, PARROTS AND PARAKEETS (Psittacidae)

Fig. 42. Barred Parakeet
(*Bolborhynchus lineola*) p. 105

Parrots form one of the best-known families of birds. They are found in Asia, Africa, Australia and many Pacific islands. In the Americas they occur all over South and Central America, the West Indies. and once occurred as far north as New York. Today Mexico and the Bahamas is their northern, and southern Argentina and Chile their southern boundary.

In Colombia parrots are for the most part found in tropical forest, but some occur in dry scrub and wooded savannas. A few species occur in mountains to 12,000 ft. or more. They feed on fruit, nuts and seeds, sometimes doing considerable damage to cultivated crops. Most species nest in cavities in trees, where their round, white eggs are laid.

Noisy and conspicuous, they fly swiftly, with rapid wing-beats, in small compact flocks, but are difficult to see when they alight, for their predominantly green plumage blends with the foliage.

In size the Colombian species vary from the three-foot-long, gaudily colored macaws, to the tiny parrotlets about six inches in length. The talking propensities of parrots are well-known. Among the South American species the best performers are that group known as Amazon Parrots (*Amazona*), heavy-bodied, mostly green birds. (51 Col.; 113 S.A.; 141 N.&S.A.; 315 wld.)

AID TO IDENTIFICATION

Size very large (over 2 ft.) 1, 2, 3, 4, 5.

Under 2 ft.; tail conspicuously long and pointed (under wing-coverts green) 7E, 8, 9, 11E, 12, 13, 14, 15, 17, 18, 23aE, (under wing-coverts red) 6, 10E, 16.

Tail short, pointed (under wing-coverts green) 19, 26E, (under wing-coverts red) 28E, (or yellow) 25.

Tail square or rounded (under wing-coverts green) 20, 27E, 30, 31E, 38E, 39, 40, 41, 44, 45E, 46, 47, 48, 49, 50E, (under wing-coverts blue) 21, 22, 23E, 24E, 32, 33, 36. 37. 42, 43, (under wing-coverts red) 34E, 35, (or yellow) 29.

102

1. BLUE-AND-YELLOW MACAW
(Ara ararauna)

Description. 29 - 35". Upperparts, wings and long, pointed tail blue. Underparts yellow. Forehead green.

Range. Eastern Panama to Venezuela, southeastern Brazil and Bolivia.

Colombia. Forest and savanna. Northern Colombia from the Pacific coast eastward to Santa Marta, the lower and middle Magdalena Valley, and east of the Andes southward to the Amazon.

It is curious that no macaw has as yet (1963) been recorded from Nariño, west of the Andes.

2. MILITARY MACAW
(Ara militaris)

Description. 27 - 30". Mostly green. Forehead and basal two-thirds of long, central tail-feathers red. Primaries, secondaries, lower back, upper and under tail-coverts blue. Throat and foreneck dark red. Under side of wings and tail olive yellow.

Range. Mexico to Venezuela and western South America, south to western Argentina.

Colombia. Forest. Tropical zone. From the Dagua Valley in Pacific Colombia eastward across the northern part of the country to the middle Magdalena and the Santa Marta regions. East of the Andes in Putumayo *(militaris)*.

3. GREAT GREEN MACAW
(Ara ambigua)

Description. 30 - 33". Resembles very closely the Military Macaw but larger, and more yellowish green.

Range. Nicaragua, southward to western Ecuador.

Colombia. Forest. Tropical zone of the Pacific slope of Colombia south to the Baudó Mts. *(ambigua)*.

4. SCARLET MACAW
(Ara macao)

Description. 33 - 38". Scarlet. Greater wing-coverts yellow. Remiges, lower back, upper and under tail-coverts blue.

Range. Mexico to Venezuela, northeastern Brazil and Bolivia.

Colombia. Open woodland and savanna of the tropical zone in northeastern Colombia, the lower Magdalena Valley and east of the Andes south to the Amazon.

5. RED-BLUE-AND-GREEN MACAW
(Ara chloroptera)

Description. 34 - 38". Very much like the Scarlet Macaw but without yellow in the plumage. Outer tail-feathers blue instead of scarlet and wing-coverts green.

Range. Eastern Panama to Venezuela southward east of the Andes to Bolivia and Argentina.

Colombia. Forest. Tropical zone. The Pacific coast from the Baudó Mts. northward and westward across northern Colombia to the lower Magdalena and the Santa Marta region. East of the Andes in the Amazonian drainage.

6. CHESTNUT-FRONTED MACAW
(Ara severa)

Description. 17 - 21". Mostly green. Forehead and border of cheeks maroon. Bend of wing and under wing-coverts rosy red; remiges blue. Under sides of wings and tail dull red.

Range. Eastern Panama to Venezuela and southward to southern Brazil and Bolivia.

Colombia. Forests of the tropical zone, often near rivers *(castaneifrons)*.

7. RED-BELLIED MACAW
(Ara manilata)

Description. 18 - 22". Mostly green. Forecrown blue. Chest and throat blue-gray, feathers edged green; belly maroon red. Remiges blue, edged green; under side of wings and tail dull yellow.

Range. Southern and eastern Venezuela, the Guianas southward to southern Brazil and east to Ecuador and Peru.

Colombia. Palm groves east of the Andes from Meta southward.

8. BLUE-CROWNED PARAKEET
(Aratinga acuticaudata)

Description. 14 - 15". Forehead and forecrown blue; rest of plumage green, yellow-er below. Base of outer tail-feathers red.

Range. Tropical South America to Argentina and Bolivia. Margarita Island.

Colombia. Scrubby, arid Caribbean region from eastern Santa Marta eastward (*haemorrhous*).

9. SCARLET-FRONTED PARAKEET
(Aratinga wagleri)

Description. 13 - 14". Green. Forehead, forecrown, spots on lower cheeks and the thighs red.

Range. Tropical western South America from northwestern Venezuela, to Peru and western Ecuador.

Colombia. Forest. Tropical and subtropical zones. West of the Eastern Andes (*wagleri*). East of the Andes (*transilis*).

10. WHITE-EYED PARAKEET
(Aratinga leucophthalmus)

Description. 14 - 15". Green. Extreme point of forehead maroon sometimes with a few red specks (or forehead with a solid red band, 1). Spots on side of neck, lesser wing-coverts red. Under wing-coverts red and yellow.

Range. Nicaragua to Panama. Eastern Colombia, eastern Venezuela, the Guianas, southward to Bolivia and Argentina.

Colombia. Open forest and palm groves. Tropical zone east of the Eastern Andes from Meta southward (*callogenys*). From Meta northward (1, *nicefori*).

11. DUSKY-HEADED PARAKEET
(Aratinga weddellii)

Description. 10½ - 11½". Whole head brownish gray to bluish gray. Greater wing-coverts, remiges, tips of tail-feathers ultramarine blue; rest of plumage green. Under side of wings and tail black.

Range. Western portion of the Amazon basin, from Ecuador to Bolivia and western Mato Grosso.

Colombia. Forest. Tropical zone east of the Andes.

12. BROWN-THROATED PARAKEET
(Aratinga pertinax)

Description. 9½ - 10½". Forehead, cheeks, foreneck and upper breast dull brown (or pale brown, 1; or grayish brown, 2). Crown and remiges bluish. Upper surface grass green, lower breast and belly yellowish green. Under surfaces of wings black, of tail greenish yellow.

Range. Western Panama through Venezuela to the Guianas. Dutch West Indies.

Colombia. Open woods, clearing and scrub. Tropical zone. Eastern Caribbean coast, the lower and middle Magdalena Valley and east of the Andes in the Zulia Valley (*aeruginosa*). East of the Andes in the llanos of Meta (1, *lehmanni*). The upper Orinoco (*venezuelae*). The valley of the río Sinú (2, *griseipecta*).

13. GOLDEN-PLUMED PARAKEET
(Leptosittaca branickii) Plate IV

Description. 13½ - 15½". General plumage grass green. Lores and a tuft of long narrow feathers springing from cheek, dull orange yellow. Center of abdomen dull red mixed with green. Under side of wing yellowish. Tail long and pointed, dull red.

Range. Southern Ecuador and central Peru.

Colombia. Temperate zone of the Central Andes.

14. YELLOW-EARED PARAKEET
(Ognorhynchus icterotis) Plate IV

Description. 16 - 18". Forecrown, lores, cheeks, lengthened plumes on ear-coverts golden yellow. Entire upper surface, sides of neck, under tail-coverts grass green. Foreneck and rest of underparts greenish yellow. Tail long, pointed, central feathers green, rest dull maroon red on inner webs. Under side of wing dusky, of tail red.

Range. Northern Ecuador.

Colombia. Subtropical to temperate zones. Locally, where there are wax palms, in the Eastern, Central and Western Andes.

15. PAINTED PARAKEET
(Pyrrhura picta) Plate IV

Description. 8 - 9". Forehead, lores, region in front of eye, patch on lower back and center of abdomen and the tail-feathers maroon red. Collar on hindneck and greater wing-coverts blue. Entire top of head dark brown (or tinged with blue, 1); ear-coverts rusty. Throat and chest dull blue, feathers broadly edged with buffy white giving a scaled appearance. Rest of plumage grass green.

Range. Venezuela and the Guianas southward to eastern Peru and northeastern Brazil.

Colombia. Forest. Tropical zone. Sinú Valley (subandina). The west slope of the Eastern Andes in Magdalena (1, caeruleiceps).

16. SANTA MARTA PARAKEET
(Pyrrhura viridicata)

Description. 9 - 10". Narrow frontal band scarlet. Ear-coverts maroon brown, throat tinged with same color. General plumage green with a scattering of orange and scarlet feathers on the lower breast. Upper wing-coverts mixed green and orange, under wing-coverts mixed orange and scarlet. Remiges blue; tail green, under surface dull red.

Range. Colombia.

Colombia. Forest. The Santa Marta Mts., in the subtropical zone.

17. MAROON-TAILED PARAKEET
(Pyrrhura melanura)

Description. 10 - 11". Forehead and crown brown more or less mixed with green, narrow line on forehead maroon. Rest of plumage mainly green, feathers of chest narrowly (or very broadly, 1) edged with ashy white. Greater median wing-coverts bright rosy red. Tail maroon, with green at base.

Range. Venezuela southward to the río Negro, western Brazil, Ecuador and Peru.

Colombia. Forest. Tropical zone. Extreme eastern and southern Colombia (melanura). East of the Andes in Meta and Caquetá (souancei). Subtropical zone on the eastern slope of the Central Andes (1, chapmani). Tropical zone of southwestern Nariño (pacifica).

18. FLAME-WINGED PARAKEET
(Pyrrhura calliptera)

Description. 9 - 10". Crown mixed ashy brown and greenish blue. Ear-coverts and center of belly maroon red. Throat and breast ashy brown tinged maroon. Lesser wing-coverts orange, greater wing-coverts golden yellow. Rest of plumage grass green. Tail maroon.

Range. Colombia.

Colombia. Forest. Subtropical to lower temperate zone of the Eastern Andes in Boyacá and Cundinamarca.

19. BARRED PARAKEET
(Bolborhynchus lineola) Fig. 42

Description. 7 - 7½". Forecrown emerald green. Upper surface olive green barred with black, the width of bars increasing toward upper tail-coverts. Shoulders black, wing-coverts tipped black forming two wing-bars. Under surface bright yellowish green. Tail feathers green, black along shaft, the central ones black on distal half.

Range. Mexico to Venezuela and Peru.

Colombia. Open forest and savanna. Subtropical zone of the Andes in Norte de Santander, Caldas and Cauca (tigrinus).

20. RUFOUS-FRONTED PARAKEET
(Bolborhynchus ferrugineifrons)

Description. 8 - 9". Narrow frontlet, lores and upper throat rusty rufous, rest of plumage dull green, brightest on upper tail-coverts, tinged olive on chest.

Range. Colombia.

Colombia. Páramo zone of Central Andes in Tolima.

21. BLUE-WINGED PARROTLET
(Forpus passerinus)

Description. 5 - 5½". Grass green, palest on under surface. ♂ with sky blue or ultramarine wing-coverts and blue (or green, 1) rump. All species of Forpus are tiny, chunky parrots with very short tails.

Range. Venezuela south to Argentina and Bolivia. Trinidad. Curaçao.

Colombia. Dry and semi-arid regions. Tropical zone. Caribbean coast west and southwest of the Santa Marta Mts. and the extreme lower Magdalena Valley (*spengeli*); east of the Santa Marta Mts. (*cyanophanes*). Valley of the río Zulia in Norte de Santander (1, *viridissimus*).

22. SPECTACLED PARROTLET
(Forpus conspicillatus) Plate IV

Description. 5 - 5½ " ♂ : Above green, rump and wing-coverts deep blue, narrow ring around eye pale blue. Below pale, dull green. ♀ very similar to ♂ Blue-winged Parrotlet, but feathers around eye tinged blue.

Range. Eastern Panama to the llanos of eastern Colombia.

Colombia. Open forest. Tropical zone east of the Andes in Boyacá and Meta and the upper Magdalena Valley north to about 10°N. (*conspicillatus*). Middle and upper Cauca Valley; west of the Western Andes in the Dagua Valley and the upper Patía Valley (*caucae*). The east slope of the Eastern Andes from Boyacá (1600 m.) to Meta (*metae*).

23. DUSKY-BILLED PARROTLET
(Forpus sclateri)

Description. 5 - 5½ ". ♂ : Very similar to the Blue-winged Parrotlet but green portions of wing darker and upper mandible black instead of yellow. ♀ differs from females of the other species by having the forecrown yellowish green in contrast to hindcrown and the maxilla as in ♂ .

Range. The Guianas, Venezuela and northern Brazil to Peru and northern Bolivia.

Colombia. Forest. Tropical zone at the eastern base of the Eastern Andes (*sclateri*). Río Guainía region (*eidos*).

24. COBALT-WINGED PARAKEET
(Brotogeris cyanoptera)

Description. 6½ - 7½ ". Chin and upper throat orange; rest of plumage green, tinged blue on head, olive on back,

[Species 23a, see Page 409.]

yellowish below. Wing-coverts and primaries deep blue edged with green. The tail in *Brotogeris* is pointed.

Range. Venezuela southward to northwestern Brazil, Ecuador and eastern Peru.

Colombia. Savanna. Tropical zone east of the Eastern Andes.

25. ORANGE-CHINNED PARAKEET
(Brotogeris jugularis) Plate IV

Description. 6½ - 7". Chin spot orange. Top and sides of head, lower back and rump blue-green; center of back olive green. Underparts yellowish green. Lesser wing-coverts bronzy brown, primary coverts ultramarine blue, wings bluish green. Tail green.

Range. Southern Mexico to northern and western Venezuela.

Colombia. Open woods. Tropical zone west of the Eastern Andes, east of them in Norte de Santander (*jugularis*). The llanos of Casanare in Arauca (*exsul*).

26. TUI PARAKEET
(Brotogeris st. thoma)

Description. 6½ ". Forecrown and streak behind eye golden yellow. General plumage green; mantle tinged blue; lower back, rump and underparts tinged yellowish. Wings and tail green.

Range. Northeastern Peru eastward to the middle Amazon. Northern Bolivia.

Colombia. Amazonian region (*st. thoma*).

27. SAPPHIRE-RUMPED PARROTLET
(Touit purpurata)

Description. 7 - 7½ ". General plumage emerald green. Bend of wing, lower back and rump glossy violet-blue; patch at sides of body olive. Scapulars dusky brown, remiges black, edged green. Central tail-feathers green, rest magenta, outer web edged purple and tipped black, outer ones tipped green.

Range. Southern Venezuela, the Guianas and northwestern Brazil.

Colombia. Forest. Tropical zone east of the Andes in Caquetá and southward to the río Guainía (*viridiceps*).

28. SCARLET-SHOULDERED PARROTLET
(Touit huetii)

Description. 7 - 7½". ♂ : Green, underparts yellower. Narrow frontal band black. Front of cheek violet-blue. Wing-coverts deep ultramarine; bend of wing, under wing-coverts and patch on sides of breast scarlet. Tail as in No. 27. ♀ has no red in tail.

Range. British Guiana and Venezuela southward to Ecuador, Brazil and northeastern Peru. Trinidad.

Colombia. Forest. Tropical zone east of the Eastern Andes.

29. RED-WINGED PARROTLET
(Touit dilectissima)

Description. 6½-7". ♂ : Green, yellower below. Forecrown blue; above and below the eye scarlet; chin and throat yellow. Lesser and innermost wing-coverts black; median and greater wing-coverts, bend of wing scarlet, feathers tipped yellow. Under wing-coverts and patch on sides of breast golden yellow. Central tailfeathers yellow at base with a subterminal green band and broad black tip. Rest of tailfeathers golden yellow tipped black. ♀ similar to ♂ but without scarlet wingcoverts.

Range. From Costa Rica southward to northwestern Ecuador and northwestern Venezuela.

Colombia. Forest. Tropical zone. The Pacific coast and the west slope of the Eastern Andes and probably the forested region between *(dilectissima)*.

30. SPOTTED-WINGED PARROTLET
(Touit stictoptera)

Description. 7½ - 8". ♂ : Green. Wing-coverts brown, tipped with whitish, some of the median wing-coverts dull orange. ♀ : Wing-coverts green with black centers; otherwise like ♂.

Range. Eastern Ecuador.

Colombia. Forest. Known definitely only from the west slope of the Eastern Andes in the subtropical zone of Cundinamarca, from the upper tropical zone of the

Macarena Mts. and the east slope of the Central Andes in Cauca *(stictoptera)*. Until recently the ♀ was thought to represent a different species [*emmae*].

31. BLACK-HEADED PARROT
(Pionites melanocephala)

Description. 9½ - 10½". Entire crown and nape black. Line from bill extending below the eye and entire upperparts including tail, green. Collar around hindneck dull cinnamon, sides of neck and throat, flanks and under tail-coverts orange-yellow; rest of underparts dirty white.

Range. The Guianas, eastern and southern Venezuela to northern Brazil and eastern Peru.

Colombia. Forest. Tropical zone east of the Eastern Andes from Meta southward *(pallida)*.

32. BROWN-HOODED PARROT
(Pionopsitta haematotis)

Description. 9½-10½". Top of head dark grayish brown becoming golden olive on the hindneck and upper mantle. Cheeks and throat dark grayish brown; collar at base of neck and ear-coverts rose pink; rest of body plumage green except for scarlet patch on sides of chest. Wing-coverts extensively blue, wing-lining blue. Tail short, central feathers green with blue tip, rest red on inner web with broad blue tips.

Range. Mexico southward to northwest Colombia.

Colombia. Forest. Tropical zone. Northwestern Colombia from the Pacific coast eastward to Bolívar *(coccinicollaris)*.

33. BEAUTIFUL PARROT
(Pionopsitta pulchra)

Description. 9-10". Differs from the Brown-hooded Parrot by having the lores, line above eye, posterior part of cheeks and the ear-coverts rosy pink, the fore-part of the cheeks and chin very pale rose. Shoulder mixed orange and yellow, median wing-coverts red; no scarlet patch on sides of chest and no rose band across breast.

Range. Western Ecuador.

Colombia. Forest. Tropical, occasionally subtropical zone of Pacific Colombia from the Baudó Mts. southward.

34. ORANGE-CHEEKED PARROT
(Pionopsitta barrabandi)

Description. 10-11". Head black, golden orange patch from base of lower mandible extending over cheeks and sides of throat. Breast golden orange. Lesser wing-coverts and thighs golden yellow, bend of wing and under wing-coverts scarlet. Rest of plumage green strongly tinged blue on belly. Tail green, yellow on inner web of feathers with a broad blue tip.

Range. Southern Venezuela and western Amazonia southward to Mato Grosso.

Colombia. Tropical zone east of the Andes from Caquetá southward *(barrabandi)*.

35. SAFFRON-HEADED PARROT
(Pionopsitta pyrilia)

Description. 9 - 10". Entire head, neck, throat and the lesser wing-coverts golden yellow, the bases of the feathers scarlet; rest of wing-coverts extensively blue; bend of wing, under wing-coverts and patch on sides of chest scarlet. Breast golden olive, rest of plumage green. Tail green, inner webs of feathers yellow broadly tipped blue.

Range. Eastern Panama; western Venezuela.

Colombia. Forest. Tropical to upper subtropical zone. Northern Colombia from the Pacific coast eastward to the east slopes of the Eastern Andes in Santander, southward to about 5°N.

36. INDIGO-WINGED PARROT
(Hapalopsittaca fuertesi)

Description. 10-11". ♂: Forecrown and sides of head greenish yellow, rest of crown blue. Body plumage mainly olive green, bluer on wing-coverts, yellower on upper tail-coverts. Shoulder crimson, remiges ultramarine blue. Tail crimson-

maroon at base, distally blue. ♀ similar, but shoulder crimson-maroon.

Range. Colombia.

Colombia. Forest. Temperate zone of the Central Andes in Caldas.

37. RUSTY-FACED PARROT
(Hapalopsittaca amazonina)

Description. 10-11". Differs from No. 36 in having the forecrown and cheeks dull red; general plumage greener, olivaceous only on the chest.

Range. Western and northern Venezuela.

Colombia. Forest. Upper subtropical and temperate zone on the western slope of the Eastern Andes *(amazonina)*.

38. SHORT-TAILED PARROT
(Graydidascalus brachyurus)

Description. 10 - 11". Green, more yellowish on upper tail-coverts and underparts. Greater wing-coverts and secondaries sharply edged with greenish yellow. Tail very short, base of outer feathers red.

Range. Eastern Peru and the entire Amazon Valley.

Colombia. Forest. Tropical zone east of the Andes from Caquetá southward *(brachyurus)*.

39. BLUE-HEADED PARROT
(Pionus menstruus) Plate IV

Description. 11 - 12". Head, hindneck, throat and breast cobalt blue, bases of the feathers of throat and breast red giving a mottled appearance. Rest of plumage green, tinged with olive on the shoulders; under tail-coverts red. Central tail-feathers green, outer tail-feathers blue, basally red on inner web. Spot at base of upper mandible red. Young birds differ from adults in having the head pale greenish blue, the forecrown rosy red.

Range. Costa Rica southward through Venezuela and the Guianas to Mato Grosso, Ecuador, Peru and Bolivia. Trinidad.

Colombia. Forest. Tropical zone west of the Eastern Andes *(rubrigularis)*. East of the Eastern Andes *(menstruus)*.

40. RED-BILLED PARROT
(Pionus sordidus)

Description. 11-12". Crown deep blue, feathers green at base. Throat and upper chest verditer blue (or purplish blue, 1). Dorsal surface dull olive green. Underparts brownish green (or pale grayish green, 2), under tail-coverts red. Remiges bright green. Outer tail-feathers blue, inner web basally red. Bill red.

Range. Western South America from Venezuela south to Bolivia.

Colombia. Forest. Tropical and subtropical zones of the Santa Marta Mts. except the eastern foothills (saturatus). Perijá Mts. on the Venezuelan border and the eastern foothills of the Santa Marta Mts. (2, sordidus). Subtropical zone of Eastern Andes (1, corallinus).

41. WHITE-CAPPED PARROT
(Pionus seniloides)

Description. 11-12". Forecrown white, feathers edged orange-red, feathers of rest of crown, nape, sides of head and neck basally white broadly margined with violet-black. Entire upper surface, sides of body and flanks green. Chest and belly plum color, under tail-coverts rosy red. Outer tail-feathers basally red on inner web, blackish on outer web, broadly tipped green. Young birds have the feathers of the head green with white bases. Lower breast and belly green.

Range. Western Venezuela; Ecuador.

Colombia. Forest. Subtropical to temperate zones of the west slope of the Eastern Andes, and the Central Andes southward through Nariño.

42. BRONZE-WINGED PARROT
(Pionus chalcopterus)

Description. 11-12". Feathers of crown, sides of head and neck and underparts bronzy brown broadly edged with deep violet-blue. Throat whitish, a narrow pinkish band on upper breast. Mantle dark bronzy green, lower back and upper tail-coverts deep blue; under tail-coverts bronzy green margined with blue. Wing-coverts and inner secondaries bronzy brown, palest on lesser wing-coverts. Tail dark blue, under tail-coverts and inner web of outer tail-feathers red. Wing-lining azure blue. Primaries cobalt blue.

Range. Western Venezuela to northern Peru.

Colombia. Forest. Upper tropical and subtropical zone of the Eastern, Central and Western Andes (chalcopterus). Upper tropical zone of Nariño (cyanescens).

43. DUSKY PARROT
(Pionus fuscus)

Description. 10½-11½". Small spot on base of upper mandible red. Head dull purplish blue. Upper parts dark purplish brown, the feathers edged paler. Below plum color shaded with ashy on the chest. Remiges deep purple-blue. Inner webs of outer tail-feathers red.

Range. Venezuela eastward through the Guianas to the lower and middle Amazon, and Maranhão, Brazil.

Colombia. Forest. Upper tropical zone of the Perijá Mountains.

Amazona

The plumage in all the six species of *Amazona* found in Colombia is almost entirely green. The remiges are blue-black for about their distal half; the tail is square, usually the basal half of the inner web of the outer tail-feathers is red. The different species may be distinguished as follows:

44. RED-LORED PARROT
(Amazona autumnalis)

Description. 14-15". Frontal band and lores crimson. Feathers of crown and hindneck edged with lilac. Wing speculum red.

Range. Southern Mexico to northwestern Venezuela and western Ecuador. Northwestern Brazil from the rio Negro westward along the rio Solimões.

Colombia. Forest. Tropical zone from the middle and lower Magdalena Valley westward to the Pacific coast as far as the upper Atrato (salvini).

45. FESTIVE PARROT
(Amazona festiva)

Description. 15-16". Frontal band and lores maroon-red, superciliary light blue. Lower back and rump crimson. No wing speculum. Tail basally green, distally yellowish green without any red.

Range. Northwestern British Guiana; Venezuela along the Orinoco. Eastern Ecuador and Peru.

Colombia. Forest. The Amazonian region (festiva).

46. YELLOW-HEADED PARROT
(Amazona ochrocephala)

Description. 14 - 16". Forehead and center of crown (or center of crown only, 1) yellow. Wing speculum red.

Range. Mexico southward to Venezuela, the Guianas, Ecuador, Peru and Brazil. Trinidad.

Colombia. Tropical zone of northern Colombia from east of the Andes in Santander westward to the Atrato river (panamensis). East of the Andes from Caquetá southward (1, nattereri). East of the Andes in Meta eastward to the Orinoco (1, ochrocephala).

47. ORANGE-WINGED PARROT
(Amazona amazonica)

Description. 13-14". Forehead, lores and superciliaries verditer blue; crown and cheeks yellow. Wing speculum orange. Orange on inner web of tail-feathers crossed by a green band.

Range. The Guianas and Venezuela southward to Ecuador, Peru and southern Brazil. Trinidad and Tobago.

Colombia. Tropical zone of northern Colombia from Bolívar eastward to the eastern llanos and southward to the Amazonian region (amazonica).

48. SCALY-NAPED PARROT
(Amazona mercenaria)

Description. 13-15". Feathers of hindneck edged black. Wing speculum red. Outer web of outer tail-feathers deep purple.

Range. Northwestern Venezuela southward through western South America to Ecuador and northern Bolivia.

Colombia. Forest. Tropical to upper temperate zones of the Eastern, Central and Western Andes and the Santa Marta Mts. (canipalliata).

49. MEALY PARROT
(Amazona farinosa)

Description. 15-18". Upperparts with a mealy, powdery appearance. Sometimes a yellow spot on crown. Wing speculum red. Distal half of tail yellowish green, with no red at base.

Range. Mexico southward to western and southern Venezuela, the Guianas, Ecuador, Peru and Brazil.

Colombia. Forest. Tropical zone west of the Andes and east of the Andes as far south as Meta (inornata). East of the Andes in Putumayo and Vaupés. (chapmani).

50. RED-FAN PARROT
(Deroptyus accipitrinus)

Description. 14-16". Fan-shaped erectile occipital crest red, the feathers broadly edged blue. Forecrown whitish, sides of head, hindcrown, throat and breast brown with pale shaft streaks. Feathers of lower breast and belly red, edged blue. Back, closed wing, and the tail green. Primaries and under surface of tail black.

Range. The Guianas and Venezuela southward to the lower Amazon, northern Brazil, Ecuador and Peru.

Colombia. Tropical zone east of the Andes (accipitrinus).

CUCKOOS (Cuculidae)

Fig. 43. Squirrel Cuckoo
(Piaya cayana) p. 112

The cuckoos of Colombia divide themselves into four main groups: the species resembling the North American varieties; the non-parasitic squirrel cuckoos, mainly chestnut in color, with long tails; the anis, blue-black in color; and the ground cuckoos — large ground-inhabiting species rather resembling pheasants at first glance.

The anis build large communal nests in which many females lay. The eggs are blue, covered by a thick, chalky deposit. The eggs are sometimes covered with fresh green leaves. (17 Col.; 23 S.A.; 30 N.&S.A.; 127 wld.)

AID TO IDENTIFICATION

Above uniform (ashy or bronzy brown) 1, 2, 3, 4, 5, (or chestnut) 8, 9E, 10, (or glossy black) 11, 12, 13.
Crown gray, back brown 6, 7.
Back striped 14.
Underparts spotted 15E, or with one wide band 16, or barred 17.

1. DWARF CUCKOO
(Coccyzus pumilus)

Description. 8″. Above ashy gray. Chin, throat and upper breast rufous; sides of body and under tail-coverts buff, rest of underparts white. Tail with a broad blackish terminal band narrowly tipped white. Bill black.

Range. Northern Venezuela.

Colombia. Open woods. Tropical occasionally to the subtropical zone of the lower Magdalena Valley.

2. BLACK-BILLED CUCKOO
(Coccyzus erythropthalmus)

Description. 11-12″. Above bronzy brown, shaded bronzy green on the tail which is narrowly tipped with white; below white. Bill black.

Range. Breeds in North America; winters south to Trinidad, Venezuela, Ecuador and Peru.

Colombia. Winter resident. Recorded from the Eastern Andes westward to the Pacific.

111

3. YELLOW-BILLED CUCKOO
(Coccyzus americanus)

Description. 11 - 12″. Very similar to the Black-billed Cuckoo but lower mandible yellow with black tip. Inner webs of basal part of primaries chestnut, outer tail-feathers black, white tips of tail-feathers very wide.

Range. Breeds in North America to lower California and the West Indies. Winters from Trinidad, Venezuela and Colombia southward to Argentina and Bolivia.

Colombia. Open woods. Winter resident, end of August to early May *(americanus)*.

4. PEARLY-BREASTED CUCKOO
(Coccyzus euleri)

Description. 10 - 11″. Similar to the Yellow-billed Cuckoo but remiges without chestnut inner margins. Pale grayish below.

Range. The Guianas, westward to the Orinoco Valley and southward to southern Brazil.

Colombia. Tropical zone. Forest and thickets. Northeastern Colombia southward east of the Andes to the Amazonian drainage.

5. MANGROVE CUCKOO
(Coccyzus minor)

Description. 11 - 12″. Similar to the Yellow-billed Cuckoo but crown grayer, eye-stripe black, and underparts bright buff instead of white.

Range. Florida and the West Indies, south through Central America to northern South America. Trinidad, Tobago, Monos, Aruba.

Colombia. Mangroves and dry thickets. Known only from "Bogotá" collections but undoubtedly the Caribbean coast *(minor)*.

6. DARK-BILLED CUCKOO
(Coccyzus melacoryphus)

Description. 9 - 9½″. Top of head and hindneck dark gray; ear-coverts black. Upperparts grayish brown; underparts rusty-buff, cheeks silvery gray. The central tail-feathers bronzy, tipped black, rest of tail-feathers black with white tips. Bill black.

Range. Venezuela, the Guianas south to Peru, Bolivia, Paraguay, and Argentina. Trinidad, the Galápagos Islands.

Colombia. Forest and thickets. Tropical, occasionally subtropical zone throughout the country including Gorgona Island.

7. GRAY-CAPPED CUCKOO
(Coccyzus lansbergi)

Description. 9½ - 10″. Top and sides of head dark gray. Upper surface including wings rufescent-brown. Entire under surface deep rusty-buff. Tail black, tipped white. Bill black, base of mandible yellow.

Range. Western Venezuela and western Ecuador.

Colombia. Scrub. Tropical zone of the Santa Marta region westward to Bolívar.

8. SQUIRREL CUCKOO
(Piaya cayana) Fig. 43

Description. 15 - 18″. Entire upper surface purplish chestnut. Throat and breast pinkish buff, rest of underparts pale gray, darkening on crissum to blackish. Tail, very long with black subterminal band and white tip. Bill olive yellow.

Range. Mexico southward to the Guianas, Venezuela, Brazil, Argentina and Bolivia. Trinidad.

Colombia. Edge of forest, and tangled scrub. Tropical and subtropical zone. Northern Colombia from the east shore of the Gulf of Urabá eastward to the lower Magdalena and east of the Andes to Norte de Santander *(mehleri)*. Extreme northwestern Colombia, the west shore of the Gulf of Urabá and north Pacific coast *(thermophila)*. Western Colombia from Nariño northward along the Pacific coast to the upper río San Juan, the Cauca Valley and the eastern slope of the northern portion of the Central Andes *(nigricrissa)*. East of the Andes in Arauca and Boyacá *(circe)*; from eastern Cundinamarca southward to Caquetá and the head of the Magdalena Valley *(mesura)*. From Vaupés probably southward to the Amazon *(cayana)*.

9. BLACK-BELLIED CUCKOO
(Piaya melanogaster)

Description. 13 - 14″. Crown and nape gray, throat rufescent-buff. Entire upper surface including wings, tail and breast chestnut. Lower breast, belly and under tail-coverts black. Tail chestnut with subterminal black bar and white tip. Bill red.

Range. The Guianas, southern Venezuela westward through Amazonia to eastern Ecuador and Peru.

Colombia. Forest. Tropical zone of eastern Colombia from Caquetá southward *(ochracea).*

10. LITTLE CUCKOO
(Piaya minuta)

Description. 9 - 9½″. Almost exactly like the Squirrel Cuckoo but only half the size and with a much shorter tail.

Range. Panama to western Ecuador. Venezuela and the Guianas to central Brazil and Bolivia.

Colombia. Scrub and undergrowth. Humid tropical zone. The west shores of the Gulf of Urabá *(panamensis);* rest of Colombia west of the Eastern Andes *(gracilis).* East of the Andes from Arauca southward *(minuta).*

11. GREATER ANI
(Crotophaga major) Plate III

Description. 16 - 18″. Glossy blue-black, feathers of the mantle and breast margined with shiny bronzy green. Tail long, purplish blue above, purple below. Bill black, compressed, with a high conspicuous ridge.

Range. Panama to Venezuela and through tropical South America east of the Andes to Argentina. Trinidad.

Colombia. Marshy areas and pastures. Tropical, occasionally to the temperate zone, except Nariño.

12. SMOOTH-BILLED ANI
(Crotophaga ani)

Description. 13 - 13½″. Purplish black, the feathers of the mantle and chest edged with shiny, bronzy purple. Tail long, blue-black. Bill compressed, high and arched, conspicuously ridged.

Range. Mexico, southward to Ecuador and east of the Andes from Venezuela to Argentina. Most of the islands of the Caribbean. Trinidad. The Pearl Islands.

Colombia. Marshy areas and wet woods. Tropical and subtropical zones, occasionally to lower temperate zones throughout the country.

13. GROOVE-BILLED ANI
(Crotophaga sulcirostris)

Description. 11½ - 12″. Like the Smooth-billed Ani in color but smaller and more shiny. Upper mandible not as conspicuously ridged; furrowed by three grooves.

Range. Texas south to the coast of Peru on the west and to Venezuela, northern Brazil and British Guiana on the east. Many of the Caribbean islands. Trinidad.

Colombia. Tropical zone. Savanna and pasture lands, usually in dry areas, often accompanying cattle. Caribbean coast, the Magdalena Valley, Nariño and east of the Andes along the Orinoco *(sulcirostris).*

14. STRIPED CUCKOO
(Tapera naevia)

Description. 10 - 11″. Crown and nape dull chestnut; rest of upperparts sandy-buff to rufescent-buff, striped with black. Under surface whitish, tinged buff on chest. Wing-coverts dusky edged with buff. Tail brown, long and graduated, the outer feathers tipped with white; under tail-coverts tinged buffy.

Range. Mexico southward to Venezuela, the Guianas, Brazil, Ecuador, Peru and eastern Bolivia. Trinidad.

Colombia. Thickets, clearings and pastures, often seen on the ground. Tropical to lower subtropical zones except Nariño *(naevia).*

15. PHEASANT CUCKOO
(Dromococcyx phasianellus)

Description. 13-14″. Crown dark chestnut, crested; post-ocular streak buffy. Sides of neck and upperparts dark brown shaded with glossy purplish; throat white, sides of throat and the breast buff, spotted with dark brown, rest of underparts white. Wing-coverts edged buffy white. Upper tail-coverts long, feathers decomposed, brown with an olive gloss, tipped white. Tail long, feathers very broad, graduated, tipped and margined with buff. Young birds have the crown like the back.

Range. Rare throughout its range. Spottily distributed from Mexico southward to Venezuela, British and French Guiana, Ecuador, Peru, Paraguay, Argentina and Bolivia.

Colombia. Forest. Known from the tropical zone from Arauca southward to Meta *(rufigularis)*.

16. RUFOUS-VENTED GROUND-CUCKOO
(Neomorphus geoffroyi)

Description. 18″. Terrestrial. Pheasant-like in appearance. Crown rusty buff; a long flat blue-black crest. Entire upper surface including tail and wing-coverts bronzy brown, very strongly shaded with glossy purple (or bronze green, bronzier on lower back and tail, 1). Primaries bronzy green, secondaries purplish green. Throat and middle of abdomen whitish, chest grayish, the feathers edged whitish. A black band across the breast. Crissum purplish brown. Bill pale bluish green.

Range. Nicaragua south to western Colombia and east of the Andes to Ecuador, Bolivia and central Brazil.

Colombia. Tropical forests of the Pacific coast south to the upper Atrato; eastward in northern Colombia to Bolívar *(salvini).* Caquetá and Putumayo *(1, aequatorialis).*

17. BANDED GROUND-CUCKOO
(Neomorphus radiolosus) Plate III

Description. 18″. Forecrown greenish black, the feathers banded with buff, center of crown, long flat crest and hindneck blue-black. Lower back, rump and closed wing purplish chestnut. Upper tail-coverts and primaries purple. Lower surface from chin to belly, broadly banded black and buffy white; under tail-coverts deep purplish maroon.

Range. Western Ecuador.

Colombia. Tropical zone. Forests on the western slope of the Western Andes at their southern end, probably south into Nariño.

BARN OWLS (Tytonidae)

Fig. 44. Barn Owl
(Tyto alba)

Barn Owls are of world-wide distribution and are all more or less alike in appearance. Almost all have a rufous phase. They often nest in buildings but when these are not available they use holes in trees or burrows. Strictly nocturnal, they are not often seen, but occasionally at dusk they may be observed flying with moth-like flight, over meadows and clearings looking for mice, frogs, bats and other prey. Their voice is varied, comprising hissing sounds, shrill cries, and clicks made with the bill. (1 Col.; 1 S.A.; 1 N.&S.A.; 11 wld.)

BARN OWL
(Tyto alba)

Description. 14 - 16″. Above grayish brown spotted and vermiculated with white, orange-rufous bases of feathers showing through. Facial disk prominent, surrounded by a dark line. Underparts white, buff or brownish buff dotted with black. Wings and tail buffy rufous to brownish rufous, barred and marbled with blackish.

Range. Virtually world-wide.

Colombia. Caribbean coast and the lower Magdalena Valley *(guatemalae)*. Subtropical and temperate zone of all three ranges and the tropical zone east of the Andes in Meta and Caquetá *(contempta)*.

OWLS (Strigidae)

Fig. 45. Spectacled Owl
(Pulsatrix perspicillata) p. 117

Most Colombian owls are strictly nocturnal and rarely seen. Pygmy Owls, Burrowing Owls and the Short-eared Owl are, however, more diurnal. In habits and appearance they do not differ from owls found elsewhere. The most distinctive is the Burrowing Owl, found only in the New World.

The Screech-Owls all look rather alike. They usually have ear-tufts, barred wings and tail, and generally brown coloration. Their distinguishing characters only are given. The Screech-Owls, as well as many other owls, have brown and rufous phases. (20 Col.; 25 S.A.; 34 N.&S.A.; 123 wld.)

AID TO IDENTIFICATION

With ear-tufts (size small) 1, 2, 4[E], 5, (size large) 6, 7, 16, 17, 18.
Without ear-tufts (size small) 3, 9, 10, 11, 19, (size large) 8, 8a[E], 12, 13, 14[E], 15.

1. VERMICULATED SCREECH-OWL
(Otus guatemalae)

Description. 8-9". Scapulars white barred with brown and wing-coverts spotted with white. Below rather dark with no conspicuous marking. Legs feathered, toes bare. Iris yellow.

Range. Mexico southward through Central America to Venezuela, eastern and western Ecuador, and Bolivia.

Colombia. Forest. Tropical zone. Only recorded from the lower slopes of the Baudó Mts., but undoubtedly much more widely spread. "Bogotá" *(vermiculatus)*.

2. TROPICAL SCREECH-OWL
(Otus choliba)

Description. 8-9". Below buffy white with narrow longitudinal dark brown streaks and numerous very dark brown cross-bars. Legs feathered, toes bare. Iris yellow.

Range. Costa Rica southward to Venezuela, Brazil, Peru, southern Bolivia and Argentina. Margarita Island. Trinidad.

Colombia. Forest. Tropical and subtropical zone. The middle and upper Magdalena Valley and east of the Eastern Andes from Boyacá southward *(crucigerus)*. The Central and Western Andes *(luctisonus)*.

116

3. RUFESCENT SCREECH-OWL
(Otus ingens)

Description. 9½ - 11". Above brown, vermiculated with black; below tawny streaked with dark brown. Rather like No. 1 but larger. Ear tufts absent.

Range. Ecuador to Bolivia.

Colombia. Forest. Known only from three specimens from the subtropical zone in the upper Cauca Valley *(columbianus)*.

4. TAWNY-BELLIED SCREECH-OWL
(Otus watsonii)

Description. 8 - 9". Very dark above; below rather like No. 2 but ground color orange-rufous instead of white. Legs feathered, toes bare. Iris yellow.

Range. Tropical South America south to Peru and Argentina.

Colombia. Forest. Tropical zone east of the Eastern Andes *(watsonii)*.

5. WHITE-THROATED SCREECH-OWL
(Otus albogularis)

Description. 11 - 12". Upperparts dark umber-brown spotted with white or buff. Throat white. Breast band umber spotted with white, rest of underparts deep buff, streaked dark brown. Legs feathered, toes bare. Iris yellow.

Range. Colombia and Venezuela southward through western South America to Bolivia.

Colombia. Forest. Subtropical to temperate zone of all three ranges *(albogularis)*.

6. CRESTED OWL
(Lophostrix cristata)

Description. 15 - 17". Prominent eyebrows, prolonged into long ear-tufts, white. Facial disk buffy, bordered posteriorly by dusky, below eye chestnut. Upperparts almost uniform deep brown, wing-coverts spotted with white. Wings and tail barred. Underparts without bars or streaks, finely vermiculated, brown on chest, rufous-buff sometimes mixed with white on rest of underparts. Legs feathered, toes bare. Iris brown.

[Species 8a, see Page 409.]

Range. Southern Mexico southward to eastern Panama. The Guianas; the middle and upper Amazon to eastern Ecuador.

Colombia. Forest. Tropical zone east of the Andes from Caquetá southward *(cristata)*. Pacific Colombia eastward to the middle Magdalena Valley *(wedeli)*.

7. GREAT HORNED OWL
(Bubo virginianus)

Description. 18 - 22". The largest Colombian Owl. Ear-tufts prominent, dark brown. Patch on chin and another on chest white. Above dark brown variegated with buff and whitish. Below barred dark brown and white. Legs and toes feathered. Iris bright yellow.

Range. From Alaska and southern Canada to Venezuela, Ecuador, Peru, Brazil and the Straits of Magellan.

Colombia. Forest. Tropical zone of northeastern Colombia east of the Andes *(scotinus)*. Tropical zone of the Caribbean coast in the lower and middle Magdalena Valley *(elutus)*. Temperate and páramo zones of the Central Andes and the mountains of Nariño *(nigrescens)*.

8. SPECTACLED OWL
(Pulsatrix perspicillata) Fig. 45

Description. 17 - 20". No ear-tufts. Feathers at base of bill white, this color prolonged backwards to form an eyebrow. Throat black bordered white below. Mask across face and entire upperparts uniform chocolate brown. Band across chest chocolate, rest of underparts deep buff. Tail barred dark brown and grayish, tipped white. Legs and feet feathered. Iris yellow.

Range. Mexico southward to Venezuela, Ecuador, Peru, Brazil, Bolivia, Argentina. Trinidad.

Colombia. Forest. Tropical zone of northeastern Colombia, southward east of the Andes to the Amazon *(perspicillata)*. From the west shores of the Gulf of Urabá southward down the Pacific coast to the Baudó Mts. *(chapmani)*.

9. ANDEAN PYGMY-OWL
(Glaucidium jardinii)

Description. 6½ - 7". No ear-tufts. Above

more or less uniform chocolate brown. Throat, patch on chest, prominent collar across hindneck white. Crown white spotted. Lower breast and belly streaked fulvous and dark brown. Wings and tail blackish barred with white. Legs feathered, toes bare. Iris yellow.

Range. Mountains of Costa Rica southward to Venezuela, Ecuador and Peru.

Colombia. Subtropical and temperate zone of the Western, Central and Eastern Andes *(jardinii)*.

10. FERRUGINOUS PYGMY-OWL
(Glaucidium brasilianum)

Description. 5½ - 6½". No ear-tufts. Very similar to Andean Pygmy-Owl but crown streaked instead of spotted. Lower breast and belly white, streaked brown. Bright ferruginous in "red" phase. Legs feathered, toes bare. Iris yellow.

Range. Southern Arizona south to Venezuela, Brazil Argentina and Bolivia. Trinidad, Margarita Island.

Colombia. Forest and scrub. Tropical zone of the Caribbean coast *(medianum)*. East of the Andes from Meta southward *(ucayalae)*.

11. BURROWING OWL
(Speotyto cunicularia)

Description. 8 - 9". Terrestrial. No ear-tufts. Legs very long. Above brown much spotted with white. Throat and patch on chest white. Band across lower throat and rest of lower parts barred brown or rufous-brown and white. Wings and tail barred buffy white and dark brown. Legs feathered in front, toes bare. Iris yellow.

Range. Plains of western North America. Through Central America and the islands of the Caribbean southward to Venezuela and the open and drier parts of South America to Tierra del Fuego.

Colombia. Savanna. The eastern llanos *(carrikeri)*. The arid tropical zone of the middle Magdalena Valley *(tolimae)*.

12. MOTTLED OWL
(Ciccaba virgata)

Description. 13 - 15". No ear-tufts. Lower part of facial ruff edged with white. Above deep brown, inconspicuously but liberally dotted and vermiculated with buffy. Below white to tawny conspicuously streaked with dark brown, somewhat clouded and barred on chest; tail with a few narrow white bars. Legs feathered, toes bare. Iris brown.

Range. Mexico southward to Venezuela, the Guianas, Argentina and Paraguay. Trinidad.

Colombia. Forest. Tropical and subtropical zone of the Western, Central and Eastern Andes, the upper Cauca Valley and the Santa Marta region *(virgata)*. The Macarena Mts. southward to the Caquetá region *(macconelli)*.

13. BLACK-AND-WHITE OWL
(Ciccaba nigrolineata)

Description. 14 - 16". No ear-tufts. Above black, superciliaries spotted with white. Hindneck, upper mantle and lower surface including legs white, narrowly barred black. Tail black with four or five narrow white bars and white tip. Iris brown to yellow. Bill and toes orange yellow. Essentially this species is white below barred with black, while the next is black below barred with white.

Range. Southern Mexico to western Venezuela and western Ecuador.

Colombia. Forest. Tropical and subtropical zones of the Andes. Not recorded from Nariño.

14. BLACK-BANDED OWL
(Ciccaba huhula)

Description. 17". No ear-tufts. Black, banded above by very narrow, wavy white lines: below black barred with narrow white lines. Tail with four white bars and white tip. Legs like rest of underparts, toes bare.

Range. British and French Guiana, Venezuela to southern and central Brazil.

Colombia. Forest. Tropical zone at the base of the Andes in Meta *(huhula)*.

15. RUFOUS-BANDED OWL
(Ciccaba albitarsus)

Description. 16½". No ear-tufts. Above blackish brown barred and spotted everywhere with orange tawny. Below bright orange tawny spotted with silvery white, giving an ocellated appearance, the white spots divided in the middle by a chestnut line. Legs feathered, toes bare. Iris yellow.

Range. The mountains of northern Venezuela and Ecuador.

Colombia. Forest. Subtropical to temperate zone of all three ranges, except the west slope of the Western Andes.

16. STRIPED OWL
(Asio clamator)

Description. 13 - 15". Ear-tufts prominent. Above tawny striped with dark brown; facial disk white bordered posteriorly with black. Underparts white to buffy boldly streaked dark brown. Wings and tail barred dark brown. Iris brown. Legs and toes feathered.

Range. Southern Mexico to southern Brazil, Argentina and Uruguay.

Colombia. Forest. Tropical zone. The Santa Marta region and the lower and middle Magdalena Valley. East of the Andes in Boyacá and Meta *(clamator)*.

17. STYGIAN OWL
(Asio stygius)

Description. 15 - 17". Ear-tufts prominent. Above sooty more or less intermixed with orange-buff. Below buffy white, breast blotched sooty, rest of underparts blotched

and barred with same. Tail barred with bright buff. Legs and toes bare.

Range. Mexico and the Greater Antilles southward to Venezuela, western Ecuador, Paraguay and Argentina.

Colombia. Forest. Subtropical to temperate zone of all three ranges *(robustus)*.

18. SHORT-EARED OWL
(Asio flammeus)

Description. 14 - 16". Ear-tufts present but inconspicuous. Upperparts dark brown with a few pale streaks. Facial disk blackish bordered behind with buff. Underparts tawny buff, heavily streaked blackish brown. Wing and tail barred bright orange-buff. Legs and feet feathered.

Range. Virtually world-wide.

Colombia. Open savanna. Subtropical and temperate zone of the Eastern Andes westward to the upper Cauca Valley *(bogotensis)*.

19. BUFF-FRONTED OWL
(Aegolius harrisii)

Description. 7 - 8". No ear-tufts. Above dark chocolate brown, darkest on head. Broad frontal band continued backward over eyes, collar on hindneck, and entire underparts yellowish buff. Wings and tail spotted with white.

Range. Northern Venezuela, Ecuador.

Colombia. Cultivated and sparsely wooded country. Subtropical probably to temperate zone. Rare, recorded from "Bogotá" and the head of the Cauca Valley *(harrisii)*.

GUACHAROS OR OILBIRDS (Steatornithidae)

Fig. 46. Oilbird
(Steatornis caripensis)

Resembling large nightjars, these strange birds form a family of their own and are found locally only in tropical South America.

Gregarious and nocturnal, the birds nest in colonies, on ledges in caves. They feed on a variety of fruits which they pluck from the trees in flight. The young become excessively fat and are used by the Indians as food and for making oil from the fat. (1 Col.; 1 S.A.; 1 N.&S.A.; 1 wld.)

OILBIRD

(Steatornis caripensis)

Description. 15 - 17". Cinnamon chestnut, brighter above, paler and pinker below. Upperparts with narrow black transverse lines. Head, wing-coverts and underparts dotted with black-encircled white spots. Primaries and outer tail-feathers with large white spots. Inner remiges barred with narrow, buffy white lines on inner web. Tail very rounded. Wings long, pointed; span about 2½ feet. Bill strongly hooked.

Range. Trinidad, the Guianas, westward through Venezuela to eastern Panama, Ecuador and Peru.

Colombia. Tropical to temperate zone of the Santa Marta region and all three Andean ranges.

POTOOS (Nyctibiidae)

Fig. 47. Common Potoo
(Nyctibius griseus) p. 122

The big species of potoos look like gigantic nightjars, some of them reaching a length of almost two feet. Solitary and nocturnal, they live on insects which they catch on the wing. They nest on top of tree stumps, and both when incubating and perching assume a stiff, erect position with the bill pointing skyward. This curious habit makes them look like part of the stump on which they are perching, and consequently difficult to detect. They live in the forest, either humid or dry. Except for the Common Potoo all are rare. They are found only in the warmer parts of the New World. (5 Col.; 5 S.A.; 5 N.&S.A.; 5 wld.)

GREAT POTOO
(Nyctibius grandis)

Description. 19-20″. Ground color of upperparts white, very finely streaked, vermiculated and freckled with blackish brown and buff. Lower surface similar but more coarsely marked on the center of the breast. Tail long, barred and marbled with dark brown. The general color impression of the bird is pale brownish gray. Young birds are much whiter than adults.

Range. Guatemala. Panama to Venezuela, Dutch Guiana. Peru. Southeastern Brazil.

Colombia. Tropical zone. The lower Atrato, the middle Magdalena Valley and east of the Eastern Andes from Meta south to the Amazon.

LONG-TAILED POTOO
(Nyctibius aethereus)

Description. 20″. Mostly deep chestnut brown, vermiculated and streaked with black, and with large drop-shaped black marks on the center of the breast. Tail very long (13″) barred and marbled with blackish brown.

Range. Spottily recorded from eastern Ecuador, Peru, British Guiana, Brazil and Paraguay.

Colombia. Forest. Tropical zone west of the Western Andes in the watershed of the río San Juan. *(chocoensis)*. East of the Andes in Vaupés *(longicaudatus)*.

121

COMMON POTOO
(Nyctibus griseus) Fig. 47

Description. 15 - 17". Grayish brown, mottled, streaked and vermiculated with cinnamon, gray and black. Broad streaks on crown and spots on breast black. Narrow streaks on underparts black. Tail long, like back in color. A very dark brown phase sometimes occurs.

Range. Mexico to Venezuela, the Guianas, Bolivia and Argentina. Trinidad, the Greater Antilles.

Colombia. Forest, clearings and savanna. Tropical zone west of the Eastern Andes *(panamensis)*. East of the Andes *(griseus)*.

WHITE-WINGED POTOO
(Nyctibius leucopterus)

Description. 13 - 14". General plumage deep brown, the feathers of crown, back and breast with large black spots. Middle wing-coverts white with dark tips forming a conspicuous wing-bar. Tail short (5½"), dark brown irregularly barred with pale brown.

Range. Western Venezuela. Eastern Ecuador. Coastal region of Brazil.

Colombia. Subtropical zone on the west slope of the Eastern Andes in Norte de Santander and "Bogotá" collections *(maculosus)*.

RUFOUS POTOO
(Nyctibius bracteatus)

Description. 9 - 12". Bright orange-rufous speckled and vermiculated above and on breast with black and white. Upper wing-coverts, scapulars and abdomen with round white spots surrounded by black. Under tail-coverts tipped white. Tail bright rufous with irregular black bars.

Range. British Guiana, Venezuela, Ecuador and Peru.

Colombia. Recorded only from "Bogotá" but undoubtedly the tropical zone east of the Andes.

NIGHTJARS AND NIGHTHAWKS (Caprimulgidae)

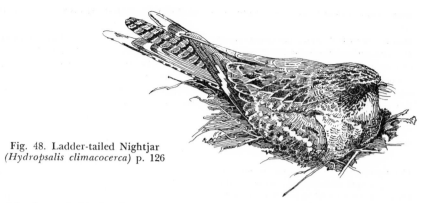

Fig. 48. Ladder-tailed Nightjar
(Hydropsalis climacocerca) p. 126

Members of this family are largely nocturnal; nighthawks however are often seen hawking for insects well before sunset. Their coloring is confined to brown, rufous, buff and black, often with white markings in the wing and tail. Some species have much elongated wing- and tail-feathers. Bills are small, but open widely to catch insects and very occasionally small birds. Well-developed rictal bristles are an aid to the capture of their prey. When perching, nightjars sit lengthwise on the branch. They nest on the bare ground, using no nesting material. The calls of the various species are loud and very distinctive, and only heard at night. Nightjars are found throughout the world with the exception of the far north, New Zealand and oceanic islands.

No key is provided because a superficial one would be of little use due to the similarity of the species and further because they are only active at night. (19 Col.; 26 S.A.; 35 N.&S.A.; 72 wld.)

SEMICOLLARED NIGHTHAWK
(Lurocalis semitorquatus)

Description. 10½ - 12". Head, chest and entire upperparts black with small rufous spots and ocelli, nape sometimes mixed with white. Scapulars, inner secondaries and wing-coverts white with black rufous-spotted tip or white vermiculated and spotted with black. Band across throat white. Lower breast, belly and under tail-coverts rufous-buff. Wings very long, protruding well beyond tail when folded. ♀ resembles ♂ but has less white on head and inner secondaries. Best identified by long narrow wings and very short tail.

Range. Nicaragua southward to Venezuela, British Guiana, Ecuador, Peru and southeastern Brazil. Trinidad.

Colombia. Forest and open country. Trop-

ical zone of the Santa Marta region *(semitorquatus)*. Subtropical to temperate zone of the Eastern and Central Andes *(rufiventris)*.

LEAST NIGHTHAWK
(Chordeiles pusillus)

Description. 6 - 7". Above grayish brown vermiculated with blackish, and spotted and speckled with rufous. White band across throat; breast grayish brown, rest of under surface regularly barred white and dark brown. Outer four primaries with a white bar, secondaries tipped buff. Tail dark brown mottled grayish and rusty, feathers tipped white except for central and outermost pair (♂), or white mottled with brown (♀). Recognizable

123

from other nighthawks by diminutive size.

Range. British Guiana westward to the Orinoco and northern Brazil. The interior of southern Brazil.

Colombia. Savanna, and thin woods. Extreme eastern Colombia along the Orinoco River *(septentrionalis)*.

SAND-COLORED NIGHTHAWK
(Chordeiles rupestris)

Description. 9 - 10″. Above sandy gray streaked and vermiculated with blackish brown, spotted with buff. Throat white, chest sandy mixed with white, rest of underparts white. Tertials and secondaries white tipped with black. Tail forked, central feathers like back, rest white tipped dusky. The pure white belly and white outer tail-feathers help identify this species.

Range. Southern Venezuela, south to Bolivia and eastward to central Brazil.

Colombia. Riverbanks and savanna. The base of the Eastern Andes in Meta *(xyostictus)*. Amazonian Colombia *(rupestris)*.

LESSER NIGHTHAWK
(Chordeiles acutipennis)

Description. 7½ - 8½″. Above mixed blackish, grayish and buffy. Throat bar white, lower breast and abdomen buff, barred brownish. White bar (buffy in ♀) on primaries about midway on length of feather. Tail blackish barred sandy all except central ones with a white subterminal bar (♂); without bar (♀).

Range. From the southwestern United States southward to Venezuela, Bolivia and southeastern Brazil.

Colombia. Scrubby lands, pastures. Tropical zone of northern and western Colombia westward to the Orinoco *(acutipennis)*. Winter resident recorded from "Bogotá" westward to the Pacific coast in December *(texensis)*. Winter resident in northern Magdalena and Bolívar *(micromeris)*. Resident in the semi-arid parts of the upper Magdalena Valley *(crissalis)*.

COMMON NIGHTHAWK
(Chordeiles minor)

Description. 8½ - 9″. Very similar to the Lesser Nighthawk but larger. The white bar on the primaries much closer to the base of the feathers, rather than near the middle of them.

Range. Breeds from Alaska and Canada southward to Panama. Winters in South America from Venezuela southward to Argentina. Trinidad.

Colombia. Open country. The following forms, all transients, (but possibly some winter) have been recorded in Colombia from the end of August to November, and again in April: *minor; sennetti; henryi; aserriensis; chapmani; howelli.* They differ from each other in minor details and can only be told apart in the hand.

BAND-TAILED NIGHTHAWK
(Nyctiprogne leucopyga)

Description. 8 - 8½″. Above dark brown vermiculated and spotted with buffy, streaked with black on crown and lower back. A white patch at sides of throat. Chest narrowly barred black and buff, rest of underparts broadly barred buffy white and dark brown. Primaries dusky without white patch. Tail-feathers except central ones with a broad white median bar.

Range. French Guiana, westward to the Orinoco and southward to southern Brazil.

Colombia. Savanna. Orinoco region *(exigua)*. Vaupés *(latifascia)*.

NACUNDA NIGHTHAWK
(Podager nacunda)

Description. 12 - 13″. ♂: Upperparts vermiculated and freckled sandy and blackish. Spots on head, inner secondaries and wing-coverts black. Chin and breast barred sandy and blackish, the chest spotted with buff. Band across throat, base of remiges, lower breast, abdomen and under tail-coverts white. Tail sandy barred with black, outer feathers very broadly tipped white. ♀: No white at tip of tail. A chunky species with sharply bicolored underparts.

Range. Venezuela, the Guianas, south to Argentina and Bolivia. Trinidad, Tobago.
Colombia. Open savanna, pasturelands. Tropical zone of the Santa Marta region and the Guajira Peninsula. The lower Magdalena Valley. East of the Andes in Meta and Vaupés *(minor)*.

PAURAQUE
(Nyctidromus albicollis)
Description. 9 - 10". ♂ : Crown grayish, finely vermiculated with dark brown, central feathers broadly streaked black. Upperparts grayish to rufescent, somewhat streaked and barred with dusky. Wing-coverts black barred and tipped with buff, scapulars with a large velvety black spot on tip of outer web, fringed buff. Ear-coverts plain tawny. Upper throat tawny buff, barred black with a wide white patch across lower throat. Breast tawny buff barred blackish; rest of underparts paler with a few dark bars. Primaries dusky with a broad white band. Outer tail-feathers mostly black, next two white, remainder sandy, marbled with black and barred with black. ♀ similar but duller, wing band much narrower tinged buff. Tail-feathers barred, only the penultimate tipped white. A very rufous phase exists in both sexes.
Range. From Texas, southward to Venezuela, Bolivia and southeastern Brazil. Trinidad.
Colombia. Dense second growth, savanna. All of tropical and subtropical Colombia, except the arid Caribbean littoral *(albicollis)*. Caribbean coast from the río Sinú, eastward and the lower Magdalena Valley *(gilvus)*.

OCELLATED POORWILL
(Nyctiphrynus ocellatus)
Description. 8½ - 9". ♂ : Above and below blackish brown; round white spots on longer wing-coverts and belly. Tail barred, all except central pair narrowly tipped white. Remiges notched with rufous on outer web. ♀ similar to ♂. The very dark coloration helps distinguish this species.
Range. Nicaragua. Western Ecuador. Eastern Ecuador south to Argentina and

Bolivia.
Colombia. Forest. Tropical zone of the Pacific coast *(rosenbergi)*.

CHUCK-WILL'S-WIDOW
(Caprimulgus carolinensis)
Description. 11 - 13". ♂ : Above wood brown streaked, spotted and vermiculated with black. A pale narrow band across lower throat. Primaries blackish barred with rufous-tawny. Inner webs of three outermost tail-feathers silky white. ♀ similar, but all tail-feathers finely mottled rufescent and black and barred with black.
Range. Breeds from Kansas to New Jersey, south to the Gulf States. Winters in Central America south to Colombia, and the Greater Antilles.
Colombia. Wooded regions. Tropical and subtropical zone. Winter resident, November to June.

RUFOUS NIGHTJAR
(Caprimulgus rufus)
Description. 9 - 10½". Very similar to the Chuck-Will's-Widow. ♂ differs principally by having only the terminal quarter of the three outer tail-feathers instead of the terminal half white. ♀ differs from the Chuck-Will's-Widow only by smaller size.
Range. Costa Rica southward to Venezuela, southern Brazil and Argentina. Lesser Antilles. Trinidad.
Colombia. Wooded regions. Tropical zone. Northwestern Colombia *(minimus)*. The Santa Marta region *(rufus)*. East of the Andes in Meta *(noctivigulus)*.

BAND-WINGED NIGHTJAR
(Caprimulgus longirostris)
Description. 8½ - 9". Above blackish. Sides of crown mottled with whitish, center of crown and rest of upperparts spotted, ocellated and barred with rufous. A conspicuous rufous band around hindneck. White bar across throat. Chest blackish spotted with buff, rest of underparts buff, barred blackish. A white band across primaries (buffy in ♀). Outermost tail-feathers with large white terminal patch (♂), or mottled with grayish (♀).

Range. Venezuela southward in western South America to Chile. Argentina.

Colombia. Brush country and open woods. Subtropical to temperate zones throughout the country *(ruficervix)*.

WHITE-TAILED NIGHTJAR
(Caprimulgus cayennensis)

Description. 8½ - 9". Rather like the Band-winged Nightjar but belly white (♂) or buffy (♀). Tail-feathers except central pair silvery white on inner web, tip dark, and with a black median bar on inner web (♂); outer tail-feathers barred rufescent and dark brown (♀).

Range. Costa Rica to Venezuela, the Guianas and northern Brazil. Lesser Antilles, Trinidad, Tobago, Curaçao, Bonaire, Margarita Island.

Colombia. Savanna, open pastureland. Tropical zone of the Caribbean coast *(albicauda)*. Subtropical zone of the Cauca Valley and middle Magdalena Valley *(apertus)*. East of the Andes in Meta and Santander and the head of the Magdalena Valley *(cayennensis)*. The arid Guajira Peninsula *(insularis)*.

SPOT-TAILED NIGHTJAR
(Caprimulgus maculicaudus)

Description. 7 - 8". Crown black, spotted with rufous. Eyebrow and collar on hind-neck rufous-chestnut, rest of upperparts buff sparsely barred with black. Large spots on wing-coverts and edges of axillaries deep buff; primaries dark brown barred with rufous. Chest and throat blackish heavily spotted with buff. Four outer tail-feathers terminating in a white bar, inner webs of feathers with three or four round white spots and notched with rufous on outer webs (♂). Without white in tail (♀).

Range. Southern Mexico. Colombia eastward to Venezuela, British and French Guiana, southward to southeastern Brazil, Bolivia and Peru.

Colombia. Forest and clearings. Tropical zone east of the Eastern Andes from Vaupés to Meta and Boyacá. Apparently common in the lower Atrato Valley in cattle ranch country.

LITTLE NIGHTJAR
(Caprimulgus parvulus)

Description. 7½ - 8½". ♂: Above brown, feathers of crown streaked with black; axillaries black edged with pale buff. Chin and throat dark brown, the feathers tipped black; breast dusky vermiculated and spotted with buffy white, rest of underparts buff, barred with dusky. Primaries with a white bar; all but central tail-feathers tipped with white, outermost two pairs on both webs, next two pairs on inner webs only. ♀ similar but primaries barred and mottled with rufous; tail without white spots.

Range. Northern Venezuela and western Ecuador. Brazil south to the Amazon, west to eastern Peru and south to Argentina.

Colombia. Brushlands. Tropical zone in the Santa Marta region *(heterurus)*.

BLACKISH NIGHTJAR
(Caprimulgus nigrescens)

Description. 7 - 7½". ♂: Entire upperparts, throat and chest blackish sparsely spotted with grayish and rufous-buff. Bar on throat, spots on breast, small spots on inner web of inner primaries and narrow tip to second and third outermost tail-feathers white. ♀ similar but without white in tail and wings.

Range. The Guianas, southern Venezuela southward to Brazil and westward to eastern Ecuador, Peru, and Bolivia.

Colombia. Forest, clearings and savanna. Amazonian region.

LADDER-TAILED NIGHTJAR
(Hydropsalis climacocerca) Fig. 48

Description. ♂ 10 - 11"; ♀ 8". ♂: Upperparts and chest pale sandy buff, vermiculated with black. Spots on wing-coverts, throat, lower breast and belly white. Primaries banded with white. Tail rather long (7"), W-shaped. Central tail-feathers pale sandy narrowly banded with blackish, outer tail-feather slightly longer than central ones, notched sandy and blackish on base of outer web, barred black and white on basal portion of inner web with a broad diagonal band of white on distal portion of feathers, rest of tail feathers considerably shorter than the outermost and central ones, blackish at base and tip, the rest white. ♀: Tail normal. Remiges barred with rufous basally.

Range. Venezuela, the Guianas southward through Amazonia to Ecuador, Peru and Bolivia.

Colombia. Sandy river banks and adjacent forest. Tropical zone east of the Andes *(climacocerca)*.

SWALLOW-TAILED NIGHTJAR
(Uropsalis segmentata)

Description. 20 - 24" (♂); 9 - 10" (♀). ♂ : Tail enormously lengthened, deeply forked, uniform dusky on inner web, outer web very narrow, notched white, shafts white. Plumage blackish barred and spotted with orange-rufous, particularly on lower back; collar on hindneck rufous. ♀ generally like ♂ but tail normal, outer tail-feathers barred rufous.

Range. The Andes of Ecuador, Peru and Bolivia.

Colombia. Temperate and páramo zones of the Eastern and Central Andes *(segmentata)*.

LYRE-TAILED NIGHTJAR
(Uropsalis lyra)

Description. 27 - 32" (♂) , 9 - 10" (♀) . ♂ : Outer tail-feathers enormously lengthened (22"), uniform dusky with black shaft, web white on last 3"; rest of tail-feathers black with rufous-chestnut bars. Plumage blackish, mottled and spotted with rufous and buff and with a conspicuous chestnut collar on hindneck. ♀ similar in color but tail not lengthened, slightly forked, blackish, barred with chestnut on all but central feathers.

Range. Venezuela, Ecuador and Peru.

Colombia. Savanna and open woodland. Upper tropical and subtropical zones of the Eastern and Central Andes *(lyra)*.

PLATE V

BUFF-TAILED
SICKLEBILL
(*Eutoxeres c. condamini*)
Page 137

FIERY TOPAZ
(*Topaza pyra*)
Page 149

VELVET-PURPLE
CORONET
(*Boissonneaua jardini*)
Page 153

VIOLET-TAILED SYLPH
(*Aglaiocercus c. coelestis*)
Page 158

GREEN-VENTED
WHITETIP
(*Urosticte b. benjamini*)
Page 148

TAWNY-BELLIED
HERMIT
(*Phaethornis
s. syrmatophorus*)
Page 135

WHITE-TAILED
STAR-FRONTLET
(*Coeligena phalerata*)
Page 152

BEARDED
HELMET-CREST
(*Oxypogon g. guerinii*)
Page 157

FORK-TAILED
WOODNYMPH
(*Thalurania
furcata verticeps*)
Page 141

EMPRESS BRILLIANT
(*Heliodoxa imperatrix*)
Page 149

SPARKLING VIOLET-E
(*Colibri c. coruscans*)
Page 138

RED-BILLED EMERALD
(*Chlorostilbon g. gibsoni*)
Page 141

128

E.L. Poole

SWIFTS (Apodidae)

Fig. 49. Fork-tailed Palm Swift
(Reinarda squamata) p. 131

Swifts differ from swallows by their very strong and rapid flight, long, narrow wings, usually blackish plumage and screaming, twittering notes. They never perch on telegraph wires, but cling to rocks or in hollow trees. The Palm Swift has the peculiar habit of attaching its nest to the under side of palm leaves.

They live entirely on insects which are caught in flight, and are usually seen in flocks or small groups. The sexes are alike. (14 Col.; 15 S. A.; 25 N. & S. A.; 77 wld.)

AID TO IDENTIFICATION

Tail slightly to deeply forked 1, 10, 11, 12, 13^E, 14^E.
Tail square, very short, spines usually protruding 2, 3, 4, 5, 6, 7, 8, 9.

1. WHITE-COLLARED SWIFT
(Streptoprocne zonaris)

Description. 8 - 8½ ". Mainly sooty black, neck encircled by white band, narrow behind, wide on upper chest. Tail forked. By far the largest Colombian swift.

Range. Mexico and the Greater Antilles, southward to Venezuela, British Guiana, Peru, Bolivia, and Argentina. Trinidad.

Colombia. Hilly and mountainous country. Tropical to subtropical zone *(albicincta)*. Temperate zone of the Central Andes *(altissima)*.

2. DARK-BREASTED SWIFT
(Chaetura chapmani)

Description. 5 - 5½ ". Very similar to the Chimney Swift and probably not distinguishable in the field. Differs by much blacker upperparts and non-contrasting throat. Tail short, square with protruding spines.

Range. Venezuela, British Guiana and Trinidad. Southern Brazil.

Colombia. Migrant (?) Known only from Antioquia in April *(viridipennis)*. The typical race undoubtedly occurs in Northeastern Colombia for it is known from the Venezuelan side of the Perijá Mts.

3. CHIMNEY SWIFT
(Chaetura pelagica)

Description. 5 - 5½ ". Dark sooty olive-brown above, grayer and paler on rump and tail-coverts. Below grayish brown; very pale (almost whitish) on chin and thoat. Tail very short with protruding spines.

Range. Breeds in North America, north of the Mexican border; winters on the upper Amazon, being reported from northeastern Peru.

Colombia. Transient. Recorded from the Eastern and Western Andes in April.

4. GRAY-RUMPED SWIFT
(Chaetura cinereiventris)

Description. 4¼-4½″. Glossy greenish black above, rump pale ashy gray. Throat whitish shading to gray on chest and blackish on belly and under tail-coverts. Tail short, square with protruding spines.

Range. Nicaragua to Venezuela, British Guiana, Brazil, Ecuador, Peru and Bolivia. Trinidad, Tobago, Grenada.

Colombia. The eastern base of the Eastern Andes in Boyacá *(schistacea)*. Eastern base of the Andes from Meta southward *(sclateri)*. Tropical and subtropical zone of the Central and Western Andes *(occidentalis)*.

5. BAND-RUMPED SWIFT
(Chaetura spinicauda)

Description. 4¾ - 5¼″. Above sooty blackish, rump crossed by a sharply defined buffy white band, upper tail-coverts black. Below grayish brown, paler on chin and throat. Tail very short, spines protruding.

Range. Costa Rica southward to Venezuela, the Guianas and the lower Amazon. Trinidad.

Colombia. Tropical zone. The Santa Marta region, the lower Magdalena and Cauca Valleys and the Pacific coast *(aetherodroma)*. Putumayo and Caquetá *(aethalea?)*.

6. ASHY-TAILED SWIFT
(Chaetura andrei)

Description. 6″. Entire upper surface deep smoky brown, below smoky brown, distinctly paler on throat. Tail very short with short protruding spines.

Range. Panama. Venezuela. Southern Brazil, Paraguay and Argentina.

Colombia. Summer visitor (?) Recorded from Magdalena in early August *(meridionalis)*.

7. SHORT-TAILED SWIFT
(Chaetura brachyura)

Description. 4-4¼″. Sooty black with a slight greenish gloss. Rump, upper and under tail-coverts and short tail pale grayish brown.

Range. The Lesser Antilles. Panama. Venezuela, the Guianas to Mato Grosso. Ecuador and Peru.

Colombia. Tropical zone on both sides of the Eastern Andes *(brachycerca)*.

8. CHESTNUT-COLLARED SWIFT
(Cypseloides rutilus)

Description. 5½-5¾″. Dark sooty black above, belly brownish black. Collar on hindneck, auriculars, lower throat and breast chestnut-rufous. Tail short, spines slightly protruding. Young birds lack the rufous coloring.

Range. Mexico southward to Trinidad, Venezuela and the Guianas, Ecuador, Peru and Bolivia.

Colombia. Upper tropical and subtropical zones of the Eastern, Central and Western Andes *(brunnitorques)*.

9. SPOT-FRONTED SWIFT
(Cypseloides cherriei)

Description. 5-5½″. Uniform sooty black, slightly paler below, grayish on chin. Sides of forehead and small post-ocular spot or streak white. Tail short, with spines protruding.

Range. Costa Rica. Western Venezuela.

Colombia. Migrant (?) Recorded once in January in Santander.

10. WHITE-CHESTED SWIFT
(Cypseloides lemosi)

Description. 6″. Above sooty black, slightly lighter and browner below, with a large white patch on chest. Crown and back faintly glossed greenish, the wings and tail glossed bluish. Tail forked, spines not stiffened. Immature birds lack the white chest and resemble the White-chinned Swift. The tarsus, however, is relatively long, 15 - 16 mm.

Range. Colombia.

Colombia. Known only from the upper Cauca Valley.

11. WHITE-CHINNED SWIFT
(Cypseloides cryptus)

Description. 5½″. Sooty brown above and below, chin pure white. Tail very slightly forked.

Range. Honduras southward to Venezuela, British Guiana and Peru.

Colombia. Known only from the upper Cauca Valley and Córdoba.

12. LESSER SWALLOW-TAILED SWIFT
(Panyptila cayennensis)

Description. 5 - 5¼". Tail deeply forked. Blue-black, except for white lores, throat, collar on hind-neck, sides of neck, chest and patch on flanks.

Range. Southern Mexico. Nicaragua to Venezuela, the Guianas, eastern Ecuador and Brazil. Trinidad and Tobago.

Colombia. Tropical zone both east and west of the Andes (cayennensis).

13. PYGMY SWIFT
(Micropanyptila furcata)

Description. 4-4¼". Blackish brown above, paler below with white center to abdomen. Concealed base of long, deeply forked tail white.

Range. Northwestern Venezuela.

Colombia. Known only from near the Venezuelan border in Norte de Santander in the tropical zone (furcata).

14. FORK-TAILED PALM SWIFT
(Reinarda squamata) Fig. 49

Description. 5-5½". Tail long and deeply forked. Greenish black above and below, the feathers edged with grayish. Center of lower parts from chin to tail-coverts white to brownish white.

Range. Venezuela, the Guianas south to eastern Brazil. Eastern Peru.

Colombia. Llanos of eastern Colombia in the vicinity of palm trees (semota).

HUMMINGBIRDS (Trochilidae)

Fig. 50. Racquet-tailed Hummingbird
(Ocreatus underwoodii) p. 155

Few people are aware of the vast size of this family, for the most part composed of tiny birds which vary in length from just over two to almost nine inches. Famous for their glittering metallic colors, many species are additionally embellished with crests, facial plumes, long tails ending in racquets and other ornaments. Females usually differ from males and are more soberly colored. Bills are usually long and straight, but in some species curved bills aid in feeding on special flowers. Hummingbirds live on nectar and small insects which they secure by probing into flowers while they hover in front of them, on rapidly beating wings. Hummingbirds do not walk or hop, but perch on twigs and branches. Their nest, composed of moss, lichens and plant fibers, is placed in the fork of a twig or saddled by cobwebs to the branch of a tree. In it two white eggs are laid. Their song is a squeaky warble — in some cases surprisingly loud.

Hummingbirds are found only in the Americas and almost all occur south of the border of the United States. In South America they are found from sea level to snow line. In very cold weather birds living high up in the Andes sometimes roost or take shelter in caves and there is some evidence that in very severe spells the birds become torpid and inactive, until the temperature rises.

In the following description metallic colors are taken with the observer's back to the light. Wings are not usually described as in almost all species the feathers are blackish, often with a slight bluish or violet gloss. Two measurements are given: the length of the bird from the forehead to the tip of the tail, and then that of the bill in parentheses. Decimals are used for this family instead of the usual fractions. (136 Col.; 247 S.A.; 319 N.&S.A.; 319 wld.)

AID TO IDENTIFICATION

Underparts uniform gray, black or white 1E, 2, 8, 9, 12E, 15E, 23E, 27, 31, 32, 40, 41, 42, 43E, 44, 45, 46, 48, 49, 57E, 58E, 61, 67, 68, 110, 127, 128E, 129, 130E, 132.

Underparts uniform or mostly uniform buff to chestnut, central tail-feathers often long 4, 5, 10, 11, 13, 14E, 16E, 17E, 18E, 19, 56, 70, 81, 83, 84, 89, 96E, 118, 131 132E, 133, 134.

Underparts spotted, or white or buff with shining green discs 22, 40, 50E, 52, 53E, 53a, 54E, 59 60, 69, 71, 72, 74, 75, 76, 78, 82, 92, 94, 98, 101, 102, 108, 114, 115, 116, 117, 119, 120, 123, 124.

Underparts streaked 3, 20, 21E.

Underparts green or white with a black stripe down center 30.

Breast or belly purple, violet or blue 45, 46, 47, 48, 50E, 51, 59, 60, 67, 92.

Throat or belly fiery orange or topaz 31, 90, 98.

Throat amethyst or rosy red, band across or patch at sides of breast white or buffy 85, 99, 100, 132E, 133.

Body plumage shining or glittering green (with blue or violet cap, throat or cheek tufts) 25, 28, 29, 52, 53E, 53a, 62, 72, 75, 76, 82, 88, 91, 101, 102, 103, 105, 126, 130E, 132, (without contrasting colors on top of head) 39E, 40, 41, 42, 43E, 44, 49, 55E, 63, 64E, 65, 67, 68, 71, 77E, 83, 90, 93, 94, 104, 106, 108, 109, 116, 117, 122, 126, 132, 134.

Above purple or all or mostly black 86, 87, 88, 93, 114, 115, 118.

Rump crossed by a white or buff band 3, 33, 34, 35E, 36E, 37E, 38.

Outer tail-feathers all or mostly white 7, 26, 54E, 80, 87, 89, (or buff to chestnut): 5, 6E, 21E, 24, 66E, 73E, 79E, 95, 96E, 97, 121, 127, 128E.

Tail long, central feathers pointed, terminal portion white or buff. No bright greens or other bright colors 8, 9, 10, 11, 12E, 13, 14E, 15E, 16E, 17E, 18E, 19.

Tail long, forked, or feathers crossed or terminating in a racquet. Bright green or other bright colors present (forked, size very small) 36E, 37E, 38, 45, 131, 132, (forked, size large) 78, 112, 113, 123, 124, 125, (crossed) 79E, (racquet) 111.

1. BLUE-FRONTED LANCEBILL
(Doryfera johannae)

Description. 3.5″ (1.1″) ♂ : Forecrown glittering violet-blue. Upper surface and sides of body shining bronze-green; upper tail-coverts shining blue-green. Center of throat, breast and abdomen blue-black. Under tail-coverts violet-blue. Tail shiny steel blue. ♀ : Forehead glittering blue-green, crown bronze, rest of upperparts like ♂. Under surface grayish green. Tail steel blue, outer feathers tipped gray.

Range. British Guiana eastward through southern Venezuela to Ecuador and Peru.

Colombia. Forest. Tropical zone of the eastern base of the Eastern Andes from Cundinamarca southward (johannae).

2. GREEN-FRONTED LANCEBILL
(Doryfera ludoviciae)

Description. 4″ (1.3-1.5″) ♂ : Forecrown glittering emerald green. Hindcrown and nape shining bronzy purple. Back bronze-green, upper tail-coverts bluer. Tail black tipped with gray. Below dark grayish, washed bronzy green. Bill thin, long, straight. ♀ Similar but with frontlet reduced in size, or absent.

Range. Costa Rica southward to western Venezuela, Ecuador, Peru and northern Bolivia.

Colombia. Forest. Subtropical zone of the Eastern and Central Andes and the east slope of the Western Andes (ludoviciae). Upper tropical and subtropical zones on the western slope of the Western Andes from the río San Juan southward (rectirostris).

3. TOOTH-BILLED HUMMINGBIRD
(Androdon aequatorialis)

Description. 4 - 4.2″ (1.5 - 1.6″) ♂ : Throat boldly streaked gray and white, rest of underparts white, blotched with gray. Crown shiny bronzy purple, rest of upperparts shiny bronze green. Upper tail-coverts white, the longest ones blue-green. Tail grayish green with a bluish green subterminal band, the outermost ones tipped white. Bill stout, straight. ♀ similar but head without purple-bronze.

Range. Eastern Panama southward to western Ecuador.

Colombia. Forest. Tropical zone of the Pacific slope from Nariño northward and turning eastward in Antioquia to the middle Magdalena Valley.

4. BRONZY HERMIT
(Glaucis aenea)

Description. 3.2″ (1.2-1.3″, bill curved). Crown dark grayish brown, rest of upperparts shiny, bronzy gold. Under surface uniform deep buff. Central tail-feathers bronzy, tipped white, rest with basal half rufous-chestnut, distal half black tipped white.

Range. Nicaragua to western Panama. Northwestern Ecuador.

Colombia. Forest. Tropical zone of the Pacific coast.

5. RUFOUS-BREASTED HERMIT
(Glaucis hirsuta)

Description. 4-4.3″ (1.2-1.4″, bill curved, lower mandible yellow with dark tip). Crown fuscous, feathers tipped bronze, rest of upperparts bronzy green, upper tail-coverts fringed white. Ear coverts dusky, chin whitish. Below dull rufous, center of lower breast and belly grayish turning to white on under tail-coverts. Central tail-feathers green, tipped white, lateral feathers chestnut with a broad black subterminal bar and a white tip.

Range. Eastern Panama to Venezuela and the Guianas southward to southeastern Brazil and Bolivia. Trinidad.

Colombia. Forest. Tropical zone. From the east shore of the Gulf of Urabá to the Pacific coast south to the río San Juan and eastward over the rest of the country to Meta, Caquetá and Putumayo *(affinis);* Amazonian Colombia at Leticia *(hirsuta).*

6. WHITE-TAILED BARBTHROAT
(Threnetes leucurus)

Description. 3.8-4.1″ (1.3-1.4″, bill slightly curved). Upperparts bronze green with feathers, especially of crown, edged with buff, central tail-feathers greener, tipped white, outer feathers pale fawn with a diagonal subterminal black band and white tip. Throat black, bordered on each side by a white line and below by a broad orange-buff band. Chest dusky bronze green, lower breast and belly buffy white.

Range. British and Dutch Guiana and Venezuela southward to Amazonian Brazil, Ecuador, Peru and Bolivia.

Colombia. Forest. Eastern base of the Eastern Andes from Meta southward *(cervinicauda).*

7. BAND-TAILED BARBTHROAT
(Threnetes ruckeri)

Description. 3.8 - 4.1″ (1.3 - 1.4″). Very like the White-tailed Barbthroat; differs principally by having the tail steel blue, tipped white, all but the central feathers basally white.

Range. Nicaragua south to western Ecuador and western Venezuela.

Colombia. Forest. Tropical zone of the Pacific coast except Nariño and across northern Colombia to the middle Magdalena Valley. The humid forest region of coastal Santa Marta *(darienensis).* Northeastern Colombia in the Zulia Valley *(venezuelensis).* Pacific slope of Nariño *(ruckeri).*

Phaethornis

The Hermits *(Phaethornis)* form a very homogeneous group of medium to small-sized hummingbirds, characterized by their dull, usually bronzy upperparts, buffy or grayish underparts and long, curved bills, (except for *bourcieri),* the lower mandible mostly red in the larger species or yellow in the smaller. The feathers of the tail are graduated, the central ones attenuated and often much longer than the rest, the distal third, white. None possesses glittering colors. The sexes are alike. They inhabit the forest, usually keeping low down near the ground in the undergrowth.

8. WHITE-WHISKERED HERMIT
(Phaethornis yaruqui)

Description. 5″ (1.7 - 1.8″). Crown and nape coppery green, rest of upper surface bronze green including sides of neck and chest. Moustacial streak white; streak behind eye white to buff. Lower parts dark gray, streak down center of throat pale gray to whitish. Under tail-coverts white. Tail blue-black, central feathers tipped white.

Range. Western Ecuador.

Colombia. Forest. Tropical zone of the Pacific coast *(sancti-johannis).*

9. GREEN HERMIT
(Phaethornis guy)

Description. 4.8 - 5″ (1.5 - 1.7″). Upper-parts, sides of throat and chest bronze green, bluer on upper tail-coverts. Mous-tacial streak, streak behind eye, down center of throat, and patch on abdomen rufescent buff, rest of underparts gray (or green, 1). Tail blue at base gradually turning blue-black, central feathers tipped white.

Range. Costa Rica, southward to Peru and eastward to Venezuela and Trinidad.

Colombia. Forest. Tropical zone of north-western Colombia (1, *coruscus*). Tropical and subtropical zones of the Western and Central Andes and the west slope of the Eastern Andes *(emiliae)*. East of the Andes in Boyacá and Meta *(apicalis)*.

10. TAWNY-BELLIED HERMIT
(Phaethornis syrmatophorus) Plate V

Description. 4.8 - 5″ (1.6 - 1.7″). Coppery green above, feathers of rump edged buff, upper tail-coverts ochraceous. Streak be-hind eye white; area below the eye black. Entire underparts ochraceous; a line down center of throat white. Tail-feathers gray at base, turning greenish black, distal half of elongated tail-feathers white, rest tipped ochraceous.

Range. Ecuador and northeastern Peru.

Colombia. Forest. Tropical and subtropical zone of the Pacific coast and the Cauca Valley *(syrmatophorus)*. Head of the Mag-dalena Valley *(columbianus)*.

11. LONG-TAILED HERMIT
(Phaethornis superciliosus)

Description. 4.8 - 5″ (1.5 - 1.8″). Top of head dusky, rest of upperparts bronze-green (or coppery green, 1), upper tail-coverts edged with ochraceous. Underparts grayish buff, paler and buffier on abdo-men, sides of throat clouded with blackish. Stripe behind eye, malar streak and stripe down center of throat buffy. Tail-feathers blue-green, with a broad subterminal black band and buff tip to all but central pair.

Range. From Mexico southward through Central America to Venezuela, the Gui-anas, the Amazon, Peru and Bolivia.

Colombia. Forest. Tropical zone of north-western and northern Colombia to the middle Magdalena Valley (1, *cassinii*). Tropical and lower subtropical zone of Santa Marta region *(susurrus)*. Tropical zone east of the Eastern Andes from Meta southward to Caquetá (1, *moorei*). The upper río Guainía near the Venezuelan and Brazilian border *(insolitus)*.

12. WHITE-BEARDED HERMIT
(Phaethornis hispidus)

Description. 5″ (1.3 - 1.4″). Top of head dusky, rest of upperparts bronzy to cop-pery green. Upper tail-coverts fringed grayish white. Streak behind eye, malar streak and gular patch white. Sides of throat and breast grayish, rest of under-parts whitish. Tail bronzy green with a black subterminal band and white tip.

Range. Central Venezuela, western Brazil to Ecuador, Peru and northeastern Bolivia.

Colombia. Forest. Tropical zone east of the Andes northward to Boyacá.

13. PALE-BELLIED HERMIT
(Phaethornis anthophilus)

Description. 4.8″ (1.2 - 1.4″). Top of head dusky, rest of upperparts bronze green, each feather edged ochraceous. Streak behind eye buff, cheeks black. Stripe on each side of throat white, feathers of throat with dark centers and pale edges giving a streaked appearance (or almost solid blackish, 1) rest of underparts isabel-line. Tail-feathers bronzy green, subter-minal band black, tip white.

Range. Pearl Islands. Western Venezuela.

Colombia. Forest. Caribbean coast through the río Sinú eastward and up the Magda-lena Valley *(anthophilus)*. "Bogotá" but probably the eastern base of the Andes (1, *fuliginosus)*.

14. STRAIGHT-BILLED HERMIT
(Phaethornis bourcieri)

Description. 4.8″ (1.2 - 1.3″, bill almost straight). Crown and upperparts bronze green, upper tail-coverts fringed with buff.

Narrow superciliary and inconspicuous malar streak buffy, gular streak white. Rest of underparts isabelline, paler on center of breast and abdomen. Tail bronze green at base with a broad subterminal black band and buff tips to all but central pair.

Range. The Guianas westward through southern Venezuela to eastern Ecuador and Peru. The upper Amazon.

Colombia. Forest. Tropical zone of Caquetá (*bourcieri*).

15. SOOTY-CAPPED HERMIT
(Phaethornis augusti)

Description. 5″ (1.2 - 1.3″). Crown dusky, upperparts coppery green, upper tail-coverts orange-rufous. Moustacial streak and streak behind eye and gular streak white, rest of underparts dingy gray, under tail-coverts buffy. Base of tail-feathers coppery green, black in center with broad white tips.

Range. Venezuela to British Guiana.

Colombia. Garden, scrub and forest. Upper tropical zone of the eastern slope of the Eastern Andes in Boyacá and the Macarena Mts. (*vicarius*).

16. DUSKY-THROATED HERMIT
(Phaethornis rupurumii)

Description. 4″ (.9 - 1″). Crown dusky brown, feathers edged paler, rest of upper surface dull coppery green, tail-coverts edged rufous. Stripe behind eye and moustacial streak buffy white. Throat black with feathers edged buff, giving a streaked appearance; rest of underparts buffy white. Tail-feathers dull green, the central pair tipped white, the lateral ones edged buff. Lower mandible yellow basally in this and the ensuing species of Hermits.

Range. British Guiana, southern Venezuela to the lower Amazon.

Colombia. Forest and scrub. Orinoco region (*rupurumii*).

17. REDDISH HERMIT
(Phaethornis ruber)

Description. 3.2″ (.8 - .9″). Crown and center of back coppery green; rump and upper tail-coverts orange-rufous. Chin and throat whitish, underparts ochraceous. Central tail-feathers coppery with only the tip white, rest coppery with ochraceous tips.

Range. Southern Venezuela and the Guianas, southward to southeastern Brazil and Bolivia.

Colombia. East of the Andes from Caquetá southward and eastward (*nigricinctus*).

18. GRAY-CHINNED HERMIT
(Phaethornis griseogularis)

Description. 3.4″ (.8 - .9″). Crown and nape coppery green; back bronze green, upper tail-coverts rufous. Broad streak behind eye buff. Sides of head black. Chin and throat grayish, rest of underparts ochraceous. Tail basally black, lateral tail-feathers with broad ochraceous tips, central tail-feathers black with white distal third.

Range. Western Venezuela, northwestern Brazil, eastern Ecuador and Peru.

Colombia. Tropical zone east of the Eastern Andes from Meta southward (*griseogularis*).

19. LITTLE HERMIT
(Phaethornis longuemareus)

Description. 3.6″ (.8 - .9″). Crown dusky, feathers edged coppery, rest of upper surface bronzy to coppery green; upper tail-coverts rufous. Feathers of chin and throat black in center, fringed gray giving a streaked appearance (or virtually like rest of underparts, 1). Streak behind eye and on sides of throat buffy, sides of head black. Breast grayish in contrast to rufescent of rest of underparts (or buffy not in contrast, 2). Tail bronzy, central feathers tipped white, lateral ones tipped rufescent.

Range. Southern Mexico south to Venezuela, the Guianas, Peru and southeastern Brazil. Trinidad.

Colombia. Forest and scrub. Tropical zone of the northern Pacific coast and lower Atrato Valley (1, 2, *nelsoni*). Tropical zone of the upper Atrato Valley southward along the Pacific coast (*subrufescens*).

Tropical zone of the lower Cauca and middle Magdalena Valleys *(striigularis)*. Tropical zone east of the Eastern Andes from Meta southward (2, *atrimentalis*).

20. WHITE-TIPPED SICKLEBILL
(Eutoxeres aquila)

Description. 4.5" (1", chord). Bill sharply curved, sickle-shaped. Upperparts shining bronze green, bluer on the upper tail-coverts. Below boldly streaked black and white. Tail very rounded, bronze green tipped white.

Range. Costa Rica southward to northeastern Peru.

Colombia. Forest and scrub. Tropical zone of the Pacific coast south to the río Dagua *(munda)*. South of the río Dagua *(heterura)*. At the head of the Magdalena Valley and the eastern base of the Andes from Meta southward *(aquila)*.

21. BUFF-TAILED SICKLEBILL
(Eutoxeres condamini) Plate V

Description. 4.5" (1.1", chord). Bill sickle-shaped. Above shining bronze green. A shiny blue-green patch at sides of breast; throat and breast streaked buffy white and black; abdomen buffy white; sides of body buff. Four central tail-feathers dark green, tipped white, lateral tail-feathers mostly cinnamon, shading to white at tips. Tail very rounded.

Range. Eastern Ecuador and eastern Peru.

Colombia. Forest. Tropical zone east of the Andes from Caquetá southward along the base of the Andes *(condamini)*.

22. SCALY-BREASTED HUMMINGBIRD
(Phaeochroa cuvierii)

Description. 4.5" (1 - 1.1"). Shining coppery green above. Below buffy grayish, the feathers with central shining bronzy disks. Tail-feathers bronzy green, outermost four with broad white tips. Bill straight and rather thick, lower mandible pale with dark tip.

Range. Guatemala south to Colombia.

Colombia. Open woods. Tropical zone of northeastern Colombia *(berlepschi)*.

23. GRAY-BREASTED SABREWING
(Campylopterus largipennis)

Description. 5" (1.1 - 1.2"). Upperparts including central tail-feathers shining green; lower parts plain gray. Outer tail-feathers steel blue tipped white. In ♂ the shaft of the two outermost primaries is very broad and swollen. In ♀ it is normal, otherwise similar to ♂. Bill straight.

Range. Venezuela, the Guianas, southward to Brazil and Bolivia.

Colombia. Forest. Tropical zone east of the Andes from Meta, southward along the base of the Andes *(aequatorialis)*. Extreme eastern Colombia on the río Vaupés *(largipennis)*.

24. LAZULINE SABREWING
(Campylopterus falcatus)

Description. 4.2 - 4.6" (.9 - 1"). ♂: Upper surface glittering green. Throat, breast, sides of neck glittering violet-blue; sides of breast glittering golden green. Center of belly glittering blue-green. Central tail-feathers bronze green with a large chestnut mark on basal half of outer web, rest chestnut with bronze-green tips. Bill curved. ♀: Shining green above. Throat glittering blue-green; rest of lower surface dark grayish with a few green disks. Tail as in ♂.

Range. Northern Venezuela and eastern Ecuador.

Colombia. Forest and scrub. Upper tropical and subtropical zones. The lower Cauca and upper and middle Magdalena Valleys. East slope of the Andes from Norte de Santander to Meta.

25. SANTA MARTA SABREWING
(Campylopterus phainopeplus)

Description. 5" (.9 - 1"). ♂: Crown and throat glittering dark blue, rest of plumage glittering green. Tail dark steel blue, central rectrices tinged green. ♀: Shining green above, gray below. Flanks tinged green. Tail green, outer rectrices tipped with gray.

Range. Colombia.

Colombia. Sometimes in banana plantations. The Santa Marta Mts. from 4,000-6,000 ft. from February to May; up to 15,000 ft. from June to October.

26. WHITE-NECKED JACOBIN
(Florisuga mellivora)

Description. 3.8 - 4.1" (.8 - .9"). ♂ : Crown shining cornflower blue; nape shining green. Large white patch on extreme upper back, rest of back shining bronze green. Throat and breast shining purplish blue, bordered below by a bronze green band; rest of underparts white. Upper tail-coverts very long, bronze green. Tail white, central and inner feathers with blue-black tips. ♀ : Bronzy to coppery golden green above. Feathers of throat and breast basally bronze green broadly edged with white giving a scaled appearance; center of abdomen white. Tail-feathers bronze green with a subterminal blue-black patch, the outermost tipped white, the rest very narrowly fringed white.

Range. Mexico, southward to Venezuela and the Guianas, Bolivia and southern Brazil. Trinidad, Tobago and islands in the southern Caribbean.

Colombia. Forest and scrub. Generally distributed throughout the country in the tropical zone *(mellivora)*.

27. BROWN VIOLET-EAR
(Colibri delphinae)

Description. 3.5 - 4.3" (.7 - .8"). ♂ : General color dull grayish brown, paler below, the feathers of lower back, upper and under tail-coverts fringed with rusty. Broad band from below eye continued backwards over ear-coverts glittering violet-blue. Moustacial streak whitish. Patch on throat glittering golden green turning to violet-blue on lower throat. Under tail-coverts rufescent. Tail pale olive bronze with a broad subterminal purple-bronze band. ♀ similar to ♂ but moustacial streak buffier.

Range. From Guatemala south to Bolivia and across northern South America to Trinidad and British Guiana.

Colombia. Forest and scrub. Tropical and lower subtropical zones of the Santa Marta region, the upper Magdalena and Cauca Valleys, and Nariño. East slope of the Andes from the Macarena Mts. southward.

28. GREEN VIOLET-EAR
(Colibri thalassinus)

Description. 3.6 - 4" (.7 - .8"). ♂ : Body plumage green, shining above, glittering on throat and breast. Patch below eye, prolonged over ear-coverts, glittering violet-blue. Tail green with a subterminal blue-black band. ♀ similar but duller.

Range. Mexico to western Panama, Venezuela south through western South America to Bolivia.

Colombia. Forest and scrub. Generally distributed throughout subtropical zone, except Nariño *(cyanotis)*.

29. SPARKLING VIOLET-EAR
(Colibri coruscans) Plate V

Description. 4.5 - 5" (.9 - 1"). Very similar to the Green Violet-Ear but larger, and with chin, upper throat and patch on center of breast violet-blue. Central tail-feathers greenish blue, the rest brilliant dark blue with a deep purplish blue subterminal band.

Range. Extreme western British Guiana, westward through Venezuela to Ecuador and southward to northwestern Argentina.

Colombia. Forest, scrub and pastureland. Subtropical to temperate zones, throughout the country *(coruscans)*.

30. BLACK-THROATED MANGO
(Anthracothorax nigricollis)

Description. 4.5" (.8 - 1"). ♂ : Above golden green. Middle of throat and abdomen black; sides of throat glittering blue, sides of body green, a more or less concealed white patch on flanks. Central tail-feathers bronze green, lateral feathers purple, edged blue. ♀ : Above green; below white with a black stripe from chin down throat to vent. Tail like ♂ but outer feathers tipped white.

Range. Panama, eastward to Venezuela and the Guianas, southward to Argentina, Paraguay and Bolivia. Trinidad and Tobago.

Colombia. Scrub, forest and plantations. Tropical zone from the lower Atrato, and Cauca Valley eastward to Meta, Vichada, Caquetá and Vaupés.

31. RUBY-TOPAZ HUMMINGBIRD
(Chrysolampis mosquitus)

Description. 3 - 3.2" (.6 - .7"). ♂ : Top of head and nape glittering ruby, extreme upper back black continued over sides of breast; rest of upperparts brown slightly glossed with olive. Throat and breast glittering topaz orange; rest of underparts dark brown. Under tail-coverts orange-rufous; tail-feathers chestnut tipped black. ♀ : Coppery green above; central tail-feathers bronzy green, rest chestnut with a subterminal black band and white tip. Entire underparts grayish white. Young ♂ resembles ♀ but has the tail bronzy purple; all but central tail-feathers tipped white.

Range. Venezuela and the Guianas southward through eastern South America to southeastern Brazil.

Colombia. Gardens and scrub. Tropical zone of the Caribbean coast, middle and upper Magdalena and Cauca Valleys. The west slope of the Western Andes as far south as the río Dagua. East of the Andes from Norte de Santander southward.

32. VIOLET-HEADED HUMMINGBIRD
(Klais guimeti)

Description. 3 - 3.2" (.4"). ♂ : Crown, chin and throat glittering violet-blue; a white spot behind the eye. Upperparts shining green. Underparts grayish with a few green disks, center of abdomen whitish. Tail bronzy green, blackish toward the tip, edged white. ♀ : Crown blue, spot behind eye white. Upperparts bronze green; below gray. Tail-feathers like ♂, but more broadly tipped white.

Range. Nicaragua to western Venezuela and southward to Peru and Bolivia.

Colombia. Scrub. Tropical and subtropical zone of both slopes of the Eastern Andes *(guimeti)*.

33. RUFOUS-CRESTED COQUETTE
(Lophornis delattrei)

Description. 2.8 - 3.2" (.4"). ♂ : Crown and long crest rufous, the longest feathers tipped with bronze green. Upper surface bronze green with a buffy white band across rump. Central tail-feathers bronzy, rest rufous edged and tipped bronze. Chin, throat and malar region glittering green, mixed with chestnut and white on the upper breast; rest of underparts pale bronzy green mixed with gray. ♀ : Front of crown, lores, throat and upper breast rufous. Upperparts bronze green, band across rump buffy white; upper tail-coverts coppery violet. Tail-feathers chestnut with a bronze green median band. Breast and belly buffy.

Range. Costa Rica to Colombia. Peru and Bolivia.

Colombia. Forest and scrub. Upper tropical and subtropical zone of the middle and upper Magdalena Valley *(lessoni)*.

34. SPANGLED COQUETTE
(Lophornis stictolopha) Plate VI

Description. 2.5 - 2.8" (.3"). ♂ : Very similar to the Rufous-crested Coquette, but crest feathers wider, the terminal spots larger and distributed over the whole crest. ♀ similar to ♀ of the Rufous-crested Coquette, but throat with a certain amount of black.

Range. Western Venezuela, eastern Ecuador and northern Peru.

Colombia. Scrub. Tropical zone on both slopes of the Eastern Andes in Tolima and Cundinamarca, west to Antioquia.

35. FESTIVE COQUETTE
(Lophornis chalybea)

Description. 3" (.5 - .6). ♂ : Forehead and area below the eye glittering green; chin and narrow line prolonged backwards under the eye velvety black; tuft of elongated narrow feathers springing from sides of throat and cheeks forming a ruff, shining green, each feather terminating in a white dot. Upperparts bronze green; band across rump buff, upper tail-coverts shining purple. Tail coppery purple. Chest whitish; rest of underparts grayish brown mixed with shining green. ♀ like the ♂ but without glittering frontlet and ruff. Chin and upper throat and area below eye buff. Outer tail feathers tipped dingy white.

Range. Venezuela south to southeastern

Brazil and Bolivia.

Colombia. Forest. Tropical zone east of the Andes from Cundinamarca southward (*verreauxii*).

36. WIRE-CRESTED THORNTAIL
(*Popelairia popelairii*)

Description. ♂ 4.1″ - ♀ 2.8″ (.5″). ♂: Crown and long, very narrow crest, chin and throat glittering green; lower throat and breast black; rest of underparts smoky brown, darkest on center of belly. Back and sides of neck and body coppery green; a white band across rump. Tail very long (2.4″), deeply forked, steel blue, shafts white on underside. ♀: Coppery green above, crown duller; a white band across rump. Throat and breast blackish, malar region and sides of belly white. Tail normal, steel blue, crossed by a gray band near the base, and tipped white.

Range. Eastern Ecuador and eastern Peru.

Colombia. Tropical zone. East of the Andes in Cundinamarca and Meta.

37. BLACK-BELLIED THORNTAIL
(*Popelairia langsdorffi*)

Description. ♂ 4.8 - ♀ 2.8″ (.5″). ♂: Crown, lores, throat and chest glittering green, chest bordered below by narrow line of glittering coppery purple; lower breast and center of belly black, flanks white. Back shining green, rump crossed by a white band, upper tail-coverts ultramarine blue. Central tail-feathers very short almost hidden by tail-coverts, outermost two greatly elongated (3.2″) and very narrow, pale grayish in color, the next pair much shorter than the outermost pair, steel blue like the central tail-feathers, shafts white on under-side. ♀: Shining bronze green above, white band across rump. Throat and belly blackish, breast with glittering green disks, flanks white. Tail slightly forked (.8″), central tail-feathers steel blue, outer tail-feathers with a gray base and steel blue subterminal band, all tipped white.

Range. Southwestern Venezuela, eastern Ecuador, eastern Peru and the upper and middle Amazon.

Colombia. Open woods. Tropical zone of southeastern Colombia from Putumayo eastward to the río Guainía (*melanosternon*).

38. GREEN THORNTAIL
(*Popelairia conversii*) Plate VI

Description. ♂ 4″ - ♀ 2.5″ (.4″). ♂: Upper surface shining green, a white band across rump. Lower surface glittering green, some of the feathers on the breast considerably bluer. Tail graduated, forked (2 - 2.2″); outer feathers much attenuated, steel blue with white shafts. ♀: Above like ♂. Throat black; lower throat, breast and center of belly bronzy green; patch on chest bluer. Tail slightly forked (.8″); outer feathers tipped white. Broad moustacial streak and flanks white.

Range. Costa Rica to western Ecuador.

Colombia. Tropical zone of the Pacific coast. There are records from eastern Colombia but they are probably wrong.

39. BLUE-CHINNED SAPPHIRE
(*Chlorestes notatus*)

Description. 3.5″ (.6 - .7″). ♂: Base of mandible red. Above dark bronzy green. Chin glittering blue, (or greenish blue chin, 1), rest of underparts glittering golden green. Tail steel blue. ♀ similar to ♂ but bases of feathers of underparts white, showing through.

Range. Venezuela, the Guianas south to Bahia on the east and eastern Peru on the west. Trinidad and Tobago.

Colombia. Forest. Tropical zone along the eastern base of the Eastern Andes and eastward to the Orinoco (*notatus*). Extreme southeastern Colombia at Leticia on the Amazon R. (1, *obsoletus*).

Chlorostilbon

The five Emerald Hummingbirds (*Chlorostilbon*) found in Colombia are all very similar. Males are shining green above and have the crown (sometimes) and underparts glittering green. Only their distinguishing characters are given below. Females are shining green above, gray below, the outer tail-feathers tipped grayish white. Most are indistinguishable from each other in the field.

40. BLUE-TAILED EMERALD
(Chlorostilbon mellisugus)

Description. 3″ (.5″). ♂ : Bill black. Lower parts emerald green glittering on belly, throat strongly tinged blue. Crown glittering golden green. Tail steel blue only slightly forked. ♀ : Shining grass green above, smoky white below, central tail-feathers greenish blue, rest deep blue.

Range. Costa Rica southward to Venezuela, the Guianas, Ecuador, Peru and Bolivia. Trinidad, the Dutch West Indies, Margarita Island. The Pearl Islands.

Colombia. Scrubby woods. Tropical and subtropical zones. The Pacific coast to Nariño where it is also found in the subtropical zone of the eastern slope of the Andes. The Cauca Valley north to Medellín, eastward to the east slope of the Central Andes in Tolima and the middle Magdalena Valley in the vicinity of Chicoral *(pumilus)*. The tropical zone in Caquetá *(napensis)*. East of the Eastern Andes in Boyacá and Meta *(caribaeus)*.

41. RED-BILLED EMERALD
(Chlorostilbon gibsoni) Plate V

Description. 3″ (.5″). ♂ : Lower mandible red basally with black tip. Upperparts dark coppery green, crown not glittering. Lower parts glittering golden green (or tinged with blue, 1). Tail steel blue, deeply forked. ♀ very like females of No. 40 but back more coppery green, central tail-feathers green, a pale grayish band near base of outer tail-feathers. Extreme base of lower mandible red.

Range. Northern and western Venezuela.

Colombia. Thickets and scrub. Tropical to subtropical zone. The upper and middle Magdalena Valley, westward from Chicoral to the east slope of the Central Andes in Tolima. East of the Andes in Norte de Santander. Possibly the upper Cauca Valley *(gibsoni)*. The Caribbean coast from the Sinú delta eastward to the Santa Marta region *(1, chrysogaster)*. Arid region from Riohacha eastward *(1, nitens)*.

42. COPPERY EMERALD
(Chlorostilbon russatus)

Description. 2.9″ (.6″). ♂ : Bill black. Upperparts reddish coppery green. Wing-coverts and tail golden coppery. ♀ : Coppery green above, grayish below. Central tail-feathers coppery bronze, outer tail-feathers bronzy at base with a broad subterminal band purplish bronze, and grayish tips.

Range. Northwestern Venezuela.

Colombia. Scrub and forest edge. Upper tropical zone of the Santa Marta Mts. and west slope of the Perijá Mts. Upper subtropical zone of the Eastern Andes in southern Boyacá.

43. NARROW-TAILED EMERALD
(Chlorostilbon stenura)

Description. 3″ (.9″). ♂ : Bill black, tail-feathers shining coppery green above and below, narrow, acuminate. ♀ : Distinguishable from ♀ of other species except *poortmani* by green central tail-feathers.

Range. Venezuela.

Colombia. Scrub. Tropical zone east of the Andes from Norte de Santander to Meta *(stenura)*.

44. SHORT-TAILED EMERALD
(Chlorostilbon poortmani)

Description. 3″ (.6″). ♂ : Crown and underparts glittering grass green. Back shining grass green. Tail shining olive green, very short. Bill black. ♀ differs from all other species except *stenura* by having the central tail-feathers green; the other feathers are green with a wide dark blue subterminal band and tipped white.

Range. Western Venezuela.

Colombia. Scrub. Tropical and lower subtropical zone of the eastern slope of the Eastern Andes, south to Meta *(poortmani)*. West slope of the Eastern Andes and the east slope at the northern end *(euchloris)*.

45. FORK-TAILED WOODNYMPH
(Thalurania furcata) Plate V

Description. ♂ 3.6 - 4″ ♀ 3 - 3.2″ (.8 - 1″). ♂ : Crown glittering purple (or glittering green, edged bluish purple posteriorly, 1; or glittering green, 2; or dark shining bronzy green, 3). Back bronze-green with a band of purple-blue across back (or plain bronze-green, 3). Chin, throat and upper breast glittering emerald green; lower breast and belly violet-blue. Tail rather long, forked, steel blue. ♀ : Shining bronze green above, rump bluer. Below gray, in some races mixed with green on lower breast and abdomen. Central tail-feathers steel blue, tipped white.

Range. Mexico southward to Venezuela, the Guianas, Bolivia and southeastern Brazil. Trinidad.

Colombia. Scrub. Upper tropical and subtropical zones of the Santa Marta Mts., the Eastern Andes and the upper Magdalena Valley *(colombica)*. Tropical and lower subtropical zone of the lower Cauca and lower Atrato Valleys southward along the Pacific coast to the río Dagua (1, *fannyi)*. Subtropical zone of both slopes of the Western Andes from the upper Dagua Valley and the mountains above Cali southward to Cerro Munchique (2, *subtropicalis)*. The lowlands of Nariño (2, *verticeps)*. Tropical zone east of the Eastern Andes from Meta southward to Putumayo (3, *viridipectus)*. Eastern Colombia from the Macarena Mts. southward to the Brazil-Venezuela border (3, *nigrofasciata)*. Extreme southeastern Colombia on the Amazon at Leticia *(simoni)*.

46. VIOLET-BELLIED HUMMINGBIRD
(Damophila julie)

Description. 3.2" (.6"). ♂ : Crown, throat, (or throat only, 1) glittering golden green. Upperparts shining golden green becoming more coppery on lower back and upper tail-coverts. Breast and belly glittering deep violet-blue. Tail, very rounded, steel blue. Lower mandible flesh color. ♀ : Above bronzy green; below dingy gray with glittering green disks on the throat. Tail steel blue, outer feathers pale tipped. Lower mandible flesh.

Range. Panama to western Ecuador.

Colombia. Forest. Tropical zone of northwestern Colombia east to the valley of the upper río Sinú (1, *panamensis)*. The Caribbean coast, the Cauca and Magdalena Valleys *(julie)*.

47. SAPPHIRE-THROATED HUMMINGBIRD
(Lepidopyga coeruleogularis)

Description. 3.5" (.7 - .8") . ♂ : Throat and upper breast glittering blue, abdomen shining green. Upperparts shining bronzy green. Tail forked, central tail-feathers coppery green, rest blue-black. Lower mandible flesh. ♀ : Upperparts including central tail-feathers bronze green, rest of tail-feathers blue-black tipped white. Below white, sides of breast and body coppery green.

Range. Costa Rica and Panama.

Colombia. Gardens and scrub. Extreme western Colombia near the mouth of the Atrato *(confinis)*. Mouth of the Magdalena river near Ciénaga Grande *(coelina)*.

48. SAPPHIRE-BELLIED HUMMINGBIRD
(Lepidopyga lilliae)

Description. 3.9" (.8"). ♂ : Throat and upper breast glittering purple-violet, lower breast and abdomen glittering blue. Sides of neck and breast shining blue-green. Above shining emerald green. Tail forked, steel blue. Lower mandible flesh. ♀ : Not known.

Range. Colombia.

Colombia. Mangroves. Restricted to the region east of the mouth of the Magdalena river near Ciénaga Grande.

49. SHINING-GREEN HUMMINGBIRD
(Lepidopyga goudoti)

Description. 3.3" (.8"). ♂ : Upperparts shining emerald green, crown bluer. Below glittering emerald green, bluer on throat (or glittering golden green, 1). Under tail-coverts green edged white. Tail forked, central feathers bronzy green, outer feathers blue-black. Lower mandible flesh. ♀ : Upperparts including central tail-feathers bronzy green, rest of tail-feathers blue-black; tail slightly forked. Throat and breast glittering green, the white bases of the feathers showing through, rest of underparts white.

Range. Northern Venezuela.

Colombia. Gardens and open woods. Tropical zone of the upper Magdalena Valley from northern Tolima to southern Huila *(goudoti)*. The lower Atrato Valley westward to the middle Magdalena Valley and the eastern Santa Marta region *(luminosa)*. East of the Andes in Norte de Santander, in the Zulia and Catatumbo Valleys (1, *zuliae*).

50. RUFOUS-THROATED SAPPHIRE
(Hylocharis sapphirina)

Description. 3.2 - 3.5″ (.8″). ♂ : Entire upperparts, lower breast and belly dark shining green. Throat chestnut, foreneck and upper chest glittering sapphire blue. Central tail-feathers and upper tail-coverts purple-bronze, outer tail-feathers purplish chestnut edged all around with black. Under tail-coverts chestnut. Bill flesh color, tip black. ♀ : Above lighter and bronzier green than males. Throat and under tail-coverts rusty, rest of underparts white with glittering blue disks on lower throat and upper chest. Tail like ♂ , but outer feathers pale tipped.

Range. Venezuela and the Guianas southward to eastern Peru, Brazil, northern Argentina and Paraguay.

Colombia. Scrub. Tropical zone east of the Eastern Andes, eastward to the Orinoco and southward to the río Guainía.

51. WHITE-CHINNED SAPPHIRE
(Hylocharis cyanus)

Description. 3.2″ (.7″). ♂ : Head, sides of neck, throat and breast glittering purple-blue, with a small patch of white in center of throat. Hindneck deep shining green gradually changing on back to bronzy on rump; upper tail-coverts dark plum color. Abdomen deep shining green. Tail and under tail-coverts steel blue. Bill flesh color. ♀ : Generally similar to the Rufous-throated Sapphire but tail steel blue instead of bronze. Chin and under tail-coverts white instead of rust.

Range. Venezuela and the Guianas southward to Peru, southeastern Brazil and Bolivia.

Colombia. Forest and plantations. Santa Marta region southward to the Zulia

Valley *(viridiventris)*. Extreme southeastern Colombia at Leticia on the Amazon *(rostrata)*.

52. BLUE-HEADED SAPPHIRE
(Hylocharis grayi)

Description. 3.5 - 3.8″ (.9″). ♂ : Head glittering sapphire blue. Upperparts shining bronzy green; underparts glittering golden green. Tail steel blue (or shining dark green, 1). Bill flesh color, tip black. ♀ : Shining bronze green above; underparts white thickly marked with shining bronze-green disks. Tail steel blue (or green, 1), outer feathers tipped white.

Range. Eastern Panama. Western Ecuador.

Colombia. Forest and scrub. Subtropical and semi-arid tropical zones of the Patía and Cauca Valleys and the arid portions of the upper Dagua Valley *(grayi)*. Lower tropical zone of the Pacific coast from the Baudó Mts. southward (1, *humboldtii*).

53. GOLDEN-TAILED SAPPHIRE
(Hylocharis oenone)

Description. 3.6 - 3.8″ (.8″). ♂ : Head, nape, throat and upper breast glittering violet (or crown glittering violet, throat and upper breast glittering greenish blue, 1). Back shining green, upper tail-coverts shining reddish copper. Underparts glittering green becoming golden green on abdomen. Tail shining golden copper both above and below. Lower mandible flesh. ♀ : Shining green above; upper tail-coverts and tail like ♂ but outer tail-feathers tipped grayish white. Below white with a few shining blue-green disks on sides of throat and breast. Lower mandible flesh.

Range. Venezuela southward through western South America to Ecuador, Peru and Bolivia. Trinidad.

Colombia. Gardens and forest. East slope of the Eastern Andes in the tropical zone from Boyacá southward along the base of the Andes *(oenone)*. Extreme southeastern Colombia at Leticia on the Amazon (1, *josephinae*).

[Species 53a, see Page 409.]

PLATE VI

(All birds shown are males unless otherwise noted)

SAPPHIRE-VENTED
PUFF-LEG
(Eriocnemis l. luciani)
Page 154

SWORD-BILLED
HUMMINGBIRD
(Ensifera ensifera)
Page 152

BLACK-TAILED
TRAIN-BEARER
(Lesbia v. victoriae)
Page 156

PERIJA METAL-TAIL
(Metallura iracunda)
Page 157

AMETHYST-THROATED
SUN-ANGEL
*(Heliangelus
amethysticollis clarisse)*
Page 153

PURPLE-CROWNED
FAIRY
(Heliothryx b. barroti)
Page 158

PURPLE-BACKED
THORN-BILL
*(Ramphomicron
m. microrhynchum)*
Page 156

RAINBOW-BEARDED
THORN-BILL
(Chalcostigma h. herrani)
Page 157

PURPLE-THROATED
WOODSTAR
(Philodice mitchellii)
Page 159

ANDEAN EMERALD
(Amazilia f. franciae)
Page 146

SPANGLED COQUETTE
(Lophornis stictolopha)
Page 139

GREEN THORNTAIL
(Popelairia conversii)
Page 140

144

E.L.Poole

54. WHITE-TAILED GOLDENTHROAT
(Polytmus guainumbi)

Description. 3.5 - 3.8″ (1″). ♂ : Entire upper surface shining golden bronze green. Throat, breast and upper abdomen glittering golden green; belly and under tail-coverts white. Tail rounded, central feathers bronze green, lateral ones bluish green, white on outer web for distal third, tip white. Bill curved, dull red. ♀ generally similar to ♂ but tail bronze green, the lateral feathers tipped white.

Range. Trinidad and Venezuela. Eastern South America to southern Brazil, Paraguay and eastern Bolivia.

Colombia. Scrub and savanna. Tropical zone. Meta *(doctus)*.

55. GREEN-TAILED GOLDENTHROAT
(Polytmus theresiae)

Description. 3.3 - 3.5″ (.8″). ♂ : Much like the White-tailed Goldenthroat but tail less rounded, shining bronze green above, shining blue-green below in strong contrast to golden green of underparts. Extreme base of tail white. Bill black. ♀ : Has only narrow white tip to tail-feathers. Otherwise like ♂.

Range. The Guianas, northern Brazil and eastern Peru.

Colombia. Scrub and savanna. The río Guainía region *(leucorrhous)*.

56. BUFFY HUMMINGBIRD
(Leucippus fallax)

Description. 3.5″ (.9″). Forecrown, sides of head and neck grayish brown, rest of upperparts including tail bronzy to olive green. Throat, breast and sides of body rusty buff; abdomen and under tail-coverts white. Central tail-feathers dull green, outer ones with a dark subterminal band, broadly tipped white. Maxilla flesh, black at tip, mandible black.

Range. Drier portions of coastal Venezuela and the islands off its coast.

Colombia. Mangroves and the arid portions of the eastern Santa Marta region and the Guajira Peninsula *(cervina)*.

57. VERSICOLORED EMERALD
(Amazilia versicolor)

Description. 3.2 - 3.4″ (.7″). Crown and upperparts shining grass green. Throat and upper breast white bordered all around by glittering bluish green; center of abdomen white. Flanks and upperparts bronzy green. Central tail-feathers dull bronzy olive, outer feathers with a broad subterminal dark bar.

Range. Venezuela and northwestern Brazil south to Paraguay and Bolivia.

Colombia. Savannas, clearings and forest. Tropical zone east of the Andes from Boyacá southward into Amazonian Colombia *(milleri)*.

58. GLITTERING-THROATED EMERALD
(Amazilia fimbriata)

Description. 3.5 - 3.8″ (1″). Above shining bronze green. Throat, breast and sides of body glittering blue-green (or golden green, 1). Center of lower breast and abdomen white. Central tail-feathers dark bronze-green (or bronzy black, 2), rest black.

Range. Venezuela and the Guianas south to Paraguay and Bolivia. Trinidad (?)

Colombia. Savanna and scrub. The extreme northern section of the eastern llanos along the río Arauca (2, *obscuricauda*). Boyacá and Cundinamarca (1, *apicalis*). Orinoco region *(fimbriata)*. Southeastern Colombia in Caquetá and Putumayo (1, *fluviatilis*). Extreme southeastern Colombia at Leticia on the Amazon *(1, laeta)*.

59. BLUE-CHESTED HUMMINGBIRD
(Amazilia amabilis)

Description. 3.5-3.7″ (.7″). ♂ : Crown and sides of throat glittering golden green; center of throat shining bronze; patch on breast glittering violet-blue, lower breast with green disks, rest of underparts gray. Back shining grass green, upper tail-coverts purplish bronzy, Central tail-feathers reddish bronze, outer ones steel blue. Lower mandible flesh color. ♀ like ♂ above, but crown shining green. Below dingy white with green disks on throat and breast. Tail as in ♂ but lateral feathers tipped white.

Range. Nicaragua southward to western Ecuador.

COLOMBIA. Forests, plantations and clearings. Tropical zone. Pacific coast and eastward across northern Colombia to the middle Magdalena (*amabilis*).

60. PURPLE-CHESTED HUMMINGBIRD
(Amazilia rosenbergi)

Description. 3.5-3.7″ (.7-.8″). ♂ : Crown and dorsal surface shining bronze green. Sides of neck, throat and upper breast glittering golden green, patch on breast glittering violet-blue. Rest of underparts grayish brown, with green disks on sides; under tail-coverts white. Central tail-feathers bronzy purplish, rest of tail-feathers blue-black. ♀ : Shining green above including central tail-feathers. Throat and breast white with green disks; abdomen gray; under tail-coverts white. Outer tail-feathers blue-black with white tips.

Range. Northwest Ecuador.

Colombia. Scrub. Tropical zone of Pacific Colombia, from the upper Atrato Valley southward.

61. ANDEAN EMERALD
(Amazilia franciae) Plate VI

Description. 3.5-3.7″ (.8-.9″). ♂ : Crown glittering blue (or green, 1). Back somewhat glittering, grass green (or coppery green, 1). Upper tail-coverts and tail coppery to coppery purple (or coppery to golden coppery green, 1). Sides of head, neck and breast glittering golden green becoming shining bronze on sides of body. Entire center of underparts white. ♀ similar but no glittering cap.

Range. Western Ecuador to northern Peru.

Colombia. Subtropical zone of the Western, Central and west slope of the Eastern Andes (*franciae*). Upper tropical zone of the Pacific slope of Nariño (1, *viridiceps*).

62. INDIGO-CAPPED HUMMINGBIRD
(Amazilia cyanifrons)

Description. 3.5-3.7″ (.7-.8″). ♂ : Cap glittering deep blue. Upperparts shining grass green; underparts glittering emerald green. Tail dull steel blue. ♀ similar but duller.

Range. Costa Rica.

Colombia. Forest. Tropical and subtropical zone. Southwestern Atlántico; slopes of the Central and Eastern Andes above the middle and upper Magdalena. East of the Andes in Norte de Santander (*cyanifrons*).

63. STEELY-VENTED HUMMINGBIRD
(Amazilia saucerottei)

Description. 3.4 - 3.6″ (.7″). Above shining green, upper tail-coverts dull purplish. Underparts glittering green. Under tail-coverts bright steel blue edged white (or bronzy grayish edged white, 1; or pale gray edged white, 2). Tail bright steel blue (or blue-black, 2). Lower mandible flesh color.

Range. Nicaragua and Costa Rica. Western Venezuela.

Colombia. Forest and scrub. Tropical zone of the Caribbean coast region, the northern portion of the Eastern Andes and the Magdalena Valley south to Tolima (*warscewiczi*). Upper tropical and subtropical zones in the semi-arid portions of the west slope of the Western Andes and the Patía Valley, to the west slope of the Central Andes (1, *saucerottei*). Interior valleys of Nariño west of the Andes in the subtropical zones (2, *australis*).

64. GREEN-BELLIED HUMMINGBIRD
(Amazilia viridigaster)

Description. 3.6-3.8″ (.7″). ♂ : Differs from *Amazilia saucerottei* in having the feathers of the rump and upper tail-coverts fringed buff and the tail shining purple. Under tail-coverts cinnamon. ♀ similar to ♂ but duller.

Range. Venezuela and British Guiana.

Colombia. Plantations, scrub and forest. Tropical zone of the eastern slope of the Eastern Andes from Meta northward (*viridigaster*).

65. RUFOUS-TAILED HUMMINGBIRD
(Amazilia tzacatl)

Description. 3.5-3.7″ (.8-.9″). ♂ : Upper parts shining bronzy green; throat and breast glittering green, lower breast and belly grayish. Upper and under tail-coverts and tail chestnut. Bill flesh color with black tip. ♀ similar but duller.

Range. Mexico to western Venezuela and western Ecuador.

Colombia. Plantations, scrub and forest. Tropical, occasionally subtropical zone. Across northern Colombia from the Pacific to Norte de Santander, south on the west to the Baudó Mts. *(tzacatl).* Pacific Colombia from the río San Juan southward. Gorgona Island *(jucunda).*

66. CHESTNUT-BELLIED HUMMINGBIRD
(Amazilia castaneiventris)

Description. 3.5-3.7″. Above shining reddish bronze, rump and upper tail-coverts grayish. Throat and breast glittering green, rest of underparts rich chestnut. Tail chestnut, tipped bronze.

Range. Colombia.

Colombia. Subtropical zone on the west slope of the Eastern Andes in Boyacá.

67. WHITE-VENTED PLUMELETEER
(Chalybura buffonii)

Description. ♂ 4.5″-♀ 4″ (1″). ♂ : Above shining green, bronzier on the tail-coverts. Underparts glittering green (or throat and sides of neck glittering green changing to glittering blue on breast and abdomen, 1). Under tail-coverts long, plume-like, snow white. Central tail-feathers blackish bronze (or steel blue, 1; or bronze green, 2), outer tail feathers for the most part blue-black. ♀ : Upperparts shining green; underparts dingy grayish. Outer tail-feathers broadly tipped white. Under tail-coverts like ♂ .

Range. From the Canal Zone to western Venezuela.

Colombia. Scrub and forest. Tropical zone of the Santa Marta Mts., up to at least 4,500 ft. on the west slope of the Perijá Mts. (2, *aeneicauda*). Tropical zone

of the middle Magdalena Valley and east of the Andes in the río Zulia region *(buffonii).* Tropical zone on the east slope of the Andes from Meta northward to western Arauca (1, *caeruleogaster*). Tropical zones at the head of the Magdalena Valley, Cauca Valley, west slope of the Western Andes south to the río Dagua *(micans).*

68. BRONZE-TAILED PLUMELETEER
(Chalybura urochrysia)

Description. ♂ 4.2 - ♀ 3.9″ (1 - 1.1″). ♂ : Above bronzy green, bronzy purple on rump and upper tail-coverts. Throat and breast glittering green (or glittering blue-green, 1); rest of underparts grayish. Under tail-coverts plume-like, snow white. Tail bronzy olive green. ♀ differs from White-vented Plumeleteer, principally in having the tail tipped with gray and the under tail-coverts gray like rest of underparts and not conspicuous.

Range. Nicaragua southward to western Ecuador.

Colombia. Forest and scrub. Tropical zone. The entire west coast eastward to east of the Gulf of Urabá and middle Magdalena Valley *(urochrysia).* A small area west of the Gulf of Urabá adjacent to the Panama border (1, *incognita*).

69. SPECKLED HUMMINGBIRD
(Adelomyia melanogenys)

Description. 3.3-3.6″ (.5-.6″). Upperparts bronzy, post-ocular streak white, cheeks blackish. Below buffy white (or bright buff, 1), speckled with dusky bronze on throat, sides of body tawny. Tail bronzy, all but central feathers tipped buff.

Range. Central Venezuela southward to Ecuador, Bolivia and northwestern Argentina.

Colombia. Forest and scrub. Subtropical zone of the Eastern Andes except at their southern end *(melanogenys).* The head of the Magdalena Valley *(connectens).* The subtropical zone of the Western and Central Andes (1, *cervina*). The upper subtropical zone of Nariño *(maculata).*

70. BLOSSOM-CROWN
(Anthocephala floriceps)
Description. 3.2-3.4″ (.6″). ♂ : Forehead and forecrown buffy white, hindcrown chestnut, spot behind eye white. Back shining green becoming bronzy on upper tail-coverts and central tail-feathers; lateral tail-feathers with basal half bronze and broad subterminal bar black, broad tips buff (or white, 1). Underparts grayish tinged buff on sides of throat, body and under tail-coverts. ♀ similar but crown bronzy green like the back. Young males have the crown dull chestnut.
Range. Colombia.
Colombia. Forest and patches of woods. Upper tropical and subtropical zone of the Santa Marta Mts. *(floriceps).* Central sections of the Central Andes on the east slope (1, *berlepschi*).

71. RUFOUS-VENTED WHITETIP
(Urosticte ruficrissa)
Description. ♂ 3.8 - ♀ 3.5″ (.7″). ♂ : Upperparts shining grass green. Throat, upper breast and sides of neck glittering emerald green, bordered below by an indistinct white line; rest of underparts shining green; under tail-coverts edged buff. Tail slightly forked, dusky bronze; central feathers much shorter than the rest broadly tipped white. ♀ : Shining green above; underparts white, thickly spangled on throat and breast with glittering green disks, on abdomen with shining green disks. Under tail-coverts buff. Tail bronzy, two outermost pairs of feathers tipped white.
Range. Eastern Ecuador, northeastern Peru.
Colombia. Forest and scrub. Subtropical zone. Head of the Magdalena Valley.

72. GREEN-VENTED WHITETIP
(Urosticte benjamini) Plate V
Description. ♂ 3.6- ♀ 3.3″ (.7-.8″). ♂ : Differs from the Rufous-vented Whitetip by being considerably smaller, by having a white post-ocular spot, a large shining purple patch on upper breast, and green under tail-coverts. ♀ : Differs by having the lores and spot behind the eye

white, and by smaller size.
Range. Western Ecuador. Northeastern Peru.
Colombia. Forest. Upper tropical and lower subtropical zones of the Pacific slope of the Western Andes from the río Munchique southward to Nariño *(benjamini).* Headwater of the río San Juan *(rostrata).*

73. GOULD'S JEWEL-FRONT
(Polyplancta aurescens)
Description. 4.8-5″ (.8″). ♂ : A broad line from base of bill and over center of crown glittering iridescent purple-blue; sides of crown and upperparts shining grass green. Lores and throat velvety black. Sides of head from behind eyes and sides of neck glittering golden green, becoming glittering green on chest. A broad band across the breast orange-rufous, rest of underparts shining green. Central tail-feathers bronze-green, rest chestnut, tipped bronze green. ♀ differs from the ♂ in being duller and lacking the glittering iridescent line on the crown.
Range. Southern Venezuela to western Brazil, eastern Ecuador and northeast Peru.
Colombia. Forest. Recorded only from Vaupés.

74. LILAC-THROATED BRILLIANT
(Heliodoxa rubinoides)
Description. 4.2-4.5″ (.9-1″). ♂ : Forehead, center of crown and chin glittering green. Upperparts bronze or coppery green, a white spot behind eye. A glittering violet (or rosy violet, 1) patch on center of throat, rest of underparts buffy rufescent with glittering green disks on upper throat, sides of neck, chest and upper abdomen. Central tail-feathers golden bronze, the lateral ones not as bright, and with pale buff shafts. ♀ resembles ♂ but lacks the brilliant gular patch.
Range. Ecuador and Peru.
Colombia. Forest and occasionally pastures and gardens. Subtropical zone from the west slope of the Eastern Andes to the east slope of the Western Andes *(rubinoides).* West slope of the Western Andes (1, *aequatorialis*).

75. VIOLET-FRONTED BRILLIANT
(Heliodoxa leadbeateri)

Description. ♂ 5.- ♀ 4.3″ (.9″) ♂ : Crown glittering blue to violet-blue, hindcrown and nape coppery golden; rest of upper surface bronze green. Chin, throat and breast glittering emerald green, rest of underparts shining bronze green. Tail forked, central feathers coppery, outer feathers black. ♀ : Forecrown shining blue-green; rest of upper surface like ♂ . Throat and breast with glittering golden green disks, shining green on abdomen. Tail not as deeply forked as in ♂ and outer feathers tipped white.

Range. Venezuela southward to Ecuador. Peru and Bolivia.

Colombia. Forest and scrub. Subtropical zone at the head of the Magdalena Valley and perhaps the upper Cauca Valley (*sagitta*). The east slope of the Eastern Andes from the Macarena Mts. northward (*parvula*).

76. GREEN-CROWNED BRILLIANT
(Heliodoxa jacula)

Description. ♂ 5- ♀ 4.3″ (.9″). ♂ : Crown, throat and breast glittering emerald green; large spot on lower throat glittering violet-blue, rest of underparts and upperparts bronze green. Tail forked, longer than in Blue-crowned Brilliant, the outer feathers deep blue, the central ones bronze. ♀ differs from the Blue-crowned Brilliant in having the crown and particularly the underparts greener, chin and throat whiter, the outer tail-feathers steel blue instead of black.

Range. Costa Rica to western Ecuador.

Colombia. Forest. Upper tropical zone. Known from the east slope of the mountains on the Panama border west of the Gulf of Urabá, the east slope of the Western Andes in Antioquia and the west slope of the Eastern Andes in northern Cundinamarca, and the east slope of the same range in Meta near Medina (*jacula*).

77. PINK-THROATED BRILLIANT
(Heliodoxa gularis)

Description. 4½″ (1.2″). ♂ : Shining dark grass green, above and below. Throat glittering rose lilac. Thighs and under tail-coverts white. Central tail-feathers like back, rest greenish bronze. ♀ : generally like ♂ but gape white, and patch on throat smaller.

Range. Eastern Ecuador, northeastern Peru.

Colombia. Recorded from Leticia, on the Amazon River.

78. EMPRESS BRILLIANT
(Heliodoxa imperatrix) Plate V

Description. ♂ 5.4 - 5.8″ ♀ 4.8 - 5″ (1″). ♂ : Feathers of forehead, extending over base of bill, throat and breast glittering emerald green; a glittering rosy violet gular spot. Lower breast and belly glittering pale golden olive green. Crown, back, upper tail-coverts shining bronze green. Tail long (2.1″), deeply forked, feathers rather narrow, dark shining blackish olive. ♀ : Shining bronze green above. Below white with golden green disks on throat, breast and belly. Tail greener than in ♂ , shorter and not as deeply forked. Young birds have the malar region chestnut-rufous.

Range. Western Ecuador.

Colombia. Forest. Subtropical zone of the west slope of the Western Andes from the headwaters of río San Juan southward through Nariño.

79. FIERY TOPAZ
(Topaza pyra) Plate V

Description. ♂ 7 - 7.5″ (1″) including lengthened tail-feathers, ♀ 5″ (1″). ♂ : Top of head, sides of neck prolonged into a broad band across chest purple-black with only a very slight gloss; nape purplish. Back, wing-coverts and belly glittering fiery orange-red. Chest shining golden red. Throat glittering golden green, golden copper in center. Upper and under tail-coverts and central tail-feathers shining golden green, rest of tail-feathers shining purple-black. The pair next to the central ones narrow, much elongated and crossed (3.8″). ♀ : Above bronzy green, grass green on crown. Upper and under tail-coverts emerald green. Throat glittering coppery red, surrounded by glittering gold, rest of underparts shining coppery green more golden on belly. Next to central pair of tail-feathers (slightly longer than rest) purple-blue, the rest in color like the ♂ except for dull cinnamon outer web to outermost tail-feather.

Range. Southwestern Venezuela, northwestern Brazil, westward to northeastern Peru and Ecuador.

Colombia. Forest. Río Vaupés region on the Brazilian frontier.

80. WHITE-TAILED HILLSTAR
(Urochroa bougueri)

Description. 4.4 - 4.6" (1.2 - 1.3"). Above shining reddish copper tinged green on lower back (or shining bronze-green becoming shining copper on upper tail-coverts, 1). Feathers of gape chestnut (or like sides of throat, 1). Chin, throat and upper breast glittering cornflower blue, edged green on sides of neck, rest of underparts dark gray with a few shining green disks. Central and outermost tail-feathers blackish green, rest mostly white broadly edged black on outer web (or central tail-feathers coppery olive, the rest white edged blackish on outer web, 1).

Range. Ecuador.

Colombia. Forest. Upper tropical and lower subtropical zones of the Pacific slope from the headwaters of the río San Juan southward through Nariño (bougueri). Subtropical zone on the east slope of the Andes in Nariño (1, leucura).

81. SHINING SUNBEAM
(Aglaeactis cupripennis)

Description. 4.5" (.8 - .9"). ♂: Crown, hindneck, center of back blackish with an olive gloss, lower back glittering violet-purple gradually passing through golden to golden green on upper tail-coverts. Indistinct collar on hindneck, entire underparts, shaft of outermost primary, orange-rufous; throat often spotted dusky. Wing-coverts and wing-feathers bronze. Central tail-feathers bronzy olive, rest bronzy on outer web, orange-rufous on inner web. ♀ similar but glittering patch on lower back much reduced.

Range. Temperate zone of the Andes of Ecuador to southern Peru.

Colombia. Open slopes. Upper temperate zone of all three ranges (cupripennis).

82. VELVET-BREAST
(Lafresnaya lafresnayi)

Description. 4" (1.2"). ♂: Bill curved. Entire upperparts shining grass green. Throat and upper breast glittering emerald green, lower breast and belly velvety black; under tail-coverts cream color (or white, 1) with shining green tips. Central tail-feathers shining golden olive, rest cream color (or white, 1) tipped bronze. ♀: Top of head dusky grayish, rest of upper surface shining green. Throat and breast buffy, finely spotted with green disks; rest of underparts buffy white. Tail and under tail-coverts as in ♂.

Range. Western Venezuela southward to central Peru.

Colombia. Forest and scrub. Santa Marta Mts. from the subtropical to temperate zone (liriope). Subtropical and temperate zone of the Eastern and Central Andes (lafresnayi). Temperate zone of the Western Andes and the southern end of the Central Andes (1, saúl).

83. PARAMO SAPPHIRE-WING
(Pterophanes cyanopterus)

Description. 6 - 6.4" (1.5"). ♂: Above and below dark, shining bluish green, bluer on underparts. Wing-coverts dark shining blue. Upper tail-coverts and tail shining olive. ♀ differs from ♂ by having the forehead and forecrown mouse gray; the underparts rufous-chestnut, with shining green disks on sides.

Range. Temperate zone of the Andes of Ecuador, Peru and northern Bolivia.

Colombia. Open slopes. Temperate zone of the Eastern Andes (cyanopterus). Temperate zone of the Central Andes southward over the east slope of the mountains in Nariño (caeruleus).

84. BRONZY INCA
(Coeligena coeligena)

Description. 4.4 - 4.7" (1.1 - 1.2"). Upperparts reddish bronze, each feather edged obscurely with green, most conspicuously on the back. Sides of head, lower breast and belly and under tail-coverts dull rufous (or pale grayish, 1; or dark grayish, 2). Feathers of throat dusky in the center margined white giving a scaly appearance. Upper tail-coverts and tail bronze, tail somewhat forked.

Range. Venezuela southward through the Andes to Bolivia.

Colombia. Wet forest. Subtropical zone of the Western Andes, the west slope of the Central Andes and the east slope at their northern end *(ferruginea)*. Subtropical zone of the Eastern Andes and the east slope of the middle portion of the Central Andes (1, *columbiana*). The Perijá Mts. (1, *zuliana*). The head of the Magdalena Valley (2, *obscura*).

85. BROWN INCA
(Coeligena wilsoni)

Description. 4 - 4.4″ (1.2 - 1.4″). A white patch on each side of the breast. Top of head shining reddish bronze gradually turning to shining olive green on the lower back. Throat glittering violet, chin and rest of underparts dull dark brown, tinged with rufous. Upper tail-coverts and tail bronzy, the latter pale tipped.

Range. Western Ecuador.

Colombia. Forest. Upper tropical and subtropical zone of the western slope of the Western Andes from the headwaters of the río San Juan southward through Nariño.

86. BLACK INCA
(Coeligena prunellei)

Description. 4 - 4.4″ (1.2″). A white patch on each side of breast. General color black, obscurely glossed with greenish on the head and golden purple on the lower back. Obscure glittering blue patch on throat. Lesser wing-coverts glittering blue. Tail and upper tail-coverts purple-black. Under tail-coverts dusky, edged with white.

Range. Colombia.

Colombia. Probably temperate zone of the Eastern Andes.

87. COLLARED INCA
(Coeligena torquata)

Description. 4.3 - 4.6″ (1.2 - 1.3). ♂ : Lower throat and breast white. Center of crown glittering purple-blue, throat dark shining green. Rest of plumage generally black becoming shining green on lower back, sides of body and wing-coverts. Upper tail-coverts and central tail-feathers blackish green, rest of tail-feathers white tipped black, most broadly on outer tail-feathers (or upper surface, throat and abdomen shining grass green, glittering on crown and throat. Upper tail-coverts and central tail-feathers golden green, rest white with golden green tips, 1). ♀ : Upper surface shining green. Throat and breast white, the throat with shining green disks. Belly gray with a few shining disks. Tail as in ♂.

Range. Venezuela southward to Ecuador and Peru.

Colombia. Forest and scrub. Subtropical and temperate zone of all three Andean ranges including Nariño *(torquata)*. Eastern slope of the Andes in Norte de Santander (1, *conradi*).

88. LILAC-SPOTTED STAR-FRONTLET
(Coeligena traviesi)

Description. 4.5″ (1.3″). ♂ : Above mostly black. Frontlet glittering bluish green; center of crown and wing-coverts shining dark greenish blue; rump and upper tail coverts shining coppery purple. Throat green, patch on lower throat glittering violet, a white patch on upper breast, rest of underparts glittering dark green. Tail bronze green, somewhat forked. Younger (?) males are shining dark green above without black, rump and tail coverts green.

Range. Colombia.

Colombia. Unknown. Known from a few "Bogota" specimens which are rather variable in appearance. Possibly a hybrid between *Coeligena torquata* and some other *Coeligena*.

89. WHITE-TAILED STAR-FRONTLET
(Coeligena phalerata) Plate V

Description. 4.1 - 4.4″ (1.1 - 1.2″). ♂ : Forehead and forecrown glittering green, changing to glittering blue posteriorly. Back and throat dark shining green; patch on lower throat glittering purple; breast glittering blue-green, belly shining green. Tail slightly forked, snowy white, sometimes stained with bronzy brown at tip. ♀ : Forecrown glittering green. Upperparts shining bronze green, tail-feathers bronzier, only the outer ones tipped buff. Under surface deep ochraceous.

Range. Colombia.

Colombia. Forest and open slopes. Santa Marta Mts. from 4,500 - 11,000 ft.

90. GOLDEN-BELLIED STAR-FRONTLET
(Coeligena bonapartei)

Description. 4.1 - 4.4″ (1.1 - 1.2″). ♂ : Forehead and forecrown, throat, sides of neck and breast glittering grass green, throat with a glittering violet-blue spot in center. Hindcrown and nape black shot with green; back shining emerald green; rump and upper tail-coverts, lower breast and belly glittering fiery gold. Tail somewhat forked, shining bronze. Wings uniform blackish (or with a patch of cinnamon on the secondaries, 1). ♀ : Above shining green, glittering fiery orange on upper tail-coverts. Throat and under tail-coverts cinnamon. Breast glittering grass green, abdomen glittering golden orange. Tail shining olive, the outer feathers tipped buff.

Range. Venezuela.

Colombia. Forest and scrub. Temperate zone of the west slope of the Eastern Andes *(bonapartei)*. The Perijá Mts. (1, *consita*).

91. DUSKY STAR-FRONTLET
(Coeligena orina)

Description. 4.2 - 4.5″ (1.2 - 1.3″). ♂ : Uniform dark shining green above and below, feathers of crown edged black. No glittering frontlet. Spot on throat glittering blue. Tail dark green without bronze sheen.

♀ : Not known.

Range. Colombia.

Colombia. Forest. Temperate zone at the northern end of the Western Andes.

92. BLUE-THROATED STAR-FRONTLET
(Coeligena helianthea)

Description. 4.2 - 4.5″ (1.2 - 1.3″). ♂ : Frontal patch glittering green. Sides of crown, hindcrown and nape deep velvety black becoming increasingly shot with shining green toward lower back. Upper tail-coverts glittering steely blue shot with purple. Throat dark shining green, large gular patch glittering purplish blue (or violet-blue, 1). Breast very dark blackish green. Belly glittering rosy violet. Tail forked, black with a bronzy gloss. ♀ : Shining grass green above. Upper tail-coverts and tail as in ♂. Throat cinnamon, breast paler with green disks; belly as in ♂.

Range. Extreme western Venezuela.

Colombia. Forest and scrub. Temperate zone of both slopes of the Eastern Andes from Bogotá northward *(helianthea)*. Páramo de Tamá, Norte de Santander (1, *tamae)*.

93. BUFF-WINGED STAR-FRONTLET
(Coeligena lutetiae)

Description. 4.2 - 4.5″ (1.2 - 1.3″). ♂ : Frontlet, throat and entire underparts glittering emerald green; spot on center of throat glittering blue. Top of head velvety black, back velvety black shot with green, upper tail-coverts bronzy purple. A cinnamon buff patch on tertials. Tail forked, blackish olive. ♀ : Shining green above. Throat cinnamon, rest of underparts shining golden green. Wings and tail like ♂.

Range. Both slopes of the Andes of Ecuador.

Colombia. Forest. Temperate zone on the west slope of the Central Andes southward into Nariño.

94. SWORD-BILLED HUMMINGBIRD
(Ensifera ensifera) Plate VI

Description. ♂ 5.8 - ♀ 4.8″ (3 - 3.8″). ♂ : Bill enormously long, somewhat upturned.

Head bronze, rest of upperparts bronzy green. Throat brownish black, some of feathers pale edged; underparts grass green. Tail forked, dark bronze green. ♀ differs from ♂ by having a white throat spotted with olive and the rest of the lower parts whitish, thickly sprinkled with green disks. Outer tail-feathers with pale outer web.

Range. The Andes of Ecuador, Peru and Bolivia.

Colombia. Scrub. Upper subtropical to temperate zone of all three ranges.

95. BUFF-TAILED CORONET
(*Boissonneaua flavescens*)

Description. 4.5 - 4.7″ (.6 - .7″). Crown and throat glittering green to golden green. Upperparts shining bronzy green to grass green. Breast shining green, belly buffy with green disks. Central tail-feathers bronze, rest of tail-feathers pale buff, tipped and edged with bronze green. Inner webs of tertials rufescent.

Range. Northern Venezuela to Ecuador.

Colombia. Forest. Upper subtropical to lower temperate zones of all three ranges (*flavescens*). Upper tropical zone of the Pacific slope of Nariño (*tinochlora*).

96. CHESTNUT-BREASTED CORONET
(*Boissonneaua matthewsii*)

Description. 4.4 - 4.7″ (.7″). ♂: Upper surface, throat and extreme upper breast glittering golden green. Breast and belly and under tail-coverts chestnut. Central tail-feathers bronze, rest chestnut, tipped and edged bronze. Tertials chestnut. ♀ similar, but throat with glittering green disks.

Range. Eastern Ecuador and Peru.

Colombia. Known only from the subtropical zone east of the Andes in southwestern Putumayo and eastern Nariño.

97. VELVET-PURPLE CORONET
(*Boissonneaua jardini*) Plate V

Description. 4.4 - 4.7″ (.7″). ♂: Most of head, neck and throat velvety black. Forecrown, upper throat, entire breast and belly glittering purple. Back and rump glittering bluish green. Under wing-coverts orange-rufous. Upper tail-coverts and central tail-feathers purple-black, rest of tail-feathers white, edged and tipped black. ♀: Generally similar to ♂ but duller sometimes with a chestnut patch on center of breast and with the buff bases of the feathers showing through on the breast and belly.

Range. Western Ecuador.

Colombia. Forest. Tropical to subtropical zone of the western slope of the Western Andes from the río San Juan southward to Nariño.

98. ORANGE-THROATED SUN-ANGEL
(*Heliangelus mavors*)

Description. 3.7″ (.7″). ♂: Forehead, throat and upper breast glittering golden orange, band across breast buff; rest of underparts buff with green disks. Entire upper surface shining green. Central tail-feathers golden green, rest bronzy tipped white. ♀ like ♂ but throat brownish black, the feathers edged rufous.

Range. Northern Venezuela.

Colombia. Forest and scrub. Upper subtropical and temperate zones of the eastern slope of the Eastern Andes at their northern end.

99. AMETHYST-THROATED SUN-ANGEL
(*Heliangelus amethysticollis*) Plate VI

Description. 3.7″ (.7″). ♂: Crown dark green (or purplish, 1), the feathers on point of forehead edged bright green (or bluish, 1). Back shining green. Chin, sides of head, sides of throat greenish black, throat glittering rosy amethyst (or amethyst, 1). Band across chest white, bordered below by a band of glittering green; rest of underparts mouse color with green disks; under tail-coverts white. Central tail-feathers shining green to bronzy green, rest of tail-feathers blue-black. ♀ like ♂ but throat dull black.

Range. Western Venezuela to Bolivia.

Colombia. Forest and scrub. Subtropical and temperate zones. The Eastern Andes at their northern end *(clarisse)*. The Perijá Mts. (1, *violiceps*), Páramo de Tamá in Norte de Santander (1, *verdiscutatus*).

100. GORGETED SUN-ANGEL
(Heliangelus strophianus)

Description. 3.7″ (.5″). ♂: Differs from the Amethyst-throated Sun-Angel only in having the tail steel blue, longer and forked instead of almost square. ♀ like the Amethyst-throated Sun-Angel but tail dark blue instead of bronzy.

Range. Western Ecuador.

Colombia. Mountains of southwestern Colombia, probably Nariño.

101. TOURMALINE SUN-ANGEL
(Heliangelus exortis)

Description. ♂ 4.6 ♀ 4.1″ (.6″). ♂: Frontal patch dark glittering green. General plumage dark shining green. Chin and upper throat glittering violet-blue, lower throat glittering rose red, chest glittering green. Tail forked, rather long, outer feathers black, central pair bronze green. ♀: Frontal patch glittering green. Entire upper surface including central tail-feathers bronzy green. Chin and throat white. Underparts shining green, the white bases of the feathers showing through. Tail shorter than in ♂ and not as deeply forked.

Range. Ecuador.

Colombia. Forest. Subtropical to temperate zone (rarely upper tropical) of all three ranges. The east slope of the Andes of Pasto at the headwaters of the río Putumayo.

102. GLOWING PUFF-LEG
(Eriocnemis vestitus)

Description. 3.4 - 3.6″ (.7 - .8″). ♂: Above shining dark green changing to glittering emerald green on rump and upper tail-coverts. Throat patch glittering purple surrounded by shining blackish green (or surrounded by glittering emerald green, 1). Lower breast and belly glittering emerald green; under tail-coverts glittering purple. Tail forked. Downy leg-puffs white. ♀

similar to ♂ above. Throat and underparts buffy, the former with purple disks, the rest with green disks. Under tail-coverts steel blue.

Range. Western Venezuela and Ecuador.

Colombia. Scrub. Temperate and lower páramo zone. The Eastern Andes *(vestitus)*. The northern extremity of the Western Andes (1, *paramillo*). The southern portion of the Central Andes south and eastward to southeastern Nariño *(smaragdinipectus)*.

103. TURQUOISE-THROATED PUFF-LEG
(Eriocnemis godini)

Description. 3.8″ (.8″). Above shining bronze green; rump and upper tail-coverts glittering green, under tail-coverts glittering purple. Under surface glittering emerald green, golden green on abdomen. Diffused gular patch glittering blue. Downy leg-puffs white. Tail forked, blue-black.

Range. Northern Ecuador.

Colombia. Probably the Central Andes. Known only from "Bogotá" specimens.

104. COPPERY-BELLIED PUFF-LEG
(Eriocnemis cupreo-ventris)

Description. 3.8″ (.7″). Above shining golden green, upper tail-coverts emerald green. Throat and breast glittering emerald green, belly glittering golden copper. Under tail-coverts glittering purple. Tail dark steel blue, somewhat forked. Downy leg-puffs white.

Range. Western Venezuela.

Colombia. Scrub. Subtropical and temperate zone. Both slopes of the Eastern Andes south to Cundinamarca.

105. SAPPHIRE-VENTED PUFF-LEG
(Eriocnemis luciani) Plate VI

Description. 4.5 - 4.8″ (.8 - .9″). Forecrown shining blue. Entire upper surface shining coppery green. Under surface glittering coppery green, under tail-coverts glittering purple. Tail steel blue, rather long, forked. Downy leg-puffs white.

Range. Ecuador to central Peru.

Colombia. Subtropical zone of the west slope of the Andes in southern Nariño (luciani).

106. GOLDEN-BREASTED PUFF-LEG
(Eriocnemis mosquera)

Description. 4.5 - 4.8" (.8"). Crown and throat shining emerald green. Upper surface shining golden green. Sides of neck and breast glittering golden copper; rest of underparts glittering coppery green. Tail forked, shining bluish green. Downy leg-puffs white.

Range. Northern Ecuador.

Colombia. Forest. Occasionally upper tropical, usually temperate zone of all three Andean ranges throughout.

107. EMERALD-BELLIED PUFF-LEG
(Eriocnemis alinae)

Description. 3.5" (.7"). Forehead glittering emerald green. Above shining coppery green. Throat and breast white, thickly sprinkled with glittering green disks turning to glittering blue in certain lights; belly and under tail-coverts glittering emerald green. Tail slightly forked, shining olive green. Downy leg-puffs white.

Range. Ecuador to central Peru.

Colombia. Upper subtropical to temperate zones of the Eastern Andes from Boyacá southward (alinae).

108. BLACK-THIGHED PUFF-LEG
(Eriocnemis derbyi)

Description. 3.8" (.9"). ♂ : Upper surface shining coppery green, rump glittering coppery violet; upper tail-coverts glittering emerald green. Under surface including under tail-coverts glittering golden green. Downy leg-puffs black. ♀ differs only by having white underparts, thickly marked with glittering golden green disks, and mostly white leg-puffs.

Range. Northern Ecuador.

Colombia. Temperate and páramo zones of the southern portion of the Central Andes and the Andes of Nariño (derbyi). The northern and central portion of the Central Andes (longirostris).

109. GREENISH PUFF-LEG
(Haplophaedia aureliae)

Description. 3.6 - 4" (.7"). Top of head coppery, rest of upper surface coppery green. Below coppery green, feathers fringed with grayish. Tail blue-black, very slightly forked. Leg-puffs white externally, pinkish buff internally.

Range. Eastern Panama southward through the Andes to northern Bolivia.

Colombia. Forest. Subtropical zone on both slopes of the Eastern Andes and the eastern slope of the Central Andes (aureliae). Upper tropical, rarely to the temperate zone on the slopes of the mountains above the Cauca Valley and the west slope of the Western Andes from the headwaters of the río San Juan south to the río Munchique (caucensis).

110. HOARY PUFF-LEG
(Haplophaedia lugens)

Description. 3.6 - 4" (.7"). Above similar to the Greenish Puff-Leg. Below grayish black, the feathers of the throat frosted with white. Tail steel blue. Leg-puffs white.

Range. Northwestern Ecuador.

Colombia. Forest. Upper tropical and subtropical zones and the Pacific slope of the mountains of Nariño.

111. RACQUET-TAILED HUMMINGBIRD
(Ocreatus underwoodii) Fig. 50

Description. ♂ 4.7 - 5" ♀ 3 - 3.2" (.5"). ♂ : Central tail-feathers shining green, elongated bare shaft (1") terminating in a large blue-black disk, rest of tail-feathers dark blue. Throat, upper breast glittering green, rest of plumage bronze green. Downy leg-puffs white. ♀ : Without long tail-feathers. Above bronze green, below white, spotted with green (or plain white, l). Tail like back, outer feathers tipped white.

Range. Northern Venezuela southward through the Andes to Bolivia.

Colombia. Forest clearings and scrub. Upper tropical to temperate zones of both slopes of the Eastern Andes except at their southern end *(underwoodii)*. The southern end of the Eastern Andes, the Central and Western Andes *(ambiguus)*. Upper tropical zone of the Pacific slope of Nariño (1, *melanantherus*).

112. BLACK-TAILED TRAIN-BEARER
(Lesbia victoriae) Plate VI

Description. Up to 10″ (.6″). ♂ : Above bronzy green, throat and upper chest glittering green. Below bronzy green, the buff bases of the feathers showing through. Tail elongated, much graduated, outer feathers much the longest (up to 6″ long). Tail-feathers black with terminal bronzy spots. Under tail-coverts buff. ♀ : Much shorter tail (up to 3.5″), outer feathers with pale outer web for the basal two-thirds. Above bronze green, below buffy white with glittering green disks on throat and bronzy disks on rest of underparts.

Range. Ecuador to southwestern Peru.

Colombia. Scrub and grassy slopes. Upper subtropical to temperate zone of the Eastern Andes. The mountains of western Nariño *(victoriae)*.

113. GREEN-TAILED TRAIN-BEARER
(Lesbia nuna)

Description. Up to 6.5″ (.4″). ♂ : Rather similar to the Black-tailed Train-bearer but considerably smaller and much greener, less bronzy. All but central tail-feathers shining emerald green instead of black with terminal bronze spots. ♀ differs from ♀ of the Black-tailed Train-bearer in the same manner as ♂.

Range. Northern Venezuela. The Andes of Ecuador to northern Bolivia.

Colombia. Subtropical and temperate zones. Recorded from the immediate vicinity of Bogotá, the extreme upper Cauca Valley, and east of the Andes at the headwaters of the Putumayo *(gouldii)*.

114. PURPLE-BACKED THORN-BILL
(Ramphomicron microrhynchum)
Plate VI

Description. 3.6 - 3.8″ (.2″). ♂ : Above shining deep purple. Throat and upper breast glittering golden green, rest of underparts bronzy green. Tail purple-black.

Noteworthy is its very small bill. ♀ : Above shining grass green, upper tail-coverts bronze, under tail-coverts chestnut. Under surface buffy white with shining green disks. Outer tail-feathers purple-black, tipped white.

Range. Western Venezuela to central Peru.

Colombia. Forest and bushy hillsides. Subtropical to temperate zones of all three ranges. Not recorded from Nariño *(microrhynchum)*.

115. BLACK-BACKED THORN-BILL
(Ramphomicron dorsale)

Description. 3.8 - 4″ (.3″). ♂ : Forecrown obscurely green. Upper surface including tail black, upper tail-coverts purple. Throat glittering golden olive, rest of under surface dull bronze green. ♀ very similar to the Purple-backed Thorn-bill but with fewer green disks below.

Range. Colombia.

Colombia. Open woods and grassy slopes. Temperate and páramo zones of the Santa Marta Mts. Probably found at much lower altitudes in winter.

116. VIRIDIAN METAL-TAIL
(Metallura williami)

Description. 3.6 - 3.9″ (.5″). ♂ : General plumage shining green, glittering on the throat. Tail shining purple in certain lights, in others greenish purple; under surface of tail rich purple (or bright bronzy green, 1). ♀ similar to ♂ above. Below rufous-buff, thickly spotted with green disks.

Range. Ecuador.

Colombia. Open slopes. Subtropical to lower páramo zones of both slopes of the Central Andes *(williami)*. Temperate zone of the Andes of Nariño (1, *primolina*).

117. TYRIAN METAL-TAIL
(Metallura tyrianthina)

Description. ♂ 3.9″ ♀ 3.4″ (.4″). ♂ : Throat glittering emerald green, rest of plumage bronzy green. Tail shining golden violet-purple (or shining purple, 1). ♀ like ♂ but throat and breast tawny ochraceous, whiter on belly with a few bronzy spots. Tail tipped white.

Range. Venezuela south through the Andes to Bolivia.

Colombia. Forest, open slopes, and brush lands. Santa Marta Mts. and the Sierra de Perijá from the upper tropical to the temperate zone (1, *districta*). Upper tropical to the lower páramo zones of the rest of Colombia *(tyrianthina)*.

118. PERIJA METAL-TAIL
(Metallura iracunda) Plate VI

Description. 4 - 4.2″ (.4″). ♂ : Above and below black with strong bronze green reflections in certain lights. Throat glittering emerald green. Tail brilliant bronzy purple-violet. ♀ : Tail coppery violet, back dusky green, below buffy.

Range. Western Venezuela.

Colombia. Subtropical and temperate zones of the Perijá Mts.

119. BRONZE-TAILED THORN-BILL
(Chalcostigma heteropogon)

Description. 4.8″ (.5″). ♂ : Crown shining green becoming bronzier on the back, turning to bronze purple on rump and upper tail-coverts. Throat glittering emerald green terminating in a glittering violet point on chest; rest of lower surface dull olive. Tail forked, bronze. ♀ similar to ♂ but throat with glittering green disks and no violet on chest.

Range. Western Venezuela.

Colombia. Temperate and páramo zone of the Eastern Andes southward to Cundinamarca.

120. RAINBOW-BEARDED THORN-BILL
(Chalcostigma herrani) Plate VI

Description. 4.5 - 4.8″ (.4″). ♂ : Center of crown narrowing to a line on the nape, chestnut. Sides of crown and upper surface shining bronzy green, blackish in certain lights turning to purple on lower back and upper tail-coverts. Throat glittering green, changing from violet-blue through green to fiery orange red, narrowing to a stripe on breast, where bordered with black. Tail purple, outer feathers broadly tipped white. ♀ similar

to ♂ but without markings on the throat.

Range. Northern Ecuador.

Colombia. Forest and brush country. Temperate and páramo zones of the Central Andes *(tolimae)*. Temperate zones of the southern end of the Western Andes and Nariño *(herrani)*.

121. BEARDED HELMET-CREST
(Oxypogon guerinii) Plate V

Description. 4.8 - 5″ (.3″). ♂ : Top and sides of head brownish black. A long thin white crest. Sides of throat and neck and elongated feathers springing from lower throat white, elongated feathers on center of throat glittering emerald green, changing to glittering blue-green on lower throat and breast (or feathers of center of throat glittering purple-blue, 1; or glittering orange-purple, 2) . Upper surface shining olive; below whitish with olive disks. Central tail-feathers shining olive, rest of tail-feathers white in center, surrounded by shining olive. ♀ : Shining green above, white below with bronze disks. Tail as in ♂ .

Range. Western Venezuela.

Colombia. Bushy slopes. Temperate and páramo zones of the Eastern Andes *(guerinii)*. Páramo zone, 11,000 - 16,000 ft., of the Santa Marta Mts. (1, *cyanolaemus*). Páramo zone of the Central Andes (2, *stübelii*).

122. AVOCET-BILL
(Opisthoprora euryptera)

Description. 4 - 4.2″ (.5″). Bill upturned at tip. Crown and sides of head shining bronze, spot behind eye white. Upper surface shining green; below shining bronze green, the feathers of throat and breast edged white, those of flanks and abdomen edged pale rufous. Central tail-feathers bronze green, remainder steel blue, narrowly tipped white.

Range. Northern Ecuador.

Colombia. Upper temperate zone of the Central Andes. Probably occurs in the mountains of Nariño. Known also from "Bogotá" and "Popayán."

123. BLUE-THROATED SYLPH
(Aglaiocercus kingi)

Description. ♂. Up to 8". ♀. 3.7 - 3.9" (.5"). ♂: Crown glittering emerald green. Back shining green. Below shining bronzy green, small patch in center of throat glittering violet-blue. Tail very long, graduated, outermost pair much the longest, shining purple, all but outer pair tipped with shining peacock blue (or base of tail-feathers purple-black, distal third glittering blue-green, 1). ♀: Crown and rump shining blue-green, rest of back bronze green. Below buffy, palest on throat where marked with bronze disks. Tail not elongated, slightly forked, central feathers shining blue-green, outermost blue-black, tipped white.

Range. Venezuela southward to Ecuador, Peru and northern Bolivia.

Colombia. Forest and scrub. Both slopes of the Eastern Andes in the subtropical zone from Norte de Santander, southward to the Bogotá region *(kingi)*. Subtropical and temperate zones of the southern portion of the Eastern and Central Andes and the extreme upper Cauca Valley (1, *mocoa)*.

124. GREEN-THROATED SYLPH
(Aglaiocercus emmae)

Description. ♂. Up to 8". ♀. 3.7 - 3.9" (.5"). ♂: Very similar to the Blue-throated Sylph but no violet-blue throat spot. Tail glittering emerald green (or purple-blue as in *kingi*, 1). ♀: Distinguishable from the ♀ of *kingi* by having the throat much more heavily marked with green disks and the center of breast and belly cinnamon, rather than pale buff.

Range. Western Ecuador.

Colombia. Forest and scrub. Subtropical zone of the northern portion of both slopes of the Eastern Andes in Norte de Santander, Santander and Magdalena (1, *caudatus)*. Subtropical and lower temperate zones of the Central and Western Andes, southward to Nariño *(emmae)*.

125. VIOLET-TAILED SYLPH
(Aglaiocercus coelestis) Plate V

Description. ♂. Up to 8". ♀. 3.7 - 3.9"

(.6 - .7"). ♂: Distinguishable from *kingi* by very much larger violet-blue throat patch, lower back strongly tinged blue. Tail mainly shining violet with almost glittering green tips to all but outer tail-feathers. ♀: Distinguishable from the other two species by shining blue crown and white chest sharply defined from rufous underparts.

Range. Western Ecuador.

Colombia. Forest and scrub. Upper tropical and subtropical zones of the Pacific slope of the Western Andes from the upper río San Juan, southward to Cerro Munchique *(pseudocoelestis)*. Western Nariño *(coelestis)*.

126. WEDGE-BILLED HUMMINGBIRD
(Schistes geoffroyi)

Description. 3.3 - 3.5" (.6"). ♂: Crown and center of throat glittering emerald green. A tuft on each side of neck glittering violet; a patch on each side of breast white (or forming a collar across breast, 1). Underparts bronze green. Upper back shining green, lower back and upper tail-coverts reddish bronze (or entire back shining green, 1). Central tail-feathers bronze green, outer tail-feathers bronze green with a broad median blue band, and a narrow white or greenish tip. ♀ like ♂ but throat dull green, and purple patch on sides of chest reduced (or differs from ♂ by having the throat white and the purple patches on sides of throat replaced by blue-green, 1).

Range. Northern Venezuela southward to Bolivia.

Colombia. Forest. Upper tropical and subtropical zones of the west slope of the Eastern Andes and the east slope of the Central Andes at the head of the Magdalena Valley *(geoffroyi)*. Western slope of the Central Andes and both slopes of the Western Andes, southward into Nariño (1, *albogularis)*.

127. PURPLE-CROWNED FAIRY
(Heliothryx barroti) Plate VI

Description. 4.7" (.6 - .7"). ♂: Crown glittering violet. Broad streak below eye black terminating in glittering violet on sides of neck. Entire upper surface shining grass green; entire under surface white. Central tail-feathers black, remainder white. ♀ like ♂ but without purple cap; throat and upper breast with a few indistinct grayish spots.

Range. Guatemala to western Ecuador.

Colombia. Forest and scrub. The Pacific coast. From the Gulf of Urabá eastward through the lower Cauca and upper Sinú Valleys to the middle Magdalena Valley *(barroti)*.

128. BLACK-EARED FAIRY
(Heliothryx aurita)

Description. 4.6 - 5″ (.8″). ♂: Similar to the Purple-crowned Fairy but crown glittering green instead of purple. ♀: Similar to Purple-crowned Fairy differing only in having the throat and breast conspicuously spotted with gray.

Range. Venezuela and the Guianas southward to southern Brazil, Ecuador, Peru and Bolivia.

Colombia. Forest and scrub. Tropical zone east of the Eastern Andes *(aurita)*.

129. LONG-BILLED STARTHROAT
(Heliomaster longirostris)

Description. 4″ (1.5″). ♂: Crown glittering blue-green. Throat glittering violet-red (or purple, 1). Moustacial streak and center of belly white; rest of underparts bronzy grayish, under tail-coverts blackish broadly tipped white. Upperparts bronzy green. Central tail-feathers bluish bronze (or coppery bronze, 1) outer tail-feathers black, outermost tipped white. ♀: Crown like back. Moustacial streak wider than in ♂. Throat like ♂ but feathers edged with white. Otherwise like ♂.

Range. Mexico southward through Central America to Venezuela, British and French Guiana, eastern Brazil, Ecuador, Peru, northern Bolivia and Mato Grosso. Trinidad.

Colombia. Forest and scrub. Tropical and subtropical zones. East of the Eastern Andes *(longirostris)*. West of the Eastern Andes (1, *stuartae*).

130. BLUE-TUFTED STARTHROAT
(Heliomaster furcifer)

Description. 5″ (1.3″). ♂: Shining bronze green above glittering on crown and middle of back. Glittering blue tufts projecting from sides of neck. Throat glittering rosy red, rest of underparts glittering blue. Tail forked, steely green. ♀: Bronzy green above, below grayish white with dusky disks on throat. Tail forked, bronzy, outer tail-feathers tipped white.

Range. Central and southern Brazil southward to Bolivia, Uruguay, Argentina.

Colombia. Recorded from Leticia, on the Amazon River.

131. PURPLE-THROATED WOODSTAR
(Philodice mitchellii) Plate VI

Description. 3 - 3.3″ (.5″). ♂: Above bronze green, throat glittering violet, bordered below by a broad white collar. Sides of body bronzy, center of abdomen gray, flanks chestnut. Tail purplish black, rather long, forked, feathers narrow. ♀ like ♂ but throat white, abdomen rufous-chestnut. Tail normal, basally rufous, followed by a broad black band, and tipped rufous.

Range. Western Ecuador.

Colombia. Forest and pastures. Tropical and lower subtropical zones of both slopes of the Western Andes and western Nariño.

132. AMETHYST WOODSTAR
(Calliphlox amethystina)

Description. ♂. 3.5″ ♀: 3″. (.7″). ♂: Above shining olive green. Throat glittering rosy red, patch on chest white, rest of underparts dull grayish green. Central tail-feathers shining olive, outer tail-feathers twice as long as central ones, dusky violet, tipped green. ♀: Above olive green, below grayish washed rufous on sides. Central tail-feathers like back, outer ones black tipped white.

Range. The Guianas, Venezuela, eastern Ecuador, Peru and most of Brazil.

Colombia. Known only from Bogotá trade skins but undoubtedly occurs in Amazonian Colombia.

PLATE VII

GRAY-CHEEKED
NUNLET
(*Nonnula rufi-
capilla frontalis*)
Page 177

WHITE-TAILED TROGO
(*Trogon viridis chionurus*
Page 164

BLUE-CROWNED
MOTMOT
(*Momotus mo-
mota aequatorialis*)
Page 169

RED-HEADED BARBET
(*Capito bourcierii orientalis*)
Page 180

RUFOUS-TAILED
JACAMAR
(*Galbula r. ruficauda*)
Page 172

TOUCAN BARBET
(*Semnornis r. ramphastinus*)
Page 180

PAVONINE QUETZAL
(*Pharomachrus pav-
oninus auriceps*)
Page 163

RUFOUS-BREASTED
PICULET
(*Picumnus r. rufiventris*)
Page 188

GREAT JACAMAR
(*Jacamerops a. aurea*, ♀)
Page 172

CRIMSON-BACKED
WOODPECKER
(*Piculus r. rivolii*)
Page 189

BARRED PUFFBIRD
(*Nystalus radiatus*)
Page 174

BLACK-CHEEKED
WOODPECKER
(*Melanerpes p. pucherani*)
Page 193

E.L.Poole

133. WHITE-BELLIED WOODSTAR
(Acestrura mulsanti)

Description. 3″ (.6 - .7″). ♂ : Upperparts and sides of body shining grass green. Throat glittering reddish violet, streak behind eye and underparts, except sides, white. Tail short, black, forked, outer feathers very narrow, hair-like. ♀ : Above bronzy green. Post-ocular streak white, broad band below eye blackish. Throat and breast buffy white, belly and under tail-coverts chestnut. Tail very short, black, broadly tipped chestnut.

Range. The Andes from Ecuador to Bolivia.

Colombia. Forest and scrub. Subtropical and lower temperate zones of the Central and the Eastern Andes from Cundinamarca southward to the Andes of Nariño.

134. GORGETED WOODSTAR
(Acestrura heliodor)

Description. 2.6 - 2.8″ (.5″). ♂ : Upper surface and sides of body dark shining green (or crown green, back blue-green, rump blue, 1). Throat glittering reddish violet, the feathers prolonged into tufts on the side of the neck. Breast dark gray. Patch on flanks white. Tail black, feathers narrow, outermost hair-like and much the shortest. ♀ : Very similar to the White-bellied Woodstar but more uniform buff below and with upper tail-coverts rufous.

Range. Western Venezuela to northern Ecuador.

Colombia. Forest and scrub. Subtropical zone of the Santa Marta Mts. (1, *astreans*). Subtropical zone of the Eastern and Central Andes *(heliodor)*. Acestrura harterti described from the Central Andes is considered to be a hybrid.

135. RUFOUS-SHAFTED WOODSTAR
(Chaetocercus jourdanii)

Description. 2.6 - 2.8″ (.5 - .6″). ♂ : Very similar to the Gorgeted Woodstar. Differs by glittering rose instead of violet throat; no white post-ocular streak; paler, whitish chest; hidden rufous base to tail. ♀ very similar to ♀ of the Gorgeted Woodstar but the upper tail-coverts are green instead of rufous.

Range. Venezuela. Trinidad.

Colombia. Forest and scrub. Upper tropical and subtropical zones of the northern portion of the Eastern Andes in Santander *(andinus)*.

TROGONS (Trogonidae)

Fig. 51. Collared Trogon
(*Trogon collaris*) p. 164

Trogons can be counted among the most beautiful of birds. From 9 to 14 inches in length (excluding the "long-tailed" Central American form* which does not occur in Colombia), males are shining emerald green or violet-blue above, red or yellow below. In females the green or blue sometimes is replaced by brown or gray. The tail is rather long, the feathers wide, graduated and square at the tip. The legs are very short, the feet weak and quite unsuited for terrestrial locomotion.

Trogons are usually found living singly or in pairs in dense forest. They are rather sluggish and if not disturbed often sit quietly without moving. They feed on fruit and insects and nest in cavities of decayed trees.

In addition to the American species, eleven are found in tropical Asia and three in Africa. (13 Col.; 14 S.A.; 22 N.&S.A.; 36 wld.)

AID TO IDENTIFICATION

Head, upperparts and breast green, belly red 1, 2, 3E, 4, 5, (with a white band across breast) 6, 8, 9, 10, 12E.
Head, upperparts and breast green or blue, lower breast and belly yellow 7, 11, 13.
Head, lower breast and belly gray, back and pectoral band green 1, 2, 3E.
Head, breast and back gray 4, 5, 6, 7, 11, 12E, 13.
Head, breast and back brown 8, 9, 10.

1. QUETZAL
(*Pharomachrus mocinno*)

Description. 12 - 13″. ♂: Short crest springing from forehead, pointing forward over base of bill, top and sides of head golden green. Upper surface including wing-coverts and lengthened upper tail-coverts, which are as long as the tail, shining metallic emerald green. Breast like *Pharomacrus m. mocinno.*

back, rest of under suface crimson. Three outermost tail-feathers entirely white, the rest black. ♀: Back as in ♂. Head, throat and underparts brownish gray except for green band across breast and pink belly and under tail-coverts. Tail black, two outermost feathers notched with white on outer web.

Range. Southern Mexico, southward to

162

western Panama. Venezuela, Ecuador, Peru and Bolivia.

Colombia. Forest. Subtropical zone from the eastern slope of the Western to the eastern slope of the Eastern Andes in Meta *(antisianus)*.

2. WHITE-TIPPED QUETZAL
(Pharomachrus fulgidus)

Description. 12 - 13″. ♂: No frontal crest. Very similar to the Quetzal, differing principally by having the three outer tail-feathers black, broadly tipped white. ♀: Much like No. 1 but head bronzy green with no frontal crest.

Range. The mountains of central and northern Venezuela. Possibly Ecuador and British Guiana.

Colombia. Forest. Subtropical zone. Probably the north portion of the Eastern Andes *(fulgidus)*. The Santa Marta Mts. *(festatus)*.

3. PAVONINE QUETZAL
(Pharomachrus pavoninus) Plate VII

Description. 13½ - 14½″. ♂: No frontal crest. Best distinguished from the above two by the tail being entirely black in both sexes. ♀ further differs in having the lower breast and belly pinkish crimson.

Range. Venezuela, northwestern Brazil, Ecuador, Peru and northern Bolivia.

Colombia. Forest. Subtropical zone east of the Eastern Andes *(hargitti);* tropical zone in Caquetá and Vaupés *(pavoninus)*. Upper tropical and subtropical zones west of the Eastern Andes and the subtropical zone of the east slope of the Eastern Andes in Nariño *(auriceps)*.

4. SLATY-TAILED TROGON
(Trogon massena)

Description. 11½-12″. ♂: Wing-coverts and inner secondaries finely vermiculated black and white. Sides of head and throat black. Entire upper surface and breast shining metallic blue-green, bluer on upper tail-coverts. Central tail-feathers bronzy green with a diffused black tip; outer tail-feathers and underside of tail

black. ♀: Entire head, breast, upper surface, wings and tail rather dark gray. Tail edged and tipped white in immature birds. Lower breast, belly and under tail-coverts carmine. Wing-coverts uniform gray.

Range. Southern Mexico to northwestern Ecuador.

Colombia. Tropical zone of northwestern Colombia *(hoffmanni)*. Tropical zone of the Pacific coast from the upper río San Juan southward *(australis)*.

5. BLUE-TAILED TROGON
(Trogon comptus)

Description. 10-11″. ♂: Distinguishable from the Slaty-tailed Trogon by somewhat bluer crown, breast and back, peacock blue rump, upper tail-coverts and central tail-feathers, the latter with a sharply defined black terminal band. ♀: Not distinguishable in the field from ♀ of the Slaty-tailed Trogon. Differs by the gray portions of the plumage being somewhat darker. Wing-coverts uniform gray.

Range. Colombia.

Colombia. Forest. Tropical zone. The lower Cauca Valley, and from the upper Atrato Valley southward to Nariño.

6. BLACK-TAILED TROGON
(Trogon melanurus)

Description. 11½-12½″. ♂: Best distinguished from the last two by having the green on the breast separated from the red underparts by a narrow white band. Terminal black band on central tail-feathers sharply defined. ♀ differs from the last two by having the wing-coverts obscurely vermiculated, and the lower breast paler gray.

Range. From the Panama Canal Zone southward to Venezuela, the Guianas, Brazil, eastern and western Ecuador, Peru and Bolivia.

Colombia. Forest. Tropical zone. Río Guainía region *(melanurus)*. Near the base of the Eastern Andes in Meta and Caquetá *(eumorphus)*. Tropical and subtropical zones of the Magdalena Valley, the Cauca Valley and the valley of the Atrato *(macrourus)*.

7. WHITE-TAILED TROGON
(*Trogon viridis*) Plate VII

Description. 10". ♂: Crown, hindneck and breast shining violet-blue. Throat, cheeks and wings black. Lower breast, belly and under tail-coverts orange-yellow. Back shining blue-green shading to peacock blue on upper tail-coverts. Outer tail-feathers black, diagonally tipped white (or mostly white, 1), central tail-feathers blue-green. ♀: Mostly gray. Belly and under tail-coverts orange-yellow, wing-coverts narrowly barred with white. Outer tail-feathers notched with white, tipped white.

Range. From Costa Rica southward to Venezuela, the Guianas, Brazil, Paraguay, Argentina, Ecuador, Peru and Bolivia. Trinidad.

Colombia. Forest and scrub. Tropical zone east of the Eastern Andes (*viridis*). Tropical and subtropical zones of the Pacific coast, south to the Baudó Mts. and across northern Colombia to the Santa Marta region and southward down the Magdalena Valley (1, *chionurus*).

8. COLLARED TROGON
(*Trogon collaris*) Fig. 51

Description. 9½-10". ♂: Entire upper surface, breast and central tail-feathers shining coppery green. Face and throat black. Wing-coverts and inner secondaries finely vermiculated black and white. A broad white band separating the green of the breast from the carmine rose of the rest of the underparts. Outer tail-feathers coarsely barred black and white, tip white. ♀: Entire upper surface and breast sandy brown to tobacco brown, wing-coverts very finely vermiculated with black. Eye-ring and breast band white. Lower breast, belly and under tail-coverts pale rose. Central tail-feathers hazel (or chestnut, 1), tipped black. Outermost tail-feathers marbled, black and white with a subterminal black bar and white tip.

Range. Mexico southward through Central America to Venezuela, the Guianas, Bolivia and southeastern Brazil. Trinidad and Tobago.

Colombia. Forest. The western slope of the Western Andes in the tropical and subtropical zones (*virginalis*). Subtropical zone of central Colombia from the east slope of the Western Andes to the west slope of the Eastern Andes (*subtropicalis*). The tropical zone of the eastern slope of the Eastern Andes from Meta northward (*exoptatus*). Tropical zone at the eastern base of the Eastern Andes from Caquetá southward and eastward (*collaris*). Extreme southern tip of Colombia at Leticia on the Amazon (1, *castaneus*).

9. MASKED TROGON
(*Trogon personatus*)

Description. 9½-10". ♂: Very similar to *T. collaris*, best differentiated by the outermost tail-feathers being black, barred sometimes obscurely, with wavy white lines and tipped with white. ♀ differs from the ♀ of *T. collaris* by having the outer tail-feathers finely barred black and white; tip white.

Range. Western Venezuela through the mountains of western South America to Bolivia. Mt. Duida, Mt. Roraima, Mt. Auyantepui in eastern Venezuela.

Colombia. Humid forest. Subtropical zone of the Santa Marta Mts. (*sanctaemartae*). Upper tropical and subtropical zones of the Eastern and Central Andes and the eastern slope of Nariño (*personatus*). Subtropical and temperate zones of the Western Andes south into western Nariño (*assimilis*).

10. HIGHLAND TROGON
(*Trogon temperatus*)

Description. 9½-10". ♂: Differs from the Masked Trogon only in having the bill much smaller and the under surface of the outer tail-feathers always very obscurely marked with wavy white lines. ♀ differs from ♀ of the Masked Trogon in having the brown portions of the plumage more rufescent, and the bill much smaller.

Range. Colombia southward to Ecuador, Peru and Bolivia.

Colombia. Forest. Subtropical to temperate zones of the Central and Eastern Andes, southward into Nariño.

11. BLACK-THROATED TROGON
(Trogon rufus)

Description. 9½-10″. ♂: Upperparts and breast shining coppery green to bluish green. Underparts lemon yellow, separated from green of breast by an indistinct white band. Tail golden coppery (or metallic green to bluish green, 1). Outer tail-feathers barred black and white, tipped white. ♀: Very similar to ♀ of the White-tailed Trogon except the lower breast and belly and under tail-coverts are pale yellow; the outer tail-feathers barred black and white.

Range. Honduras southward through Central America to Venezuela, the Guianas, southern Brazil, Paraguay, Argentina and Bolivia.

Colombia. Forest. Tropical zone. Extreme northwestern Colombia (tenellus). The Pacific coast except extreme northwest and eastward across the lower Cauca to the middle Magdalena Valley (cupreicauda). The eastern base of the Eastern Andes from southern Meta eastward and southward (1, sulphureus).

12. BLUE-CROWNED TROGON
(Trogon curucui)

Description. 9 - 9½″. ♂: Top of head and breast shining violet blue-green; bar across breast white, rest of lower parts carmine rose. Back shining coppery green shading to blue-green on upper tail-coverts. Central tail-feathers blue-green, outer tail-feathers barred black and white. ♀: Upperparts, throat and breast gray. Lower breast grayish white; belly and under tail-coverts carmine rose. Wing-coverts and inner remiges black with narrow white bars. Outer tail-feathers barred black and white on outer web.

Range. Eastern Ecuador, the upper and middle Amazon, southward to Bolivia. Paraguay, Uruguay and southeastern Brazil.

Colombia. Tropical zone east of the Eastern Andes from Meta southward (peruvianus).

13. VIOLACEOUS TROGON
(Trogon violaceus)

Description. 8-8½″. ♂: Head and upper breast dark violet-blue (or top of head black, 1). Back shining blue-green, upper tail-coverts and tail peacock blue. Wing-coverts and inner remiges finely vermiculated black and white. Lower breast, belly and under tail-coverts orange yellow. Outer tail-feathers basally black, distally white barred with black, and with white tips. ♀: Dark gray, lower breast, belly and under tail-coverts yellow. Wing-coverts and inner remiges black with narrow white bars. Outer webs of outer tail-feathers barred black and white.

Range. Mexico south to western Ecuador and east of the Andes from Venezuela and the Guianas southward to the Amazon, Ecuador and Peru. Trinidad.

Colombia. Forest. Tropical zone of the northern Colombia and the Santa Marta region (caligatus). Tropical zone of the Pacific coast (1, concinnus). East of the Andes from Meta southward to Putumayo and Amazonas (crissalis). Vaupés (ramonianus).

KINGFISHERS (Alcedinidae)

Fig. 52. Ringed Kingfisher
(Ceryle torquata)

Kingfishers form a large family of world-wide distribution, but are very poorly represented in the Americas. Most live near water where they feed on fish which they capture with their stout, pointed bills by diving into the water after them. The Pygmy Kingfisher, however, lives largely on insects which it catches on the wing.

Kingfishers nest in holes in banks. The smaller species are usually found along small, quiet woodland streams; the larger ones frequent lagoons, lakes, and larger rivers. (6 Col.; 6 S.A.; 6 N.&S.A.; 87 wld.)

AID TO IDENTIFICATION

Above gray 1, 2.
Above green with white nuchal collar 3, 4, (without collar) 5, 6.

1. RINGED KINGFISHER
(Ceryle torquata)

Description. 15-16″. ♂ : Upper surface blue-gray. Feathers of the crown, prolonged into a crest, streaked with black. Spot before eye, chin, throat, sides of neck, nuchal collar and under wing-coverts white. Lower throat and rest of underparts chestnut. Primaries black, notched on inner web with white. Central tail-feathers gray, rest black crossed by broken white bars. ♀ : differs from ♂ by having a broad gray band across chest

bordered by a white band below. Under wing-coverts chestnut.

Range. Mexico, south through Central America and South America to Tierra del Fuego. The Lesser Antilles. Trinidad.

Colombia. Larger rivers and lagoons. Tropical occasionally to the temperate zone throughout except Nariño *(torquata)*.

2. BELTED KINGFISHER
(Ceryle alcyon)

Description. 11-12″. ♂ : Similar above to the Ringed Kingfisher but much smaller

166

in size. Underparts white, with a broad blue-gray breast band and blue-gray flanks. ♀: differs from ♂ by having a broad breast band mixed gray and rufous followed below by a second narrow rufous band; flanks rufous.

Range. Breeds in North America; winters southward to Panama, occasionally on the Venezuelan coast and coastal islands. The West Indies. Trinidad and Tobago. Curaçao, Bonaire.

Colombia. Recorded once from the Santa Marta region *(alcyon)*.

3. AMAZON KINGFISHER
(Chloroceryle amazona)

Description. 10-11½". ♂: Throat, sides of neck and nuchal collar, white; lower neck and chest chestnut; rest of underparts white, the flanks streaked with shining oily green. Entire upperparts including tail shining oily green. Primaries notched with white on inner webs. Outer tail-feathers with white spots on both webs. ♀ similar to the ♂ but without chestnut. A patch on each side of the breast shining oily green.

Range. Southern Mexico southward through Central and South America to Argentina. Trinidad.

Colombia. Forest, tree-fringed rivers and ponds. Generally distributed throughout the country with the exception of the southwest *(amazona)*.

4. GREEN KINGFISHER
(Chloroceryle americana)

Description. 7½-8". ♂: Very similar to the Amazon Kingfisher but very much smaller, and wings more conspicuously spotted with white. ♀: Like ♀ of Amazon Kingfisher but throat and lower breast tawny buff instead of white with a band across chest and spots forming a second band, oily green.

Range. Texas, southward through Central America to southern Bolivia and Argentina. Trinidad, Tobago.

Colombia. Rivers and creeks. Throughout the tropical zone; recorded as high as 4,500 ft. *(americana)*.

5. GREEN-AND-RUFOUS KINGFISHER
(Chloroceryle inda)

Description. 8½-9". ♂: Above shining oily green; wings, rump and outer tail-feathers spotted with buffy white to white. Throat pale buff to orange-buff, deepening to rich orange-chestnut on the rest of the lower parts. ♀ similar to ♂ but with a band across chest barred white and oily green.

Range. Nicaragua south through South America to western Colombia and east of the Andes to Ecuador, Peru and southern Brazil.

Colombia. Rivers and creeks. Tropical zone throughout the country. Not recorded from the southwest.

6. PYGMY KINGFISHER
(Chloroceryle aenea)

Description. 5-5½". This tiny kingfisher differs in color from the Green-and-Rufous Kingfisher only in having the center of belly and under tail-coverts white in both sexes.

Range. Southern Mexico southward through Central America to Bolivia and southern Brazil. Trinidad.

Colombia. Mangroves, forest streams and ponds, and drainage ditches in plantations. Tropical zone occasionally to the lower temperate. Caribbean coast; Eastern Andes in the Bogotá region; east of the Eastern Andes, south to the Amazon *(aenea)*. Southwestern Colombia *(aequatorialis)*.

MOTMOTS (Momotidae)

Fig. 53. Blue-crowned Motmot
(Momotus momota) p. 169

Motmots constitute a small family of tropical American birds, for the most part green, with rather long and heavy curved bills. They have (except for the Tody Motmot) long, graduated tails, the central feathers of which usually terminate in a racquet. Most species are over a foot long. Sluggish and solitary in habits, they often sit in the undergrowth flicking their tails from side to side, pendulum-wise. The hooting notes of certain Blue-crowned Motmots resemble the syllables "hu-dú." Motmots live in the lower levels of the forest, feed on fruit, insects and small reptiles, and nest in crevices and tunnels in the ground. The sexes are similar. (4 Col.; 4 S.A.; 8 N.&S.A.; 8 wld.)

TODY MOTMOT
(Hylomanes momotula)
Description. 7". Remarkable among motmots for its small size and short tail. Superciliary bright verditer blue; stripe below and behind eye black, bordered below by a white line. Crown and upper mantle dull chestnut; back and upper tail-coverts grass green. Line at each side of throat buffy white; breast and sides of body olive green, center of abdomen whitish. Tail olive brown. Bill rather long and heavy. Tail conspicuously rounded.

Range. Southern Mexico to northwestern Colombia.

Colombia. Forest undergrowth. Tropical zone west of the Western Andes, southward to the Baudó Mts. *(obscurus).*

BROAD-BILLED MOTMOT
(Electron platyrhynchum)
Description. 13 - 15". Bill flat, broad, curved. Crown, upper mantle, sides of neck, throat and breast cinnamon-rufous. Lores, stripe below eye and conspicuous spot on breast black. Chin and belly verditer green. Back grass green. Tail blue, central pair ending in a bare shaft and racquet with black tip.

Range. Honduras southward to western Ecuador. East of the Andes from Ecuador south to Bolivia and eastward to the middle Amazon and Goyaz.

Colombia. Forest. Tropical zone of the Pacific coast and the Atrato Valley *(platyrhynchum).* Lower Cauca Valley northward to the Gulf of Urabá and Córdoba *(colom-*

bianum). Eastern base of the Eastern Andes from Caquetá southward *(pyrrholaemum).*

RUFOUS MOTMOT
(Baryphthengus ruficapillus)

Description. 18" Very similar in general color to the Broad-billed Motmot but much larger and bill smaller in proportion and not flat. No verditer green on chin, stripe below eye much broader and cinnamon-rufous on breast extending to upper belly; breast spot much smaller.

Range. Tropical Central America from Nicaragua southward to western Ecuador and northern Argentina.

Colombia. Forest. Entire tropical Pacific coast extending eastward through the lower Cauca Valley to the middle Magdalena Valley *(semirufus).* Tropical southeastern Colombia northward to Caquetá *(martii).*

BLUE-CROWNED MOTMOT
(Momotus momota) Plate VII; Fig. 53

Description. 15 - 17" (or 18 - 21", 1). Center of crown black, forehead, and sides of crown shining turquoise blue deepening into ultramarine blue on the hindcrown. Lores, side of head black—this color prolonged backwards over the ear-coverts where bordered narrowly above and below by shining turquoise blue.

More or less distinct chestnut collar on hindneck. Upperparts olive green (or grass green, 1), primaries edged blue. Throat and chest cinnamon strongly tinged olive, rest of underparts cinnamon (or underparts olive green, 1); a black spot narrowly bordered with bright turquoise blue in center of breast. Tail long, green near base, becoming bluer distally and terminating in a blue racquet which is tipped with black,

Range. From northeastern Mexico, southward through Central America to Venezuela, Argentina and Bolivia. Trinidad and Tobago.

Colombia. Forest and scrub. Tropical zone. Pacific coast near the Panama border eastward to both sides of the Gulf of Urabá *(reconditus).* The upper río Sinú (intermediate with *reconditus*) eastward to Santa Marta and the western base of the Perijá Mts. and southward down the Magdalena Valley to Tolima *(subrufescens).* The foothills of the Serranía de Macuira in the Guajira Peninsula *(spatha).* Humid forest region of northwestern Norte de Santander *(osgoodi).* Subtropical, occasionally the lower temperate zones of the mountains of Colombia except Santa Marta (1, *aequatorialis).* Tropical zone along the base of the Eastern Andes from Arauca and Boyacá southward *(microstephanus).* Along the río Orinoco *(momota).*

JACAMARS (Galbulidae)

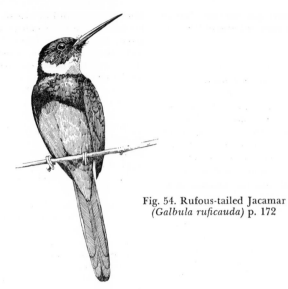

Fig. 54. Rufous-tailed Jacamar
(*Galbula ruficauda*) p. 172

These beautiful birds, found only in tropical America, are recognizable by their long, thin and very pointed bills and often brilliant coloring. Some are metallic, shining green above, mostly rufous below; others largely black, shot with purple or green. They inhabit forest clearings and second growth. Rather fearless, they perch on exposed branches often over forest paths from which they survey their surroundings, darting swallow-like after dragonflies and other insects, or sitting stolidly for long periods. The sexes are virtually similar.

Jacamars nest in tunnels which they excavate in banks, and in which they lay their almost round, white eggs. (11 Col.; 15 S. A.; 15 N. & S. A.; 15 wld.)

AID TO IDENTIFICATION

Upperparts chestnut 1[E], ashy brown or black 2, 3[E], 4[E], glossy black with elongated central tail-feathers 6[E].

Upperparts and central tail-feathers metallic green or violet (outer tail-feathers like central ones 5[E], 10[E], 11, (outer tail-feathers rufous or cinnamon) 7[E], 8[E], 9.

1. CHESTNUT JACAMAR
(Galbalcyrhynchus leucotis)

Description. 8 - 8½". Forehead, crown, chin, wings and tail greenish black, ear-coverts white. Rest of plumage dark chestnut. Bill rather heavy, kingfisher-like, pink with dark tip; feet red.

Range. Eastern Ecuador, Peru and Bolivia eastward down the Amazon Valley as far as the rio Purús, western Brazil.

Colombia. Forest clearings. Base of Eastern Andes, Caquetá southward *(leucotis)*.

2. DUSKY-BACKED JACAMAR
(Brachygalba salmoni)

Description. 7 - 7¼". Entire upper surface dark ashy brown, glossed with greenish black. Chin and throat white. A broad band across breast greenish black, rest of underparts tawny-rufous. Wings and tail black glossed with green. Bill black.

Range. Eastern Panama.

Colombia. Forest clearings. Northern Colombia in Antioquia *(salmoni)*; Córdoba and Bolívar *(carmenensis)*.

170

3. PALE-HEADED JACAMAR
(Brachygalba goeringi) Plate VIII

Description. 6½ - 7″. Crown and upper mantle ashy brown. Back, wings and tail blackish brown glossed with greenish. Throat white, breast and band across hindneck pale ashy brown. Line down center of breast, belly and under tail-coverts white. A chestnut band across middle of belly. Sides of body dark brown. Bill black.

Range. Northern Venezuela.

Colombia. Open woods and clearings. Tropical zone. East of the Eastern Andes in the Casanare Valley, in Boyacá and Arauca.

4. BROWN JACAMAR
(Brachygalba lugubris)

Description. 7 - 7¼″. Crown and mantle ashy brown, the feathers tipped paler; rump darker and glossed with greenish black. Chin and upper throat whitish, breast and sides of body dark rufescent brown, center of abdomen fulvous white. Wings and tail blue-black. Bill black.

Range. Venezuela and the Guianas southward to Brazil and Bolivia.

Colombia. Forest. Tropical zone. Eastern base of the Eastern Andes in Meta *(fulviventris);* in Caquetá *(caquetae).*

5. BRONZY JACAMAR
(Galbula leucogastra)

Description. 8½ - 9½″. Top and sides of head bronzy blue, chin and upper throat black. Large triangular patch on lower throat white (buff, ♀). Entire upper surface and chest purple-violet shot with bronze green. Tail-feathers bronze green, the outermost edged and tipped with white. Belly mixed black and white. Bill black.

Range. Venezuela and the Guianas; the middle Amazon westward to Ecuador and Peru.

Colombia. Forest. Tropical zone east of the Andes. Putumayo and Vaupés *(leucogastra).* Eastern Nariño in the valley of the río San Miguel along the Ecuador boundary *(chalcothorax).*

6. PARADISE JACAMAR
(Galbula dea)

Description. 11 - 13″. Central tail-feathers conspicuously lengthened (up to 7″). Top of head, chin and upper throat dusky ashy, somewhat paler over eye forming an indistinct eyebrow. Throat and upper breast white; sides of head, lower breast and belly blue-black mixed with white on sides of body. Upperparts bronzy purple-black. Wings bronzy green. Tail bluish green. Bill black.

Range. The Guianas and Venezuela southward to the Amazon, westward from its mouth to Ecuador, Peru and Bolivia.

Colombia. Forest. Tropical zone. Extreme southeastern Colombia *(brunneiceps).*

7. YELLOW-BILLED JACAMAR
(Galbula albirostris)

Description. 7¾ - 8¼″. Crown and feathers at base of bill metallic purple. Throat cinnamon-buff, triangular patch on lower throat white (or without white patch, ♀); rest of underparts chestnut. Upper surface and central tail-feathers bronze green (or emerald green, 1). Outer tail-feathers chestnut (or bronzy brown, 1). Upper mandible dusky (or dusky on distal half only, 1), lower mandible yellow. The only jacamar in Colombia with a yellow lower mandible.

Range. Venezuela and the Guianas southward to eastern Brazil, and westward to Ecuador and northern Peru.

Colombia. Forest. Tropical zone east of the Eastern Andes from Meta southward to Putumayo and Amazonas *(chalcocephala).* Vaupés *(1, albirostris).*

8. WHITE-CHINNED JACAMAR
(Galbula tombacea)

Description. 8½ - 9″. Forehead and forecrown dark ashy; chin and upper throat whitish, lower throat green, tinged blue. Belly and outer tail-feathers chestnut (or cinnamon, ♀). Hindcrown dark blue, rest of plumage golden bronze to bronze green depending on the light.

Range. Ecuador and Peru eastward to the middle Amazon.

Colombia. Forest often near streams and ponds. Tropical zone east of the Eastern Andes from Meta southward. *(tombacea).*

9. RUFOUS-TAILED JACAMAR
(Galbula ruficauda) Plate VII; Fig. 54

Description. 10¼ - 11¼ ". ♂: Entire upper surface including central tail-feathers, sides of head and neck and band across breast metallic bronzy gold; chin and throat white (or chin and upper throat dusky, rest white, 1). Lower breast, belly and under tail-coverts and outer tail-feathers chestnut. ♀ similar but chin and throat buff, lower underparts cinnamon-buff.

Range. Southern Mexico to western Ecuador. Venezuela, the Guianas southward to southern Brazil, Paraguay, Argentina and northern Bolivia. Trinidad and Tobago.

Colombia. Forest and clearings. Tropical zones. Entire Pacific coast up to 3,000 ft. (1. *melanogenia).* Northern Colombia from the lower Atrato eastward to the llanos east of the Andes in Boyacá and Arauca *(ruficauda).* The Santa Marta region and the lower Magdalena Valley *(pallens).* The Zulia and Catatumbo Valleys *(brevirostris).*

10. GREEN-TAILED JACAMAR
(Galbula galbula)

Description. 8½ - 9". Very similar to the Rufous-tailed Jacamar. Differs principally in the shorter tail, in which all the feathers are bronzy bluish green. Top and sides of head strongly tinged blue instead of coppery green.

Range. The Guianas, southern Venezuela, northern and eastern Brazil.

Colombia. Forest. Tropical zone. The Orinoco and río Vaupés regions.

11. GREAT JACAMAR
(Jacamerops aurea) Plate VII (♀)

Description. 10½ - 12". ♂: Upperparts shining coppery green, more bluish on the head and usually shot with purple or entirely fiery purple on the back. Throat like back, a broad white patch across lower throat (or without white patch, ♀) entire rest of underparts tawny-rufous. Tail-feathers graduated, central pair shining coppery green, outer ones bluer. The bill in this species is rather heavy and somewhat curved.

Range. Costa Rica southward to Venezuela, the Guianas, the Amazon Valley, and eastward to Ecuador, Peru and northern Bolivia.

Colombia. Forest. Pacific coast southward to Nariño and across northern Colombia to the middle Magdalena Valley *(penardi).* Tropical zone east of the Eastern Andes from Meta southward *(aurea).*

PUFFBIRDS (Bucconidae)

Fig. 55. White-necked Puffbird
(Notharchus macrorhynchos)

Puffbirds are a small family of medium-sized birds found only in tropical America. They have big heads, short, thick necks and heavy, hooked bills *(Bucco)* or rather thin, curved ones *(Monasa* and most others). When sitting quietly with their feathers puffed out they present a bulky appearance. In color they are rather dull. Some species are black and white, while many are clothed in various shades of brown. They live on insects which they catch either in flight or on the ground. They nest in holes in trees or in burrows which they excavate in banks. They live in the forest, usually perching not very high up; they are not at all shy, often allowing a close approach. They are rather silent, their notes consisting of soft whistles and high-pitched wheezy notes. The sexes are alike.

Probably due to their very sedentary habits no puffbird has reached Trinidad or other islands adjacent to the continent. (22 Col.; 32 S.A.; 32 N.&S.A.; 32 wld.)

AID TO IDENTIFICATION

Black and white 1, 2, 3.
Black or gray and black 19E, 20, 21E.
Brown or rufous or with brown or rufous in the plumage 5E, 8, 11E, 12, 13, 14, 18, 22E; with a band across breast or throat 4E, 6, 7E, 9, 10E; size very small, under 6½", streaked below 15, plain rufescent below 16E, 17.

1. WHITE-NECKED PUFFBIRD
(Notharchus macrorhynchos) Plate VIII
Description. 10". Most of upper surface, and stripe through eye black. Forecrown, collar on hindneck and underparts white. Broad band across breast black; flanks black narrowly barred white. Wings and tail black.
Range. Southeastern Mexico, southward to western Ecuador. Venezuela, the Guianas southward to Brazil, Ecuador, Peru and Bolivia.
Colombia. Open woodland. Tropical zone

of northern Colombia; cultivated lands in the upper Cauca Valley *(hyperrhynchus)*.

2. BLACK-BREASTED PUFFBIRD
(Notharchus pectoralis)
Description. 8½ - 9". Upperparts, wings and tail blue-black. Ear-coverts white continued backward to form a collar across hindneck. Wing-coverts fringed white. Upper throat and center of belly white. Broad band across breast blue-black. Sides of body blackish, feathers fringed white.
Range. Eastern Panama.

173

Colombia. Forest and occasionally clearings. Tropical zone of the entire Pacific coast eastward to the Magdalena Valley.

3. PIED PUFFBIRD
(Notharchus tectus)

Description. 6 - 6¼". Upper surface blueblack, scapulars broadly tipped white. Feathers of the forecrown tipped white; lores and eyebrow white. Band across breast black, rest of underparts white. Tail black, the feathers with a terminal and median white spot on inner web only, except for center pair

Range. Costa Rica southward to western Ecuador. Southern Venezuela and the Guianas, northern and eastern Brazil, Ecuador and Peru.

Colombia. Forest. Entire Pacific coast, eastward to the lower Cauca and middle Magdalena Valley *(subtectus)*.

4. CHESTNUT-CAPPED PUFFBIRD
(Bucco macrodactylus)

Description. 6½ - 6¾". Crown chestnut. Collar across hindneck bright rusty buff, rest of back chestnut-brown speckled with pale fulvous. Lores and eyebrow and stripe below ear-coverts white; ear-coverts and band across lower throat extending to sides of neck black. Throat pale buff, upper breast whitish buff, lower breast and belly buff to pale isabelline marbled with wavy blackish lines. Tail very rounded, chestnut brown.

Range. Southern Venezuela to western Brazil, Ecuador, Peru, northern Bolivia.

Colombia. Forest. Tropical zone east of the Eastern Andes from Meta southward *(macrodactylus)*.

5. SPOTTED PUFFBIRD
(Bucco tamatia)

Description. 7 - 7¼". Upperparts brown, mantle and wing-coverts spotted with fulvous. Forehead, eyebrow and throat rusty orange. Ear-coverts grayish brown, bordered below by a white stripe, this bordered by a broad black patch on sides of neck. Lower breast and belly white heavily spotted with black.

Range. The Guianas and southern Venezuela south to Brazil, Ecuador and Peru.

Colombia. Forest. The Orinoco region *(tamatia)*. Amazonas *(pulmentum)*.

6. SOOTY-CAPPED PUFFBIRD
(Bucco noanamae)

Description. 7½ - 7¾". Upper surface dull dark brown, grayer on the crown. Ear-coverts and an inconspicuous nuchal band hoary gray, feathers of back and upper tail-coverts fringed rufescent. Forehead, eyebrow, and throat white. Lores and broad band across upper breast commencing on sides of neck black. Rest of underparts fulvous white spotted with black, the spots edged buff.

Range. Colombia.

Colombia. Forest and scrub. Tropical zone of the valleys of the Atrato and San Juan rivers of Pacific Colombia, eastward to the west shore of the Gulf of Urabá.

7. COLLARED PUFFBIRD
(Bucco capensis)

Description. 7¼ - 7½". Crown, back and tail cinnamon-rufous crossed with very narrow wavy black lines. Collar across hindneck uniform black, bordered above by a uniform cinnamon-buff band. Sides of head, eyebrow uniform orange-cinnamon. Throat white, breast crossed by a black band which joins that across the hindneck; rest of lower parts fulvous. Bill orange with dusky ridge.

Range. The Guianas and Venezuela southward to Peru; both banks of the Amazon.

Colombia. Forest. Tropical zone east of the Eastern Andes in Meta eastward to the Orinoco *(dugandi)*. From the Caquetá region southward to the north bank of the Amazon *(capensis)*.

8. BARRED PUFFBIRD
(Nystalus radiatus) Plate VII

Description. 8 - 8½". Crown, back, wings and tail broadly banded rufous and black. Collar across hindneck uniform cinnamon. Chin white. Sides of neck and the breast cinnamon-buff barred with narrow black lines; abdomen plain pinkish buff.

Range. Panama to western Ecuador.

Colombia. Forest. Pacific coast eastward across northern Antioquia to the middle Magdalena Valley.

9. RUSSET-THROATED PUFFBIRD
(*Hypnelus ruficollis*)

Description. 8¾ - 9½". Above grayish brown spotted with dirty white; an ill-marked white nuchal collar. Lores, space below eye, and the ear-coverts and chin white. Center of throat deep rusty, fading to white on upper breast which is crossed by a black band; rest of underparts buffy, sides of body more (or less, 1) spotted with black. Tail grayish brown.
Range. Northwestern Venezuela.
Colombia. Open woods and dry scrub. Tropical zone of northern Colombia and the lower and middle Magdalena Valley. The arid coastal region of the Guajira Peninsula (1, *decolor*). The Catatumbo and Zulia Valleys (*coloratus*).

10. TWO-BANDED PUFFBIRD
(*Hypnelus bicinctus*)

Description. 8¾ - 9¼". Above very similar to Russet-throated Puffbird. Below rusty buff with a broad band of black across lower throat, another narrower band across breast and the suggestion of a third band below this.
Range. Northern Venezuela. Margarita I.
Colombia. Savanna, scrub and woods. Tropical zone east of the Andes in Boyacá and Meta (*bicinctus*).

11. WHITE-CHESTED PUFFBIRD
(*Malacoptila fusca*)

Description. 8 - 8½". Upperparts dark brown, blackish on head, boldly streaked with fulvous. Throat and sides of head brown, breast streaked fulvous. Moustacial streak and a conspicuous patch on the breast white. Lower breast broadly streaked fulvous and dark brown. Belly white. Tail brown. Base of bill yellow.
Range. Southern Venezuela, the Guianas southward and westward to western Brazil, Ecuador, Peru and northern Bolivia.
Colombia. Forest. Tropical zone east of the Andes from Meta southward (*fusca*).

12. BLACK-STREAKED PUFFBIRD
(*Malacoptila fulvogularis*)

Description. 8 - 8½". Above very similar to the White-chested Puffbird but streaks narrower. Throat and large breast patch cinnamon; moustacial streak buffy white. Lower breast broadly streaked black and

white, belly fulvous white. Bill all black.
Range. Ecuador, Peru and Bolivia.
Colombia. The llanos of Meta (*substriata*). Head of the Magdalena Valley in the subtropical zone (*huilae*).

13. WHITE-WHISKERED PUFFBIRD
(*Malacoptila panamensis*)

Description. 8 - 8½". ♂: Below very similar to the Black-streaked Puffbird (or with center of throat and breast deeper cinnamon and much more sharply defined from pale abdomen, 1). Above rufous-brown to dark grayish brown, spotted with white and fulvous. Lower mandible yellowish green. ♀ similar to ♂ but cinnamon of breast much paler.
Range. Southern Mexico south to western Ecuador.
Colombia. Forest undergrowth. Western Colombia, south to the río San Juan and eastward to the lower Cauca (*chocoana*). Northern Colombia from Bolívar east to the middle Magdalena Valley (*panamensis*). Western Colombia from the río Dagua southward to Nariño (1, *poliopis*).

14. MOUSTACHED PUFFBIRD
(*Malacoptila mystacalis*)

Description. 8¾ - 9¼". Above sandy brown to rufescent-brown, spotted on the mantle with fulvous white. Forehead, lores and moustacial streak white. Throat and breast orange-cinnamon (or cinnamon-chestnut, 1). Belly white, sides of belly inconspicuously streaked and mottled with brown. Lower mandible bluish gray with black tip (or yellowish with black tip, 1).
Range. Western Venezuela.
Colombia. Heavy forest. Upper tropical and lower subtropical zones of the Santa Marta Mts. Both slopes of the Eastern and Central Andes and the Macarena Mts. (*mystacalis*). Upper tropical and subtropical zones of the west slope of the Western Andes from the río San Juan southward (1, *pacifica*).

15. LANCEOLATED MONKLET
(*Micromonacha lanceolata*)

Description. 5¼ - 5¾". Forehead white bordered posteriorly by a narrow black band. Lores white. Crown uniform russet brown. Back brown, each feather margined with pale fulvous. Underparts white,

PLATE VIII

(All birds shown are males unless otherwise noted)

**GOLD-FRONTED
PICULET**
(*Picumnus auri-
frons lafresnayi*)
Page 188

**WHITE-CROWNED
MANAKIN**
(*Pipra pipra minima*)
Page 251

PALE-HEADED JACAMAR
(*Brachygalba goeringi*)
Page 171

GRAY SCREAMING PIHA
(*Lipaugus vociferans*)
Page 263

WHITE COTINGA
(*Carpodectes hopkei*)
Page 259

MASKED TITYRA
(*Tityra semi-
fasciata columbiana*)
Page 265

**WHITE-FRONTED
NUNBIRD**
(*Monasa morphoeus fidelis*)
Page 177

WHITE-WINGED BECAR
(*Pachyramphus poly-
chopterus dorsalis*)
Page 264

**WHITE-NECKED
PUFFBIRD**
(*Notharchus macro-
rhynchos hyperrhynchus*)
Page 173

**ORANGE-FRONTED
BARBET**
(*Capito squamatus,* ♀)
Page 179

GREAT ANTSHRIKE
(*Taraba major
transandeanus*)
Page 218

E.L.Poole

boldly streaked with black. Tail short, black at base, then brown with a subterminal black bar and paler brown tip.
Range. Costa Rica and western Panama. Eastern Ecuador, Peru and western Brazil.
Colombia. Forest. So far, recorded east of the Andes from the Macarena Mts. and from the upper río San Juan on the west slope of the Western Andes and western Nariño *(lanceolata).*

16. BROWN NUNLET
(Nonnula brunnea)

Description. 5¾ - 6¼". Above uniform sepia brown. Lores and lowerparts rusty cinnamon, paler on belly. Wings and tail dark brown. Bill slender.
Range. Eastern Ecuador and Peru.
Colombia. The eastern base of the Eastern Andes from Meta southward.

17. GRAY-CHEEKED NUNLET
(Nonnula ruficapilla) Plate VII

Description. 5¾ - 6¼". Crown chestnut (or nearly like back, 1) sides of head gray. Back brown; throat and breast cinnamon-rufous (or cinnamon-buff, 1) becoming whitish on belly. Bill slender.
Range. From the Canal Zone southward to eastern Peru and Mato Grosso, Brazil.
Colombia. Forest and scrub. Northernmost west shore of the Gulf of Urabá adjacent to the Panama border or near the Panama border on the Pacific coast. The Caribbean coastal region and lower Atrato Valley (1, *pallescens*). Middle Magdalena Valley *(frontalis).*

18. WHITE-FACED PUFFBIRD
(Hapaloptila castanea)

Description. 10 - 10½". Lores and forehead white, outlined with black. Chin and upper throat white; rest of under surface chestnut. Upper surface grayish olive, grayest on top and sides of head. Wings and tail dusky, glossed olive.
Range. Western Ecuador.
Colombia. Humid forest. Upper tropical and subtropical zones of the Western Andes and Nariño.

19. BLACK-FRONTED NUNBIRD
(Monasa nigrifrons)

Description. 11¼ - 11¾". Forehead, lores and chin black. Upper back blackish gray

glossed with greenish; lower back and under surface dark gray. Tail glossy bluish black. Bill red.
Range. Ecuador, Peru, Brazil and Bolivia.
Colombia. Forest. Tropical zone east of the Eastern Andes *(nigrifrons).*

20. WHITE-FRONTED NUNBIRD
(Monasa morphoeus) Plate VIII

Description. 10¾ - 11¼". Forehead and chin white (or forehead only white, 1, 2, 3). Upper throat and forecrown black, rest of plumage ash gray (or head and breast black, sharply defined from the gray of the rest of the underparts, 2; or less sharply defined, 3). Wings uniform gray (or wing-coverts pale gray in contrast to black primaries, 2; or wing-coverts not so pale, 3). Tail blue-black. Bill red.
Range. Eastern Nicaragua southward through Panama. Southern Venezuela, Ecuador, Peru, Brazil and northern Bolivia.
Colombia. Forest. Tropical zone of the Pacific coast southward to the upper río San Juan (2, *pallescens*). The east shore of the Gulf of Urabá eastward to the río Sinú (3, *fidelis*). Tropical zone of the lower Cauca and middle Magdalena Valleys (1, *sclateri*). East of the Eastern Andes from Meta southward *(peruana).*

21. YELLOW-BILLED NUNBIRD
(Monasa flavirostris)

Description. 9½ - 10". Black; belly ashy, shoulders and under wing-coverts white. Bill yellowish green to yellowish white.
Range. Ecuador, Peru and western Brazil.
Colombia. Forest. Tropical zone east of the Eastern Andes.

22. SWALLOW-WING
(Chelidoptera tenebrosa)

Description. 6". Gregarious. More active than most puffbirds. Wings long, pointed, swallow-like in flight. Head, neck, breast, upper back, wings and tail black with a green gloss. Lower back, rump and upper and under tail-coverts white. Lower breast gray, belly cinnamon to cinnamon-chestnut. Tail rather short. Bill black.
Range. Most of tropical South America.
Colombia. Forest clearings, open woods and savanna. Tropical zone east of the Eastern Andes *(tenebrosa).*

BARBETS (Capitonidae)

Fig. 56. Black-spotted Barbet
(*Capito niger*) p. 179

Barbets are found in the tropics of Africa and Asia as well as Central and South America. In the New World most of the species occur in northern and northwestern South America. None has reached islands adjacent to the continent. They are brilliantly colored, medium- to small-sized birds, with rather thick bills. They live in the forest, nest in holes in trees and eat fruit and insects. Most of the species have a very monotonous call, usually one rather harsh note endlessly repeated. (9 Col.; 11 S.A.; 12 N.&S.A.; 72 wld.)

AID TO IDENTIFICATION

Mostly olive or bright green above 1E, 7E, 8.
Mostly black above 2, 3, 4, 5, 6E.
Mostly olive brown above, bill banded 9.

1. SCARLET-CROWNED BARBET
(*Capito aurovirens*)

Description. 7¼ - 7½". ♂ : Back, wings and tail olive. Entire crown and nape scarlet, eyebrow grayish white, sides of head brownish, chin white, throat and breast orange, belly yellowish olive. ♀ differs from ♂ by having the crown and nape hoary white, the breast and throat less intense orange.

Range. Ecuador, Peru and western Brazil.

Colombia. Forest. Tropical zone east of the Andes from Caquetá southward.

2. SPOT-CROWNED BARBET
(*Capito maculicoronatus*)

Description. 7 - 7½". ♂ : Crown black spotted with white. Forehead, sides of crown and head, upper surface, wings and tail blue-black. Chin, throat, upper breast, center of abdomen and under tail-coverts white. A band across breast pale yellowish orange. Flanks black and scarlet. ♀ similar to ♂ but whole throat and breast blue-black like back, without yellow.

Range. Panama.

Colombia. Second growth woodland. Trop-

178

ical zone of extreme northwestern Colombia adjacent to the Panama border and east to the west shore of the Gulf of Urabá *(pirrensis)*. From the east shore of the Gulf of Urabá southward down the Atrato Valley to the Dagua Valley. The lower Cauca and middle Magdalena Valleys *(rubrilateralis)*.

3. ORANGE-FRONTED BARBET
(Capito squamatus) Plate VIII (♀)

Description. 7 - 7¼ ". ♂ : Forehead and forecrown orange to scarlet-orange, middle and hindcrown white. Sides of head, back, wings and tail blue-black, the tertials broadly edged white. Entire under surface dingy white, stained with pale sulphur yellow in chest. ♀ differs from ♂ in having the feathers of the back and wing-coverts narrowly edged with white giving a scaled appearance and the chin, throat and breast blue-black.

Range. Western Ecuador.

Colombia. Scrub. Tropical zone of western Nariño.

4. WHITE-MANTLED BARBET
(Capito hypoleucus)

Description. 7 - 7½ ". Forehead and forecrown dark crimson. Hindcrown, hindneck and mantle white. Sides of head, wings, tail and rest of upperparts blueblack. Thoat and upper breast white, a pale dull violet or buffy brown band across chest, rest of underparts yellowish white; flanks pale yellow.

Range. Colombia.

Colombia. Tropical zone of the lower Cauca and middle Magdalena Valleys.

5. FIVE-COLORED BARBET
(Capito quinticolor)

Description. 7". ♂ : Upper surface black, feathers of crown, nape and hindneck tipped with blood red, those of the back, rump, upper tail-coverts and secondaries tipped with greenish yellow. Wing band greenish yellow. Cheeks, chin and throat white, tinged yellow; breast and center of abdomen orange-yellow; flanks and under tail-coverts olive, mottled with black.

Wings and tail olive brown. ♀ differs from the ♂ in having the crown and hindneck finely streaked with yellow instead of spotted with blood red.

Range. Colombia.

Colombia. Tropical zone of the Pacific coast from the río San Juan southward to Nariño.

6. BLACK-SPOTTED BARBET
(Capito niger) Fig. 56

Description. 7¾ - 8¼ ". ♂ : Forecrown dull golden yellow deepening to bronzy brown on hindcrown (or forecrown scarlet becoming yellow on hindcrown, 1). Long eyebrow golden yellow (or whitish, 1). Throat orange (or scarlet, 1). Sides of head, wing-coverts and back black, the latter bordered on each side with a yellow band (or whitish band, 1). Underparts pale yellow spotted on flanks with black. Wing-bar yellowish, quills edged with olive. Tail dark olive green. ♀ : Crown like ♂. Back black, the feathers edged with pale yellow. Wing-coverts edged with orange-yellow (or whitish, 1). Throat orange heavily spotted with black (or uniform crimson, 1). Breast and sides of body yellow (or yellowish white, 1) heavily spotted with black on sides; center of breast clear yellow (or yellowish white, 1), becoming whitish on belly.

Range. Venezuela and the Guianas southward to central and western Brazil, Ecuador and Peru.

Colombia. Forest and second growth. Tropical zone at the base of the Andes in Meta *(punctatus)*. East of the Andes from the Caquetá region southward *(macintyrei)*. Extreme eastern Colombia along the río Guainía (1, *transilens*). North bank of the Amazon (1, *nitidior*).

7. LEMON-THROATED BARBET
(Capito richardsoni)

Description. 5¾ - 6¼ ". ♂ : Back moss green, a broad nuchal collar slaty blue. Crown, sides of head and chin dark crimson, throat and side of neck yellow. Breast band salmon, becoming scarlet on lower breast, rest of underparts yellowish white, streaked green. Wings and tail olive green.

♀: Upper surface moss green. Forehead, lores and ear-coverts black, forecrown and sides of neck and throat grayish green. Streak behind eye and surrounding ear-coverts yellow. A broad band across upper breast golden yellow, lower breast yellowish green, flanks streaked yellowish and dark olive green. Wings and tail olive.

Range. Ecuador and Peru.

Colombia. Forest and scrub. Tropical zone east of the Eastern Andes from Meta southward *(richardsoni)*.

8. RED-HEADED BARBET
(Capito bourcierii) Plate VII

Description. 6½ - 7". ♂: Entire back, wings and tail grass green. A narrow nuchal collar sky blue. Narrow line surrounding bill black. Entire head, throat and upper breast scarlet, fading to orange and then yellow on lower breast. Sides of body streaked yellowish white and green. ♀: Forehead black, forecrown golden-yellow, hindcrown olive. Ocular region and ear-coverts and sides of neck sky blue margined posteriorly with golden yellow. Throat pale green, band across breast golden yellow, lower breast olive-yellow, belly and flanks streaked dull yellow and green. Back, wings and tail green.

Range. Costa Rica southward to western Venezuela, Ecuador and Peru.

Colombia. Forest and scrub. Upper tropical and subtropical zone of the Western Andes south to the río Dagua; the upper Cauca Valley *(occidentalis)*. Tropical zone of western Nariño *(aequatorialis)*. Tropical and subtropical zones in Meta and at the head of the Magdalena *(bourcierii)*. East of the Andes from Putumayo southward *(orientalis)*.

9. TOUCAN BARBET
(Semnornis ramphastinus) Plate VII

Description. 7½ - 8". ♂: Bill heavy and swollen, yellowish green with black tip. Forehead, crown, nape, area in front of eye and at base of lower mandible shining black; hindcrown bordered laterally by a broad white stripe. Feathers of hind-crown elongated so as to lie over mantle, shining black. Sides of head, ear-coverts, sides of neck, throat and breast blue-gray, the ear-coverts bordered posteriorly by black. A broad band of scarlet across breast, this color staining the center of lower breast and upper abdomen (or lower breast and abdomen yellow, 1). Sides of body yellow. Mantle olive brown, lower back and rump golden yellow. Wings and tail dark gray. ♀ similar to ♂ but lacks the elongated nuchal feathers.

Range. Western Ecuador.

Colombia. Forest. Upper tropical and subtropical zones of both slopes of the Western Andes (1, *caucae*). Western Nariño *(ramphastinus)*.

TOUCANS (Ramphastidae)

Fig. 57. White-throated Toucan
(Ramphastos tucanus) p. 182

The toucans constitute one of the most characteristic families of tropical American birds. They are at once distinguishable from other South American birds by their immense and often brightly colored bills, which not infrequently are almost half as long as the bird itself. Their tails are rather long and rounded and at times carried upright when perching. The sexes are usually similar.

There are four main groups of toucans: the typical toucans, mostly black with white or sulphur throats and breast; the mountain toucans with blue to blue-gray underparts, olive brown backs; the toucanets, most of them bright green; and the araçaris, usually with slaty olive or black upper parts and chest, and yellow bellies crossed by one or more red or black bands.

Toucans are gregarious, live in the forest where they feed on fruit, and nest and roost in holes in trees. They are active and noisy, inquisitive and not particularly shy. Their notes sometimes resemble the yelping of a pack of hounds.

They are found from southern Mexico, southward through Central America to southern Brazil, Peru, northern Argentina and Bolivia. (20 Col.; 37 S.A.; 37 N.&S.A.; 37 wld.)

AID TO IDENTIFICATION

Back black or mostly black (breast yellow) 1, 2, 3, 5, (breast white) 4E, 5, (banded below) 9E, 11, 12.
Back olive 6, 7, 8, 10E, 14E, 15E, 16.
Back red 13E.
Back bright green 17, 18E, 19, 20.

181

1. KEEL-BILLED TOUCAN
(Ramphastos sulfuratus)

Description. 18 - 20". Upper surface, lower breast and belly, wings and tail black, mantle tinged maroon. Ear-coverts, throat and breast golden yellow, the latter bordered below by a narrow red band. Upper tail-coverts white; under tail-coverts crimson. Bare skin around eye pea green; iris greenish yellow. Base of upper and lower mandible and most of ridge of bill pea green; long wedge-shaped area along cutting edge of upper mandible orange; area on lower mandible below this blue, broad tip to bill crimson.

Range. Southern Mexico southward to Central America. Northern Venezuela.

Colombia. Heavy forest. Tropical to lower subtropical zone. Northern Colombia from the Panama border eastward to the Santa Marta region *(brevicarinatus)*.

2. CHESTNUT-MANDIBLED TOUCAN
(Ramphastos swainsonii)

Description. 22 - 23". Differs from Keel-billed Toucan by larger size and differently colored bill. Area around eye and iris yellowish green. Bill 5 - 6¼". Ridge of culmen greenish yellow, distal half of maxilla sulphur-yellow; basal portion of bill dark red, becoming blackish toward the distal half of the lower mandible.

Range. Honduras southward to Ecuador and eastward to Venezuela.

Colombia. Forest. Tropical and occasionally lower subtropical zones of western Colombia and eastward to the middle Magdalena Valley.

3. BLACK-MANDIBLED TOUCAN
(Ramphastos ambiguus)

Description. 22 - 26" (or 19 - 21", 1). Similar in color to the preceding two but bill different. Bare skin around eye olive. Bill 6 - 7¾" (or 5 - 6", 1). A wedged-shaped area at base of upper mandible and entire lower mandible black to reddish black; rest of upper mandible bright yellow except for a green area at center of ridge and another bordering black wedge of upper mandible.

Range. Panama southward to western Ecuador. Western Venezuela, eastern Ecuador and Peru.

Colombia. Tropical and subtropical zones of the lower Cauca Valley, the middle and upper Magdalena Valley, the Perijá Mts. and the east slope of the northern portion of the Eastern Andes south to Meta *(ambiguus)*. Tropical zone of the Pacific coast (1, *brevis*).

4. WHITE-THROATED TOUCAN
(Ramphastos tucanus) Fig. 57

Description. 19 - 22". Differs from the four described above by having the throat and breast white, tinged with pale sulphur yellow, and yellow instead of white upper tail-coverts. Skin around eye light blue, iris dark brown. Bill 6 - 7". Base of upper mandible orange-yellow, base of lower mandible light blue, ridge of culmen yellowish green, tip of bill yellow: rest of bill dark red (or black, 1).

Range. Venezuela and the Guianas southward to eastern and central Brazil, northern Argentina and Bolivia.

Colombia. Tropical zone east of the Eastern Andes in Arauca and Boyacá *(tucanus);* from Meta southward (1, *cuvieri*).

5. CHANNEL-BILLED TOUCAN
(Ramphastos vitellinus)

Description. 17 - 21". Similar in color to the White-throated Toucan but much smaller (or with the throat and breast bright sulphur yellow in contrast to white ear-coverts, 1). Skin around eye blue. Base of mandible blue, of maxilla yellow. Ridge of bill pale yellow, rest of bill black (or base of mandible and maxilla blue with a small area of yellow at extreme base, 1).

Range. Eastern Colombia, Venezuela and the Guianas southward to Brazil, Ecuador and Bolivia. Trinidad.

Colombia. Tropical zone east of the Eastern Andes from Arauca southward *(culminatus)*. Northern Colombia from the Gulf of Urabá eastward to the lower Cauca and middle Magdalena Valleys (1, *citreolaemus*).

6. GRAY-BREASTED MOUNTAIN TOUCAN
(Andigena hypoglauca) Plate IV

Description. 17 - 19". Crown and nape and ear-coverts glossy black; chin blackish, throat, breast, center of belly and nuchal collar blue-gray; flanks chocolate brown Back olive brown; rump golden yellow. Under tail-coverts and sides of rump crimson cherry. Wings and upper tail-coverts slaty olive. Tail blackish, central feathers tipped rufous. Skin around eye light blue, iris dark brown. Bill 3½ - 4". Extreme base of lower mandible bright yellow, a band at base of upper and lower mandibles and distal half of lower mandible black. Median portion of lower mandible and portion of maxilla above it greenish yellow. Ridge and distal portion of upper mandible orange red, separated from the yellow by a black line.

Range. Mountains of Ecuador and eastern Peru.

Colombia. Temperate zone of the western slope of the Central Andes between 8,000 and 11,000 ft. in Caldas and Cauca *(hypoglauca)*.

7. PLATE-BILLED MOUNTAIN TOUCAN
(Andigena laminirostris)

Description. 19 - 21". Crown and nape glossy black, upperparts and wings golden olive, darker and greener on wings. Rump lemon yellow, upper tail-coverts dark slaty green. Underparts blue; a patch at sides golden yellow. Thighs maroon-brown; under tail-coverts crimson. Tail dark gray, the central tail-feathers tipped rufous. Skin above eye yellow-green, below it yellow; iris red. Bill 3¼ - 4". Extreme base of upper mandible and basal half of lower mandible dark red. A bony, raised, rectangular plate near base of upper mandible ivory, rest of bill black.

Range. Western Ecuador.

Colombia. Upper tropical to lower temperate zones of the Andes of Nariño from 3300 to 9500 ft.

8. BLACK-BILLED MOUNTAIN TOUCAN
(Andigena nigrirostris)

Description. 19 - 21". Crown, nape and upper mantle glossy black. Back and outer wing-feathers olive brown, rump lemon yellow, upper tail-coverts greenish. Cheeks, ear-coverts and throat white. Breast and belly pale blue; flanks chocolate. Under tail-coverts crimson. Tertials and tail gray, the latter tipped with chestnut. Skin in front of eye light blue, behind the eye light yellow. Iris dark red. Bill 3½ - 4½". Upper and lower mandible black (or base of bill red, rest black, 1; or base of bill and distal half of ridge of maxilla dark red, 2).

Range. Western Venezuela to northern Ecuador.

Colombia. Subtropical and temperate zones of both slopes of the Eastern Andes from 6000 to 9500 ft. southward to Meta *(nigrirostris)*. Both slopes of the Central Andes and the west slope of the Eastern Andes at the head of the Magdalena Valley from 5800 to 9000 ft.; east of the Andes near the Ecuador boundary (1, *spilorhynchus*). Both slopes of the Western Andes south to Caldas (2, *occidentalis*).

9. MANY-BANDED ARAÇARI
(Pteroglossus pluricinctus)

Description. 16 - 18". Crown, nape and upper mantle glossy black; ear-coverts deep maroon-chestnut. Center of back slaty grayish green; lower back and rump crimson; upper tail-coverts, wings and tail dark greenish olive. Throat and upper breast glossy black, rest of lower parts yellow with a black band across lower breast and mixed black and scarlet band across upper abdomen. Flanks dull chestnut; under tail-coverts yellow, tinged chestnut. Bill 4 - 5". Base of bill outlined by a thin yellow line. Upper mandible mostly ivory white, ridge of culmen and entire lower mandible black.

Range. Southern Venezuela southward to eastern Peru and northwestern Brazil.

Colombia. Tropical zone east of the Eastern Andes from Arauca southward.

10. CHESTNUT-EARED ARAÇARI
(Pteroglossus castanotis)

Description. 17½ - 18½ ". Crown and nape black; throat, sides of head and neck and broad band across hindneck maroon. Back, wings and tail dark slaty green; rump crimson, upper tail-coverts maroon-red. Upper breast black, rest of underparts yellow, stained with crimson on breast, and crossed by a broad crimson band on abdomen. Thighs deep maroon. Skin about eye greenish, iris white. Bill 4 - 5". Bill black, band on maxilla pale brown; line surrounding base of bill and "teeth" yellow.

Range. Ecuador, Peru and Brazil southward to Paraguay, Argentina and Bolivia.

Colombia. Tropical zone east of the Eastern Andes from Boyacá south to Amazonas *(castanotis)*.

11. COLLARED ARAÇARI
(Pteroglossus torquatus)

Description. 15 - 16½". Entire head and throat blue-black. Narrow band across hindneck chestnut. Upper mantle glossy blackish green; lower back and upper tail-coverts crimson; wings and tail dark slaty olive. Breast mottled yellow and crimson with a large black mark in center. Abdomen yellow crossed by a black band which is bordered below by crimson. Thighs chestnut. Skin around eye dark reddish, iris light yellow. Bill 3½ - 4½". Ridge and tip of upper mandible black, rest ivory; entire lower mandible black; bill outlined basally by a conspicuous yellow band.

Range. Yucatan, southward through Central America to northern and western Venezuela.

Colombia. Forest and scrub. Tropical zone of the Caribbean coast region often in semi-arid areas; the lower Cauca and lower and middle Magdalena Valleys; eastern base of the Eastern Andes in the Zulia Valley *(nuchalis)*. Tropical zone of northwestern Colombia in the Gulf of Urabá region *(torquatus)*.

12. STRIPE-BILLED ARAÇARI
(Pteroglossus sanguineus)

Description. 16 - 18". Differs from the Collared Araçari by being slightly larger, by the absence of nuchal collar, and by different bill pattern. Skin in front of eye bluish black, behind it dark red, iris yellow. Bill 3¾ - 4¼". Ridge of culmen, narrow stripe above "teeth" and lower mandible black. Upper mandible and tip of bill brownish ivory. Narrow line outlining base and "teeth" yellowish.

Range. Northwestern Ecuador.

Colombia. Tropical zone of the Pacific coast and both shores of the Gulf of Urabá.

13. IVORY-BILLED ARAÇARI
(Pteroglossus flavirostris) Plate IV

Description. 14 - 15". Crown and nape glossy black. Throat, sides of head chestnut, a narrow band across base of throat black. Broad band across chest crimson followed by a broad band of black, narrowly margined below with crimson. Belly and under tail-coverts yellow. Upper mantle dark maroon, rump crimson. Center of back, wings and tail and flanks olive. Skin before eye black, above and below it dark red. Iris dark red. Bill 3 - 3½", ivory white. Nostril orange-yellow, "teeth" black. A longitudinal mark near base at cutting edge of lower mandible brown.

Range. Southern Venezuela and western Brazil, eastern Peru and northern Bolivia.

Colombia. Forest. Tropical zone east of the Eastern Andes from Meta south to Amazonas *(flavirostris)*.

14. LETTERED ARAÇARI
(Pteroglossus inscriptus)

Description. 14 - 15". Entire head glossy black (or dark chestnut, ♀). Back, wings and tail dark slaty green; rump crimson. Underparts yellow stained with brown on lower breast; thighs chestnut. Skin about eye green, red posteriorly. Iris dark red. Bill 2½ - 3½". Upper mandible dull yellow, ridge and tip and thin, wavy, vertical black lines rising from cutting edge black. Lower mandible black.

Range. Eastern Ecuador, eastern Peru, Brazil and northern Bolivia.

Colombia. Forest. Tropical zone east of the Eastern Andes from Meta southward to Amazonas *(humboldti)*.

15. LEMON-COLLARED TOUCANET
(Selenidera reinwardtii)

Description. 11 - 13 ". ♂ : Lengthened ear-coverts forming a tuft on the sides of the head golden yellow, rest of head, nape, throat, breast and center of abdomen glossy black. Sides of abdomen mixed olive and yellow; flanks chestnut; under tail-coverts crimson. Upperparts bright olive green; a narrow band across upper mantle lemon yellow. Wings and tail olive green, the latter tipped chestnut except for outermost feathers. Bill 2 - 2½ ". Basal two-thirds reddish brown, ridge and distal third black. ♀ : Has the black portions of the plumage replaced by chestnut and ear-tufts yellow but sometimes bronzy olive, yellow at the tip only. Otherwise similar to the ♂. Skin about eye yellowish green. Bill similar to ♂.

Range. Eastern Ecuador and eastern Peru.

Colombia. Forest. Tropical zone east of the Eastern Andes in Caquetá and Putumayo *(reinwardtii)*.

16. YELLOW-EARED TOUCANET
(Selenidera spectabilis)

Description. 16 - 17½ ". Crown and nape black (or chestnut, ♀). Ear-coverts golden yellow (or black, ♀). Throat, breast, and center of abdomen glossy black. Sides of body orange yellow; flanks chestnut; under tail-coverts crimson. Entire upper surface including wings bright olive green. Tail slaty gray. Skin above eye blue-green, below yellow-green, skin at angle of bill yellow. Iris light red. Bill 3 - 4" Upper portion of upper mandible greenish gray to yellowish green. Lower portion of upper mandible dark brownish black.

Range. Nicaragua southward to Panama.

Colombia. Forest. Tropical zone of the Pacific coast south to the Baudó Mts. and eastward to the lower Cauca and middle Magdalena Valleys.

17. YELLOW-BILLED TOUCANET
(Aulacorhynchus calorhynchus)

Description. 14½ - 15¾ ". Entirely grass green except for blue-gray throat and bright blue patch below the eye. Bill 2½ - 3½ ". Upper mandible and tip of lower mandible olive yellow. Base of upper mandible and most of lower mandible black. Extreme base of lower mandible olive yellow. A white line surrounding base of bill.

Range. Northwestern Venezuela.

Colombia. Forest. Upper tropical and subtropical zone of the Santa Marta Mts. and the Perijá Mts.

18. CHESTNUT-TIPPED TOUCANET
(Aulacorhynchus derbianus)

Description. 15½ - 16½ ". General plumage grass green. Throat whitish, patch at base of bill and line surrounding eye bright blue. An indefinite blue patch on nape. Tips of central tail-feathers chestnut. Bill 3". Bill mostly black, dark crimson at base of both mandibles and tip of upper.

Range. Western British Guiana, southern Venezuela, eastern Ecuador, Peru and northern Bolivia.

Colombia. Subtropical zone. Southeastern Colombia, but no definite locality.

19. EMERALD TOUCANET
(Aulacorhynchus prasinus) Plate IV

Description. 12 - 14". General plumage bright grass green, paler below and more yellowish at sides of body. Throat grayish blue (or white, 1). Under tail-coverts and tips of tail-feathers chestnut. Bill 2½ - 3". Ridge of upper mandible yellowish green. Rest of bill blackish; base of lower mandible dark red (or black, 2). A broad sharply defined white line outlining base of bill.

Range. Mexico southward through Central America to western Venezuela and southern Peru.

Colombia. Forest. Subtropical and lower temperate zone. Santa Marta Mts. (2, *lautus*). From the Perijá Mts. southward on the west slope of the Eastern Andes and the east slope of the Central Andes (1, *albivitta*). West slope of the Central Andes and the northern part of the Western Andes *(griseigularis)*. Southern portion of the Western Andes *(phaeolaemus)*.

20. CRIMSON-RUMPED TOUCANET
(Aulacorhynchus haematopygius)

Description. 15½ - 16½ ". Crown dull green; spot above and below eye blue. Ear-coverts pale green in contrast to green of crown and nape. Upper back olive green, lower back, upper tail-coverts and wings bright grass green, rump crimson, upper tail-coverts grass green. Below bright green, a broad bright blue band across breast, rather diffused and variable in intensity. Tail bluish green, central tail-feathers tipped with chestnut. Bill 3 - 3¼ ". Bill dark crimson, part of ridge and central portion of lower mandible black. Conspicuous line at base of upper mandible and patch at base of lower mandible white.

Range. Northwestern Venezuela, western Ecuador.

Colombia. Forest. Subtropical zone of both slopes of the Western Andes, eastward to the Eastern Andes in Cundinamarca, Meta, Boyacá, Santander, and Caquetá. The Perijá Mts. *(haematopygius)*. Pacific slope of Nariño *(sexnotatus)*.

WOODPECKERS AND PICULETS (Picidae)

Fig. 58. Chestnut Piculet
(*Picumnus cinnamomeus*) p. 188

As might be expected, the vast forests of South America support a large and varied population of woodpeckers ranging in size from three inches to over a foot in length and showing a wide range of color. In habits they resemble woodpeckers from elsewhere. As do woodpeckers in other parts of the world, the South American species climb trees and fly with the same undulating flight.

The tiny piculets form a very distinctive group. Among the smallest of birds, they inhabit wooded pasturelands, forest clearings, desert scrub, open forests and the forest edge in the tropical zone. They clamber about on small twigs which form the ends of branches and search for their food much in the manner of titmice. Like nuthatches they often climb head downward and, like them, do not have stiffened tailfeathers. Unlike most woodpeckers their heads are not crested but they fly with the undulating flight characteristic of the family. They dig their nesting holes in soft-wooded trees, usually only a few feet above the ground. They are not shy and for their size their tapping is very loud. Of the 25 species of piculets found in South America, seven occur in Colombia. In addition to the South American species one is found in the West Indies, three in southeastern Asia and one in Africa. (35 Col.; 79 S.A.; 118 N.&S.A.; 208 wld.)

AID TO IDENTIFICATION

Under five inches: 1, 2E, 3, 4, 5E, 6, 7E.

Over six inches: Back barred black and white 22, 24.
   Back black or black and white 19, 20, 21E, 23, 32, 33E, 34, 35.
   Back crimson or yellow 9, 17E.
   Back chestnut barred with black or not barred 14E, 15E, 16, 18E.
   Back olive (breast and belly barred) 10, 13, 27, 28E, 29, 30, 31.
      (not barred or belly only barred) 8, 11E, 12, 25, 26E.

187

1. CHESTNUT PICULET
(Picumnus cinnamomeus) Fig. 58

Description. 4 - 4¼ ". General plumage chestnut-rufous. Forehead white, center of crown dotted with yellow and spotted posteriorly with white (or center of crown black margined at sides and posteriorly with white spots, ♀).* Tail black, inner webs of central tail-feathers and diagonal band on two outer tail-feathers buffy white.

Range. Northern Venezuela.

Colombia. Thickets in the semi-arid portions of the Caribbean coast region, southward in the Magdalena Valley, at least to Gamarra *(cinnamomeus)*. The middle Magdalena Valley *(persaturatus)*.

2. RUFOUS-BREASTED PICULET
(Picumnus rufiventris) Plate VII

Description. 4½ - 4¾ ". Crown black, spotted with crimson (or black dotted with white, ♀); sides of head, nuchal collar and entire underparts rufous-chestnut. Back dark olive. Tail black, inner web of central tail-feathers and transverse band on two outer tail-feathers buffy.

Range. Eastern Ecuador, western Brazil, Peru and Bolivia.

Colombia. Tropical zone from Meta southward along the eastern base of the Eastern Andes *(rufiventris)*.

3. OLIVACEOUS PICULET
(Picumnus olivaceus)

Description. 4 - 4¼". Crown black, forecrown dotted with orange (or white, ♀), hindcrown with white. Upperparts pale grayish olive, upper tail-coverts whitish. Lower parts pale yellowish clouded on chest and streaked on belly with grayish olive. Inner remiges margined with pale yellowish olive. Tail similar to Scaled Piculet.

Range. Honduras to western Ecuador.

Colombia. Forest and cultivated lands. Tropical and subtropical zone of both slopes of the Central and the west slope of the Eastern Andes *(olivaceus)*. The east slope of the Eastern Andes in Norte de Santander *(tachirensis)*. The east slope of the Western Andes at their northern end and west slope in the valley of the upper río San Juan *(antioquensis)*. Pacific slope of Nariño *(harterti)*.

4. GRAYISH PICULET
(Picumnus granadensis)

Description. 4 - 4¼ ". Crown black, forecrown dotted with golden yellow (or white, ♀), hindcrown dotted with white. Back gray, lower parts soiled white. Inner remiges margined with straw color. Tail similar to Scaled Piculet.

Range. Colombia.

Colombia. Forest and scrub. Upper tropical and subtropical zones of the middle and upper Cauca Valley. The Dagua and Patía Valleys.

5. GOLD-FRONTED PICULET
(Picumnus aurifrons) Plate VIII

Description. 4". Crown smoky brown, dotted on forehead with orange (or white, ♀), on hindcrown with white. Upperparts banded yellowish and olive green; lower parts dirty white, banded with black. Tail similar to Scaled Piculet.

Range. Eastern Ecuador, northeastern Peru and the Amazon Valley.

Colombia. Forest and scrub. Eastern base of the Andes from Meta southward *(lafresnayi)*.

6. SCALED PICULET
(Picumnus squamulatus)

Description. 4 - 4¼ ". Crown black forecrown speckled with orange (or white, ♀), on hindcrown with white. Back olive. lower parts dirty white, feathers both above and below margined with black giving a scaled appearance. Tail black, inner webs of central tail-feathers and diagonal band across two outer tail-feathers white.

Range. Northern Venezuela.

Colombia. Forest and open woodland. Eastern slope of the Eastern Andes up to 4500 ft. in Meta, Boyacá and Arauca *(squamulatus)*. The Santa Marta region and the Zulia Valley *(röhli)*.

*All immature piculets have the crown unspotted.

7. ORINOCO PICULET
(Picumnus pumilus)

Description. 4 - 4¼ ". Forecrown blackish speckled with yellow (or white, ♀), hindcrown pale brown speckled with white. Back olive. Lower parts yellowish white narrowly barred with black. Tail black, inner web of central tail-feathers and diagonal band on two outer tail-feathers yellowish white.

Range. Colombia.

Colombia. Known only from the west bank of the middle Orinoco River in Vichada.

8. SPOT-BREASTED WOODPECKER
(Chrysoptilus punctigula)

Description. 8¾ - 9¼ ". ♂: Forehead and forecrown black, anterior portion of crown, the nape and malar streak crimson; lores and sides of head and neck white. Back olive, barred (or spotted, 1) with black, rump saffron yellow spotted black. Throat black, heavily spotted with white (or white streaked with black, 1). Breast olive, sometimes stained with crimson, fading to yellowish on remainder of underparts which are spotted (or speckled, 2) with black. ♀ like ♂ but without crimson malar streak and crimson of crown restricted to the nape.

Range. Eastern Panama to Venezuela and the Guianas southward to the Amazon Valley, eastern Peru and northern Bolivia.

Colombia. Scrub. Tropical zone of the Caribbean coast region to the west base of the Santa Marta Mts. (1, ujhelyii). Tropical zone east of the Eastern Andes in Meta (2, punctipectus). Tropical zone east of the Andes from Caquetá southward (speciosus). Tropical zone south of the Caribbean littoral west of the Andes southward to Santander (1, striatigularis).

9. CRIMSON-BACKED WOODPECKER
(Piculus rivolii) Plate VII

Description. 11½ - 12". ♂: Top of head crimson, sides of head yellowish white bordered below by a broad crimson malar streak. Hindneck scarlet deepening to crimson on mantle; rump, upper tail-coverts barred mustard yellow and black (or black, 1), tail black. Throat black, feathers of breast basally white, edged

black and fringed crimson giving a scaled appearance; rest of underparts mustard yellow. Outer webs of primaries olive. ♀ differs from ♂ by having the forecrown black, and by lacking the red malar streak.

Range. Western Venezuela southward in the Andes to Bolivia.

Colombia. Forest. Upper subtropical and temperate zone of the Eastern Andes (rivolii). Northern portion of the Western Andes (1, quindiuna). Upper tropical and subtropical zones of the southern portion of the Western and Central Andes and Nariño (1, brevirostris).

10. GOLDEN-OLIVE WOODPECKER
(Piculus rubiginosus)

Description. 8 - 9". ♂: Entire crown, nape, (or sides of crown and nape crimson, rest of crown gray, 1) and malar streak crimson, lores and sides of head soiled white. Upper surface and wings golden olive, stained crimson, wing lining yellowish white. Throat streaked black and white (or solid black, 2). Lower surface banded black and yellow (or yellowish white, 1); rump often paler than back and more or less banded. Tail black, edged olive. ♀ differs from ♂ by having the forecrown blackish becoming grayish on center of crown and malar streak black instead of red.

Range. Southern Mexico southward through Central America to Venezuela, British Guiana, Brazil, Ecuador, Peru, Bolivia and northern Argentina. Trinidad and Tobago.

Colombia. Forest and second growth. Santa Marta Mts. in the upper tropical and subtropical zones (1, alleni). Western slope of the Eastern Andes in the Department of the Magdalena (palmitae). Eastern slope of the Andes from Norte de Santander southward to Meta (buenavistae). The eastern slope of the Eastern Andes near the Ecuador boundary (nuchalis). Subtropical zone of both slopes of the Central Andes (2, gularis). In the subtropical and occasionally lower temperate zones of both slopes of the Western Andes. West slope of the Central Andes at the southernmost end and the upper Patía Valley *(pacificus)*. Pacific slope of the Andes of Nariño (1, *rubripileus)*. East of the Andes in Nariño (1, *michaelis)*.

11. YELLOW-THROATED WOODPECKER
(Piculus flavigula)

Description. 8 - 8½". ♂: Differs from the White-throated Woodpecker principally by having the throat and sides of head golden yellow, and no red malar stripe. ♀ differs by having the throat and sides of head golden yellow, the crown dull golden yellow instead of olive yellowish.

Range. The Guianas, Venezuela, Ecuador, Peru, and Brazil.

Colombia. Forest. Tropical zone east of the Andes from Meta southward *(magnus)*.

12. WHITE-THROATED WOODPECKER
(Piculus leucolaemus)

Description. 7¾ - 8½". ♂: Crown, nape and malar streak crimson; ear-coverts olive; broad line below eye and below ear-coverts golden yellow. Upper surface bright golden olive green. Throat white, breast olive, spotted with white; lower breast and belly yellowish white, banded with black, wing lining rufous-chestnut. ♀ differs from ♂ by having the crown golden olive, only the nape scarlet and no red malar streak.

Range. Western and eastern Ecuador, western Brazil, Peru and Bolivia.

Colombia. Tropical zone of the Eastern Andes in northwestern Cundinamarca *(leucolaemus)*. Pacific coast from the Baudó Mts. southward *(litae)*.

13. GOLDEN-GREEN WOODPECKER
(Piculus chrysochloros)

Description. 9 - 9½". ♂: Crown, nape and malar streak crimson, sides of head olive, stripe below eye yellow. Upper surface bright olive green. Throat whitish banded with olive (or plain orange-buff, 1); rest of under surface banded olive and greenish white (or olive and orange-buff, 1). Wings olive, inner webs of feathers cinnamon-chestnut. Tail olive. ♀

differs from ♂ by having the crown green like the back (or old gold in contrast to back, 1).

Range. Panama southward to Venezuela, British Guiana, Brazil, Ecuador, Peru, Bolivia and Argentina.

Colombia. Forest. Southern Córdoba (1, *aurosus)*. Middle and lower Magdalena Valley and tropical zone of the Santa Marta region undoubtedly eastward to the Zulia Valley *(xanthochlorus)*. Tropical zone east of the Andes from Meta southward *(capistratus)*.

14. CHESTNUT WOODPECKER
(Celeus elegans)

Description. 11 - 12". ♂: Uniform chestnut, deepest below and on crest. Malar streak crimson. Rump buff to yellowish buff. Inner remiges uniform chestnut (or barred black and buff on inner web, 1). Tail blackish. ♀: Lacks the crimson malar streak.

Range. The Guianas and Venezuela southward to eastern Brazil, northern Mato Grosso, eastern Ecuador, Peru and Bolivia. Trinidad.

Colombia. Forest. Tropical zone east of the Eastern Andes from Meta southward to the Amazon *(citreopygius)*. Vichada and Vaupés (1, *jumana)*.

15. SCALE-BREASTED WOODPECKER
(Celeus grammicus)

Description. 9 - 9½". Chestnut, back evenly barred with black (or back uniform, wing-coverts only barred, 1). Rump yellowish buff. Malar streak crimson (without it, ♀); feathers of lower throat, breast and upperparts of belly edged with black giving a more (or less, 1) scaled appearance. Tail basally chestnut, distally black.

Range. The Guianas, Venezuela southward to eastern Ecuador, Peru, western Brazil and northern Bolivia.

Colombia. Forest. Tropical zone along the base of the Andes from Meta southward (1, *verreauxii)*. Eastern Colombia along the río Guainía *(grammicus)*.

16. CINNAMON WOODPECKER
(Celeus loricatus)

Description. 9 - 9½". ♂ : Above dark cinnamon more or less spotted and banded with black, sometimes almost uniform above (or barred with black, 1). Throat and side of neck crimson, hind portion of crown occasionally tinged crimson. Lower surface buff, scalloped and spotted on breast with black (or, occasionally, markings on lower parts obsolete, 2). ♀ : Similar, but lacks the crimson throat and sides of neck.

Range. Nicaragua to western Ecuador.

Colombia. Forest. Tropical zone of the Pacific coast from the middle Atrato Valley southward and the lower Cauca to the west side of the middle Magdalena Valley (1, loricatus). The Lebrija Valley, Santander (2, degener). The lower Magdalena Valley, the valley of the río Sinú westward across northern Colombia to the Pacific coast (mentalis).

17. CREAM-COLORED WOODPECKER
(Celeus flavus)

Description. 10½ - 11". ♂ : Malar streak scarlet. Entire body plumage and conspicuous crest chamois (or sulphur yellow, 1). Wings chestnut, inner webs of primaries black, tertials partially yellow, lesser wing-coverts blackish, greater ones chestnut edged black (or wings dull brown, wing-coverts edged yellow, 1). Tail brownish black. ♀ : Lacks scarlet malar streak.

Range. Venezuela, the Guianas and northern Brazil to Bahia. Eastern Peru, northern Bolivia.

Colombia. Forest. Tropical zone east of the Andes in Vaupés, Vichada and Meta (flavus). Eastern base of the Andes in Caquetá southward to Amazonas (1, peruvianus). At Morelia in Caquetá a specimen of the typical race has been taken but it was perhaps a straggler to the region.

18. RINGED WOODPECKER
(Celeus torquatus)

Description. 10 - 11". Head and throat buffy brown, malar streak red (or without malar streak, ♀). Neck, upper mantle and breast black, rest of underparts buffy cinnamon barred black. Back, wings and tail rufous-chestnut more or less barred with black.

Range. Venezuela, the Guianas, Brazil, Peru, and Bolivia.

Colombia. Known only from the forests at the foot of the Macarena Mts., Meta (occidentalis).

19. LINEATED WOODPECKER
(Dryocopus lineatus)

Description. 13 - 14" (or 11½ - 13", 1). ♂ : Crown, long crest and malar streak crimson. Line from lores running below eye and continuing down side of neck and breast white. Ear-coverts dark gray, throat white streaked with black. Entire upper surface, wings and tail black, scapulars white. Upper breast black; lower breast, abdomen and under tail-coverts white, barred with black (or buff, spotted with dusky brown, 1). Under wing-coverts white. ♀ differs from ♂ in having the anterior half of crown and malar streak black instead of crimson.

Range. Mexico southward to western Ecuador. Venezuela southward through Peru and Brazil to Argentina and Bolivia. Trinidad.

Colombia. Forest. Tropical zone west of the Eastern Andes except Nariño (nuperus). Tropical zone east of the Andes (lineatus). Southwestern Cauca southward (1, fuscipennis).

20. ACORN WOODPECKER
(Melanerpes formicivorus)

Description. 7½ - 8½". Forehead and hindcrown black, forecrown white; a band across nape scarlet (or no scarlet band, ♀). Ear-coverts, chin and upper throat black. A broad band across lower throat pale yellow, joined to the white forecrown by a line passing in front of the eye. Band across chest greenish black with a few red spots in center. Abdomen white, breast and sides of body streaked black and white. Mantle glossy greenish black. Wings dull black, base of primaries white,

PLATE IX

TYRANNINE
WOODCREEPER
(*Dendrocincla
t. tyrannina*)
Page 198

WEDGE-BILLED
WOODCREEPER
(*Glyphorynchus spir-
urus sublestus*)
Page 198

LONG-BILLED
WOODCREEPER
(*Nasica longirostris*)
Page 199

YELLOW-THROATED
SPINETAIL
(*Certhiaxis cinna-
momea fuscifrons*)
Page 207

STREAK-CAPPED
SPINETAIL
(*Cranioleuca hellmayri*)
Page 207

MANY-STRIPED
SPINETAIL
(*Asthenes flam-
mulata multostriata*)
Page 209

STRIPE-NECKED
SPINETAIL
(*Siptornis striaticollis*)
Page 209

DOUBLE-BANDED
SOFTTAIL
(*Xenerpestes min-
losi umbraticus*)
Page 209

STREAKED
TUFTEDCHEEK
(*Pseudocolaptes
b. boissonneautii*)
Page 211

CHESTNUT-WINGED
HOOKBILL
(*Ancistrops
s. strigilatus*)
Page 211

BUFF-FRONTED
FOLIAGE-GLEANER
(*Philydor rufus riveti*)
Page 212

RUDDY
FOLIAGE-GLEANER
(*Automolus rubi-
ginosus rufipectus*)
Page 213

FLAMMULATED
TREEHUNTER
(*Thripadectes
f. flammulatus*)
Page 214

PLAIN XENOPS
(*Xenops minutus neglectus*)
Page 214

SHARP-TAILED
STREAMCREEPER
(*Lochmias nema-
tura sororia*)
Page 216

BLACK-CRESTED
ANTSHRIKE
(*Sakesphorus cana-
densis pulchellus*)
Page 219

DUSKY ANTBIRD
(*Cercomacra tyran-
nina rufiventris*)
Page 231

SPOT-WINGED
ANTSHRIKE
(*Pygiptila stel-
laris occipitalis*)
Page 221

BARE-CROWNED
ANTBIRD
(*Gymnocichla
n. nudiceps*)
Page 233

IMMACULATE ANTBIRD
(*Myrmeciza i. immaculata*)
Page 235

STRIATED ANTTHRUSH
(*Chamaeza nobilis rubida*)
Page 237

showing a conspicuous band in flight; tail black.

Range. Pacific coast and southwestern United States southward through Central America to western Panama.

Colombia. Open woodland. Subtropical and occasionally temperate zone of all three Andean ranges, southward to the head of the Cauca and Magdalena Valleys. Not on the east slope of the Eastern Andes *(flavigula).*

21. YELLOW-TUFTED WOODPECKER
(Melanerpes cruentatus)

Description. 7½ - 8¼". Forehead and hindcrown blue-black, center of crown crimson (or black, ♀). Eyebrow yellowish white becoming golden yellow posteriorly, the two joining on the nape to form a golden yellow band. Sides of head, throat and breast, mantle and wing-coverts shining blue-black. Lower back and upper tail-coverts white. A broad band down center of lower breast and abdomen scarlet; sides of body barred black and white. Wings and tail dull black, inner webs of remiges notched with white.

Range. Tropical South America east of the Andes southward to the Amazon and on the west to northern Bolivia.

Colombia. Forest. Tropical zone east of the Eastern Andes south to the Amazon *(cruentatus).*

22. GOLDEN-NAPED WOODPECKER
(Melanerpes chrysauchen)

Description. 7 - 7½". ♂ : Forehead buffy white, crown crimson, nape golden yellow. Stripe through eye, down sides of neck, and continued down sides of back black. Broad band down center of back including upper tail-coverts white. Throat white, rest of underparts isabelline barred on sides with black, center of belly scarlet. Wings and tail black, inner remiges and central tail-feathers with a few white spots. ♀ like ♂ but red of crown confined to nape.

Range. Costa Rica to western Panama.

Colombia. Upper tropical zone of the middle Magdalena Valley *(pulcher).*

23. BLACK-CHEEKED WOODPECKER
(Melanerpes pucherani) Plate VII

Description. 7 - 8". ♂ : Forehead and extreme forecrown golden yellow, hindcrown and nape scarlet. Eyebrow and ear-coverts black, streak behind eye white. Mantle and inner remiges black, barred with white; lower back and upper tail-coverts pure white. Throat whitish, breast dirty olive, rest of underparts yellowish olive barred with black; center of abdomen crimson. Tail black, the central feathers notched with white. ♀ : Differs by having the crimson confined to the nape, the center of crown being black, mottled with white.

Range. Southern Mexico to western Ecuador.

Colombia. Forest and clearings. Tropical zone of coastal Colombia *(pucherani.)*

24. RED-CROWNED WOODPECKER
(Melanerpes rubricapillus)

Description. 6¾ - 7¼". ♂ : Forehead whitish, crown and nape scarlet. Sides of head, throat and underparts dark isabelline, center of belly scarlet-orange. Back barred black and white, rump and upper tail-coverts white. Primaries black barred only toward base. Central tail-feathers mostly white, rest black, the outermost notched and tipped with white. ♀ differs by having only the nape scarlet.

Range. The Bay Islands of Honduras, southern Costa Rica, Panama, the Pearl Islands, Venezuela. Tobago and Margarita Island.

Colombia. Open woodland and scrub. Arid tropical zone of the Caribbean coast and Magdalena Valley. East of the Andes in the Orinoco region *(rubricapillus).* The eastern Guajira Peninsula *(paraguanae).*

25. SMOKY-BROWN WOODPECKER
(Veniliornis fumigatus)

Description. 6 - 6½". General plumage smoky olive brown (or tinged red on mantle, 1), throat grayish. Entire crown crimson (or dark brown, ♀). Wings dull brown barred with white on inner webs. Tail blackish.

Range. Mexico southward to Venezuela, Ecuador, Peru and Bolivia.

Colombia. Forest and open woodland. The Panama border (1, *sanguinolentus*). Subtropical to lower temperate zone in the Santa Marta Mts. *(exsul)*. Upper tropical to temperate zones of the rest of Colombia west of the Andes and east of them in Meta *(fumigatus)*.

26. LITTLE WOODPECKER
(Veniliornis passerinus)

Description. 6½ - 7". ♂: Forecrown and sides of head brownish olive, hindcrown scarlet. Upperparts bright yellowish olive. Remiges with white notches on inner web. Underparts dark olive, the breast slightly spotted, belly narrowly banded with yellowish white. The wing-coverts slightly spotted with yellowish. Tail-feathers blackish. ♀ differs from ♂ in having the crown olive, dotted with whitish, and tail obscurely barred with olive.

Range. Venezuela and the Guianas southward to Paraguay, Argentina and southern Bolivia.

Colombia. Eastern slope of the Eastern Andes in Meta and Boyacá *(fidelis)*. Putumayo *(agilis)*.

27. GOLDEN-COLLARED WOODPECKER
(Veniliornis cassinii)

Description. 7 - 7¾". ♂: Crown crimson, nuchal band dull yellow; back olive green (or golden olive, 1). Lower parts white banded with black (or tinged on chest with red, 1). Wing-feathers notched with whitish on inner web. Tail blackish banded with olive. ♀ like ♂ but forecrown olive brown, hindcrown and nape dull yellow.

Range. The Guianas and Venezuela south to the north bank of the middle Amazon.

Colombia. Forest and scrub. Tropical zone east of the Andes in Caquetá *(caquetanus)*. Tropical zone of the Pacific coast from the lower Atrato southward (1, *chocoensis*).

28. RED-STAINED WOODPECKER
(Veniliornis affinis)

Description. 7 - 7¾". ♂: Crown and nape crimson, nuchal band yellow; upperparts golden olive. Below whitish coarsely banded with blackish olive. Webs of remiges notched with white, wing-coverts stained crimson; tail blackish banded with olive. ♀ differs from ♂ in having the crown smoky brown, nuchal collar dull yellow.

Range. Venezuela southward to southern Brazil, Ecuador, Peru and northern Bolivia.

Colombia. Forest clearings and scrub. Tropical zone east of the Eastern Andes *(orenocensis)*.

29. RED-RUMPED WOODPECKER
(Veniliornis kirkii)

Description. 6½ - 7". ♂: Crown, nape, rump and upper tail-coverts scarlet. Nuchal collar golden yellow; back golden olive. Underparts evenly banded white and dark olive. Flight feathers notched with white on inner webs, tail blackish, the outer feathers barred with olive. ♀ differs from ♂ in having a smoky brown crown with a broad yellow nuchal collar.

Range. Costa Rica to western Ecuador, Venezuela. Trinidad and Tobago.

Colombia. Forest, scrub and mangroves. Tropical zone west of the Eastern Andes including Santa Marta *(cecilii)*.

30. YELLOW-VENTED WOODPECKER
(Veniliornis dignus)

Description. 7 - 7½". ♂: Crown, nape and region behind ear-coverts crimson; stripe through eye blackish bordered above and below by white. Back and wings bright olive more or less stained with crimson. Throat grayish; breast banded pale yellow and dark olive; abdomen clear pale yellow. Wing-coverts with a few yellowish spots. Inner webs of remiges notched with white; central tail-feathers blackish, outermost ones barred with buff. ♀ like ♂ but crown blackish, nuchal collar crimson.

Range. Western Venezuela, eastern Ecuador and Peru.

Colombia. Forest. Upper tropical and subtropical zones of the three Andean ranges except the east slope of the Eastern Andes. Andes of Nariño *(dignus)*.

31. BAR-BELLIED WOODPECKER
(Veniliornis nigriceps)

Description. 7¾ - 8¼ ". ♂ : Crown and nape scarlet margined laterally by a yellowish white band spotted dusky. Ear-coverts smoky gray. Entire back olive yellow stained with crimson on mantle. Entire under surface greenish white evenly banded with blackish green. Inner webs of remiges notched with white. Tail-feathers blackish, the outer ones barred with yellowish. ♀ like ♂ but crown olive brown.

Range. The Andes of Ecuador, Peru and Bolivia.

Colombia. Forest. Upper subtropical and temperate zones. The Central Andes and the Andes of Nariño (equifasciatus).

32. CRIMSON-CRESTED WOODPECKER
(Phloeoceastes melanoleucos)

Description. 13½ - 14¼ ". ♂ : Crown, crest, and sides of head crimson, spot on cheek white, margined above by black. Area at base of bill white, outlined in black before the eye (or not outlined in black, 1; or head entirely crimson except for white ear-coverts, 2). Stripe on sides of neck continuing down sides of mantle and joining to form a V, white. Rest of back, closed wing and the tail black (or brownish, 2). Throat and breast black, rest of lower parts whitish buff (or cinnamon-buff, 1, 2) barred with black. Inner margins of flight feathers basally white (or buff, 2). ♀ differs from ♂ in having the center of the crown and stripe below eye black, area behind eye and sides of crest crimson. Forehead and broad moustacial streak white continued down sides of neck (or entire crown crimson with no black stripe below eye, 2).

Range. Panama, Venezuela and the Guianas southward to Ecuador, Peru, Bolivia, Paraguay, southern Brazil and Argentina. Trinidad.

Colombia. Forest. Tropical, occasionally to lower temperate zone. East of the Andes from Meta eastward to the Orinoco and southward to Amazonas (melanoleucos). The Santa Marta region and the west slope of the Eastern Andes westward (1, malherbii). Tropical zone of the Pacific slope of Nariño (2, gayaquilensis).

33. RED-NECKED WOODPECKER
(Phloeoceastes rubricollis)

Description. 13½ - 14¼ ". ♂ : Head, neck, throat and upper breast crimson; lower breast and rest of underparts and wing lining dark cinnamon-rufous. Back, wings and tail black. ♀ differs from ♂ in having the forehead and broad wedge-shaped stripe below eye white outlined in black.

Range. Southern Venezuela, the Guianas, northern and western Brazil, Ecuador, Peru and Bolivia.

Colombia. Forest. Tropical zone east of the Eastern Andes from Meta southward (rubricollis).

34. POWERFUL WOODPECKER
(Phloeoceastes pollens)

Description. 14 - 14½ ". ♂ : Crown and crest scarlet; forehead and sides of head black. Nasal plumes and stripe below eye continuing down sides of neck to sides of breast, and sides of mantle where they join to make a V, white. Center of upper back black, lower back white, upper tail-coverts black. Throat and upper breast, closed wings and tail black, the flight feathers barred white on inner web and tipped white. Below buff barred black. ♀ differs from ♂ by lacking the scarlet on the head.

Range. Western Venezuela, Colombia, Ecuador and Peru.

Colombia. Forest. Upper tropical and temperate zone of all three Andean ranges including Nariño (pollens).

35. CRIMSON-BELLIED WOODPECKER
(Phloeoceastes haematogaster)

Description. 10½ - 11¼ ". ♂ : Crown, margined in front by a narrow black line, nape and neck crimson; stripe through eye black, bordered above and below by a buff line. Throat and foreneck black; rest of underparts dark crimson. Upper back black, lower back and rump crimson, upper tail-coverts black, tipped dark crimson. Wings and tail black, the remiges with large buffy white spots, and tipped white. ♀ differs from ♂ by having the white stripe below the eye continued down the sides of the neck and the crimson of the underparts more or less banded with black and buff.

Range. Panama to western Ecuador. Eastern Ecuador and Peru.

Colombia. Forest. Tropical zone east of the Eastern Andes from Boyacá southward along the base of the Andes *(haematogaster)*. West of the Andes from the middle Magdalena Valley westward and southward to Nariño *(splendens)*.

WOODCREEPERS (Dendrocolaptidae)

Fig. 59. Spot-crowned Woodcreeper
(Lepidocolaptes affinis) p. 202

Woodcreepers form a large and characteristic tropical American family, reminiscent of the brown creepers of temperate regions. Dull in color, mostly clothed in shades of brown, they vary in length from less than six inches to over a foot. They climb trees and branches, supported by their stiffened tails much in the manner of woodpeckers; however they do not tap like them, but, like nuthatches, explore the bark for insects. Some have short, almost conical bills while others have very long, sometimes curved ones. Most species have a rather long, straight, heavy and slightly-hooked bill. Tails are long with the shafts of the feathers very stiff, the sharply-pointed tips protruding.

Woodcreepers inhabit forest and second growth and most of the species occur in the tropical zone. They nest in cavities in trees and are rather solitary in habits. The sexes are alike. (27 Col.; 44 S.A.; 48 N.&S.A.; 48 wld.)

AID TO IDENTIFICATION
Bill very long, slender, scythe-shaped 23, 24, 25, 26[E].
Bill not scythe-shaped:
  Without obvious markings on crown or back 1, 2, 2a, 3, 4, 5, 6, 8[E].
  Streaked, spotted, or barred on crown or back (below barred or partially so) 10, 11, (below streaked) 7[E], 9, 13[E], 21, 22, (below spotted or scaled) 12, 14[E], 15, 16[E], 17, 18, 19, 20.

197

1. TYRANNINE WOODCREEPER
(Dendrocincla tyrannina) Plate IX

Description. 10½ - 11½". Above dark brown; below olive brown, throat paler and grayer on breast, the latter with pale inconspicuous shaft streaks. Wings, tail, upper and under tail-coverts chestnut. Bill heavy, about the length of the head.

Range. Western Venezuela, Ecuador and northern Peru.

Colombia. Forest. Upper tropical to lower temperate zone of the Andes. Not recorded from Santa Marta or Nariño *(tyrannina)*. Páramo de Tamá in Norte de Santander on the Venezuelan border *(hellmayri)*.

2. PLAIN-BROWN WOODCREEPER
(Dendrocincla fuliginosa)

Description. 8¼ - 9½". Above and below uniform brown, grayer on throat, more rufescent on abdomen. Lores and ear-coverts gray, obsolete moustacial streak black. Wings, tail and upper tail-coverts chestnut. Lower mandible bluish.

Range. Honduras southward to Ecuador, Peru, the Amazon Valley and Bolivia. Trinidad and Tobago.

Colombia. Forest. Tropical zone of northern Colombia from the Perijá and Santa Marta Mts. southward up the Magdalena and Cauca Valleys *(lafresnayei)*. Sinú and Atrato Valleys southward in western Colombia to Nariño *(ridgwayi)*. Tropical zone in the eastern foothills of the Eastern Andes from Meta southward *(phaeochroa)*. Lowlands of Boyacá, Arauca and Norte de Santander *(barinensis)*.

3. RUDDY WOODCREEPER
(Dendrocincla homochroa)

Description. 7½ - 8". Uniform chestnut brown, throat paler. Crown, wings, tail and upper tail-coverts bright chestnut.

Range. Southern Mexico southward through Central America to western Venezuela.

Colombia. Forest. Tropical zone of northern Chocó and probably eastward in northern Colombia *(ruficeps)*. Arauca and the Perijá Mts. *(meridionalis)*.

[Species 2a, see Page 409.]

4. LONG-TAILED WOODCREEPER
(Deconychura longicauda)

Description. 8½ - 9½". Upperparts dull brown, crown with minute pale shaft streaks. Throat, sides of head and narrow eyebrow fulvous. Chest and rest of underparts pale olive brown, the breast conspicuously spotted with fulvous. Wings, tail and upper tail-coverts bright rufous-chestnut. Tail rather long. Bill rather short.

Range. Costa Rica southward to Venezuela, the Guianas, the Amazon Valley, eastern Ecuador, Peru and Bolivia.

Colombia. Forest. Tropical zone of northern Colombia from the upper río Sinú eastward to the middle Magdalena Valley *(longicauda)*. Southeastern Colombia on the río Guainía *(connectens)*.

5. OLIVACEOUS WOODCREEPER
(Sittasomus griseicapillus) Plate X

Description. 5¾-6¾". Head, neck, underparts grayish olive (or grayish, 1). Mantle olive, tinged with rufescent. Primaries and secondaries blackish with a buff patch on the inner web of all but the three outermost feathers. Inner remiges, tail, lower back and rump, upper and under tail-coverts bright rufous-chestnut. Bill rather short.

Range. Southern Mexico south through Central America to Venezuela, southeastern Brazil, Paraguay, Argentina, Ecuador, Peru and eastern Bolivia. Tobago.

Colombia. Forest. Tropical zone of northern Colombia from Córdoba east to the foothills of the Perijá Mts. *(levis)*. East of the Andes from Meta southward *(1, amazonus)*.

6. WEDGE-BILLED WOODCREEPER
(Glyphorynchus spirurus) Plate IX

Description. 5¾-6¼". General plumage wood brown. Throat buffy white (or cinnamon-buff, 1), arrow-shaped spots on breast white. Lower back and tail bright chestnut. Remiges dark brown, all but the three outermost with a conspicuous buffy bar on basal portion of inner web. Bill short, mandible slightly upturned.

Range. Southern Mexico southward over most of tropical South America from Venezuela to southern Brazil and Bolivia.

Colombia. Forest. Tropical and subtropical zones. West of the Western Andes in the upper Atrato and río San Juan (subrufescens), eastward to the lower Cauca and east of the Andes in Boyacá and Arauca (sublestus). The upper Sinú Valley eastward to the middle Magdalena Valley and east slope of the Andes in Norte de Santander (integratus). Tropical zone east of the Andes from Meta southward (1, rufigularis).

7. LONG-BILLED WOODCREEPER
(Nasica longirostris) Plate IX

Description. 14-15″. Crown and hindneck dark brown with pale shaft streaks, these expanding on hindcrown and hindneck into white stripes; rest of upper surface, wings and tail bright reddish chestnut. Throat, foreneck and streak above eye white, rest of underparts rufous-brown, the feathers of the lower neck and breast broadly streaked with white. Bill about 3″ long.

Range. The upper Orinoco Valley. French Guiana. Northern Brazil, eastern Ecuador, Peru and northeastern Bolivia.

Colombia. Forest. Tropical zone east of the Eastern Andes from Vichada and Caquetá southward to the Amazon (longirostris).

8. CINNAMON-THROATED WOODCREEPER
(Dendrexetastes rufigula)

Description. 10¼-10¾″. Head and back olive brown, forecrown tinged rufescent; lower back, rump, wings, upper tail-coverts and tail chestnut. Throat, lower breast and abdomen dull cinnamon-buff, chest darker with a few pale, black-bordered streaks. Bill about 1.5″.

Range. The Guianas southward to the Amazon and westward to eastern Ecuador, Peru and northeastern Bolivia.

Colombia. Forest. Tropical zone east of the Andes from Caquetá southward to Amazonas (devillei).

9. STRONG-BILLED WOODCREEPER
(Xiphocolaptes promeropirhynchus)
Plate X

Description. 12 - 13¾″. General color rufescent-brown. Crown dark brown with pale shaft streaks extending onto upper mantle (or without shaft streaks on mantle 1). Sides of head streaked dark brown and white; an ill-defined dark moustacial streak. Throat plain buffy white. Breast streaked with pale fulvous, center of belly marked with a few broken bars of black and fulvous (or without bars, 2). Bill 1.8 - 2.2″, heavy, curved, dark gray.

Range. Southern Mexico to western Panama. Venezuela, western Brazil, Ecuador, Peru and northern Bolivia.

Colombia. Forest. Subtropical zone of the Santa Marta Mts. (2, sanctae-martae). Subtropical to temperate zone of the slopes of the Andes above the Magdalena Valley (promeropirhynchus). Upper tropical to temperate zone of the west slope of the Central Andes (virgatus). Tropical zone of the Sinú Valley (rostratus). East of the Andes in the Macarena Mts. (1, macarenae).

10. BARRED WOODCREEPER
(Dendrocolaptes certhia) Plate X

Description. 10 - 11½″. Crown and underparts brown barred with black, throat paler. Mantle rufescent brown regularly to obsoletely barred with black. Wings, rump and upper tail-coverts rufous-chestnut. Bill about 1.5″.

Range. Southeastern Mexico south to Venezuela, the Guianas southward to the Amazon, eastern Ecuador, Peru, Bolivia.

Colombia. Forest. Tropical zone. Pacific coast eastward to the west bank of the Magdalena (colombianus). Santa Marta region southward east of the Magdalena River to Santander (hyleorus). Northeastern corner of Norte de Santander (punctipectus). Tropical zone east of the Andes from Meta southward (radiolatus). Banks of the Orinoco (certhia).

11. BLACK-BANDED WOODCREEPER
(Dendrocolaptes picumnus)

Description. 11½-12″. Crown and upper mantle brown streaked with fulvous, center of back more rufescent with traces of black bars. Throat pale fulvous, breast brown broadly streaked with pale fulvous; rest of under surface buffy brown banded with black. Rump, wings, tail and upper tail-coverts rufous-chestnut. Bill about 1.25".

Range. Guatemala southward to western Panama, Venezuela, the Guianas, central and western Brazil, eastern and western Ecuador, Peru and Bolivia.

Colombia. Forest. Subtropical zone west of the Eastern Andes and the Perijá Mts. but not Santa Marta or Nariño (multistrigatus). Subtropical zone of the Santa Marta Mts. (seilerni). East of the Andes from Meta southward (validus).

12. STRAIGHT-BILLED WOODCREEPER
(Xiphorhynchus picus) Plate X

Description. 8½ - 9". Crown brown with fulvous-white drop-shaped spots lengthening into streaks on extreme upper mantle. Throat, foreneck, ear-coverts and eyebrow white, the feathers of the upper breast white margined with black; rest of underparts brown. Back, wings and tail rufous-chestnut. Bill about .9-1".

Range. Panama, Venezuela and the Guianas southward to eastern Brazil; westward to Ecuador, Peru and northern Bolivia. Margarita I. Trinidad.

Colombia. Scrub lands. Tropical zone. Northwestern Colombia (extimus). Lower Magdalena Valley eastward to the Perijá Mts. (dugandi). The Guajira Peninsula to the base of the Santa Marta Mts. (picirostris). The Zulia Valley probably southward, east of the Andes to Meta (saturatior). Caquetá region (borreroi). Orinoco region in Vichada (picus).

13. STRIPED WOODCREEPER
(Xiphorhynchus obsoletus)

Description. 7½-8" (or 7-7½", 1). Crown dark brown conspicuously marked with pale fulvous drop-shaped spots. Mantle rufous-brown broadly streaked with fulvous lines bordered with black. Rump, wings and tail rufous-chestnut. Throat pale buff, lower parts olivaceous brown broadly streaked on breast, less so on

upper abdomen, with fulvous white, each stripe margined with black. Bill .9-1".

Range. The Guianas, western and southern Venezuela southward to the lower Amazon Valley and westward to Ecuador, Peru and Bolivia.

Colombia. Forest edge. Orinoco and río Guainía regions northward to eastern Boyacá and Arauca (notatus). Caquetá region northward to the Macarena Mts. (1, palliatus).

14. OCELLATED WOODCREEPER
(Xiphorhynchus ocellatus)

Description. 8¼-9". Crown and nape dark brown the feathers fulvous spotted, mantle brown narrowly streaked with a few fulvous lines. Rump, wings and tail chestnut. Throat, sides of neck and upper breast deep buff, the feathers edged with black. Rest of lower parts brown, paler and a little more rufescent in center. Extreme upper breast with drop-shaped fulvous spots edged blackish, lower breast with a few rather inconspicuous pale streaks. Bill .9-1.1".

Range. Southern Venezuela, the middle and upper Amazon Valley to eastern Peru and southward to southern Bolivia.

Colombia. Forest. Tropical zone of the eastern base of the Andes (napensis). The río Guainía and río Vaupés regions (ocellatus).

15. AMAZONIAN WOODCREEPER
(Xiphorhynchus spixii)

Description. 8¼ - 9". Crown blackish brown spotted with fulvous. Back rufous brown with narrow fulvous streaks edged with black on upper mantle. Throat fulvous white darkening to buff on lower throat where the feathers are edged with black, rest of lower parts brownish buff, feathers of breast with round fulvous spots edged with black. Rump, upper tail-coverts, wings and tail chestnut. Bill 1-1.1".

Range. Amazonia. From the mouth of the Amazon River westward to northern Bolivia, eastern Peru and eastern Ecuador.

Colombia. Forest. Upper tropical zone of the east slope of the Eastern Andes in Meta and the head to the Magdalena Valley (buenaevistae).

16. ELEGANT WOODCREEPER
(Xiphorhynchus elegans)

Description. 8¼ - 9″. Very similar to Amazonian Woodcreeper but differs by having the marks on the mantle larger and more drop-shaped, and the spotting of the breast more conspicuous.

Range. Western Brazil, eastern Peru north of the Amazon and eastern Ecuador.

Colombia. Forest. Tropical zone of the Caquetá region *(ornatus).*

17. BUFF-THROATED WOODCREEPER
(Xiphorhynchus guttatus)

Description. 9¼ - 9¾″ (or 10¾ - 11¾″, 1). Crown and sides of head and neck dark brown with drop-shaped buff spots margined with black. Back umber brown (or rufous brown, 1) streaked on upper mantle with fulvous. Throat isabelline; breast and sides of body grayish brown (or rufescent-brown, 1) broadly streaked on breast with fulvous-white (or buff, 1), the streaks margined with black. Rump, upper tail-coverts, wings and tail rufous-chestnut (or chestnut, 1). Bill about 1.3 (or 1.4 - 1.5″, 1).

Range. Guatemala south to Venezuela, the Guianas, southern Brazil and northern Bolivia. Margarita I. Trinidad and Tobago.

Colombia. Forest. Tropical zone. Upper tropical zone of the Cauca Valley *(rosenbergi).* From the Panama border eastward to the upper Magdalena Valley and Arauca *(nanus).* Catatumbo lowlands *(demonstratus).* East of the Andes from Meta southward (1, *guttatoides).* Orinoco region in Vichada *(polystictus).*

18. BLACK-STRIPED WOODCREEPER
(Xiphorhynchus lachrymosus) Plate X

Description. 9-9¾″. Crown and mantle black (or brownish black, 1), head streaked and the mantle much more broadly striped with fulvous white. Lower back, rump, upper tail-coverts, wings and tail rufous-chestnut, the wing-coverts edged with black. Throat and lower parts buff, feathers of lower neck, breast and upper abdomen margined black giving a scaled appearance. Bill 1.1-1.3″ (or 1.3-1.5″, 1).

Range. Nicaragua to western Ecuador.

Colombia. Forest. Tropical zone. Atrato Valley and the Pacific coast (1, *lachrymosus).* Upper Sinú, lower Cauca and middle Magdalena Valleys *(alarum).*

19. SPOTTED WOODCREEPER
(Xiphorhynchus erythropygius)

Description. 9¼-10¼″. Very much like the Olive-backed Woodcreeper but differs by having the crown uniform or very slightly streaked, the mantle more rufescent. Throat spotted with dark olive instead of scaled. Wings and tail chestnut.

Range. Mexico to western Ecuador.

Colombia. Forest. Tropical and subtropical zones of the west slope of the Western Andes southward into Nariño *(aequatorialis).* Tropical zone of extreme northwestern Colombia and probably the lower Cauca Valley *(insolitus).*

20. OLIVE-BACKED WOODCREEPER
(Xiphorhynchus triangularis)

Description. 9¼-10″. Crown and mantle dull olive brown, crown, sides of head and upper mantle with fulvous shaft stripes. Lower back rufescent; rump, upper tail-coverts and tail chestnut. Wing-coverts, outer margins of primaries olivaceous, inner webs chestnut, inner remiges dull chestnut. Throat fulvous, the feathers edged with black giving a scaled appearance. Breast and belly olive brown, spotted with fulvous. Bill 1-1.1″.

Range. Western Venezuela, eastern Ecuador, Peru and Bolivia.

Colombia. Forest. Upper tropical and subtropical zones of the Eastern and Central Andes and the tropical and subtropical zones of the Western Andes *(triangularis).*

21. STREAK-HEADED WOODCREEPER
(Lepidocolaptes souleyetii)

Description. 8 - 8½″ (or 7½ - 8″, 1). Top of head and nape dark brown conspicuously streaked with pale fulvous. Back plain, pale rufous-brown; rump, wings and upper tail-coverts rufous. Throat fulvous, rest of underparts olive brown, broadly streaked fulvous black-margined lines. Bill .9-1″, slender and somewhat curved.

Range. Mexico southward to western Ecuador. Venezuela, British Guiana to

northern Brazil, east Ecuador and Peru.
Colombia. Open woodland, cocoa and coffee plantations. Tropical zone. Santa Marta region and Atlántico (1, *littoralis*). Tropical zone of northwestern Colombia, the Cauca and middle and upper Magdalena Valleys and east of the Andes from the río Zulia southward to Meta *(lineaticeps)*. Tropical zone of the Pacific coast of Nariño *(esmeraldae)*.

22. SPOT-CROWNED WOODCREEPER
(Lepidocolaptes affinis) Fig. 59

Description. 8½-9″. Crown and mantle rufous-brown, the crown with pale spots edged with black. Eyebrow, throat and and ear-coverts white, the feathers lightly edged with black. Lower parts brown to olive brown, broadly streaked with white, the white stripes edged with black (or breast and abdomen with narrow more drop-shaped white marks giving an almost spotted appearance, 1). Rump, upper tail-coverts, wings and tail rufous-chestnut. Bill 1 - 1.1″, slender and somewhat curved.
Range. From southern Mexico to Venezuela, Ecuador, Peru and Bolivia.
Colombia. Forest and open woodland. Subtropical zone of the Santa Marta Mts. occasionally down to 3000 ft. *(sanctaemartae)*. Subtropical zone of the Eastern Andes from Bogotá northward *(lacrymiger)*. Subtropical to temperate zones from the west slope of the Western Andes eastward to the Central Andes and the west slope of the Eastern Andes from Bogotá southward (1, *sneiderni*). Subtropical to temperate zones of the east slope of the Andes in Nariño *(frigidus)*. Upper tropical and subtropical zones of the Pacific slope of Nariño *(aequatorialis)*.

23. GREATER SCYTHEBILL
(Campylorhamphus pucheranii)

Description. 11½ - 12″. General color dull chestnut brown faintly marked on crown, hindneck, throat and upper breast with pale shaft streaks. Streak behind and below eye white. Wings, tail and upper tail-coverts dark chestnut. Bill 2.1″, brown, less curved than in other species.
Range. Eastern and western Ecuador.

Colombia. Forest. Upper tropical and subtropical zones both slopes of the Western Andes from Valle southward.

24. RED-BILLED SCYTHEBILL
(Campylorhamphus trochilirostris)
Plate X

Description. 9 - 10″. General color rufescent-brown. Crown dark brown streaked with pale fulvous, the streaks continuing over nape and upper mantle. Throat fulvous, breast and lower throat broadly streaked with fulvous. Wings, upper tail-coverts and tail rufous-chestnut. Bill 2.5 - 2.6″, much curved, reddish brown.
Range. Panama to Venezuela and southward to southern Brazil, Argentina, Paraguay and Bolivia.
Colombia. Forest. Tropical zone. Pacific coast southward to the Baudó Mts. *(brevipennis)*. Western Nariño *(thoracicus)*. Córdoba eastward to the middle Magdalena Valley and eastward to the llanos of Meta *(venezuelensis)*.

25. BROWN-BILLED SCYTHEBILL
(Campylorhamphus pusillus)

Description. 10¼ - 10¾″. Rather similar to the Red-billed Scythebill but much darker with the throat deep buff and streaks on crown, breast, and mantle broader and very much buffier (or plumage tinged olive, especially below, 1). Bill 1.8 - 2″, much curved; upper mandible dark brown, lower light brown.
Range. Costa Rica to western Panama. Western Venezuela. Western Ecuador.
Colombia. Forest. Upper tropical and lower subtropical zones west of the Eastern Andes excepting the Caribbean coast. East of the Andes in Boyacá *(pusillus)*. The Sierra de Perijá (1, *tachirensis*).

26. CURVE-BILLED SCYTHEBILL
(Campylorhamphus procurvoides)

Description. 8 - 9″. Differs from Red-billed Scythebill by smaller size, plain back and very much narrower streaks on breast. Bill 2 - 2.2″, much curved, reddish brown.
Range. Southern Venezuela, British and French Guiana southward to the middle Amazon and rio Madeira, central Brazil.
Colombia. Forest. Tropical zone east of the Andes from Norte de Santander southward to Caquetá *(sanus)*.

OVENBIRDS (Furnariidae)

Fig. 60. Pale-legged **Ovenbird**
(Furnarius leucopus) p. 204

Ovenbirds, spinetails and their numerous allies form a very large tropical American family of small to medium-sized birds variable both in appearence and habits. Most are more terrestial than the nearly related woodcreepers but some are much like them. Particularly resembling them are the treerunners, tufted-cheeks and xenops. Unlike them, cinclodes and leaf-scrapers somewhat resemble thrushes; spinetails resemble titmice; softtails look like warblers; but most, except for the conspicuously striped treehunters, are just brown birds of the tangled undergrowth. The sexes are alike or nearly so.

They feed chiefly on insects which they search for on the ground, in trees, or low down in the undergrowth. Bills are not unusual, except in xenops in which the mandible is sharply upturned; leafscrapers in which it is long and slender; and the cinclodes which have rather heavy and long decurved bills. Tails are always much graduated, sometimes rounded, sometimes long and very pointed with protruding shafts (spinetails). However the tail except for the treerunners, is not used as a prop as it often is in the woodcreepers.

They inhabit every type of country from tropical jungle and desert to snow line. Many species inhabit the cooler regions of southern South America. Nests are very diverse and vary from natural cavities in trees, or tunnels which are excavated in the ground, to elaborate structures of twigs with complicated entrances or domed mud nests, resembling a Dutch oven, for which the family is named. (68 Col.; 213 S.A.; 217 N.&S.A.; 217 wld.)

AID TO IDENTIFICATION

Plumage without streaks or spots, except sometimes on throat.
Closed wings or the wing-coverts not in contrast to back (crown like back, tail conspicuously long) 5, 13, (crown like back, tail of normal length) 17, 18, 28E, 30, 38, 41, 43, 47E, 48E, 49E, 50, 51E, 52, 59, 63, 64, 65E, 66E, 67, (crown in sharp contrast to back) 3, 19, 31E, 41, 42, 53E.

203

Closed wings or the wing-coverts in sharp contrast to back (tail long, pointed) 6*, 7E, 8, 9, 10E, 11, 12E, 14, 15, 16E, 20, 21E, 22, 23, 24E, (tail of normal length) 43, 44E, 45, 46E, 49.

Plumage uniform above, streaked, spotted or speckled below 1, 2, 25E, 29, 32, 33, 35, 36, 41, 42, 56, 68.

Plumage streaked above (and below) 4, 27, 34, 38, 39E, 40, 54, 55, 58, 61E, 62E, (above only) 26, 37, 55, 57E, 60.

1. ANDEAN CINCLODES
(Cinclodes fuscus) Plate X

Description. 7½ - 8¼ ". Above dull earthy brown; long and conspicuous eyebrow buffy white. Underparts dirty white, the throat spotted with dusky, the feathers of the breast edged with dusky and sides of body clouded with brown. Wings dark brown, the inner wing-feathers with a broad rufous band near the base. Central tail-feathers like the back, outer tail-feathers tipped and edged with rufous.

Range. Western Venezuela southward through the Andes to Tierra del Fuego.

Colombia. Banks of rocky mountain streams in the upper temperate and páramo zones. The Santa Marta Mts. and the Eastern and Central Andes *(oreobates)*. Páramo zone of the Andes of Nariño *(paramo)*.

2. STOUT-BILLED CINCLODES
(Cinclodes excelsior)

Description. 8¾ - 9¼ ". Generally similar to the Andean Cinclodes but larger, the bill longer, heavier and more curved, the tips and margins of outer tail-feathers duller.

Range. Andes of Ecuador.

Colombia. Páramo zone. The Central Andes *(columbianus)*; the Andes of Nariño *(excelsior)*.

3. PALE-LEGGED OVENBIRD
(Furnarius leucopus) Fig. 60

Description. 7¼ - 8". Crown and nape gray; eyebrow buffy white; sides of head, back, closed wings and tail bright orange-rufous. Throat and center of abdomen white, chest and sides of body rufous (or pale rufous-buff, 1). Primaries black (or

dark brown, 1) with an orange-rufous band near base.

Range. Venezuela, British Guiana southward through Brazil to Paraguay, Argentina and Bolivia. Southwestern Ecuador, northwestern Peru.

Colombia. Humid forest and dry scrub. Tropical zone. Caribbean coastal region (1, *longirostris*). Forested portions of the middle Magdalena Valley westward to southwestern Bolívar *(endoecus)*.

4. ANDEAN SPINETAIL
(Leptasthenura andicola) Plate X

Description. 6½ - 7¼". Crown and nape chestnut streaked with black, rest of upper surface dark brown broadly streaked with white. Eyebrow and throat white; chest white streaked with dusky, rest of underparts pale brown more or less streaked with white. Wings dark brown (or wing-coverts and inner remiges margined with rufous, 1). Tail long, much graduated, central tail-feathers dark brown sharply pointed, the outer feathers with white outer webs.

Range. Western Venezuela, Ecuador, and Peru.

Colombia. Matted vegetation near ground, often near rivulets. Temperate and páramo zone. The Santa Marta Mts. (1, *extima);* the Eastern Andes in Boyacá (1, *exterior);* the Central Andes *(andicola)*.

5. WHITE-CHINNED SPINETAIL
(Schizoeaca fuliginosa)

Description. 7½ - 8¼". Eyebrow and underparts gray, chin white. Upperparts, wings and tail dark chestnut. Tail long, much graduated, the feathers pointed and loosely webbed.

---

*Many immature spinetails *(Synallaxis)* are uniform brown above, paler brown below, with brown wings and tail, and are difficult to tell apart.

Range. Western Venezuela, Ecuador and Peru.

Colombia. Temperate and páramo zones of the Eastern Andes eastward to the Táchira border of Venezuela *(fuliginosa)*. The Central and Western Andes, and the Andes of Nariño *(fumigata)*.

6. AZARA'S SPINETAIL
(Synallaxis azarae)

Description. 6½ - 7¼". Forehead, back, and sides of body olive brown. Crown, nape, wing-coverts, outer webs of remiges and tail rufous. Throat speckled black and white. Breast and sides of head gray, lower breast and center of abdomen white. Tail long and much graduated, feathers normal not pointed.

Range. Western Venezuela, Ecuador, Peru and Bolivia.

Colombia. Bushy pastures and tangled thickets. Upper tropical to temperate zones of the Western, Central and west slope of the Eastern Andes at the head of the Magdalena Valley. Páramo zone of Nariño *(media)*. Subtropical and temperate zones of the Eastern Andes from Bogotá northward *(elegantior)*.

7. DUSKY SPINETAIL
(Synallaxis moesta)

Description. 6 - 6½". Forehead blackish; crown, nape, wing-coverts, outer webs of remiges rufous. Back dark olive (or dark grayish olive, 1). Throat speckled black and white. Underparts olive grayish (or iron gray, 1). Tail chestnut, much graduated, tail feathers pointed but not conspicuously lengthened or narrowed.

Range. Eastern Ecuador, northeastern Peru.

Colombia. Scrub. Tropical and lower subtropical zones. The Eastern Andes in Meta *(moesta)*; in Caquetá *(obscura)*; extreme southeastern Nariño (1, *brunneicaudalis)*.

8. SILVERY-THROATED SPINETAIL
(Synallaxis subpudica)

Description. 6¾ - 7¾". Forehead and back olive brown. Crown, nape, wing-coverts and basal edge to outer webs of remiges rufous. Chin, lores, sides of head and underparts grayish, whitish in center of abdomen. Throat black the feathers with silvery gray edges. Tail graduated and long with feathers not narrowed.

Range. Colombia.

Colombia. Subtropical to temperate zone of the Eastern Andes.

9. PALE-BREASTED SPINETAIL
(Synallaxis albescens)

Description. 6¼ - 7¼". Forehead, back, wings and tail grayish olive brown; crown and shoulders rufous. Throat white with an irregular, somewhat concealed black patch on lower throat. Lores white. Breast pale gray, abdomen white. Tail rather short.

Range. Costa Rica to Venezuela, the Guianas and southward to southeastern Brazil, Ecuador, Peru, Bolivia, Argentina and Paraguay. Trinidad. Margarita I.

Colombia. Shrubbery and tall grass. Tropical and lower subtropical zones of all three Andean ranges *(insignis)*. Santa Marta Mts. between 1800-5800 ft. East of the Eastern Andes in the Zulia Valley *(occipitalis)*. Caribbean coast region from the lower Atrato eastward to the western base of the Santa Marta Mts. *(littoralis)*. Salty, scrubby flats. The Guajira Peninsula and eastern base of Santa Marta Mts. *(perpallida)*. West shore of the Gulf of Urabá *(hypoleuca)*.

10. DARK-BREASTED SPINETAIL
(Synallaxis albigularis)

Description. 6¼ - 6¾". Forehead and forecrown, sides of head and breast dark gray. Crown from level of eye, nape and shoulder rufous-chestnut. Throat white with a somewhat concealed black patch on lower throat. Back, flanks and tail olive brown. Center of abdomen white. Tail comparatively short, webbing rather decomposed.

Range. Eastern Ecuador, western Brazil and eastern Peru.

Colombia. Grassland and scrub. Tropical zone east of the Andes from Meta southward to Putumayo *(rodolphei)*.

11. SLATY SPINETAIL
(Synallaxis brachyura) Plate X

Description. 7 - 7½". Forehead dark gray. Crown and nape rufous (or rufous-chestnut, 1). Shoulders and outer webs or remiges rufous-chestnut. Throat speckled with white. Rest of plumage iron gray tinged olive on back and tail. Tail long, about 3½" (or 2¾", 1).

Range. Honduras to western Ecuador. Central Brazil (Goiáz).

Colombia. Low bushes and tall grass in open country; also forest. Tropical zone of the middle Magdalena and lower Cauca Valleys *(brachyura)*. The Pacific coast (1, *chapmani)*.

12. PLAIN-CROWNED SPINETAIL
(Synallaxis gujanensis)

Description. 6¼ - 7". Crown and sides of head grayish becoming olive brown on back. Below dirty white faintly tinged on chest with grayish. Sides of body grayish olive. Wing-coverts, outer webs of remiges and the tail orange-rufous. Tail rather short, about 2¼", feathers pointed.

Range. Venezuela and the Guianas southward to southern Brazil, eastern Peru, Paraguay and Bolivia.

Colombia. Forest. Tropical and lower subtropical zone of the east slope of the Eastern Andes in Meta *(columbiana)*.

13 RUFOUS SPINETAIL
(Synallaxis unirufa)

Description. 6¼ - 7". Uniform rufous-chestnut (or hazel, 1), paler below (lightly marked pale eyebrow, 2); lores black. Tail long, feathers decomposed.

Range. Western Venezuela southward to eastern Ecuador and Peru.

Colombia. Forest. Subtropical to temperate zone of the Andes *(unirufa)*. Páramo de Tamá on the Venezuelan border (1, *meridana)*. The Perijá Mts. (2, *muñotztebari)*.

14. RUSTY-HEADED SPINETAIL
(Synallaxis fusco-rufa)

Description. 6¾ - 7½". Whole head, throat and breast orange-rufous, paler on belly. Back and flanks olive gray, wing-coverts, outer margins of remiges orange-rufous. Tail chestnut, rather long, web somewhat decomposed.

Range. Colombia.

Colombia. Bushes and tangled thickets. Upper tropical and subtropical zone of the Santa Marta Mts.

15. STRIPE-BREASTED SPINETAIL
(Synallaxis cinnamomea)

Description. 6½ - 7". Upper surface dark reddish brown; post-ocular streak and ear-coverts dark rufous. Throat black spotted with white. Underparts brown, streaked pale cinnamon. Wing-coverts and edges of remiges chestnut. Tail mahogany brown, rather short, 2", feathers not pointed.

Range. Northern Venezuela. Trinidad and Tobago.

Colombia. Forest undergrowth. Upper tropical and subtropical zones of both slopes of the Eastern Andes from Tolima and Cundinamarca northward *(cinnamomea)*.

16. RUDDY SPINETAIL
(Synallaxis rutilans)

Description. 5½ - 6½". Upper surface, sides of head, neck, breast and wing-coverts dark mahogany red (or forehead chestnut, rest of upperparts olive brown, 1). Throat black; belly dark grayish olive. Wings and tail black. Tail rather short, about 2".

Range. Southern Venezuela, the Guianas, Brazil, Ecuador, Peru and Bolivia.

Colombia. Forest. Tropical zone. From Meta southward to the Caquetá region *(caquetensis)*. Extreme eastern Colombia along the río Guainía (1, *dissors)*.

17. WHITE-BROWED SPINETAIL
(Synallaxis gularis)

Description. 5½ - 6¼". Above uniform reddish brown to rufous-brown. Eyebrow and throat white, rest of lower surface dull cinnamon (or rest of under surface ashy gray, sides of body brown, 1). Tail short, chestnut.

Range. Western Venezuela southward to Ecuador and Peru.

Colombia. Forest in tangled undergrowth. Temperate zone. West slope of the Eastern Andes in Cundinamarca westward across the Central Andes to the Western Andes and Nariño (*gularis*). East slope of the Eastern Andes in Boyacá and Norte Santander (1, *cinereiventris*). The Perijá Mts. (1, *brunneidorsalis*).

18. YELLOW-THROATED SPINETAIL
(Certhiaxis cinnamomea) Plate IX

Description. 6¼ - 6¾″. Above uniform cinnamon-rufous. Forehead, lores and sides of head grayish. Eyebrow whitish. Throat pale yellow; underparts white tinged with buffy. Primaries basally rufous, distally black. Tail of normal length, but with the bare shafts protruding. Bill rather long, .6″.

Range. Northern Venezuela and the Guianas southward through central and eastern Brazil to Paraguay, Argentina and Bolivia. Trinidad.

Colombia. Mangroves, marshes, thorny scrub. Tropical zone from the upper Atrato Valley eastward to the western Santa Marta district and up the Magdalena Valley to western Santander (*fuscifrons*).

19. WHITE-WHISKERED SPINETAIL
(Poecilurus candei)

Description. 6¼ - 6¾″. Crown olive gray, center of feathers blackish. Lores, ear-coverts and lower throat black, silvery in certain lights. Chin, upper throat and malar streak, separating the black of the ear-coverts and the black of the throat, white. Area above ear-coverts rufous (or gray like crown, 1). Center of abdomen white, sides of body and upperparts including basal half of tail rufous (or cinnamon, 2); distal half of tail black.

Range. Northwestern Venezuela.

Colombia. Weedy pastureland, reeds, grassy scrub. Arid Caribbean coast region (*candei*). Middle Magdalena Valley from about 9° N. southward (1, *atrigularis*). Thorny scrub, edge of mangrove. Caribbean coast southeast and east of the Santa Marta Mts. (2, *venezuelensis*).

20. STREAK-CAPPED SPINETAIL
(Cranioleuca hellmayri) Plate IX

Description. 6 - 6½″. Crown orange-rufous, broadly striped with black; eyebrow whitish. Upperparts olive brown. Throat whitish, rest of underparts pale smoky olive. Wings and tail rufous. Tail graduated, rather long, feathers rather broad, pointed.

Range. Colombia.

Colombia. Forest, often among bromelias. Subtropical zone of the Santa Marta Mts.

21. CRESTED SPINETAIL
(Cranioleuca subcristata)

Description. 6 - 6½″. Similar to No. 20 but crown only tinged rufous, obscurely streaked with black (or prominently streaked, 1).

Range. Coastal mountains of Venezuela.

Colombia. Forest. Tropical zone. East of the Eastern Andes in Arauca and Boyacá (*subcristata*). Norte de Santander near the Venezuelan border (1, *fuscivertex*).

22. BOGOTA SPINETAIL
(Cranioleuca curtata)

Description. 6¼ - 6¾″. Crown, wings and tail orange-rufous. Back olive brown. Eyebrow grayish, cheeks brown; throat whitish, rest of lower surface drab brown. Tail feathers pointed, with the shafts slightly protruding.

Range. Ecuador and Peru.

Colombia. Forest. Subtropical zone. The Eastern Andes (*curtata*). East slope of the Eastern Andes at their southern end and the head of the Magdalena Valley (*cisandina*).

23. RED-FACED SPINETAIL
(Cranioleuca erythrops)

Description. 6¼ - 6¾″. Very similar to No. 22 but the cheeks orange-rufous instead of drab brown.

Range. Costa Rica and western Panama to western Ecuador.

Colombia. Thickets and tangled vines. Upper tropical and subtropical zones of the Western Andes, and west slope of the Central Andes. Western Nariño.

PLATE X

ORANGE-FRONTED
SOFTTAIL
(*Metopothrix aurantiacus*)
Page 210

RED-BILLED
SCYTHEBILL
(*Campylorhamphus
trochilirostris
venezuelensis*)
Page 202

STRONG-BILLED
WOODCREEPER
(*Xiphocolaptes promero-
pirhynchus rostratus*)
Page 199

OLIVACEOUS
WOODCREEPER
(*Sittasomus grisei-
capillus levis*)
Page 198

PEARLED TREERUNNER
(*Margarornis
squamigera perlata*)
Page 210

BLACK-STRIPED
WOODCREEPER
(*Xiphorhynchus
l. lachrymosus*)
Page 201

BARRED WOODCREEPER
(*Dendrocolaptes
certhia colombianus*)
Page 199

STRAIGHT-BILLED
WOODCREEPER
(*Xiphorhynchus
picus picirostris*)
Page 200

ANDEAN SPINETAIL
(*Leptasthenura
andicola exterior*)
Page 204

SLATY SPINETAIL
(*Synallaxis
brachyura chapmani*)
Page 206

GRAY-THROATED
LEAFSCRAPER
(*Sclerurus albi-
gularis propinquus*)
Page 215

ANDEAN CINCLODES
(*Cinclodes fuscus paramo*)
Page 204

E.L.Poole

24. RUSTY-BACKED SPINETAIL
(Cranioleuca vulpina)

Description. 5¾ - 6¼". Very similar to No. 22 but eyebrow white; back rufous, almost the same color as crown.

Range. Venezuela southward to Brazil, eastern Peru and Bolivia.

Colombia. Thickets near river banks. Orinoco region from Vichada southward *(alopecias).*

25. SPECKLE-BREASTED SPINETAIL
(Cranioleuca gutturata)

Description. 6 - 6½". Crown, wings, and tail rufous-chestnut; back olive brown. Chin and upper throat pale yellow; rest of underparts dull buffy-white, speckled on lower throat and breast with black.

Range. Southern Venezuela, French Guiana southward to western Brazil, eastern Ecuador, Peru, northern Bolivia and northwest Brazil.

Colombia. Forest. Tropical zone east of the Eastern Andes from Caquetá southward *(peruviana).*

26. STREAK-BACKED SPINETAIL
(Asthenes wyatti)

Description. 6 - 6½". Sparrow-like in appearance. Upper surface umber brown, streaked with blackish. Lores and eyebrow white. Chin orange-rufous, white in immature birds (or pale buff, 1). Chest grayish brown, lower breast and belly buffy. Shoulders and basal portion of remiges rufous-chestnut. Tail graduated, central feathers dark brown, outer ones dull rufous.

Range. Western Venezuela southward through the Andes to Peru, Bolivia and northwestern Argentina.

Colombia. Low bushes and rocky outcrops. Temperate and páramo zone. The Santa Marta Mts. (1, *sanctae-martae*). Northern portion of the Eastern Andes *(wyatti).*

27. MANY-STRIPED SPINETAIL
(Asthenes flammulata) Plate IX

Description. 6¾ - 7¼". Crown rufous striped with black; back dark brown striped with white or fulvous. Chin and

upper throat deep orange-rufous (or whole throat and upper breast buff, 1; or upper throat only whitish buff, 2). Rest of lower surface and cheeks white, streaked with dark brown (or cheeks buff like throat, 1). Wing-coverts streaked black and fulvous, basal portion of remiges chestnut. Tail much graduated, central tail-feathers dark brown, very pointed, outer feathers dull rufous.

Range. Andes southward to Ecuador and Peru.

Colombia. Temperate and páramo zones. Eastern Andes *(multo-striata)*. Central Andes (1, *quindiana*). Andes of Nariño (2, *flammulata*).

28. RUFOUS-FRONTED THORNBIRD
(Phacellodomus rufifrons)

Description. 6¾ - 7½". Upperparts, wings and tail dull grayish olive brown. Feathers of crown somewhat stiffened and lanceolate. Lores, eyebrow and underparts isabelline, flanks and under tail-coverts browner.

Range. Venezuela. Eastern Brazil, Paraguay, Argentina. Northern Peru. Northern Bolivia.

Colombia. Grasslands and borders of woods. Tropical zone. East of the Andes in Boyacá *(inornatus).*

29. STRIPE-NECKED SPINETAIL
(Siptornis striaticollis) Plate IX

Description. 4½ - 4¾". Crown, area below eye, wing-coverts and tail rufous-chestnut. Forehead and eyebrow white. Lower surface drab greenish, tinged on throat with chestnut and streaked on throat and upper breast with white.

Range. Ecuador.

Colombia. Forest. Subtropical zone. Slopes above the middle and upper Magdalena Valley.

30. DOUBLE-BANDED SOFTTAIL
(Xenerpestes minlosi) Plate IX

Description. 4½ - 4¾". Warbler-like but clings to the under sides of leaves. Forecrown black, the feathers stiff, obscurely streaked with white (or no white streaks, 1). Hindcrown, back and tail dark olive gray. Wings blackish with two white wing-bars. Lores, eyebrow and under surface yellowish white. Tail very rounded.

Range. Eastern Panama.

Colombia. Forest. Tropical zone of the middle Magdalena Valley in Santander and western Boyacá *(minlosi)*. Upper Sinú Valley westward to the Pacific coast to the lower río San Juan (1, *umbraticus*).

31. ORANGE-FRONTED SOFTTAIL
(Metopothrix aurantiacus) Plate X

Description. 4½ - 4¾". Warbler-like. Similar in habits to *Xenerpestes*. Forehead and forecrown orange-yellow, the feathers stiff. Back, wings and tail olive, wing-coverts pale edged. Chin and throat golden yellow, becoming buffy yellow on breast and belly and olive on under tail-coverts. Tail very rounded.

Range. Eastern Ecuador, western Brazil, eastern Peru and northern Bolivia.

Colombia. Forest and scrub. Tropical zone east of the Andes from the upper Putumayo region southward.

32. PEARLED TREERUNNER
(Margarornis squamigera) Plate X

Description. 6¼ - 6½". Profusely spotted below. Crown, nape and extreme upper mantle brown, tinged chestnut. Sides of neck spotted with yellowish white. Back, wings and tail bright chestnut, the wing-feathers with a pale basal band. Eyebrow, stripe below eye and entire throat yellowish white. Feathers of rest of underparts basally umber brown, each feather terminating in a large round yellowish white spot surrounded by black. Under tail-coverts streaked with yellowish white. Tail with protruding spines. Climbs like a woodcreeper.

Range. Venezuela southward through the Andes to Ecuador, Peru and Bolivia.

Colombia. Forest. Upper tropical to temperate zone of the Andes. Not Santa Marta *(perlata)*.

33. FULVOUS-DOTTED TREERUNNER
(Margarornis stellata)

Description. 6½ - 7". Entire upper surface, wings and tail bright reddish chestnut.

Throat and lores white, the feathers on lower part of throat edged with black. Sides of head and rest of underparts dark cinnamon. Feathers of breast just below throat with small white spots surrounded with black. Climbs like a woodcreeper.

Range. Andes southward to Ecuador and northern Peru.

Colombia. Wet, mossy forest. Upper tropical and subtropical zones of the Western Andes and Nariño.

34. SPOTTED TREERUNNER
(Premnornis guttuligera)

Description. 6¾ - 7¼". Above brown, streaked on mantle with fulvous. Throat and sides of head and eyebrow fulvous. Breast densely streaked fulvous the streaks oval edged blackish, abdomen uniform brown. Wings dark brown, the feathers edged rufous. Tail and upper tail-coverts rufous-chestnut.

Range. Northwestern Venezuela, Ecuador and Peru.

Colombia. Wet, mossy forest. Subtropical zone. West slope of the Eastern Andes westward to the east slope of the Western Andes.

35. SPOTTED BARBTAIL
(Premnoplex brunnescens)

Description. 5½ - 6". Above dark brown, the crown slightly more olivaceous, the feathers obscurely edged darker. Eyebrow and throat ochraceous. Rest of underparts dark brown, profusely marked with drop-shaped ochraceous spots outlined with black. Tail blackish brown with protruding shafts.

Range. Costa Rica southward to Venezuela, Ecuador, Peru and Bolivia.

Colombia. Undergrowth in humid forest. Subtropical zone of the Santa Marta Mts. *(coloratus)*. The Andes of Colombia *(brunnescens)*.

36. BUFFY TUFTEDCHEEK
(Pseudocolaptes lawrencii)

Description. 8 - 8½". Crown, nape dark brown with pale shaft streaks; back rufous-chestnut, unstreaked. Throat and white line below eye extended backward and forming a tuft on sides of neck. Upper breast white, the feathers edged with black. Rest of underparts cinnamon-chestnut. Wings and tail chestnut, wing-coverts centered black. Tail very rounded, feathers pointed. Bill straight, .9 - 1".

Range. Costa Rica to western Panama. Western Ecuador.

Colombia. Upper tropical zone of the west slope of the Western Andes (johnsoni).

37. STREAKED TUFTEDCHEEK
(Pseudocolaptes boissonneautii)
Plate IX

Description. 8¾ - 9¼". Rather similar to No. 36 but differing by having the crown sometimes uniform black; the back warm brown streaked with pale fulvous, lower back rufous, unstreaked; the throat and breast more extensively white, with faint dark edges (or definite black edges, 1), lower breast and belly paler. Wings dark brown, wing-coverts pale edged.

Range. Western Venezuela southward to Ecuador, Peru and northern Bolivia.

Colombia. Forest. Subtropical to temperate zones. Northern Boyacá, Santander and Norte de Santander (meridae). Southern Nariño, both east and west of the Andes (1, oberholseri). Rest of Colombia from the west slope of the Eastern Andes in the vicinity of Bogotá westward and southward (1, boissonneautii).

38. STRIPED WOODHAUNTER
(Hyloctistes subulatus)

Description. 7½ - 8" (or 6½ - 7", 1). Above brown. Feathers of crown edged with black with pale shaft streaks, shaft streaks continued on mantle (or mantle uniform, 1). Upper tail-coverts and tail rufous-chestnut, under wing-coverts ochraceous-orange. Chin and throat buffy, rest of underparts olivaceous brown, the feathers of the breast with pale shaft streaks (or without shaft streaks, 1). Wings like back; tail rufous-chestnut.

Range. Nicaragua to western Ecuador. Venezuela to northern and western Brazil.

Colombia. Forest. Tropical zone. Córdoba and northern Chocó (1, cordobae). The

Pacific coast from the Baudó Mts. southward (1, assimilis). The eastern base of the Andes from Caquetá southward (subulatus).

39. CHESTNUT-WINGED HOOKBILL
(Ancistrops strigilatus) Plate IX

Description. 7 - 8". Bill shrike-like. Above dark umber brown streaked with pale fulvous. Eyebrow and ear-coverts fulvous. Below pale chamois obscurely streaked with dusky. Wings chestnut, inner webs of primaries black; tail cinnamon-rufous.

Range. Eastern Ecuador southward to central Brazil and eastern Peru.

Colombia. Forest. Tropical zone east of the Andes from Meta southward (strigilatus).

40. LINEATED FOLIAGE-GLEANER
(Syndactyla subalaris)

Description. 7½ - 8¼". Above brown darkest on head; rump, upper tail-coverts and tail chestnut. Crown and mantle finely (or broadly, 1) streaked with fulvous. Throat buff, rest of underparts brown, breast and upper belly finely (or broadly, 1) streaked with fulvous. Wings like back.

Range. Costa Rica southward to western Ecuador. Eastern Ecuador and Peru.

Colombia. Forest. Subtropical zone. Extreme northwestern Colombia (tacarcunae). The Andes except area occupied by next race (striaticollis). Both slopes of the northern portion of the Eastern Andes and the head of the Magdalena Valley (1, striolata).

41. MONTANE FOLIAGE-GLEANER
(Anabacerthia striaticollis)

Description. 6¾ - 7¼". Crown olive brown, back umber brown; wings like back, primary-coverts dark tipped. Throat and eyebrow fulvous, ring around eye white, lores and malar streak dusky. Lower parts plain olivaceous buff, (or streaked with fulvous white on breast, 1). Tail rufous-chestnut.

Range. Venezuela southward to eastern Ecuador, Peru and Bolivia.

Colombia. Forest. Upper tropical and subtropical zone. The Andes except area occupied by the next races *(striaticollis)*. Upper tropical and subtropical zone of the Santa Marta Mts. *(anxius)*. East slope of the Andes in extreme southeastern Nariño (1, *montana*).

42. SCALY-THROATED FOLIAGE-GLEANER
(Anabacerthia variegaticeps)

Description. 7¼ - 7¾". Crown dusky olive with fine white shaft streaks; back rufescent-brown. Wings like back. Throat yellowish white mottled with dusky. Eyebrow and circle around eye orange-rufous. Breast rufescent becoming dull brown on belly, obscurely pale streaked on breast. Tail chestnut.

Range. Mexico to western Ecuador.

Colombia. Forest. Upper tropical and subtropical zone west of the Western Andes *(temporalis)*.

43. RUFOUS-RUMPED FOLIAGE-GLEANER
(Philydor erythrocercus)

Description. 7 - 7½". Upperparts and wings olivaceous (or wings blackish, 1), upper tail-coverts tinged with orange-rufous (or rump and upper tail-coverts orange-rufous, 1), tail orange-rufous. Eyebrow and post-ocular region ochraceous (or orange-rufous, 1). Underparts pale ochraceous, palest on throat, tinged olive on sides of body. Young birds are much "redder" both above and below.

Range. Mexico to western Ecuador. Eastern Ecuador, eastern Peru and northern Peru.

Colombia. Forest. Tropical and subtropical zones west of the Eastern Andes, not Santa Marta (1, *erythronotus*). Tropical zone east of the Andes in the Caquetá region *(subfulvus)*.

44. CINNAMON-RUMPED FOLIAGE-GLEANER
(Philydor pyrrhodes)

Description. 7 - 7¼". Upperparts olivaceous brown; wings slaty blackish. Eyebrow, rump, and entire under surface cinnamon,

upper tail-coverts and tail bright pale cinnamon.

Range. The Guianas and Venezuela southward to eastern Ecuador, northern Brazil, Peru and Bolivia.

Colombia. Forest. Tropical zone east of the Andes from Meta southward.

45. BUFF-FRONTED FOLIAGE-GLEANER
(Philydor rufus) Plate IX

Description. 8 - 8½". Above olive brown (or rufescent brown, 1). Eyebrow and throat cinnamon shaded over rest of underparts (or not, 1) with brown. Primaries and primary-coverts and outer tail-feathers chestnut. Central tail-feathers duller, tinged olivaceous.

Range. Costa Rica southward to western Ecuador, Venezuela, eastern Peru, Bolivia and southern Brazil.

Colombia. Forest. Subtropical zone of the west slope of the Eastern Andes (1, *panerythrus*). Upper tropical and subtropical zone of the Western Andes southward to Nariño *(riveti)*.

46. CHESTNUT-WINGED FOLIAGE-GLEANER
(Philydor erythropterus)

Description. 7¾ - 8¼". Above gray, tinged olive on lower back, rump and upper tail-coverts. Lores ochraceous. Lower parts ochraceous-buff, brightest on throat. Wings and tail chestnut.

Range. Eastern Ecuador, eastern Peru to the middle Amazon, Mato Grosso and northern Bolivia.

Colombia. Forest. Tropical zone east of the Eastern Andes *(erythropterus)*.

47. RUFOUS-TAILED FOLIAGE-GLEANER
(Philydor ruficaudatus)

Description. 7¼ - 7¾". Upper surface including wings olive. Eyebrow and underparts pale yellowish ochraceous, brightest on throat. Tail chestnut.

Range. French Guiana and southern Venezuela, southward to Maranhão. Western Brazil, Ecuador, Peru and Bolivia.

Colombia. Forest. Tropical zone east of
the Eastern Andes from Meta southward
to Putumayo.

48. OLIVE-BACKED
FOLIAGE-GLEANER
(Automolus infuscatus)

Description. 7¾ - 8¼ ". Slightly crested.
Upper surface and wings olive (or olive
tinged rufescent particularly on crown, 1).
Tail and upper tail-coverts chestnut.
Throat white, rest of underparts white
tinged olive, faintly flammulated on chest
with dusky. Flanks and under tail-coverts
olive.

Range. The Guianas and Venezuela southward to the mouth of the Amazon and
westward to eastern Ecuador and Peru.

Colombia. Forest. Tropical zone at the
eastern base of the Eastern Andes in
Caquetá and Putumayo *(infuscatus)*.
Eastern Colombia in the río Guainía
region (1, *badius*).

49. CRESTED FOLIAGE-GLEANER
(Automolus dorsalis)

Description. 7¾ - 8½ ". Slightly crested.
Upperparts, ear-coverts and wings rufescent-brown. Eyebrow and throat yellowish
white, rest of underparts dirty white;
under tail-coverts dull brown. Upper tail-
coverts and tail dark chestnut.

Range. Eastern Ecuador and eastern Peru.

Colombia. Forest. Tropical zone at the
base of the Eastern Andes in Caquetá and
Putumayo.

50. RUDDY FOLIAGE-GLEANER
(Automolus rubiginosus) Plate IX

Description. 8¾ - 9¼ ". Upperparts and
wings ruddy brown (or deep umber
brown, 1; or bay, 2). Throat and breast
cinnamon (or chestnut, 2), rest of underparts cinnamon to cinnamon brown (or
deep wood brown, 2), flanks darker. Lores
and ear-coverts silvery grayish (or cinnamon, 3). Tail chestnut (or black, 2).

Range. Mexico southward to western Ecuador, Venezuela, French Guiana, eastern
Ecuador, Peru and northern Bolivia.

Colombia. Forest. Tropical and subtropical zone. Santa Marta region *(rufipectus)*.
West slope of the Eastern Andes (3,
sasaimae). East slope of the Eastern Andes
in Meta (3, *cinnamomeigula*). East base
of the Andes in Caquetá and Putumayo
(1, *caquetae*). Northwestern Antioquia (1,
saturatus). Pacific coast from the Baudó
Mts. southward (2, *nigricauda*).

51. BROWN-RUMPED
FOLIAGE-GLEANER
(Automolus melanopezus)

Description. 8¾-9¼ ". Head somewhat
crested. Above warm brown slightly
tinged olive on mantle. Cheeks tawny,
throat pale cinnamon, rest of underparts
pale buffy-brown, darker on sides. Under
wing-coverts bright cinnamon-orange.
Lesser wing-coverts, upper tail-coverts and
tail rufous-chestnut.

Range. Eastern Ecuador, western Brazil.

Colombia. Forest. Tropical zone. Eastern base of the Eastern Andes in Putumayo.

52. BUFF-THROATED
FOLIAGE-GLEANER
(Automolus ochrolaemus)

Description. 7¾-8½ ". Upper surface
brown with an olive tinge, wings browner. Inconspicuous eyebrow buffy; throat
pale ochraceous (or white, 1); breast
ochraceous-brown, darker and more olive
on sides of body. Upper tail-coverts and
tail rufous-chestnut.

Range. Mexico southward to western
Ecuador. Southern Venezuela, the Guia-
nas, central and western Brazil, eastern
Ecuador, Peru, and Bolivia.

Colombia. Thick forest undergrowth.
Tropical zone. Northern Colombia from
the Pacific coast eastward to the western
base of the Eastern Andes (1, *pallidigu-
laris*). Eastern base of the Andes from
Meta southward *(turdinus)*.

53. CHESTNUT-CROWNED
FOLIAGE-GLEANER
(Automolus rufipileatus)

Description. 7¾-8¼ ". Head somewhat
crested. Entire crown chestnut. Lores

whitish. Back reddish brown, wings tinged chestnut. Entire under surface dull ochraceous-brown. Upper tail-coverts and tail chestnut.

Range. Venezuela, British Guiana southward to Maranhão. Eastern Ecuador, Peru and Bolivia.

Colombia. Forest. Tropical zone east of the Eastern Andes from Arauca southward (consobrinus).

54. FLAMMULATED TREEHUNTER
(Thripadectes flammulatus) Plate IX

Description. 10-10¾". Crown, mantle, throat and breast black, broadly striped with buff; rump uniform ruddy brown; belly brown broadly streaked with buff. Wings, tail and upper tail-coverts chestnut. Wing-coverts brown with pale shaft streaks.

Range. Northern Venezuela. Ecuador, and northeastern Peru.

Colombia. Humid forest. Upper tropical to temperate zone of the Andes and the Santa Marta Mts. (flammulatus).

55. STREAK-BREASTED TREEHUNTER
(Thripadectes virgaticeps)

Description. 9-9½" (or 8-8½", 1). Crown olive, the feathers with white shaft streaks and black edges. Upper mantle olive brown with pale shaft streaks gradually shading into warm brown without streaks and becoming chestnut on rump and upper tail-coverts. Wings warm brown. Throat and extreme upper breast pale cinnamon, the feathers edged with black giving a streaked appearance; rest of underparts bright cinnamon slightly shaded with olive on the chest and brown on the sides of body. Tail chestnut.

Range. Venezuela and Ecuador.

Colombia. Humid forest. Upper tropical and subtropical zones. West of the Western Andes from the Baudó Mts. southward (sclateri). Head of the Magdalena Valley and east of the Andes in southeastern Nariño (1, magdalenae).

56. BAY-RUMPED TREEHUNTER
(Thripadectes ignobilis)

Description. 8-8½". Crown, back and wings deep reddish brown. Rump and tail bay. Underparts dark wood brown, paler in center of abdomen, the throat streaked with buff. Eyebrow buff, ear-coverts with whitish shaft streaks. Bill shorter and thicker than in other species.

Range. Northwestern Ecuador.

Colombia. Upper tropical and subtropical zones of the western slope of the Western Andes and Nariño.

57. BLACK-BILLED TREEHUNTER
(Thripadectes melanorhynchus)

Description. 8¾ - 9¼". Crown blackish with pale shaft streaks, mantle dark brown with pale shaft streaks. Wings dark brown. Rump, upper tail-coverts and tail chestnut. Throat pale cinnamon, the feathers edged with black, rest of underparts rather pale ochraceous-brown.

Range. Ecuador, Peru and northern Bolivia.

Colombia. Subtropical zone of the east slope of the Eastern Andes in Meta.

58. STRIPED TREEHUNTER
(Thripadectes holostictus)

Description. 8¾ - 9¼". Above very similar to No. 57 but streaks wider. Throat and upper breast ochraceous, feathers edged with black, lower breast ochraceous-brown, the feathers with pale centers. Rest of underparts uniform ochraceous-brown.

Range. Western Ecuador. Northwestern Venezuela, eastern Ecuador, Peru and Bolivia.

Colombia. Forest. Upper tropical and subtropical zones from the west slope of Eastern Andes westward (holostictus). Pacific slope of Nariño (striatidorsus).

59. PLAIN XENOPS
(Xenops minutus) Plate IX

Description. 4¾-5¼". Lower mandible conspicuously upturned. Above uniform olive brown. Remiges dark brown with a diagonal band of cinnamon near the base of the inner feathers. Tertials basally cinnamon, distally black, tipped cinnamon. Eyebrow and throat dirty white, conspicuous line below ear-coverts silvery white, rest of underparts olivaceous-brown. Upper tail-coverts and two central tail-feathers cinnamon-rufous, next two black, outermost black at the base, the distal half diagonally cinnamon.

Range. Mexico southward through Central America to western Ecuador. Venezuela and the Guianas southward to southeastern Brazil, Ecuador, Peru and Bolivia.

Colombia. Forest and second growth. Tropical and lower subtropical zones. The Santa Marta Mts. *(neglectus).* West of the Andes *(littoralis).* East of the Eastern Andes *(remoratus).* Orinoco region in Vichada *(ruficaudus).* Northern extremity of the Perijá Mts. *(olivaceus).*

60. STREAKED XENOPS
(Xenops rutilans)

Description. 6 - 6½". Lower mandible conspicuously upturned. Crown blackish brown, streaked with fulvous. Mantle rufous-brown spotted with fulvous, lower back and upper tail-coverts rufous. Eyebrow and throat white, a silvery white line below ear-coverts. Underparts olive brown (or pale grayish brown, 1), broadly streaked fulvous white. Central and outer two tail-feathers rufous, others partially black (or virtually no black, 2).

Range. Costa Rica southward to Venezuela, the Guianas, southeastern Brazil, Bolivia and Argentina. Trinidad.

Colombia. Forest. Subtropical zone west of the Eastern Andes and on the east slope of the Eastern Andes in Nariño *(heterurus).* East slope of the Andes in Santander and the Perijá Mts. (1, *perijanus).* Santa Marta Mts. (2, *phelpsi).*

61. SLENDER-BILLED XENOPS
(Xenops tenuirostris)

Description. 4¼-4½". Similar to No. 60 but smaller, bill more slender and not as upturned.

Range. The Guianas, southwestern Venezuela south through western Brazil and eastern Peru to northern Bolivia.

Colombia. Forest. Eastern base of the Eastern Andes in Caquetá *(acutirostris).*

62. RUFOUS-TAILED XENOPS
(Xenops milleri)

Description. 4¼-4½". Differs principally from No. 61 by lacking the silvery white streak below the ear-coverts and having no black in the tail.

Range. French Guiana and southern Venezuela southward to western Brazil, and eastern Peru.

Colombia. Forest. Tropical zone at the eastern base of the Eastern Andes in Meta *(milleri).*

63. GRAY-THROATED LEAFSCRAPER
(Sclerurus albigularis) Plate X

Description. 7-7½". Entire upper surface ruddy-brown becoming chestnut on upper tail-coverts. Throat silvery gray; broad band across chest rufous-chestnut; rest of underparts dull wood brown. Tail black, feathers stiffened as in all the leafscrapers. Bill slender, .75".

Range. Costa Rica to western Panama. Venezuela, Ecuador, Peru and Bolivia. Trinidad and Tobago.

Colombia. Humid forest. Subtropical zone. Santa Marta Mts. *(propinquus).* East slope of the Eastern Andes *(albigularis).* Northern end of the Perijá Mts. *(kunanensis).*

64. TAWNY-THROATED LEAFSCRAPER
(Sclerurus mexicanus)

Description. 6½ - 7". Upperparts dark reddish brown becoming chestnut on rump and upper tail-coverts. Throat tawny rufous, breast chestnut (or breast tinged chestnut, 1) ; rest of underparts wood brown. Tail short, black. Bill .5" (or bill .75 - 1".).

Range. Mexico southward to western Ecuador. Venezuela, the Guianas, Bahia, western Brazil and eastern Peru.

Colombia. Forest. Upper tropical zone. Eastern base of the Eastern Andes in Meta, the Perijá Mts. and westward across northern Colombia; not Santa Marta *(andinus)*. Tropical and subtropical zones of both slopes of the Western Andes southward to Nariño (1, *obscurior*).

65. SHORT-BILLED LEAFSCRAPER
(Sclerurus rufigularis)

Description. 6½ - 7". Rather like No. 64 but bill much shorter and coloration less intense; the throat dark buff deepening to reddish brown on breast. Back umber brown, becoming rufescent on the upper tail-coverts. Tail black.

Range. Eastern and southern Venezuela, the Guianas, Brazil and northern Bolivia.

Colombia. Forest. Tropical zone at the base of the Macarena Mts. *(fulvigularis)*. Undoubtedly also on the Amazon at Leticia *(brunnescens)*.

66. BROWN LEAFSCRAPER
(Sclerurus caudacutus)

Description. 7½ - 7¾". Dark brown, darkest on belly. Throat white, the feathers black edged. Tail black.

Range. Venezuela and the Guianas southward to the Amazon, eastward to eastern Ecuador, Peru and Bolivia.

Colombia. Forest. Tropical zone. From Meta southward to Caquetá *(brunneus)*.

67. SCALY-THROATED LEAFSCRAPER
(Sclerurus guatemalensis)

Description. 7 - 7½". Above dark umber brown. Throat white, the feathers edged with black. Chest rufescent brown, feathers with faint pale shaft stripes. Rest of underparts dark wood brown. Tail blackish.

Range. Mexico southward to western Ecuador.

Colombia. Forest. Tropical zone. Upper Sinú Valley *(ennosiphyllus)*. From the west bank of the middle Magdalena westward to the west coast of Colombia *(salvini)*.

68. SHARP-TAILED STREAMCREEPER
(Lochmias nematura) Plate IX

Description. 6¼ -6¾". Above dark reddish brown; upper tail-coverts black. Underparts dark umber brown, the feathers of underparts including throat with white centers giving a heavily spotted appearance. Wings like back. Tail short, black. Bill long, slender .75".

Range. Eastern Panama southward to Venezuela, the Guianas, eastern Ecuador, Peru, Bolivia and Argentina.

Colombia. Forest near small streams. Subtropical zone of the eastern slope of the Eastern Andes westward to the east slope of the Western Andes *(sororia)*.

ANTBIRDS (Formicariidae)

Fig. 61. Yellow-breasted Antwren
(Herpsilochmus axillaris) p. 229

Antbirds form one of the largest tropical American families. Some can be counted among the smallest of birds, while the largest are about the size of a jay. Chiefly inhabitants of the forest mostly in the tropical zone, many live on or near the ground in thick undergrowth and tangled vines. Often mixed bands, composed of several species of antbirds, accompanied by ovenbirds, small woodpeckers and other insectivorous birds, are encountered moving rapidly through the undergrowth of the forest. Other species of antbirds join birds of other families around the swarms of army ants and snap up arthropods flushed by the ants. Other species of antbirds are aboreal, while some live in open thickets.

Although not brilliant in color, they are attractively patterned, and many have a concealed white patch in the middle of the back. Often the lower back is very densely feathered, the feathers forming a thick pad. Males of many of the most characteristic species are either black or gray, resembling each other closely and consequently difficult to tell apart. The sexes often differ; females are usually brown, more definitely patterned and easier to differentiate than males. Tails are usually short to very short, legs often rather long, adapted to a terrestrial life; the bill is not unusual, except that in some species it is rather heavy, hooked and shrike-like. An interesting group are the terrestrial antpittas which resemble short-tailed, long-legged thrushes. Antpittas vary from the size of a robin to that of a sparrow.

Nests are placed in low bushes, hollow tree stumps, or on the ground. They are variable: some suspended, vireo-like, from branches of bushes, others elaborately constructed of twigs with a passageway made of twigs leading to the entrance. (124 Col.; 220 S.A.; 222 N.&S.A.; 222 wld.)

AID TO IDENTIFICATION

All or mostly gray 10E, 11E, 12E, 13, 14E, 15E, 16E, 17E, 18E, 23, 24, 25E, 28E, 35E, 45E, 47E, 56E, 57, 58, 60E, 62, 71E, 72E, 77E, 97E, (with black throat) 37E, 41, 42E, 43E, 44E, 59E, 64E, 65E, 68E, 70E.

All or mostly black 9, 11E,19E, 20, 26, 40, 51, 53, 58, 59E, 61, 63, 69, 78E, 79E, 80, 99E.

Plumage barred 1, 2E, 6, 7, 8E, 91, 102, 103, 109, 110.

Striped or streaked 9, 21, 24, 25E, 29, 30E, 31E, 32E, 33E, 34, 48E, 53, 67E, 90, 108E, 112, 119, 122.

Spotted 18E, 46E, 61, 65E, 66E, 94, 95E, 97E, 98E, 100, 123E.

Underparts white or mostly white 3, 4, 5, 6, 14E, 24, 43E, 46E, 52, 55E, 64E, 68E, 73E, 88E, 89E, 93, 94, 95E, 107, 108E, 117, 118, 119, 121, 122, 123E.

Below chestnut or orange-rufous to ochraceous 2E, 10E, 11E, 16E, 17E, 18E, 20, 22, 35E, 41, 45E, 51, 52, 57, 59E, 60E, 65E, 69, 70E, 71E, 72E, 74, 77E, 78E, 83E, 92E, 93aE, 99E, 103, 104, 105, 106.

Below partially or all pale to bright yellow 23, 29, 33, 49, 50, 54, 66E, 67E, 117.

Lower back and rump chestnut in contrast to rest of upperparts 37E, 38E, 39E, 53, 55E, 83E.

Mostly dull brown, olive brown and gray, or brown and black 12E, 13, 14E, 15, 22, 23, 24, 26, 27E, 29, 30E, 36, 38E, 40, 42E, 44E, 56E, 62, 63, 74, 75, 76, 79E, 80, 81E, 82E, 84E, 85, 86, 87, 96E, 101, (legs very long, tail very short) 103, 104, 111, 113, 114, 115, 116, 120.

1. FASCIATED ANTSHRIKE
(Cymbilaimus lineatus) Plate XII

Description. 7¼ - 7¾ ". Bill very thick and heavy, conspicuously hooked. ♂: Crown black, sometimes lightly barred with white. Upperparts, including tail, black narrowly barred with white. Entire under surface white narrowly barred with black. ♀: Crown chestnut. Back and tail black barred with ochraceous-cinnamon. Underparts ochraceous-cinnamon, narrowly barred with black. Iris reddish in both sexes.

Range. Nicaragua southward to western Ecuador. Venezuela, the Guianas, Brazil, eastern Ecuador, Peru and Bolivia.

Colombia. Forest. Tropical zone. East of the Andes from Norte de Santander southward to Amazonas *(intermedius)*. The Magdalena Valley westward to the Pacific coast and Nariño *(fasciatus)*.

2. UNDULATED ANTSHRIKE
(Frederickena unduligera)

Description. 9¼ - 9¾ ". Bill thick, conspicuously hooked. Crested. ♂: Entire upper surface black with thin, wavy, grayish lines, the feathers of the crest edged with grayish. Throat and extreme upper breast black, rest of underparts black, heavily waved and freckled with grayish white. Wings and tail black, lightly barred and notched with grayish. ♀: Head chestnut, the feathers barred with black. Back rufescent brown, barred with black. Entire underparts bright rusty rufous, barred with black. Tail and upper tail-coverts black, barred with gray.

Range. Western Brazil, eastern Ecuador and Peru.

Colombia. Forest. Tropical zone. East of the Andes from Caquetá southward *(fulva)*.

3. GREAT ANTSHRIKE
(Taraba major) Plates VIII and XI (♀)

Description. 8 - 8½ ". Bill thick, strongly hooked. Head crested. ♂: Entire upper surface, wings and tail black, wing-coverts tipped with white forming two wing-bars. Concealed dorsal patch and tip to tail-feathers white. Below white. ♀: Rufous-chestnut (or chestnut, 1) above including wings and tail; white below.

Range. Guatemala southward to western Ecuador and northwestern Peru. Venezuela, the Guianas southward to Argentina and Bolivia. Trinidad.

Colombia. Humid scrub. Tropical rarely subtropical zones. Pacific coast eastward to the lower Cauca Valley (1, *obscurus*). Southwestern Nariño *(transandeanus)*. The Sinú Valley eastward to the middle Magdalena, southwestern Santa Marta region, Arauca, Boyacá and Meta *(granadensis)*. The Orinoco region in Vichada *(semifasciatus)*. Eastern base of the Andes from Caquetá southward *(melanurus)*.

4. BLACK-CRESTED ANTSHRIKE
(Sakesphorus canadensis) Plate IX

Description. 6¼ - 6½ ". Bill rather thick, hooked. Head conspicuously crested. ♂: Forecrown, throat and cheeks black, the feathers edged with white; hindcrown, crest, breast and line down center of lower breast black. Back rufous-brown (or blackish brown, 1); wings and tail black. Wing-coverts, inner secondaries and tail edged with white, the latter tipped white. Sides of breast and belly white, sides of body grayish. ♀: Crown and crest chestnut. Back rufescent (or cinnamon-rufous, 2). Sides of head mottled black and white. Underparts buffy, slightly streaked on breast with black (or rufescent buff, darker on sides, conspicuously streaked on breast with black, 3). Wings and tail as in ♂.

Range. Venezuela and the Guianas, northwestern Brazil. Trinidad.

Colombia. Open woodland and bushy open country. Tropical zone. The Guajira Peninsula and adjacent Santa Marta region (2, *phainoleucus*). Caribbean coast from the Panama border to the western base of the Santa Marta Mts. *(pulchellus)*. East of the Andes in Meta and the Orinoco region (3, *intermedius?*). The Amazonian region (1, *loretoyacuensis*).

5. BLACK-BACKED ANTSHRIKE
(Sakesphorus melanonotus)

Description. 6½ - 7" ♂: Differs from No. 4 by having the back black with a concealed white patch. The lower back and rump gray, upper tail-coverts black, tipped white. The breast more extensively black. ♀: Differs by having the crown blackish. Back grayish brown, with a concealed white patch. Underparts buff. Tail dull chestnut, tipped with white, outer web of outer tail-feathers buffy white.

Range. Northwestern Venezuela.

Colombia. Semi-arid scrub. Tropical zone. Santa Marta region, then southward to Norte de Santander.

6. BARRED ANTSHRIKE
(Thamnophilus doliatus) Plate XII

Description. 6½-7". In all the species of *Thamnophilus* the bill is rather thick and hooked. ♂: Crown black, base of feathers white (or without white bases, 1). Back, wings and tail black, the back barred, the wings and tail notched with white. Throat white, heavily streaked with black (or lightly streaked, 1). Lower surface coarsely barred black and white (or with broken black bars on breast and sides of body, 1). ♀: Crown, tail and wings chestnut, back uniform orange-rufous (or with a few broken black bars, 2), hindneck streaked buff and black. Throat whitish, rest of underparts tawny buff. Iris straw yellow in both sexes.

Range. Mexico southward through Central America to western Ecuador and western Peru. Venezuela and the Guianas southward to Argentina, Paraguay and Bolivia. Trinidad, Tobago, Margarita I.

Colombia. Open woodland and forest undergrowth. Tropical zone. Norte de Santander in the Catatumbo basin (2, *nigrescens*). From southern Norte de Santander to Meta *(fraterculus)*. The Amazon region (1, *subradiatus*). West of the Andes in the upper Magdalena Valley (1, *albicans*). Caribbean coast from Córdoba to the lower Magdalena Valley (1, *nigricristatus*).

7. BAR-CRESTED ANTSHRIKE
(Thamnophilus multistriatus)
Plate XI (♀)

Description. 6¾-7". ♂: Similar to No. 6 but crown and tail barred with white. ♀: like ♂ below but upperparts, wings and tail chestnut. Sides of head and collar on hindneck streaked black and white.

Range. Colombia.

Colombia. Forest border. Upper tropical and subtropical zone. West slope of the Eastern Andes and east slope of the Central Andes and western Nariño *(multistriatus)*. East slope of the Andes in Boyacá and Norte de Santander *(oecoto-*

nophilus). West slope of the Western Andes in the upper río San Juan Valley *(selvae)*. From the Dagua and upper Patía Valleys to the slopes above the Cauca river in the upper part of the valley *(brachyurus)*.

8. LINED ANTSHRIKE
(Thamnophilus palliatus)

Description. 6¾ - 7¼ ". ♂ : Very similar to No. 6. Crown black without white base to feathers. Above black much more finely barred white. Below black barred with white rather than white barred with black. ♀ : very similar to ♀ of No. 7 and not distinguishable in the field. Differs principally by having the flanks more strongly tinged with buffy.

Range. Eastern Ecuador, eastern Peru, Brazil south of the Amazon, northern Bolivia.

Colombia. Forest border and thickets. Tropical zone east of the Andes. From Meta northward to the Catatumbo region *(tenuepunctatus);* from Meta southward to Putumayo *(tenuifasciatus)*.

9. BLACK ANTSHRIKE
(Thamnophilus nigriceps)

Description. 5½-5¾ ". ♂ : Entirely black. Under wing-coverts partially white. ♀ : Head, nape and breast blackish broadly streaked with buffy white; rest of underparts pale sandy brown obscurely streaked buff. Back, wings, tail and under tail-coverts rufous.

Range. Eastern Panama.

Colombia. Forest undergrowth. Tropical zone. Lower Atrato and upper Sinú Valleys eastward to the lower Magdalena and southwestern Santa Marta *(nigriceps)*. The Magdalena Valley from Santander south to northern Tolima *(magdalenae)*.

10. BLACKISH-GRAY ANTSHRIKE
(Thamnophilus nigrocinereus)

Description. 6¼ -6½ ". ♂ : Crown, upper back, wings and tail black. A concealed dorsal patch, edges of wing-coverts, narrow tip to outer tail-feathers white. Underparts and lower back dark gray. ♀ :

Crown and sides of head dark gray, underside chestnut-rufous. Sides of body, back, wings and tail brown. A small concealed dorsal patch, white.

Range. Venezuela, French Guiana, and the Amazon Valley to eastern Peru.

Colombia. Forest. Tropical zone east of the Eastern Andes from Meta southward *(cinereoniger)*.

11. WHITE-SHOULDERED ANTSHRIKE
(Thamnophilus aethiops)

Description. 6½-6¾ ". ♂ : Lustrous black (or dark gray, with black crown, 1). Upper wing-coverts dotted with white. ♀ : Rufescent brown (or chestnut, 2), tail black (or brown, 1).

Range. Eastern and southern Venezuela, eastern Ecuador, Brazil, eastern Peru and Bolivia.

Colombia. Forest. Tropical zone east of the Andes. Southeastern Nariño *(aethiops)*. Caquetá (1, *wetmorei*). Vaupés (1, 2, *polionotus*).

12. BLACK-CAPPED ANTSHRIKE
(Thamnophilus schistaceus)

Description. 5¾-6". ♂ : Gray, paler below. Crown, nape and tail black. ♀ : Crown chestnut. Feathers around eye and lores gray with white shaft lines. Upperparts and wings olive brown; tail browner. Throat grayish white, rest of underparts olive brown, center of abdomen buffy.

Range. Western and eastern Ecuador. Peru, Bolivia and eastward down the Amazon Valley to the rio Tapajóz.

Colombia. Forest. Tropical zone. East of the Andes from Meta southward to the Amazon *(capitalis)*.

13. UNIFORM ANTSHRIKE
(Thamnophilus unicolor)

Description. 6½ - 6¾ ". ♂ : Uniform dark gray; wings and tail dusky gray. ♀ : Crown chestnut, upper surface, wings and tail chestnut brown. Throat, sides of head grayish tawny, rest of underparts tawny brown.

Range. Eastern and western Ecuador, northern Peru.

Colombia. Forest and forest edge. Upper tropical and lower subtropical zones. West of the Andes except Santa Marta. East of the Andes in southeastern Nariño *(grandior).*

14. MOUSE-COLORED ANTSHRIKE
(Thamnophilus murinus)

Description. 5¾ - 6". ♂: Above slaty gray. A small, concealed white dorsal patch. Feathers of crown with blackish centers. Feathers below eye gray with white shaft streaks. Wing-coverts tipped with pale gray forming a double wing-bar. Throat pale gray, center of abdomen and tips to tail-feathers white. Breast and sides of body pale gray. ♀: Above olive brown; crown, wings and tail dull chestnut, wing-coverts and tail tipped paler. Throat, center of abdomen and under tail-coverts white. Breast and sides of body olive.

Range. Southern Venezuela and the Guianas westward to eastern Ecuador, eastern Peru and northwestern Brazil.

Colombia. Forest. Tropical zone. Río Guainía and the río Vaupés regions *(murinus).*

15. SLATY ANTSHRIKE
(Thamnophilus punctatus)
Plates XI (♀) and XII

Description. 6-6½". ♂: Crown black; eyebrow and sides of head mixed black and gray. A partially concealed white dorsal patch. Back slate gray clouded with black (or virtually black, 1); upper tail-coverts black, tipped white. Wings black, wing-coverts conspicuously spotted and edged with white, inner secondaries broadly edged white. Underparts uniform pale gray, under tail-coverts with white tips. Upper tail-coverts black with white tips. Tail black with white tips, the outermost feathers with a white patch near center on outer web. ♀: Crown dull chestnut. Back olive brown (or crown scarcely different from back, 1). Underparts ochraceous-olive, grayish on throat. Wings and tail brown, marked like ♂, buff on wings and white on tail.

Range. Honduras south to western

Ecuador. Venezuela and the Guianas southward to southeastern Brazil and eastern Peru.

Colombia. Forest, scrub, open bush country. Tropical zone. Santa Marta region, southward through the Magdalena Valley to northern Tolima and westward to the lower Cauca and Atrato Valleys. The Caribbean coast eastward to the middle Magdalena Valley, the Catatumbo region and Arauca *(subcinereus)*; in Meta *(1, interpositus)*. The Pacific coast *(atrinucha)*. Gorgona Island *(gorgonae).*

16. AMAZONIAN ANTSHRIKE
(Thamnophilus amazonicus)

Description. 6¼ - 6¾" (or 5¾ - 6", 1). ♂: Not distinguishable in the field from No. 15. Virtually the only difference is its slightly larger size, (or similar to No. 15, but slightly smaller and upperparts virtually without black clouding, crown gray, only center of feathers black, 1). ♀: Whole head, throat and breast rufous-orange; belly rusty white. Back olive, shaded with rufous on upper mantle (or crown and nape chestnut; entire underparts cinnamon-rufous. Back and rump olive, the feathers of the back with broad black centers, 1). Wings and tail as in ♂.

Range. Venezuela, French Guiana southward to eastern Brazil and northern Bolivia.

Colombia. Forest. Tropical zone east of the Andes. From Meta southward to the Amazon *(amazonicus)*. Extreme eastern Colombia in the Orinoco and Vaupés regions (1, *cinereiceps).*

17. SPOT-WINGED ANTSHRIKE
(Pygiptila stellaris) Plate IX

Description. 5¾ - 6". ♂: Crown and nape black. Back dark gray; large concealed interscapular patch white, terminal portion of the white feathers black forming a black patch. Wings and short tail gray, wing-coverts with many small white spots. Entire lower surface blue-gray. ♀: Forecrown, sides of head and entire under surface ochraceous. Back, inner secondaries and short tail blue-gray. Wing-coverts olive brown; primaries and secondaries brown, the inner webs rufous.

Range. The Guianas southward to the mouth of the Amazon and westward through northern Brazil to eastern Ecuador, eastern Peru and northern Bolivia.

Colombia. Forest. Tropical zone east of the Andes in Caquetá, Putumayo and Vaupés *(occipitalis)*.

18. PEARLY ANTSHRIKE
(Megastictus margaritatus)
Plates XI ($♀$) and XII

Description. 5¾ - 6″. Bill shrike-like but not as thick as most of the preceding species. $♂$: Above blue-gray. Wings, tail, upper tail-coverts black, the wing-coverts and inner secondaries with large round white spots, the upper tail-coverts and tail-feathers broadly tipped white. Throat grayish white, rest of underparts pale blue-gray. $♀$: Olive brown above; wing-coverts, tertials and tail blackish brown marked as in $♂$ but spots larger and buff instead of white. Underparts ochraceous, paler on throat.

Range. Southern Venezuela, western Brazil, eastern Ecuador, eastern Peru.

Colombia. Forest. Tropical zone east of the Andes, from Caquetá and Vaupés southward.

19. BLACK BUSHBIRD
(Neoctantes niger) Plate XII

Description. 6¼ - 6½″. Upper mandible nearly straight, lower mandible somewhat upcurved. $♂$: Entirely lustrous black with a concealed white interscapular patch. Tail rather short. $♀$ like $♂$ but breast chestnut.

Range. Eastern Ecuador, northeastern Peru, northwestern Brazil.

Colombia. Forest. Tropical zone east of the Andes in southeastern Nariño.

20. RECURVE-BILLED BUSHBIRD
(Clytoctantes alixi) Plate XII

Description. 6½ - 6¾″. Bill large, upper mandible slightly concave, lower mandible sharply upturned. $♂$: Entire upper surface dark ashy gray with a concealed white interscapular patch. Lores, throat

and breast black. Sides of body and belly dark ashy gray. Wings brownish black, wing-coverts obscurely pale tipped. Tail rather short grayish black. $♀$: Brown; forehead, sides of head and sides of body chestnut. Wings and tail blackish.

Range. Possibly, but not probably, eastern Ecuador.

Colombia. Very dense second growth near ground. Tropical zone in Caldas, Antioquia, Córdoba, Bolívar and eastward to Santander.

21. SPECKLE-BREASTED ANTSHRIKE
(Xenornis setifrons)

Description. 6¼ - 6½″. Lower mandible slightly upturned. $♂$: General impression dark brown. Forehead and sides of head dark gray. Above deep reddish brown, the feathers tawny-ochraceous centrally and margined with blackish giving a somewhat streaked appearance. Rump and upper tail-coverts uniform dark wood brown. Wings dark red-brown, wing-coverts and tertials tipped with pinkish ochraceous. Throat and upper breast and center of abdomen buff, the feathers edged dark brown giving a somewhat streaked appearance, rest of underparts brown, more rufescent on chest and grayish in center of abdomen. Tail dark blackish gray. $♀$ like $♂$ but feathers at sides of head tawny-ochraceous edged black giving a streaked appearance.

Range. Eastern Panama.

Colombia. Forest. Tropical zone near the base of the Baudó Mts. in Chocó.

22. RUSSET ANTSHRIKE
(Thamnistes anabatinus)

Description. 6¼ - 6¾″. Bill heavy and shrike-like. Above olive (or tawny olive, 1). Crown tinged chestnut (or bay, 1). Wings and tail brownish chestnut (or chestnut-rufous, 3). Throat yellowish ochraceous (or ochraceous, 2), breast and eyebrow ochraceous-olive, rest of under surface olive. A concealed interscapular patch orange-rufous, the feathers with a black subterminal bar (in $♂$ only).

Range. Southeastern Mexico southward to western Ecuador. Western Venezuela, eastern Ecuador, Peru and northern Bolivia.

Colombia. Forest. Tropical zone. The Atrato Valley and the Pacific coast (1, *intermedius*). Northwestern Colombia in Córdoba (3, *coronatus*). Eastern Andes north of Bogotá (2, *gularis*). East of the Andes from Bogotá southward *(aequatorialis)*.

23. PLAIN ANTVIREO
(Dysithamnus mentalis) Plate XII

Description. 4¾ - 5¼". Bill shrike-like. ♂: Above gray (or crown and nape gray, rest of upperparts olive gray, 1) with a concealed white interscapular patch. Wings and tail gray, wing-coverts with white tips. Below pale gray, palest on throat and center of abdomen (or throat white, rest of underparts olive gray, center of abdomen sulphur yellow, 1). ♀: Crown chestnut; back olive brown, wings and tail chestnut brown, wing-coverts obscurely pale tipped. Underparts olive brown, whiter on throat and center of abdomen (or olive yellow more olive on sides, 1).

Range. Guatemala southward to western Ecuador. Venezuela to southeastern Brazil, northern Argentina, Paraguay and northern Bolivia. Trinidad and Tobago.

Colombia. Forest. Upper tropical and subtropical zones. Eastern slope of the Santa Marta Mts., the Eastern Andes and the eastern slope of the Central Andes *(semicinereus)*. Western Andes and the west slope of the Central Andes *(extremus)*. Northwest Colombia near the Panama border and lower Cauca Valley *(suffusus)*. East of the Andes in Norte de Santander (1, *viridis*). East of the Andes in southeastern Nariño *(napensis)*.

24. SPOT-CROWNED ANTVIREO
(Dysithamnus puncticeps)

Description. 5". Bill shrike-like. ♂: Feathers of crown black mesially, bordered with gray and terminating with a white tip on each web giving a checkered appearance. Back, wings and tail gray with a slightly olivaceous tinge; wing-coverts spotted with white. Throat and upper breast white narrowly streaked with black. Lower breast and center of belly white. Sides of body olive. ♀: Crown rufous-brown, the wing-coverts tipped with buff. Throat whitish lightly streaked with black. Breast and rest of underparts tawny buff, olivaceous on the sides.

Range. Costa Rica to western Ecuador.

Colombia. Forest. Tropical zone. West shores of the Gulf of Urabá *(puncticeps)*. Pacific coast in the lower Atrato Valley and lower río San Juan eastward to the lower Cauca *(intensus)*. Western Nariño *(flemmingi)*.

25. WHITE-SPOTTED ANTSHRIKE
(Thamnomanes plumbeus)

Description. 6". Bill shrike-like. ♂: Plumbeous gray, the breast blackish. Bend of wing white, wing-coverts edged with white. Feathers of breast and belly with white shafts. ♀: Crown chestnut, sides of head gray with white shaft streaks. Back, wings and tail tawny brown. Feathers of throat, breast, and upper belly blue-gray with broad white centers giving a streaked appearance. Sides of body olive.

Range. Northwestern Venezuela. Eastern Ecuador. Southeastern Brazil.

Colombia. Tropical zone east of the Andes in Meta *(leucostictus)*.

26. WESTERN ANTSHRIKE
(Thamnomanes occidentalis)

Description. 6¼ - 6½". Bill shrike-like. ♂: Slaty black above with a concealed white interscapular patch; dark slaty gray below. Wing-coverts spotted with white. ♀: Crown and nape chestnut, back maroon-brown. Wings dark brown, wing-coverts spotted with white. Eyebrow and sides of head, neck, throat and breast slaty gray, the feathers with white shafts. Belly, flanks and under tail-coverts olive brown. Tail dark brown.

Range. Eastern Ecuador.

Colombia. Upper tropical zone of the western slope of the Western Andes in southwestern Cauca *(occidentalis)*.

PLATE XI

(All birds shown are males unless otherwise noted)

SLATY ANTSHRIKE
(*Thamnophilus punc-
tatus atrinucha*, ♀)
Page 221

WHITE-PLUMED
ANTBIRD
(*Pithys albi-
frons peruviana*)
Page 237

BAR-CRESTED
ANTSHRIKE
(*Thamnophilus
m. multistriatus*, ♀)
Page 219

PEARLY ANTSHRIKE
(*Megastictus mar-
garitatus*, ♀)
Page 222

OCELLATED
ANTTHRUSH
(*Phaenostictus
mcleannani chocoanus*)
Page 239

DOT-WINGED ANTWREN
(*Microrhopias
q. quixensis*, ♀)
Page 229

GREAT ANTSHRIKE
(*Taraba major
transandeanus*, ♀)
Page 218

RUFOUS-BREASTED
ANTTHRUSH
(*Formicarius rufi-
pectus carrikeri*)
Page 237

STREAK-CHESTED
ANTPITTA
(*Grallaria perspi-
cillata periophthalmica*)
Page 244

WING-BANDED
ANTTHRUSH
(*Myrmornis t. torquata*)
Page 239

OCELLATED TAPACULO
(*Acropternis o. orthonyx*)
Page 248

BLACK-CROWNED
ANTPITTA
(*Pittasoma m. michleri*)
Page 241

E. L. Poole

27. DUSKY-THROATED ANTSHRIKE
(Thamnomanes ardesiacus)

Description. 5¾ - 6". Bill shrike-like. ♂: Entirely rather dark blue-gray. Throat obscurely spotted with black. Under tail-coverts and tail narrowly tipped white. ♀: Olivaceous brown above, wings and tail browner. Throat buffy white; rest of underparts tawny buff, brightest on under tail-coverts, clouded on breast with olive. Eye-ring whitish.

Range. The Guianas and eastern Venezuela to eastern Ecuador, eastern Peru and the upper and middle Amazon.

Colombia. Forest. Tropical zone east of the Andes from Meta southward to Putumayo *(ardesiacus).*

28. CINEREOUS ANTSHRIKE
(Thamnomanes caesius)

Description. 6 - 6½". Bill hooked but comparatively slender. ♂: Entirely gray with a concealed white interscapular patch. Under wing-coverts white. ♀: Rather like ♀ of No. 27 but much more deeply colored. Olive brown above. Wings and tail rufous brown. Throat buffy, breast olive brown, rest of underparts rusty cinnamon. Eye-ring rufous.

Range. The Guianas, Venezuela southward to Ecuador, Peru, Bolivia and southern Brazil.

Colombia. Forest. Tropical zone from the eastern base of the Eastern Andes in Meta, Caquetà and Putumayo to Vichada and Vaupés *(glaucus).*

29. PYGMY ANTWREN
(Myrmotherula brachyura)

Description. 3½ - 3¾" (or 3 - 3¼", 1). ♂: Crown and back striped black and white with a concealed white interscapular patch, rump gray. Wing black, wing-coverts spotted with large white spots, the remiges edged with white. Throat white, rest of underparts pale yellow striped with black on sides of breast. Tail black, very short, hardly longer than the tail-coverts. ♀ similar to ♂ except for the white of head and ear-coverts replaced by buffy, and buff-tinged chest.

Range. Panama southward to Venezuela, the Guianas, the middle and upper Amazon, Ecuador, Peru and northern Bolivia.

Colombia. Forest. Tropical zone. East of the Eastern Andes from Meta south to Putumayo and east to Vaupés *(brachyura);* the Pacific coast (1, *ignota).*

30. SHORT-BILLED ANTWREN
(Myrmotherula obscura)

Description. 3½". ♂: Very similar to No. 29, but crown and back blacker, much less striped; moustacial streak, broader and more conspicuous. Bill and tail shorter. ♀: Differs in the same manner, and further by having the throat and breast buff.

Range. Eastern Ecuador, northern Peru and western Brazil.

Colombia. Forest. Tropical zone. East of the Eastern Andes from Meta southward to the Amazon.

31. CHERRIE'S ANTWREN
(Myrmotherula cherriei)

Description. 4 - 4¼". ♂: Crown, back, sides of head and underparts black striped with white, below white striped with black. Wings black, wing-coverts spotted with white, wing-feathers edged white. Upper tail-coverts and tail black, tipped white, the tail-feathers edged white. Tail not conspicuously short. ♀ like ♂ but ground color of crown, nape, sides of head and underparts ochraceous-buff.

Range. Southern Venezuela, northwestern Brazil.

Colombia. Forest. Tropical zone, southern Meta eastward to the Orinoco.

32. STRIPE-CHESTED ANTWREN
(Myrmotherula longicauda) Plate XII

Description. 4½ - 4¾". ♂: Above black, striped with white. Wings and tail as in No. 31. Throat and belly white, only breast lightly striped with black. ♀: Striped black and ochraceous above. Wings and tail like ♂. Throat and belly white, breast ochraceous.

Range. Ecuador, Peru and northern Bolivia.

Colombia. Forest. Tropical zone east of the Andes in Putumayo and southeastern Nariño *(söderströmi).*

33. YELLOW-THROATED ANTWREN
(Myrmotherula ambigua)

Description. 4 - 4¼ ". ♂ : Crown streaked black and white, back streaked pale yellow and black, concealed yellow interscapular patch. Rump and upper tail-coverts gray. Underparts pale yellow, moustacial streak continued down the side of breast blackish. Wings black the wing-coverts spotted, the flight-feathers edged with white. Tail black, the feathers edged and tipped with white. ♀ like ♂ in pattern of upperparts, wings and tail, but head and nape tawny olive, striped with black instead of black and white. Underparts pale yellow, buffy at sides of body.

Range. Southern Venezuela and northwestern Brazil.

Colombia. Forest. Tropical zone east of the Andes in Vaupés.

34. STREAKED ANTWREN
(Myrmotherula surinamensis)

Description. 4 - 4¾ ". ♂ : Crown, nape and back black striped with white, lower back pale gray. Throat and breast white, striped with black. Belly white. Wing-coverts spotted and edges of flight-feathers margined with white. Tail-feathers black, tipped and edged with white. ♀ : Top and sides of head orange-rufous, the crown and nape striped with black. Back black striped with white. Rump and upper tail-coverts gray tinged ochraceous. Throat buffy, breast orange-ochraceous, rest of underparts buffy white. Wings and tail as in ♂ .

Range. Panama to western Ecuador. The Guianas, eastern and southern Venezuela, eastern Ecuador, Peru and the Amazon Valley.

Colombia. Forest and scrub. Tropical zone. East of the Andes in Meta *(multostriata)*. West of the Andes in the middle Magdalena, lower Cauca, upper Sinú Valleys and the Pacific coast *(pacifica)*.

35. PLAIN-THROATED ANTWREN
(Myrmotherula hauxwelli)

Description. 4¼ ". ♂ : Above and below gray; a concealed interscapular patch white. Wings slaty, edgings on the wing-coverts forming two white wing-bars, and inner secondaries tipped with white. Upper tail-coverts black, tipped white. Tail short, slaty black. ♀ : Upperparts and flanks and edges to primaries olive brown. Wing-coverts, tertials and tail-coverts black conspicuously edged with rufous-buff, those of the wing-coverts forming a double bar. Underparts orange-rufous. Tail brownish black, tipped buff.

Range. Ecuador, Peru, Bolivia and the Amazon Valley.

Colombia. Forest. Tropical zone. East of the Andes from Meta southward *(suffusa)*.

36. CHECKER-THROATED ANTWREN
(Myrmotherula fulviventris)

Description. 4¼ - 4¾ " (or 4¾ - 5", 1). ♂ : Above drab brown, more rufescent on upper tail-coverts. Wings and tail rufescent brown, the wing-coverts blackish, tipped with buff forming a double wing-bar. Throat checkered, black and white. Rest of underparts brownish buffy, (or grayish buff, 1). ♀ similar to ♂ but throat uniform with the rest of the underparts.

Range. Honduras southward to western Ecuador.

Colombia. Forest undergrowth. Tropical, rarely subtropical zone. Pacific coast and middle Cauca Valley *(fulviventris)*. Middle Magdalena Valley westward to the upper Sinú Valley *(1, salmoni)*.

37. CHESTNUT-SADDLED ANTWREN
(Myrmotherula ornata)

Description. 4¼ - 4¾ ". ♂ : Gray, center of back chestnut; throat black. Wing-coverts black conspicuously spotted with white. Upper and under tail-coverts olive gray. Remiges and rectrices grayish brown. ♀ : Wings, tail and chestnut of back as in ♂ . Crown, nape, upper back and upper tail-coverts olive brown. Throat checkered black and white. Rest of underparts pale ochraceous olive.

Range. Eastern Ecuador, eastern Peru, Bolivia and western Brazil, the south bank of the Amazon to the rio Tocantins.

Colombia. Forest. Tropical zone east of the Andes in Meta *(ornata)*. Southern Meta southward *(saturata)*.

38. RUFOUS-BACKED ANTWREN
(Myrmotherula haematonota)

Description. 4½ - 4¾″. ♂: Crown and nape olive brown, back chestnut. Wing-coverts black tipped with white, remiges edged rufescent brown. Throat checkered black and white, sides of head gray, breast gray, lower belly and under tail-coverts olive brown. Upper tail-coverts and tail brown. ♀: Wing-coverts tipped with rufous-buff. Sides of head, throat and rest of lower parts ochraceous; otherwise like ♂.

Range. Venezuela, northwestern Brazil, eastern Peru, and south bank of the upper Amazon.

Colombia. Forest. Tropical zone east of the Andes in Caquetá (pyrrhonota).

39. RUFOUS-TAILED ANTWREN
(Myrmotherula erythrura)

Description. 4¾ - 5¼″. Tail rather long for this group. ♂: Forehead, sides of head and neck, throat and breast pearl gray. Crown, nape and upper back olivaceous brown, rest of back chestnut, tail rufous-brown. Wings dark olive brown, the wing-coverts spotted with buff. Belly, flanks, upper and under tail-coverts olive brown. ♀ similar to ♂ but throat cinnamon and breast and belly olive buff instead of mostly gray.

Range. Eastern Ecuador, northern Brazil, southward to southern Peru.

Colombia. Forest. Tropical zone. East of the Andes from Meta southward (erythrura).

40. WHITE-FLANKED ANTWREN
(Myrmotherula axillaris)

Description. 3¾ - 4½″. ♂: Above slaty black; wings and tail black, wing-coverts spotted, the tertials and tail-feathers tipped with white. Underparts black; long silky plumes springing from flanks, white. ♀: Crown and upper back grayish olive, tinged rufous on lower back and upper tail-coverts (or upper parts olive brown becoming rufous on upper tail-coverts, 1). Wings and tail brown, wing-coverts tipped with fulvous (or plain, 1) the flight-feathers edged with rufous. Below buff

(or ochraceous buff, 1). Throat whitish.

Range. Honduras southward to western Ecuador. Venezuela, the Guianas southward to southeastern Brazil, Ecuador, Peru and Bolivia. Trinidad.

Colombia. Forest. Tropical zone. Pacific coast eastward to the Gulf of Urabá, the lower Cauca and upper Sinú Valleys (albigula). Southwestern Santa Marta region, the lower and middle Magdalena Valley and east of the Eastern Andes, from Santander southward to eastern Nariño and eastward to Vichada and Vaupés (1, melaena).

41. SLATY ANTWREN
(Myrmotherula schisticolor) Plate XII

Description. 4 - 4½″. ♂: Upper surface, remiges and rectrices, sides of head and body slaty gray, wing-coverts blacker, tipped with white. Throat and breast black (or throat and foreneck only black, 1; or throat, breast and center of belly black, 2). ♀: Upperparts brownish olive (or crown and nape olive, 2); underparts tawny ochraceous. Wings and tail brown, tertials edged with gray.

Range. Southern Mexico south to western Ecuador. Venezuela, Ecuador and northern Peru.

Colombia. Forest. Upper tropical and subtropical zones. The west coast from Nariño northward, and eastward to the west slope of the Central Andes in Antioquia and Valle (schisticolor). West portion of the Santa Marta Mts. (1, sanctae-martae). Both slopes of the Eastern Andes from Meta southward on the east slope; in Cundinamarca on the west slope, and the head of the Magdalena Valley (2, interior).

42. RIO SUNO ANTWREN
(Myrmotherula sunensis)

Description. 3½ - 4″. ♂: In color and pattern similar to No. 41, but smaller and with a much shorter tail, about 1″. ♀: Olive-gray above, more olive on crown; wings and tail brown; throat buffy white, underparts pale grayish brown, under tail-coverts ochraceous.

Range. Eastern Ecuador and Peru.

Colombia. Tropical zone in southeastern Nariño (sunensis).

43. LONG-WINGED ANTWREN
(Myrmotherula longipennis)

Description. 4 - 4½ ". ♂ : Very similar to No. 41 but somewhat paler, throat and upper breast black and tail white tipped. ♀ : Upperparts, wings and tail rufescent brown. Sides of head, eye-ring, throat and upper breast ochraceous-buff, rest of underparts white.

Range. Southern Venezuela, the Guianas and northeastern Brazil westward to eastern Peru, eastern Ecuador.

Colombia. Forest. Tropical zone. East of the Andes from Putumayo and Caquetá eastward to Vaupés *(longipennis)*.

44. PLAIN-WINGED ANTWREN
(Myrmotherula behni)

Description. 4 - 4½ ". ♂ : Similar to No. 43, but wing-coverts uniform gray like the rest of the wing instead of black tipped white. Tail without white tip. ♀ : Above russet brown, below pale russet brown, eye-ring and throat whitish.

Range. Southern Venezuela and British Guiana.

Colombia. Forest. Upper tropical zone. East of the Andes in southern Meta *(behni)*.

45. GRAY ANTWREN
(Myrmotherula menetriesii)

Description. 4 - 4¼ ". ♂ : Uniform blue-gray, paler below; wing-coverts gray with a subterminal black bar and white edge. Tail and under tail-coverts gray narrowly tipped white. ♀ : Gray above, tinged with olive on crown. Below uniform cinnamon-buff. Wings and tail brownish gray.

Range. Southern Venezuela and the Guianas, northeastern Brazil to Ecuador, Peru and Bolivia.

Colombia. Forest. Tropical zone. East of the Eastern Andes from Meta southward to Putumayo and eastward to Vichada and Vaupés *(pallida)*.

46. BANDED ANTBIRD
(Dichrozona cincta)

Description. 4½ - 5" Bill rather long, tail short. ♂ : Crown and mantle chestnut brown with a concealed white interscapulum. Rump, lower back and upper tail-coverts black, the rump crossed with a white band. Sides of head grayish, lores and eyebrow white becoming gray posteriorly. Underparts white, the breast spotted with black, flanks olive brown. Lesser wing-coverts black, spotted with white, median and greater wing-coverts broadly tipped ochraceous forming two conspicuous wing-bars. Primaries edged chestnut brown. Inner secondaries mostly blackish, banded ochraceous near the base. Tail black, outer feathers mostly white. ♀ : similar to ♂ but without the white interscapulum, and the lesser wing-coverts tipped ochraceous instead of white.

Range. Southern Venezuela, eastern Ecuador, Peru, Bolivia and the upper Amazon Valley.

Colombia. Forest. Tropical zone. Southern Meta southward to Caquetá and eastward to Vaupés *(cincta)*.

47. SPOT-TAILED ANTWREN
(Herpsilochmus sticturus)

Description. 5¼ - 5½ ". ♂ : Crown and nape black, forehead with a few white streaks. Back gray, concealed interscapular patch white, the feathers tipped black forming a black patch in center of back. Long eyebrow white; stripe behind eye black; ear-coverts white. Wings black, lesser wing-coverts spotted with white, the greater and median wing-coverts broadly tipped white. Remiges black edged white. Below pale gray, darkest on sides of body. Tail black, outer feathers broadly, the others more narrowly, tipped white. Central tail-feathers black with three or four large white marks on inner web. The description is taken from a specimen of the typical race. The ♂ of *dugandi* is not known. ♀ like ♂ but crown rufous with pale shaft streaks and no white dorsal spot. Lower parts tinged buff.

Range. The Guianas and southern Venezuela.

Colombia. Tropical zone east of the Andes. Known only from Caquetá *(dugandi)*.

48. SPOT-BACKED ANTWREN
(Herpsilochmus dorsimaculatus)

Description. 5 - 5¼". ♂ : Differs from No. 47 in having the upper back broadly striped black and white. ♀ : Crown black, forehead spotted ochraceous, rest of crown spotted with white. Back black and white; sides of neck and chest bright buff.

Range. Southern Venezuela, northwest Brazil.

Colombia. Forest. Tropical zone east of the Andes in Vaupés.

49. YELLOW-BREASTED ANTWREN
(Herpsilochmus axillaris) Fig. 61

Description. 5 - 5¼". ♂ : Crown and nape black spotted with white; eyebrow and sides of head white, speckled with black. Back gray, tinged olive. Wings black, wing-coverts and flight-feathers margined with yellowish white. Chin and throat white, rest of underparts pale yellow, suffused with olive on sides of body. Central tail-feathers gray with narrow white tip, succeeding feathers black broadly tipped white, outermost pair white, black at base only. ♀ : Crown and nape dull chestnut. Eyebrow and sides of head white, speckled with black. Upperparts olive brown; wing-coverts and tail as in ♂, flight-feathers edged olive brown. Below like ♂.

Range. Eastern Ecuador and Peru.

Colombia. Upper tropical and subtropical zones on the west slope of the Western Andes in Caldas and Cauca *(senex)*.

50. RUFOUS-WINGED ANTWREN
(Herpsilochmus rufimarginatus)

Description. 5 - 5¼". ♂ : Crown and stripe through eye black, broad eyebrow white. Back mixed black and gray. Wing-coverts and inner secondaries black margined with white, primaries and secondaries chestnut on the outer web. Tail and lower parts much as in No. 49. ♀ : Crown chestnut, stripe through eye dusky brown, broad eyebrow, ear-coverts and throat white, rest of underparts yellowish (or pale ochraceous, 1). Upper surface olive (or olive brown, 1). Wings and tail as in ♂.

Range. Eastern Panama to Venezuela and southward to northern Bolivia and southeastern Brazil.

Colombia. Forest. Upper tropical to subtropical zone. Western Bolívar (1, *exiguus)*. East slope of the Eastern Andes in Arauca, Boyacá and Meta *(frater)*.

51. DOT-WINGED ANTWREN
(Microrhopias quixensis) Plates XI (♀) and XII

Description. 4¼ - 4½" (or 5¼ - 5½", 1). ♂ : Above and below lustrous black. Large partially concealed dorsal mark white (or center of mantle black and white becoming almost entirely white on lower back and rump, 1). Lesser and median wing-coverts spotted, the greater wing-coverts broadly tipped with white, under wing-coverts white. Central tail-feathers black, outer tail-feathers black, broadly tipped white. ♀ : Upperparts, wings and tail as in ♂ but not quite as deep black, tinged grayish on forehead. Entire under surface deep chestnut (or chin and throat black, breast and belly deep chestnut, 1).

Range. Southern Mexico, southward to western and eastern Ecuador and Peru. Brazil south of the Amazon. French Guiana and adjacent northeastern Brazil.

Colombia. Forest and scrub. Tropical zone. Entire Pacific coast eastward to the lower Cauca Valley and the west bank of the Magdalena in Antioquia *(consobrina)*. East of the Andes in southeastern Nariño (1, *quixensis)*.

52. BLACK-BREASTED ANTWREN
(Formicivora grisea)

Description. 4¾ - 5¼". ♂ : Upperparts and wings mouse brown, wing-coverts black, edged white. Sides of head, throat, center of breast and abdomen black. Broad eyebrow, sides of breast and flanks white, the flank feathers long and silky. Tail very rounded, feathers blackish, outer ones broadly tipped white. ♀ : Upperparts, wings and tail like ♂. Throat, eyebrow and underparts mostly white or buffy white (or spotted on chest with black, 1; or eyebrow and entire underparts cinnamon rufous, 2).

Range. Venezuela, the Guianas, eastern and central Brazil; not western South America south of Colombia. Margarita Island. The Pearl Islands.

Colombia. Open woodland and scrub. Tropical zone. Northern Córdoba and Atlántico southward up the Magdalena Valley *(hondae)*. Arid scrub in the Santa Marta region and the Guajira Peninsula (1, *intermedia*). Eastern base of the Eastern Andes in the Catatumbo and Zulia lowlands (1, *fumosa*). Vaupés (2, *rufiventris*).

53. LONG-TAILED ANTBIRD
(Drymophila caudata)

Description. 6¼-6¾". ♂: Crown and mantle streaked black and white (or center of crown plain black, 1; mantle streaked black, white and rufous, 2). Rest of back, the belly and flanks orange-rufous. Throat and breast streaked black and white (or streaked on sides only, 3). Wing-coverts black, spotted white and tipped buff. Remiges edged ochraceous. Tail 2½", much graduated, grayish olive with a black subterminal patch and white tip. ♀: Generally like ♂ but black and white streaked portions of plumage cinnamon rufous and black, palest on chest.

Range. Venezuela southward to Ecuador, central Peru and northern Bolivia.

Colombia. Forest, scrub and fern brakes. Upper tropical and subtropical zones. The Central and Western Andes and western Nariño *(caudata)*. The Santa Marta region and the subtropical zone at the northern end of the Eastern Andes, east of the Andes in extreme southeastern Nariño (1, 2, *hellmayri*). Tropical zone in Norte de Santander near the Venezuela boundary *(1, 3, klagesi)*.

54. RUFOUS-RUMPED ANTWREN
(Terenura callinota)

Description. 4½-4¾". Warbler-like. ♂: Crown black; eyebrow, nape, throat and breast pale gray. Back and upper tail-coverts olive green, feathers of center of back and rump orange-rufous, those of the back edged with black. Shoulder bright yellow, median and greater wing-coverts black edged pale yellow, flight-feathers edged olive green. Center of breast whitish, sides of breast and rest of underparts olive yellow, yellow in center of belly. Under wing-coverts bright yellow. Tail olive. ♀ like ♂ but without black cap, shoulders olive instead of bright yellow, and no orange-rufous patch in center of back.

Range. Panama. Extreme western Venezuela. British Guiana. Ecuador and Peru.

Colombia. Forest. Upper tropical and subtropical zones of the Western Andes and west slope of the Eastern Andes and western Nariño *(callinota)*.

55. ASH-WINGED ANTWREN
(Terenura spodioptila)

Description. 3¾-4". ♂: Crown black, lores and eyebrow and ear-coverts whitish. Hindneck, and upper mantle and upper tail-coverts ashy gray, rest of back chestnut. Median and greater wing-coverts and flight feathers dark ashy gray, the wing-coverts tipped white. Underparts grayish white. Tail ashy gray, outer feathers with narrow white tips. ♀: Forehead rufescent, darker and duller on rest of crown. Hindneck and upper mantle brownish olive, rest of back rufous-chestnut. Underparts dirty white. Wings and tail grayish brown, wing-coverts tipped white.

Range. Southern Venezuela, British Guiana and northwestern Brazil. French Guiana and adjacent Brazil.

Colombia. Forest. Tropical zone in Caquetá eastward to Vaupés *(signata)*.

56. GRAY ANTBIRD
(Cercomacra cinerascens)

Description. 6½-7". ♂: Blue-gray with a concealed white interscapular patch, greater coverts sometimes with a small terminal white dot. Tail-feathers tipped white. ♀: Crown and nape dull olive brown becoming gray on rump and upper tail-coverts; underparts dull ochraceous-brown. Wing-coverts tipped white. Tail ashy gray tipped white.

Range. Southern Venezuela, the Guianas and southward to eastern Ecuador, Peru and Brazil.

Colombia. Forest. Tropical zone at the eastern base of the Eastern Andes from Meta southward *(cinerascens)*.

57. DUSKY ANTBIRD
(Cercomacra tyrannina) Plate IX

Description. 6 - 6¼ ". ♂ : Very like No. 56, but more ashy, the wing-coverts edged white and the tail-feathers with obsolescent white tips. ♀ : Forehead and lores rufous-brown. Entire upper surface, wings and tail and sides of body olive brown. Throat, breast and center of abdomen bright orange-rufous.

Range. Southern Mexico southward to western Ecuador. Venezuela, British and Dutch Guiana, northeastern and eastern Brazil.

Colombia. Forest and scrub. Tropical and subtropical zones. Upper Sinú and Cauca Valleys eastward to the eastern base of the Andes in Meta then southward to the río Guainía region *(tyrannina)*. East of the Eastern Andes in Arauca and Boyacá *(vicina)*. West bank of the Gulf of Urabá southward on the west slope of the Western Andes to Nariño *(rufiventris)*.

58. JET ANTBIRD
(Cercomacra nigricans)

Description. 6¾ - 7". ♂ : Glossy black including wings and tail; concealed interscapular patch, shoulders, edges of wing-coverts and broad tips to tail-feathers white. ♀ : Dark gray (or blackish gray, 1); concealed interscapular patch, streaks on throat, shoulders, edges to wing-coverts and tips of tail-feathers white. *Immature:* Paler gray than adult ♀ , the feathers of lower surface with broad white centers giving a scalloped appearance.

Range. Panama southward to western Ecuador. Venezuela, northern Brazil.

Colombia. Woodland undergrowth. Tropical zone. Southwestern lowlands of the Santa Marta region westward to the upper Sinú and middle Magdalena Valley. East of the Andes from Meta to Caquetá *(nigricans)*. Pacific coast eastward to the Cauca Valley (1, *atrata*).

59. BLACK ANTBIRD
(Cercomacra serva)

Description. 6 - 6¼ ". Bill somewhat compressed. ♂ : General plumage grayish black, almost pure black on throat and breast. Shoulders, tips of wing-coverts, and large concealed interscapular patch, white. ♀ : Entire upper surface including wings, tail and flanks grayish olive. Edges of flight-feathers and wing-coverts rufescent. Concealed interscapulum white. Entire underparts and preocular spot rich cinnamon-orange.

Range. Ecuador, Peru and Bolivia.

Colombia. Tropical zone. Southeastern Colombia in Putumayo *(serva)*.

60. BLACKISH ANTBIRD
(Cercomacra nigrescens)

Description. 6½ - 6¾ ". ♂ : Above dark gray, concealed interscapulum white, lores and underparts paler gray. Shoulders and tips of wing-coverts white. Wings and tail grayish black. ♀ : Forehead and forecrown, sides of head and entire underparts cinnamon-orange. Upperparts rufescent brown tinged olive; concealed interscapulum white. Edges of primaries rufescent. Tail brown.

Range. Dutch and French Guiana, southward to the middle Amazon and Mato Grosso; westward to eastern Ecuador and Peru.

Colombia. Tropical zone in southeastern Nariño *(aequatorialis)*.

61. STUB-TAILED ANTBIRD
(Sipia berlepschi)

Description. 6 - 6¼ ". Tail short, 1.75". ♂ : Deep black; concealed interscapulum white. ♀ like ♂ but duller black below, profusely spotted with white on chin, throat and breast. Wing-coverts dotted with white.

Range. Northwestern Ecuador.

Colombia. Forest. Tropical zone of the Pacific coast from the upper Atrato Valley southward to western Nariño.

62. ESMERALDAS ANTBIRD
(Sipia rosenbergi)

Description. 6 - 6¾ ". Tail short, 2". ♂ : General plumage dark iron gray, concealed interscapulum white. Wing-coverts black, tipped white. ♀: Head and underparts gray; back and edges to flight-feathers umber brown; wing-coverts blackish, tipped white; interscapulum white. Tail blackish brown.

Range. Northwestern Ecuador.

Colombia. Forest. Tropical zone of the Pacific coast from the upper río San Juan southward to western Nariño.

63. WHITE-BACKED FIRE-EYE
(Pyriglena leuconota)

Description. 7 - 7¾". Tail long, 3.5". Bill rather short. Iris bright red. ♂: Entirely glossy black except for partially concealed white interscapulum. ♀ like ♂ but back and wings dark chestnut brown.

Range. Western Ecuador. Eastern Ecuador, Peru and Bolivia. Central and eastern Brazil.

Colombia. Forest. Upper tropical and subtropical zones. Head of the Magdalena Valley and east of the Andes in Caquetá and southeastern Nariño (castanoptera).

64. WHITE-BROWED ANTBIRD
(Myrmoborus leucophrys)

Description. 6 - 6¼". Tail rather short, 1.9". ♂: Forehead, forecrown and long, broad eyebrow white. Lores, ear-coverts, chin and throat black. Rest of plumage dark blue-gray. ♀: Forehead and forecrown and long, broad eyebrow cinnamon-rufous; hindcrown rufescent brown. Lores, ear-coverts and cheeks black. Upperparts, wings and tail olive brown; wing-coverts tipped with buff. Underparts white; sides of breast and body grayish olive, under tail-coverts olive brown.

Range. Venezuela and the Guianas, northern, central and western Brazil, Ecuador, Peru and northern Bolivia.

Colombia. Forest. Tropical zone. Eastern base of the Eastern Andes from Boyacá southward to Putumayo (erythrophrys). Southeastern Nariño (leucophrys).

65. BLACK-FACED ANTBIRD
(Myrmoborus myotherinus)

Description. 5¼ - 5½". ♂: Tail short, 1.6". Forehead and eyebrow pale gray; sides of head and throat deep black. Crown, upperparts and tail dark gray. Concealed interscapular patch white. Breast and belly light gray. Wing-coverts black, margined with white forming a double wing-bar. ♀: Above, including tail, dark olivaceous brown. Sides of head black, a pale streak above ear-coverts. Throat white, rest of underparts cinnamon; a band of black dots across upper breast. Wing-coverts black edged with cinnamon-buff, forming a double wing-bar.

Range. Southern Venezuela southward to the middle Amazon, eastern Ecuador, eastern Peru and northern Bolivia.

Colombia. Forest. Tropical zone. Eastern base of the Andes from Meta southward to Putumayo and Vaupés (elegans). Extreme southeastern Nariño (napensis).

66. WARBLING ANTBIRD
(Hypocnemis cantator)

Description. 5 - 5¼". Tail rather short, 1.5". ♂: Crown black with a line of white spots down the center. Eyebrow extending to nape white, line behind eye black. Sides of head and mantle spotted black and white; a concealed white interscapular patch. Rump dull rufous, tail dark brown with an inconspicuous subterminal black spot and pale tip. Wing-coverts black, tipped white. Throat and breast white, the feathers conspicuously edged with black (or sulphur yellow with few black edgings, 1). Center of belly white; flanks and under tail-coverts bright orange-rufous. ♀ like ♂ but white of upperparts replaced with ochraceous buff and breast tinged buff. Center of crown streaked buff.

Range. Southern Venezuela, the Guianas through Amazonia to eastern Ecuador, Peru and Bolivia.

Colombia. Forest undergrowth. Tropical zone. East of the Andes in Caquetá and Putumayo (saturata). Vaupés (1, flavescens).

67. YELLOW-BROWED ANTBIRD
(Hypocnemis hypoxantha)

Description. 4¾ - 5″. ♂: Crown black with a white band down center. Frontal spot and long eyebrow yellow, streak through eye black; area below eye and ear-coverts yellow bordered below by a black moustacial streak. Throat, breast and center of abdomen bright yellow, the breast streaked with black. Back and wings olive. Extreme upper mantle streaked with yellow. Wing-coverts black, tipped with white. Tail olive brown, with a white dot at tip. ♀ like ♂ but duller, band on center of crown pale yellowish.

Range. Eastern Ecuador, eastern Peru and the upper and middle Amazon.

Colombia. Forest. Tropical zone east of the Andes in Caquetá and Putumayo (hypoxantha).

68. BLACK-CHINNED ANTBIRD
(Hypocnemoides melanopogon)

Description. 4¾ - 5″. Tail very short, 1.5″. ♂: Above dark blue-gray, below paler gray, chin and throat dull black. Wing-coverts black bordered with white, tail black narrowly tipped white. ♀: Upperparts, wings and tail as in ♂. Throat white edged with blackish gray. Breast and flanks flammulated with olive gray, center of abdomen white.

Range. Venezuela and the Guianas southward to the mouth of the Amazon and eastward to Peru.

Colombia. Forest. Tropical zone east of the Andes from Meta, eastward to Vichada and southward to Vaupés and Caquetá (occidentalis).

69. BARE-CROWNED ANTBIRD
(Gymnocichla nudiceps) Plate IX

Description. 6¾ - 7″. ♂: Top and sides of head bare, the skin bright, light blue. Plumage black, concealed interscapulum and narrow margins of wing-coverts white. Outer tail-feathers narrowly tipped white. ♀: Ocular region bare, bright blue. Upperparts rufescent brown, underparts deep orange-rufous. Concealed dorsal patch white. Wing-coverts edged orange-rufous. Tail dark brown.

Range. Guatemala to Panama.

Colombia. Woodland and thickets. Tropical zone. Santa Marta region and the lower and middle Magdalena Valley (sancta-martae). Northwestern Chocó (nudiceps).

70. BLACK-HEADED ANTBIRD
(Percnostola rufifrons)

Description. 7 - 7¼″. ♂: Crown and throat black, rest of plumage including tail dark blue-gray, somewhat paler below. Wing-coverts black, narrowly edged with white. ♀: Crown and nape dark rufous-brown. Back and tail dark grayish olive. Flight-feathers olive brown, wing-coverts black broadly edged ochraceous buff. Throat, sides of neck and the breast rufous, rest of underparts cinnamon-buff.

Range. Southern Venezuela, the Guianas and the lower Amazon westward to northwest Brazil and eastern Peru.

Colombia. Tropical zone in Vaupés (minor).

71. SPOT-WINGED ANTBIRD
(Percnostola leucostigma)

Description. 6¼ - 6¾″. ♂: Above dark slaty gray. Wings and tail blackish gray, the wing-coverts with round, white spots. Below pale gray, darkest on flanks and under tail-coverts. ♀: Top and sides of head gray. Back brown, olivaceous on upper mantle, more rufescent on upper tail-coverts. Wings rufous-brown, the wing-coverts with round rufous-buff spots. Chin whitish, rest of underparts orange-rufous. Tail slaty blackish.

Range. Southern Venezuela, the Guianas, northern and western Brazil to eastern Peru and eastern Ecuador.

Colombia. Forest. Tropical zone. Arauca, Boyacá and eastern Cundinamarca southward to Putumayo (subplumbea). Vaupés (infuscata).

72. SLATE-COLORED ANTBIRD
(Percnostola schistacea)

Description. 6¼ - 6¾″. ♂: Very similar to No. 71 but differing by shorter bill and tail; the underparts slightly paler than upperparts and the white spots on the wing-coverts much smaller. ♀: Top of head dark chestnut the feathers with pale shaft streaks; sides of head and entire underparts rich orange-chestnut. Back, flanks and wings russet brown, wing-coverts with round cinnamon spots, much larger than in ♂. Upper tail-coverts and tail slaty gray.

Range. Eastern Ecuador, eastern Peru, and western Brazil.

Colombia. Forest. Eastern base of the Andes in Putumayo.

73. SILVERED ANTBIRD
(Sclateria naevia)

Description. 6¼ - 6½". Bill long and straight, .9". Legs pale flesh. ♂: Upper-parts, wings and tail slaty black, wing-coverts dotted with white. Underparts white, the feathers flammulated with gray, under tail-coverts grayish. Tail short. ♀: Upper surface and wings dark olive brown, wing-coverts dotted with rufous. Eyebrow, sides of head and sides of body chestnut, central portion of underparts white. Under tail-coverts ochraceous. Tail blackish brown.

Range. Venezuela and the Guianas south to Mato Grosso and Bolivia. Trinidad.

Colombia. Swamps and forest. Vichada and southeastern Nariño southward to the Amazon *(argentata)*.

74. WHITE-BELLIED ANTBIRD
(Myrmeciza longipes)

Description. 5¼ - 5½". Legs rather long, flesh color. ♂: Lores, ear-coverts, throat and upper breast black. Forehead, eye-brow, lower breast gray. Crown, back, wings and tail bright chestnut. Sides of body gray becoming cinnamon-buff on flanks and under tail-coverts. ♀: Crown and nape gray (or reddish brown, 1; or dark brown, 2). Back, wings and tail as in ♂ but wing-coverts with a subterminal black bar. Sides of head buff (or lores and ear-coverts black, 1); eyebrow gray. Throat and breast, sides of body and under tail-coverts rusty buff, center of abdomen white.

Range. Panama to Venezuela and the Guianas to the north bank of the lower Amazon. Trinidad.

Colombia. Mostly terrestrial. Forest, often near streams. Tropical zone. Santa Marta region westward through the lower Mag-dalena Valley to northern Bolívar *(2, panamensis)*. Middle and upper Magda-lena Valley *(boucardi)*. Eastern bases of the Eastern Andes in the Zulia-Cat-atumbo basins *(1, longipes)*. East of the Andes in Meta *(1, griseipectus)*.

75. DULL-MANTLED ANTBIRD
(Myrmeciza laemosticta)

Description. 5¼ - 5¾". ♂: Crown, nape, sides of head, breast and upper belly dark gray; throat black, the black spreading over the upper breast, (or throat black sharply defined, 1). Back brown becoming rufescent on rump and upper tail-coverts (or back olive brown becoming rufescent brown on lower back and upper tail-coverts, 1; or dark brown, 2). Feathers of interscapular patch white at base with a median black bar and brown tip. Belly, sides of body and under tail-coverts brown. Wings rufescent brown (or dark brown, 2); lesser wing-coverts black, tipped white, greater coverts brown, tipped cinnamon. Tail reddish brown (or black, 2). ♀ similar to ♂ but throat checkered (or barred, 1), black and white.

Range. Costa Rica to northwestern Vene-zuela and northwestern Ecuador.

Colombia. Forest. Tropical zone. Córdoba *(bolivari)*. Lower Cauca and middle Magdalena Valleys *(1, palliata)*. Pacific coast from the río Dagua southward; possibly east of the Andes in southeastern Nariño *(2, nigricauda)*.

76. CHESTNUT-BACKED ANTBIRD
(Myrmeciza exsul)

Description. 5¾ - 6". ♂: Very similar to the brown-tailed forms of No. 75 but crown and nape blackish; throat grayish black, not sharply defined from gray of underparts. No interscapular patch. Wing-coverts spotted (or dotted, 1) with white (or wing-coverts unmarked, 2). ♀: Above very similar to No. 75 but no interscapular patch. Below different; chin and throat gray, breast chestnut; belly, flanks and under tail-coverts dark reddish brown.

Range. Nicaragua to western Ecuador.

Colombia. Forest undergrowth. Tropical zone. Northwestern Colombia eastward to the Sinú, lower Cauca and middle Magdalena Valleys *(cassini)*. West shore of the Gulf of Urabá *(2, niglarus)*. Pacific coast from the upper Atrato Valley southward into Nariño; possibly east of the Andes in eastern Nariño *(1, maculifer)*.

77. PLUMBEOUS ANTBIRD
(Myrmeciza hyperythra)

Description. 7¼ - 7½". Tail short, 2½". ♂: Plumbeous gray. Tail and wing-coverts black, the wing-coverts spotted with white. ♀: Entire upper surface and sides of head ashy gray. Wings and tail ashy brown; wing-coverts ashy gray, spotted with buff and white. Underparts bright orange-rufous; flanks and under tail-coverts rufous-brown.

Range. Eastern Peru, western Brazil, northeastern Bolivia.

Colombia. Forest. Tropical zone, east of the Andes in Caquetá .

78. WHITE-SHOULDERED ANTBIRD
(Myrmeciza melanoceps)

Description. 7¼ - 7½". Bill large, shrike-like. ♂: Entirely black except for partly concealed white shoulder. ♀: Head, throat and upper breast black. Back, wings and tail chestnut-rufous. Center of underparts cinnamon-buff, sides of body and under tail-coverts tawny rufous. Facial skin blue in both sexes.

Range. Eastern Ecuador, western Brazil and eastern Peru.

Colombia. Forest. Tropical zone east of the Andes from Meta to Amazonas.

79. SOOTY ANTBIRD
(Myrmeciza fortis)

Description. 7½ - 7¾". Bill rather heavy, shrike-like. ♂: Crown, throat and upper breast black, rest of plumage sooty gray; bend of wing only, white. ♀: Crown bay. Back, wings, and tail dark reddish brown, brighter on the wings. Sides of head, throat, breast and center of abdomen ashy gray; flanks and under tail-coverts dark brown. Facial skin blue in both sexes.

Range. Eastern Ecuador to southeastern Peru and western Brazil.

Colombia. Forest. Tropical zone east of the Andes from Caquetá southward to Amazonas *(fortis)*.

80. IMMACULATE ANTBIRD
(Myrmeciza immaculata) Plate IX

Description. 7½ - 7¾". ♂: Very much like No. 78 but bare skin of face light blue, less white on wing-coverts and the tail longer, 3½". ♀: Facial skin blue, forehead, ear-coverts and chin black, rest of plumage maroon brown, somewhat paler below (or with a gray median line on belly, 1). Tail black.

Range. Costa Rica southward to western Venezuela and Ecuador.

Colombia. Forest. Upper tropical and subtropical zones of the west slope of the Eastern and Central Andes in Cundinamarca, Tolima and Valle. East of the Andes in Boyacá and Meta *(1, immaculata)*. West of the Western Andes from Antioquia southward to Nariño *(berlepschi)*.

81. BLACK-THROATED ANTBIRD
(Myrmeciza atrothorax)

Description. 5¾ - 6¼". ♂: Forehead, sides of head, breast and belly plumbeous-gray. Rump and upper tail-coverts grayish black. A concealed white interscapulum. Upperparts and wings olive brown, the wings darker; wing-coverts dotted with white. Chin, throat, upper breast and tail black. ♀ like ♂ above but wing-coverts dotted buff. Sides of head gray; throat and center of lower breast and abdomen white; breast and sides of body chestnut; flanks and under tail-coverts olive brown. Tail black.

Range. Southern Venezuela and the Guianas southward to central and western Brazil, Ecuador, Peru and Bolivia.

Colombia. Forest. Tropical zone. Eastern base of the Andes in Meta *(metae)*.

82. GRAY-BELLIED ANTBIRD
(Myrmeciza pelzelni)

Description. 5¼ - 5½". ♂: Crown dark brown becoming reddish brown on back;

wings like back, wing-coverts with large, round buff spots. Lores, sides of head and eyebrow pale gray. Throat and breast black; lower breast and abdomen ashy gray; flanks and under tail-coverts reddish brown. Tail dark brown. ♀: Upperparts and sides of head like ♂. Wing-coverts and innermost secondaries reddish brown with a subterminal black bar and large buff tip. Throat and breast white, feathers at sides of throat and center of breast edged with black. Belly, flanks and under tail-coverts brown.

Range. Known only from southeastern Venezuela and adjacent Brazil.

Colombia. Forest. Tropical zone. Southeastern Vaupés.

83. CHESTNUT-TAILED ANTBIRD
(Myrmeciza hemimelaena)

Description. 5¼ - 5½". Tail short 1¼". ♂: Feathers of crown and upper mantle black, bordered with dark gray; rest of back, tail and wings chestnut. Wing-coverts black, tipped white, innermost secondaries tipped buff. A concealed white interscapular patch, the feathers with a subterminal black bar and chestnut tip. Sides of head, throat and chest black. Center of abdomen white, sides of abdomen and breast dark gray; flanks and under tail-coverts rufous-brown. ♀: Crown, nape and upper back olive gray, the feathers dark-centered, lower back and upper tail-coverts browner, dorsal patch as in ♂. Wing-coverts with terminal buff spots. Throat and breast cinnamon-orange, belly pale cinnamon, flanks olive brown. Tail chestnut.

Range. Northeastern Peru, western and central Brazil south to Bolivia.

Colombia. Tropical zone east of the Andes in Putumayo (hemimelaena).

84. RUFOUS-CAPPED ANTTHRUSH
(Formicarius colma)

Description. 7½ - 7¾". Tail short, 2". ♂: Crown and nape chestnut. Forehead, sides of head, throat and breast black, becoming grayish on abdomen and tinged with olive on flanks. Back and wings olive brown; outermost greater wing-

coverts and base of primaries cinnamon. Tail olive, black distally. ♀ like ♂ but throat white, thickly spotted with black, center of abdomen buffy white.

Range. Venezuela, the Guianas, Brazil, Ecuador and Peru.

Colombia. Forest. Tropical zone east of the Eastern Andes from Meta southward to Putumayo and Vaupés (nigrifrons).

85. BLACK-FACED ANTTHRUSH
(Formicarius analis)

Description. 8 - 8½". Tail short, 1¾", carried erect when walking as in all members of the genus. Above olive brown (or bronzy brown, 1: or dark olive brown, 2). Sides of neck cinnamon (or without cinnamon, 2). Throat black, upper breast dark gray becoming paler on abdomen. Flanks olive brown to bronzy brown, under tail-coverts chestnut. Tail basally like the back with a dark tip (or black, 2).

Range. Southeastern Mexico southward to Venezuela, the Guianas, Brazil, Ecuador, Peru and Bolivia.

Colombia. Forest. Mostly terrestrial. Tropical zone. Western base of Santa Marta Mts. (1, virescens). The northern extremity of the Perijá Mts. (griseoventris). Norte de Santander in the Catatumbo lowlands and Arauca westward into the middle Magdalena and Cauca and upper Sinú Valleys (saturatus). Northwestern Colombia and Atrato Valley (panamensis). East of the Andes from Meta southward to Putumayo (2, connectens).

86. BLACK-HEADED ANTTHRUSH
(Formicarius nigricapillus)

Description. 7¾ - 8". Tail short, 2". Crown and throat black, becoming sooty black on nape and breast and turning gray on center of abdomen and flanks. Upper mantle olive brown gradually turning browner and becoming dark chestnut brown on upper tail-coverts; under tail-coverts chestnut. Tail black.

Range. Costa Rica to western Panama. Western Ecuador.

Colombia. Forest and scrub. Tropical, rarely subtropical, zone of the Pacific coast from central Chocó southward (destructus).

87. RUFOUS-BREASTED ANTTHRUSH
(Formicarius rufipectus) Plate XI

Description. 8 - 8½″. Tail short, 2″. ♂: Crown, nape and upper tail-coverts chestnut maroon, rest of upperparts dark olive gray. Lores, sides of head and throat black. Chest dark chestnut becoming buffy cinnamon on center of abdomen. Sides of body olive gray; under tail-coverts chestnut. Tail black. ♀: Similar, but crown much darker, blackish on forehead.

Range. Costa Rica southward to western Ecuador. Eastern Ecuador, eastern Peru.

Colombia. Forest. Upper tropical to temperate zones. West slope of the Western Andes to the west slope of the Central Andes from Antioquia southward to Nariño *(carrikeri)*.

88. SHORT-TAILED ANTTHRUSH
(Chamaeza campanisona)

Description. 8½ - 9″. Thrush-like. Tail short, 2¼″; legs not markedly long. Above uniform olive brown, tinged rufescent on crown. Lores and line behind eye, white. Tail like back with a black subterminal band and white tip. Throat white, speckled with dusky, rest of lower parts white, tinged buff on breast, the feathers edged with dusky giving a scaled appearance. Under tail-coverts pale cinnamon-buff.

Range. Venezuela, British Guiana, southward to southeast Brazil, eastern Ecuador, Peru, Bolivia and Paraguay.

Colombia. Forest. Subtropical zone. East of the Andes in Meta *(columbiana)*.

89. STRIATED ANTTHRUSH
(Chamaeza nobilis) Plate IX

Description. 9½ - 10″. Crown, nape and sides of neck dark reddish brown, back and wings reddish brown with an olive tinge. Lores orange-cinnamon; eyebrow and eyering white. Underparts as in No. 88 but dark edges to feathers blacker and under tail-coverts paler. Tail like back with a subterminal black bar and white tip.

Range. Eastern Ecuador and eastern Peru, western and central Brazil.

Colombia. Forest. Tropical zone. East of the Andes in Meta, Caquetá and Putumayo *(rubida)*.

90. RUFOUS-TAILED ANTTHRUSH
(Chamaeza ruficauda)

Description. 8 - 8½″. Upperparts rufous-brown, wings and tail darker. Lores and eyebrow white. Throat white, thickly spotted with black. Below fulvous white, the feathers broadly margined with black. Under tail-coverts buff, barred with black.

Range. Coast ranges of Venezuela. Southeastern Brazil.

Colombia. Forest. Subtropical zone. The slopes of the Eastern and Central Andes above the Magdalena Valley *(turdina)*.

91. BARRED ANTTHRUSH
(Chamaeza mollissima)

Description. 8¼ - 8½″. Bill short, .5″. Above chestnut brown, wings and tail darker. Lores, eyebrow, ear-coverts and entire underparts regularly barred buffy and black.

Range. Eastern Ecuador. Northern Bolivia.

Colombia. Forest. Subtropical and temperate zone of all three Andean ranges *(mollissima)*.

92. WHITE-PLUMED ANTBIRD
(Pithys albifrons) Plate XI

Description. 5¼ - 5½″. Crown and area behind eye black. Forehead, sides of crown white, the feathers prolonged into two "horns" about 1″ long. Throat white, the feathers lengthened, forming a beard, bordered by black. Rest of undersurface, collar around hindneck, upper tail-coverts and tail chestnut. Back and wings dark gray.

Range. The Guianas and southern Venezuela eastward to eastern Ecuador and eastern Peru.

Colombia. Forest and scrub. Tropical zone at the eastern base of the Andes from Arauca southward to Putumayo *(peruviana)*.

93. BICOLORED ANTBIRD
(Gymnopithys leucaspis)

Description. 6¼ - 6½ ". Above chestnut brown, the crown brighter (or crown dark chestnut, back dark brown, 1; or crown like back, 2). Lores, ear-coverts and area behind eye black (or lores, cheeks and ear-coverts black, area behind eye leaden gray, 3). Throat, center of breast and belly white. Sides of breast black; flanks and sides of body brown. Wings and tail like back.

Range. Honduras southward to western Ecuador. Eastern Ecuador, northwestern Brazil and eastern Peru.

Colombia. Forest undergrowth. Tropical zone. Base of the Eastern Andes in Meta *(leucaspis)*. Putumayo *(castanea)*. The Nechí and Magdalena Valleys (1, *ruficeps)*. Northwestern Colombia from the Panama border to the upper Sinú Valley (1, 3, *bicolor)*. Upper Atrato Valley southward to the Dagua (2, 3, *daguae)*. Pacific slope of Nariño (1, *aequatorialis)*. Vaupés *(lateralis)* .

94. SPOTTED ANTBIRD
(Hylophylax naevioides)

Description. 5¼ - 5½ ". ♂ : Crown, nape, and ear-coverts ashy gray. Back chestnut with a concealed white interscapular patch; wing-coverts black the lesser coverts tipped white, the median and greater coverts broadly tipped chestnut, innermost secondaries black edged and tipped with chestnut. Primaries and secondaries black, margined centrally on outer web with olivaceous. Throat black, rest of underparts white, the breast crossed by a band of large black spots; sides of body gray, spotted with black. Tail olive brown with a black subterminal bar and buffy tip. ♀ : Crown brown, back rusty brown, wings and tail like ♂ but spots on wing-coverts cinnamon-buff instead of chestnut. Below white, tinged buff, the breast crossed by a band of blackish brown spots; sides of body olivaceous.

Range. Nicaragua to western Ecuador.

Colombia. Forest of the tropical zone. From the Panama border southward to western Nariño *(naevioides)*. The Sinú Valley to the west bank of the Magdalena in Antioquia *(subsimilis)*.

95. SPOT-BACKED ANTBIRD
(Hylophylax naevia) Plate XII

Description. 4¾ - 5". ♂ : Crown, nape and ear-coverts dark gray. Mantle and wings black, profusely spotted with large buff spots. Concealed interscapular patch white. Rump, upper tail-coverts and collar around hindneck olivaceous (or sides of head gray, crown and back reddish brown; concealed white dorsal patch, the feathers tipped black each with buff apical spots. Tail reddish brown, 1). Breast white crossed by a band of black spots; flanks and belly cinnamon-buff. Tail dull chestnut with a darker subterminal area and buff tip. ♀ : Crown olivaceous gray, ear-coverts and lores dark gray; sides of throat black; center of throat white. Below cinnamon-buff, brightest on chest which is crossed by a series of black spots. Rest of plumage like ♂ but spots on mantle larger (or differing in the same manner as the ♂ , 1).

Range. Southern Venezuela, British and French Guiana. Eastern Ecuador, eastern Peru, western and central Brazil southward to northern Bolivia.

Colombia. Forest. Tropical zone. Eastern base of the Andes from southern Meta southward to Putumayo *(theresae)*. Vaupés (1, *consobrina)*.

96. SCALE-BACKED ANTBIRD
(Hylophylax poecilonota)

Description. 5¼ - 5¾ ". ♂ : Crown, mantle, sides of head, rump and entire underparts leaden gray. Center of back, wings and tail black, feathers of back, wing-coverts and innermost secondaries fringed white, giving a scaled appearance. Upper tail-coverts tipped white. Tail black with a row of white spots across the central part of the feathers and narrowly tipped white. ♀ : Crown and sides of head rufous-brown (or rufous-chestnut, 1); back olive brown (or reddish brown, 1); feathers of center of back, upper tail-coverts, wings and tail as in ♂ . Throat rufous, rest of underparts cinnamon brown (or rufous, 1).

Range. Southern Venezuela, the Guianas, Brazil, eastern Ecuador, eastern Peru and northern Bolivia.

[Species 93a, see Page 410.]

Colombia. Forest of the tropical zone. Southern Meta eastward to Vaupés (duidae). Caquetá and Putumayo (1, lepidonota).

97. BLACK-SPOTTED BARE-EYE
(Phlegopsis nigro-maculata)

Description. 7 - 7½". Tail short, 2.25". Entire head, throat, breast and upper belly glossy black, rest of underparts olive brown; under tail-coverts rufous. Back, lesser and median wing-coverts sandy olive brown with large, drop-shaped black spots. Wings and tail chestnut. Bare skin surrounding eye red.

Range. Eastern Ecuador, eastern Peru, northern Bolivia, and eastward in Brazil along the south bank of the Amazon to its mouth and to northern Maranhão.

Colombia. Forest. Tropical zone of Meta southward to Putumayo (nigro-maculata).

98. ARGUS BARE-EYE
(Phlegopsis barringeri)

Description. 7½". Tail not conspicuously short, 3". ♂: Entire head, throat, breast and center of belly glossy black. Back, median and greater wing-coverts reddish brown, the feathers subterminally black surrounding a round buff spot. Upper and under tail-coverts chestnut, marked with black medially. Flight-feathers dark brown, edged exteriorly with chestnut, the primaries with a black speculum. Basal half and narrow tip to tail feathers chestnut, distal half black. Skin about eye red. ♀: Unknown.

Range. Colombia.

Colombia. Forest. Tropical zone. Known from a single specimen from eastern Nariño (río San Miguel).

99. RUFOUS-WINGED BARE-EYE
(Phlegopsis erythroptera)

Description. 6¾ - 7". ♂: Tail short, 2.25". Black. Feathers of back narrowly fringed with white, upper tail-coverts edged chestnut. Wing-coverts black, the lesser coverts narrowly fringed white, the median and greater coverts broadly edged chestnut. Outer primaries basally chestnut, distally black; secondaries black, margined basally on outer web with chestnut; inner

remiges black with broad chestnut tips. Tail black. Skin around eye red. ♀: Reddish brown above, orange rufous below, wings and tail blackish. Wings with double wing-bar and spot on outer web of central portion of remiges buff.

Range. Southern Venezuela, western and central Brazil, eastern Ecuador and Peru.

Colombia. Forest. Tropical zone east of the Andes in Caquetá and Putumayo (erythroptera).

100. OCELLATED ANTTHRUSH
(Phaenostictus mcleannani) Plate XI

Description. 8¼ - 8¾". Tail long, 4". Crown and nape grayish brown (or sooty brown, 1). Collar on hindneck chestnut; back and wing-coverts sandy brown, the feathers with large black subterminal spots and fringed with buff. Primaries and secondaries edged with olivaceous brown. Throat and upper chest and ear-coverts glossy black, bordered by a chestnut band. Feathers of breast and upper belly chestnut with large round black centers; abdomen brown. Tail slaty black. Bare facial skin light violet-blue; feet and legs flesh color.

Range. Nicaragua to western Ecuador.

Colombia. Forest. Tropical zone. Pacific coast eastward to the upper Sinú and lower Cauca Valleys and southward on the Pacific coast to the Dagua Valley (choco-anus). Western Nariño (1, pacificus).

101. WING-BANDED ANTTHRUSH
(Myrmornis torquata) Plate XI

Description. 6". Tail very short, 1.33"; bill rather long, .9". ♂: Crown deep chestnut, the feathers with pale shaft streaks. Feathers of back grayish olive, broadly margined with deep chestnut; feathers of the center of the back with concealed white bases and black tips forming a black patch in center of back. Post-ocular streak and sides of neck white, the feathers edged black; throat and upper breast black (bordered irregularly with white, 1); rest of underparts dark gray. Wing-coverts black broadly edged with cinnamon-buff forming three wing-bars. Remiges blackish with a cinnamon-

PLATE XII

DOT-WINGED ANTWREN
(*Microrhopias q. quixensis*)
Page 229

SLATY ANTSHRIKE
(*Thamnophilus punc-tatus atrinucha*)
Page 221

STRIPE-CHESTED
ANTWREN
(*Myrmotherula longi-cauda söderströmi*)
Page 225

FASCIATED ANTSHRIKE
(*Cymbilaimus line-atus fasciatus*)
Page 218

BARRED ANTSHRIKE
(*Thamnophilus doli-atus nigricristatus*)
Page 219

PLAIN ANTVIREO
(*Dysithamnus men-talis extremus*)
Page 223

BLACK BUSHBIRD
(*Neoctantes niger*)
Page 222

PEARLY ANTSHRIKE
(*Megastictus m. mar-garitatus*)
Page 222

SLATY ANTWREN
(*Myrmotherula
s. schisticolor*)
Page 227

UNICOLORED TAPACULO
(*Scytalopus unicolor latrans*)
Page 247

RECURVE-BILLED
BUSHBIRD
(*Clytoctantes alixi*)
Page 222

SPOT-BACKED ANTBIRD
(*Hylophylax naevia theresae*)
Page 238

240

E.L.Poole

buff (or white, 1) spot near base of inner web forming a band. Upper and under tail-coverts and tail chestnut. ♀ like ♂ but throat and upper breast cinnamon-chestnut, under wing-coverts buff (or white, 1).

Range. Nicaragua. Eastern Panama. Venezuela, the Guianas, eastern Ecuador and northern and western Brazil.

Colombia. Forest. Tropical zone. Northern Chocó, the río Sinú region and the middle Magdalena Valley *(stictoptera)*. East of the Andes in Caquetá *(1, torquata)*.

102. BLACK-CROWNED ANTPITTA
(Pittasoma michleri) Plate XI

Description. 8″. Tail very short, 1.5″. Legs very long, slate gray. Upper mandible black, lower, flesh color. ♂: Crown and nape glossy black; lores and below eye white speckled with black. Ear-coverts and sides of neck chestnut. Back rufescent olive brown, more or less streaked and spotted with black on mantle. Wings and tail chestnut, wing-coverts with a narrow subterminal black bar and buffy white tip. Throat black speckled with white and chestnut. Underparts barred black and white. ♀: Differs by buff tinged underparts, the feathers with broken black bars, and barred throat.

Range. Eastern Costa Rica and Panama.

Colombia. Dense forest. Tropical zone. Extreme northwestern Chocó *(michleri)*.

103. RUFOUS-CROWNED ANTPITTA
(Pittasoma rufopileatum)

Description. 7″. Tail very short, 1.5″; legs long, lead color; bill black. ♂: Crown and nape rufous; lores and broad stripe above and behind the eye black. Sides of head and throat cinnamon-rufous. Upperparts olive brown, the feathers of the mantle broadly edged with black. Wing-coverts tipped with buffy white. Underparts dull brownish olive, the middle of the breast and abdomen buffy white (or breast cinnamon, rest of underparts buffy white regularly barred with black, center of abdomen less heavily barred, 1). ♀: Above like ♂, lores and eyebrow mixed

black and white (or becoming mixed ochraceous orange and black behind the eye, 1). Wing-coverts with large terminal buff spots. Throat and lower parts ochraceous orange; sides of body brown, faintly barred dusky.

Range. Northwestern Ecuador.

Colombia. Forest. Tropical zone. The Baudó Mts. and lower río San Juan Valley *(rosenbergi)*. Pacific slope of Nariño (1, *harterti)*.

104. OCHRE-BREASTED ANTPITTA
(Grallaricula flavirostris)

Description. 4¾″. Tail very short, .8″; legs long. Upperparts olive brown, tinged slaty on crown. Lores and eye-ring deep rusty cinnamon. Throat and upper breast ochraceous orange, lower breast and abdomen white somewhat streaked on sides with black (or flanks rusty ochraceous tinged olive, center of abdomen only white, 1). Wings and tail rufescent brown.

Range. Costa Rica southward to western Ecuador. East of the Andes in Ecuador, Peru and northern Bolivia.

Colombia. Forest. Tropical and subtropical zones. East of the Andes in Meta *(flavirostris)*. The west slope of the Western Andes and western Nariño (1, *ochraceiventris)*.

105. RUSTY-BREASTED ANTPITTA
(Grallaricula ferrugineipectus)

Description. 4¾″. Tail very short, 1″; legs long. Lores buffy white, feathers behind eye white. Above olivaceous brown, wings and tail somewhat darker. Underparts deep ochraceous-buff (or deep orange-buff, 1). patch on lower throat and center of abdomen white.

Range. Northern Venezuela; northern Peru.

Colombia. More open parts of humid forest in low bushes. Upper tropical and subtropical zones. Santa Marta Mts. *(ferrugineipectus)*. West slope of the Eastern Andes in Cundinamarca (1, *rara)*.

106. SLATE-CROWNED ANTPITTA
(Grallaricula nana)

Description. 4¾". Tail short, 1.25"; legs long. Forehead, lores and eye-ring deep ochraceous; crown and nape dark slaty gray. Back, wings and tail ochraceous brown. Underparts deep orange-rufous; patch on lower throat and center of abdomen white.

Range. British Guiana, northern and eastern Venezuela. Eastern Ecuador.

Colombia. Undergrowth in forests. Subtropical and temperate zones. The east slope of the Eastern Andes in Norte de Santander (nana). Western Andes in Valle and Cauca and the Central Andes from Antioquia to Huila (occidentalis).

107. HOODED ANTPITTA
(Grallaricula cucullata)

Description. 4¾"". Tail very short, 1"; legs long. Entire head orange-rufous. Back, wings and tail olive brown. A patch at base of throat and center of abdomen white. Breast and sides of body ashy gray. Bill orange-yellow.

Range. Western Venezuela (Táchira).

Colombia. Undergrowth in forests. Subtropical zone of the Western, Central and probably the Eastern Andes (cucullata).

108. THRUSH-LIKE ANTPITTA
(Myrmothera campanisona)

Description. 6¼ - 6¾". Tail very short, 1.5"; legs long. Upperparts, wings and tail olive brown. Throat and belly white, feathers of breast edged olive brown (or feathers of breast and flanks heavily margined with olive, 1; or feathers of breast flammulated with yellowish white, 2). Under wing-coverts cinnamon-rufous.

Range. Venezuela, the Guianas to central Brazil, eastern Ecuador and eastern Peru.

Colombia. Forest. Tropical zone east of the Andes. In Meta (2, modesta). Caquetá and Putumayo (dissors). Eastern Nariño (1, signata).

109. UNDULATED ANTPITTA
(Grallaria squamigera)

Description. 8¾ - 9½". Tail short; legs long. Crown, nape, and upper mantle ashy gray, lower back tinged olivaceous, wings and tail somewhat browner. Lores buffy; throat white, bordered on each side by a black line. Underparts rusty buff, deepest on abdomen and under tail-coverts; breast and belly coarsely barred with black.

Range. Venezuela, southward through the Andes to Ecuador, Peru and Bolivia.

Colombia. Forest. Subtropical and temperate zone of the Western, Central and Eastern Andes (squamigera).

110. GIANT ANTPITTA
(Grallaria gigantea)

Description. 9¾ - 10¼". Bill thick and heavy; tail short; legs long. Forehead and lores deep tawny buff, forecrown olivaceous brown, hindcrown and nape strongly tinged ashy gray. Back olivaceous brown (a few of the feathers with subterminal bars of rusty ochraceous and black, imm.). Wings and tail browner than back. Sides of head and entire underparts deep rusty buff, barred with broken black bars; under tail-coverts deeper colored and unbarred.

Range. Both slopes of the Andes of Ecuador.

Colombia. Forest. Upper subtropical to lower temperate zones. Eastern slope of the Central Andes in Huila (lehmanni).

111. SCALED ANTPITTA
(Grallaria guatimalensis)

Description. 7 - 7¼". Tail short; legs long. Forecrown and back olivaceous brown, hindcrown and nape strongly tinged gray, all the feathers of crown and back edged black giving a scaled appearance. Lores whitish (or rusty, 1). Malar streak and irregular patch on lower throat buffy white. Throat and breast olive brown; rest of under surface tawny ochraceous, whitish on center of belly and deepest on under tail-coverts. Wings and tail brown.

Range. Southern Mexico to Venezuela and northern Brazil; southward on the west to southern Peru. Trinidad.

Colombia. Forest, often near streams. Tropical zone. Baudó Mts. (1, chocoensis). Subtropical zone of the Western Andes (subsp.?). Northern side of the Santa Marta Mts. southward to the lower Magdalena and eastward to Arauca (carmelitae). Putumayo (regulus).

112. MOUSTACHED ANTPITTA
(Grallaria alleni)

Description. 8". Tail short; legs long. Crown and nape slate color; lores and ear-coverts dark brown. Back and wings olivaceous brown. Broad malar streak white, the feathers margined with black. Upper throat russet brown bordered below by a white bar. Breast olive brown streaked with white. Belly creamy white; flanks, under tail-coverts and under wing-coverts tawny ochraceous. Tail ochraceous orange.

Range. Colombia.

Colombia. Forest. Subtropical zone. West slope of the Central Andes in Caldas.

113. CHESTNUT-NAPED ANTPITTA
(Grallaria nuchalis)

Description. 8 ¾ - 9 ¼ ". Tail short; legs long. Crown, nape, sides of head bright chestnut; lores grayish white. Back, wings and tail reddish olive brown, rufescent on wings and tail. Throat mixed gray, black and white, rest of underparts plumbeous gray.

Range. Ecuador.

Colombia. Forest. Upper subtropical to lower temperate zone of both slopes of the Central Andes and west slopes of the Eastern Andes *(ruficeps)*.

114. BICOLORED ANTPITTA
(Grallaria rufo-cinerea)

Description. 7". Tail short; legs long. Entire upper surface including sides of head, wings and tail dark reddish brown. Entire under surface deep ashy gray, tinged with rufous on the throat.

Range. Colombia.

Colombia. Upper subtropical to lower temperate zones of both slopes of the Central Andes in Antioquia and Caldas.

115. TAWNY ANTPITTA
(Grallaria quitensis)

Description. 7 - 7 ¼ ". Upper surface, wings and tail olive brown, rufescent on upper tail-coverts; lores white. Under surface tawny buff, the centers and tips of feathers whitish, giving a mottled appearance.

Range. Ecuador, northern Peru.

Colombia. Forest. Upper subtropical to temperate zones. Eastern Andes in Boyacá and probably Cundinamarca *(alticola)*. Central Andes from Antioquia southward to the Andes of Nariño *(quitensis)*.

116. BROWN-BANDED ANTPITTA
(Grallaria milleri)

Description. 6 ½ ". Tail short; legs long. Upperparts, sides of head and throat, breast-band and flanks umber brown tinged rufescent on breast; wings and tail darker. Lores, throat, center of abdomen grayish white.

Range. Colombia.

Colombia. Forest. Temperate zone in the Central Andes in Caldas.

117. WHITE-BELLIED ANTPITTA
(Grallaria hypoleuca)

Description. 7 ½ - 7 ¾ ". Tail short; legs long. Upperparts, sides of body, wings and tail deep chestnut, brightest and reddest on ear-coverts and hindneck. Throat, center of abdomen white, rest of underparts grayish (or underparts pale primrose yellow, 1). Flanks chestnut brown.

Range. Eastern Ecuador.

Colombia. Forest. Subtropical zone. West slope of the Eastern Andes in Cundinamarca *(hypoleuca)*. Headwaters of the río Magdalena *(castanea)*. West slope of the Western Andes southward to western Nariño (1, *flavotincta)*.

118. SANTA MARTA ANTPITTA
(Grallaria bangsi)

Description. 7 ½ - 8". Tail short; legs long. Above grayish olive brown. Lores and eye-ring white. Throat pale cinnamon-buff. Underparts white, streaked with olive gray. Feathers of flanks lengthened, olive gray with white centers; under tail-coverts buff. Wings and tail sepia brown.

Range. Colombia.

Colombia. Forest. Subtropical zone of the Santa Marta Mts.

119. CHESTNUT-CROWNED ANTPITTA
(Grallaria ruficapilla)

Description. 8 - 8¼ ". Tail short; legs long. Crown, nape and sides of head orange-rufous; back, wings and tail olive brown. Underparts white, the feathers of the breast and sides of body margined with brownish olive and black giving a streaked appearance.

Range. Northern Venezuela, Ecuador and northwestern Peru.

Colombia. Tangles at forest edge. Upper tropical and subtropical zones, west of the Eastern Andes. Not Santa Marta (ruficapilla). East slope of the Eastern Andes in Norte de Santander (nigro-lineata).

120. RUFOUS ANTPITTA
(Grallaria rufula)

Description. 6¼ - 6½ ". Tail short; legs long. Rufous-brown, center of belly buffy (or whitish, 1; or above olive brown, below grayish brown, 2).

Range. Western Venezuela southward through the Andes to Ecuador, Peru and Bolivia.

Colombia. Forest. Temperate zone of the Andes (rufula). Temperate zone of the Santa Marta Mts. (1, spatiator). Temperate zone of the Perijá Mts. (2, saltuensis).

121. FULVOUS-BELLIED ANTPITTA
(Grallaria fulviventris)

Description. 6¾ - 7". Tail short; legs long. Crown, nape and auriculars slaty black. Back and wings dark greenish olive (or dark brownish olive, 1). Lores, throat and center of abdomen white, breast buff, the feathers edged black giving a streaked appearance. Flanks bright rufous.

Range. Nicaragua to Panama. Eastern Ecuador.

Colombia. Forest. Tropical zone. The west shore of the Gulf of Urabá southward to western Nariño (barbacoae). Caquetá (1, caquetae). Southeastern Nariño (fulviventris).

122. STREAK-CHESTED ANTPITTA
(Grallaria perspicillata) Plate XI

Description. 6½ - 6¾". Tail short; legs long. Conspicuous buff (or pale buff, 1) eye-ring. Crown and nape slaty; back brown (or olive, 1) with a few fulvous streaks. Wing-coverts tipped with fulvous, under wing-coverts cinnamon. Margins of outer primaries fulvous. Throat white, malar streak black. Breast fulvous white, belly white, breast and sides of body streaked black.

Range. Nicaragua southward to western Ecuador.

Colombia. Forest. Tropical zone. Extreme northwestern Colombia (perspicillata). Upper Sinú Valley, lower Cauca and middle Magdalena Valleys (1, pallidior). From the Baudó Mts. southward to Nariño (periophthalmica).

123. SPOTTED ANTPITTA
(Grallaria macularia)

Description. 6¾ - 7". Tail short; legs long. Very similar to No. 122 but differs by blue-gray crown, olive green unstreaked back, chest spotted rather than streaked with black, and sides of body unstreaked rusty buff.

Range. The Guianas and southern Venezuela southward through the Amazon Valley to eastern Peru and northern Bolivia.

Colombia. Forest. Tropical zone. Amazonas (diversa).

GNATEATERS (Conopophagidae)

Fig. 62. Chestnut-belted Gnateater
(Conopophaga aurita)

Gnateaters, sometimes called antpipits, are closely related to antbirds which they resemble. Most are brown above, gray or white below with contrasting caps and throats, and have a prominent silvery white line behind the eye. They are found only in South America.

They live in the undergrowth on the forest floor where they scratch among the leaves for insects. They are shy and difficult to see. (3 Col.; 11 S.A.; 11 N.&S. A.; 11 wld.)

CHESTNUT-BELTED GNATEATER
(Conopophaga aurita)

Description. 5 - 5¼". Tail very short, 1". ♂ : Crown dark, dull chestnut. Back olive brown, the feathers edged with black; wings and tail like back. Lores, sides of head and entire throat deep black. Long line behind eye silvery white. Chest bright chestnut, sides of body olive brown, center of abdomen and under tail-coverts buffy. ♀ similar to ♂ but lores and eyebrow white, sides of head brown and throat buff.

Range. The Guianas, northern, western and central Brazil, eastern Ecuador. Eastern Peru.

Colombia. Forest. Tropical zone. Caquetá and Putumayo *(inexpectata)*.

CHESTNUT-CROWNED GNATEATER
(Conopophaga castaneiceps)

Description. 5¼ - 5¾". Tail short, 2". ♂ : Forecrown bright chestnut becoming duller on hindcrown and nape. A long silvery white line behind the eye. Back

dark grayish olive, the feathers edged with black. Wings and tail dark olive. Sides of head and lower surface dark ashy gray; center of abdomen whitish. ♀ : Crown, sides of head and broad band across breast orange-rufous. Line behind eye silvery white. Throat and center of abdomen white. Back, wings and tail olivaceous.

Range. Eastern Ecuador and Peru.

Colombia. Forest. Subtropical zone. Both slopes of the Central and Eastern Andes and the Sinú Valley *(castaneiceps)*. West slope of the Western Andes and the Baudó Mts. *(chocoensis)*. (It is probable that more than two races inhabit Colombia. More specimens are needed to prove it.)

RINGED GNATEATER
(Corythopis torquata)

Description. 5½ - 6". Tail normal. Above, including wings and tail uniform olive brown. Sides of head gray. Underparts white, a broad black band across chest; sides of body streaked with black. *Immature:* Differs from the adult by having

245

the breast band and streaks and sides olive, like the back.

Range. Southern Venezuela, the Guianas, the Amazon Valley, eastern Ecuador, Peru, and northern Bolivia.

Colombia. Known from "Bogotá" and Putumayo. Undoubtedly ranging southward and eastward (*sarayacuensis*).

TAPACULOS (Rhinocryptidae)

Fig. 63. Red-belted Tapaculo
(Liosceles thoracicus)

Tapaculos form an interesting group of peculiar birds of varied aspect. In the tropics of South America most species are found high up in the mountains, but many occur in the colder parts of southern South America. In Colombia most of the species belong to the genus *Scytalopus*. These are small dark gray, wren-like birds with barred flanks and shorts tails, short, sharply pointed bills and large feet. They live in the moss and tangled undergrowth of humid mountain forests where they creep about very much like mice. The young birds are dark brown, barred with black and are quite different from the adults. Their large nests, composed of roots and moss, are placed in crevices among rocks or in holes under roots of trees. (8 Col.; 25 S.A.; 26 N.&S.A.; 26 wld.)

AID TO IDENTIFICATION

Tail of normal length:
    Above brown, below white, breast band chestnut 1[E].
    Small, all gray 7.
    Chestnut and black, spotted all over with white 8.
Tail short:
    Plumage mostly pale, silvery gray 3, 5.
    Plumage mostly dark gray to slaty black 2, 4, 5, 6.

1. RED-BELTED TAPACULO
(Liosceles thoracicus)

Description. 8 - 8¼". Tail rather long, 3". Crown and nape dark grayish brown, lores and narrow eyebrow white, sides of head and neck gray. Back, wings and tail dark reddish brown; wing-coverts with a subterminal black bar surrounding a fulvous white spot. Throat and breast white, the breast crossed by a broad chestnut band (or a narrow pale chestnut band tinged with yellow, 1). Sides of breast gray, the feathers streaked and barred with white. Belly, flanks and under tail-coverts dark brown, barred with fulvous white.

Range. Central Brazil westward to eastern Peru and eastern Ecuador.

Colombia. Forest. Tropical zone east of the Andes. Putumayo *(dugandi)*. Southeastern Nariño (1, *erithacus*).

2. UNICOLORED TAPACULO
(Scytalopus unicolor) Plate XII

Description. 5 - 5¼". Bill rather slender. Entirely slaty gray including wings and tail. *Immature*: Dark brown above, barred black and rufous below.

Range. Western Venezuela southward through the Andes to Ecuador, Peru and Bolivia.

Colombia. Mossy forest. Upper subtropical to temperate zone of all three Andean ranges southward through Nariño *(latrans)*.

247

3. ANDEAN TAPACULO
(*Scytalopus magellanicus*)

Description. 5 - 5¼ ". Bill rather slender, maxilla slightly concave. Entire head, mantle, breast and belly silvery gray. Lower back, rump and upper tail-coverts and flanks rufous. Wings and tail rufous-brown (or very like No. 2 but smaller and much paler gray and bill shorter, 1).

Range. Venezuela southward in the Andes to Chile.

Colombia. Forest. Temperate zone. Northern end of the Western and Central Andes (1, *canus*). Eastern Andes in the vicinity of Bogotá (*griseicollis*).

4. RUFOUS-VENTED TAPACULO
(*Scytalopus femoralis*)

Description. 6 - 6¼ ". Bill much thicker than preceding species. Tail rather long for the group, 2 - 2¼ ". Crown, nape and mantle sooty brownish gray (or crown sometimes with a white spot in center, 1). Lower back, rump and upper tail-coverts dark reddish brown. Wings and tail dark blackish brown. Sides of head, throat and breast dark gray, the feathers of the lower breast edged whitish. Flanks and under tail-coverts barred rufous-brown and black, (or all black with only faint indications of barring, and with a large white crown spot, 2).

Range. The Andes from Ecuador southward to Bolivia.

Colombia. Mossy forest. Upper tropical and subtropical zone of all three Andean ranges (*confusus*). Santa Marta Mts. (1, *sanctae-martae*). Sierra de Perijá (2, *nigricans*). Eastern slope of the Andes in Boyacá (*atratus*). East slope of the Andes in southeastern Nariño. (*micropterus*).

5. BROWN-RUMPED TAPACULO
(*Scytalopus latebricola*)

Description. 4¾ - 5¼ ". Very similar to No. 3 from the Eastern Andes but larger and bill much higher at base. In color it differs by being darker below and the rufous of the lower back and underparts slightly marked with blackish (or head and mantle dark slaty gray, throat and breast paler gray. Belly, flanks and under tail-coverts rufescent brown barred with black. Lower back and upper tail-coverts dark brown barred with black on upper tail-coverts. Wings and tail dark sooty brown, 1).

Range. Northern and western Venezuela and Ecuador.

Colombia. Mossy forest. Upper subtropical to temperate zone. Santa Marta Mts. (*latebricola*). Eastern and Central Andes (1, *meridanus*). Upper Magdalena Valley (*spillmani*).

6. PALE-THROATED TAPACULO
(*Scytalopus panamensis*)

Description. 5 - 5½ ". Very similar to No. 4 from the Eastern and Central Andes, differing from it by having a white eyebrow (or no white eyebrow, 1), and a much shorter tail.

Range. Eastern Panama, Ecuador.

Colombia. Mossy forest. Upper tropical to temperate zones. East slope of Mt. Tacarcuna (*panamensis*). Western Andes and Nariño eastward to the west slope of the Central Andes (1, *vicinior*).

7. ASH-COLORED TAPACULO
(*Myornis senilis*)

Description. 6 - 6½ ". Ashy gray, wings and tail slightly darker. Resembles a *Scytalopus* except for long tail, 2.5".

Range. Andes of Ecuador.

Colombia. Forest. Temperate zone of the Eastern Andes and the Central Andes.

8. OCELLATED TAPACULO
(*Acropternis orthonyx*) Plate XI

Description. 8½ - 9". Forehead, lores, sides of head and neck, throat, lower back, rump, upper and under tail-coverts chestnut. Rest of plumage black, everywhere marked with round white spots; spots on head smallest and tinged rufescent. Wings dark brown, tail blackish. Hind claw very long and straight, 1".

Range. Northern Venezuela and Ecuador.

Colombia. Forest. Subtropical to temperate zone of the Eastern Andes in Cundinamarca and the Central Andes in Antioquia, Caldas and Cauca (*orthonyx*).

MANAKINS (Pipridae)

Fig. 64. Red-capped Manakin
(Pipra mentalis) p. 250

The members of this family form an exclusively tropical American group of small, brightly colored, forest-inhabiting birds. Varying in size from that of a small wren to a sparrow, they live mostly in the thick undergrowth of the forest and feed on fruit.

In addition to unimpressive vocal sounds they produce loud snapping noises with their wings, the wing-feathers being stiffened in some cases to produce these sounds. This is most highly developed in the Club-winged Manakin, in which species the shafts of the inner remiges are very much stiffened, thickened and club-like at their extremity.

Many of the species have the feathers of the crown brightly colored, contrasting with the rest of the plumage. The sexes are usually different. (24 Col.; 52 S.A.; 55 N.&S.A.; 55 wld.)

AID TO IDENTIFICATION

Body plumage black 2[E], 3, 4, 5, 6, 12[E], 14, 17.

Back blue 15, 16.

Below olive brown, cinnamon, or partly chestnut 9, 20[E], 21, 24[E].

Throat-feathers lengthened, beard-like (plumage gray, black and white) 18, (plumage yellow and black) 19.

Olive green (over 4″) 1, 10, 11, 14, 15, 16[E], 21, 22, 23[E]; legs yellow or orange 18, 19; tail ending in filaments or central feathers protruding 7[E], 15; (under 4″) 4, 5, 6, 8, 13[E], 17.

Above grass green or dark green 2, 3, 11, 12.

249

1. WING-BARRED MANAKIN
(Piprites chloris)

Description. 5¼ - 5¾". Forehead and lores yellowish. Entire upperparts olive green, the hindcrown, nape and ear-coverts shaded with gray. Lesser wing-coverts edged grayish olive, greater coverts broadly edged yellowish white. Inner remiges with broad, pale tips. Below yellowish green, yellow in center of abdomen (or breast gray and belly white, under tail-coverts yellow, 1). Tail blackish tipped yellowish white.

Range. The Guianas, southern Venezuela and eastern Ecuador, southward to Argentina, Paraguay and Bolivia.

Colombia. Forest. Tropical zone. Northern portion of the Perijá Mts. (perijanus). Western slope of the Central Andes and the eastern base of the Eastern Andes from Meta southward to eastern Nariño (antioquiae). Vaupés, the río Guainía near the junction of the Casiquiare (1, chlorion). Vaupés, río Guainía region south of the range of chlorion (tschudii).

2. BLUE-RUMPED MANAKIN
(Pipra isidorei)

Description. 3½ - 3¾". ♂: Crown and nape white with a bluish sheen, feathers pointed. Back, wings and tail deep glossy black, rump and upper tail-coverts sky blue. Underparts dull black, shaded on throat, belly and under tail-coverts with dull blue. ♀: Crown and nape yellowish green; rest of upper surface grass-green, brightest on upper tail-coverts. Throat pale yellowish green, breast and sides of body dull green, center of abdomen pale yellow. Wing-feathers black margined with grass green; tail green.

Range. Eastern Ecuador and northern Peru.

Colombia. Tropical zone east of the Andes in Meta and probably southward to eastern Nariño (isidorei).

3. BLUE-CROWNED MANAKIN
(Pipra coronata)

Description. 3¾". ♂: Crown cornflower blue, purplish blue on the margins, feathers pointed; rest of plumage includ-ing forehead deep velvety black (or underparts dull black shaded with greenish blue on belly and on under tail-coverts, 1). ♀: Differs from No. 2 principally by having the crown and nape uniform with the back.

Range. Costa Rica southward to western Ecuador. Southern Venezuela, eastern Ecuador, western Brazil, Peru and northern Bolivia.

Colombia. Forest undergrowth. Tropical zone west of the Eastern Andes (minuscula). East of the Andes from Meta southward to Caquetá (caquetae). Southeastern Nariño southward to Amazonas (1, carbonata).

4. RED-CAPPED MANAKIN
(Pipra mentalis) Fig. 64

Description. 4½". ♂: Top and sides of head crimson; thighs and under wing-coverts mustard yellow, otherwise deep velvety black. ♀: Upper surface, wings and tail dull olive green, breast and sides strongly shaded with olive green, center of abdomen dull mustard yellow.

Range. Mexico to western Ecuador.

Colombia. Forest. Tropical zone west of the Western Andes (minor).

5. GOLDEN-HEADED MANAKIN
(Pipra erythrocephala) Plate XIII

Description. 4". ♂: Top and sides of head orange yellow, (or yellow, 1) narrowly edged across the nape with scarlet. Sides of thighs scarlet, rest of plumage shiny blue-black. ♀: Similar to No. 4 but slightly smaller and tail much shorter.

Range. Eastern Panama, Venezuela and the Guianas southward to northern Peru and Brazil. Trinidad.

Colombia. Forest undergrowth. Tropical zone. Pacific coast southward to about 4°N. and eastward through the lower Atrato, Sinú, Cauca and middle Magdalena Valleys to the eastern base of the Santa Marta Mts. eastward to Arauca and western Meta (erythrocephala). The valley of the río Lebrija (flammiceps). East of Eastern Andes from Boyacá southward to Putumayo and Vaupés (1, berlepschi).

6. WHITE-CROWNED MANAKIN
(Pipra pipra) Plate VIII

Description. 4½". ♂: Crown and nape white, bases of feathers black (or white, 1; the white feathers prolonged to upper back, 2). Rest of plumage shiny blue-black. ♀: Crown and sides of head grayish olive (gray in immature ♂). Back bright olive green, wings and tail dusky, the feathers margined with olive. Below olive yellow. *Immature:* gray below shaded with green on the breast.

Range. Costa Rica to western Panama, western and southern Venezuela southward to southeastern Brazil and southern Peru.

Colombia. Forest. Upper tropical zone. Sinú Valley *(bolivari)*. Western slope of the Western Andes at their southern end (1, *minima*). Upper Magdalena Valley (1, 2, *unica*). East slope of the Eastern Andes from Norte de Santander southward to Caquetá *(coracina)*. Extreme eastern Colombia in Vaupés *(pipra)*.

7. WIRE-TAILED MANAKIN
(Teleonema filicauda) Plate XIII

Description. 4¾ - 5". ♂: Crown, nape and upper back scarlet. Forehead, sides of head and entire underparts golden yellow. Lower back, rump, wings and tail velvety black. Inner remiges with a large white patch on inner web. Shafts of tail-feathers lengthened, wire-like, protruding for about 2" beyond the tail. ♀: Upperparts, wings, tail and under tail-coverts olive green. Underparts dull yellow, shaded with olive on throat and breast. Shafts of tail-feathers as in ♂.

Range. Venezuela, northwestern Brazil, eastern Ecuador and eastern Peru.

Colombia. Forest. Tropical zone east of the Eastern Andes from Norte de Santander southward to Amazonas *(filicauda)*.

8. STRIPED MANAKIN
(Machaeropterus regulus) Plate XIII

Description. 4". ♂: Crown scarlet, feathers silky. Upper surface and wings bright olive green. Tail short, barely longer than tail-coverts, stiff, grayish green above, below whitish with white shafts. Inner remiges stiffened, white on the inner web. Throat whitish, rest of underparts chestnut, striped with white and stained with crimson on the breast, the feathers, particularly at the sides, somewhat lengthened. ♀: Upper surface, wings and tail bright olive green. Underparts whitish, breast crossed by a dull orange band.

Range. Venezuela, northwestern Brazil, eastern Ecuador, northeastern Peru. Southeastern Brazil.

Colombia. Forest. Tropical and upper tropical zone. The west slope of the Eastern Andes from Santander and Cundinamarca westward to the west slope of the Western Andes in Caldas *(antioquiae)*. East of the Eastern Andes from Arauca and Boyacá southward to Putumayo *(striolatus)*. Not recorded from Santa Marta and Nariño.

9. CLUB-WINGED MANAKIN
(Allocotopterus deliciosus) Plate XIII

Description. 4". ♂: Mostly dark chestnut, this color becoming deeper (almost blackish) on the lower back and abdomen where mixed with white. Forecrown crimson, margined posteriorly with black. Bend of wing yellow, outer remiges black, the inner ones white on the inner web, the innermost mostly white with thickened club-shape white shafts. Tail very short, the central feathers bronzy, the outer ones mostly white. ♀: Upperparts, wings and tail bright olive green, inner remiges white on inner web. Throat white, sides of throat tinged chestnut. Breast, sides of body olive, center of abdomen yellow.

Range. Western Ecuador.

Colombia. Upper tropical zone of the southern portion of the Pacific coast in Valle, Cauca and Nariño.

10. YELLOW-HEADED MANAKIN
(Chloropipo flavicapilla)

Description. 5¼ - 5½". ♂: Crown and nape bright golden yellow, the feathers lengthened into a broad, flat crest. Upperparts, wings and tail golden olive.

Throat and breast olive, rest of under surface pale yellow. ♀: Upperparts olive green. Throat and breast olive, rest of underparts dull yellow.

Range. Colombia.

Colombia. Forest. Subtropical zone of the Western and Central Andes. The southern end of the Eastern Andes on their western slope.

11. GREEN MANAKIN
(Chloropipo holochlora)

Description. 5½ - 5¾" Upperparts, wings and tail dark grass green (or olive green, 1). Throat grayish olive, breast olive, rest of underparts dull yellowish green.

Range. Eastern Panama. Eastern and western Ecuador to southern Peru.

Colombia. Tropical zone. West of the Andes from the headwaters of the Atrato southward to Nariño (1, *litae*). East of the Andes from Meta southward to Putumayo *(holochlora)*.

12. BLACK MANAKIN
(Xenopipo atronitens)

Description. 5½". ♂: Glossy blue-black. Wings and tail brownish black. ♀: Dark green, paler and more yellowish below. Under wing-coverts grayish white.

Range. The Guianas and southern Venezuela to northwestern Brazil.

Colombia. Tropical zone. Extreme eastern Colombia in Vaupés.

13. DWARF TYRANT-MANAKIN
(Tyranneutes stolzmanni)

Description. 3½ - 3¾". Above, including wings and tail, olive green. Throat and breast pale olive, rest of underparts pale yellow. Iris yellowish white. The only small green manakin with a yellowish white iris.

Range. Southern Venezuela, eastern Ecuador, northwestern Brazil, eastern Peru, northern Bolivia and south of the Amazon eastward to Pará.

Colombia. Forest. Tropical zone east of the Andes from Meta southward to Putumayo.

14. GOLDEN-WINGED MANAKIN
(Masius chrysopterus)

Description. 5". ♂: Chiefly velvety black. Frontal feathers golden yellow, erect, pointing forward over bill, center of crown shining golden yellow; feathers of hindcrown produced backward over nape, enamel-like, tobacco brown (or reddish brown, 1; or orange, 2; or orange-red, 3). Chin, throat and expanded patch on chest, under wing-coverts, inner margins of remiges golden yellow. Central and outer tail-feathers black, rest yellow on inner web. ♀: Mostly olive green, yellower below; the chin, center of throat, patch on breast yellowish white.

Range. Western Venezuela to Ecuador and Peru.

Colombia. Forest. Upper tropical and sub-tropical zones. West slope of the Western Andes from the lower río San Juan southward to Nariño *(coronulatus)*. West coast north of the lower río San Juan, northward and eastward to the middle Cauca Valley (1, *bellus*). West slope of the Eastern Andes in Cundinamarca and Huila and the east slope of the Central Andes in the upper Magdalena Valley (2, *chrysopterus*). East of the Andes in southeastern Nariño (3, *pax*).

15. LANCE-TAILED MANAKIN
(Chiroxiphia lanceolata) Plate XIII

Description. 5¾ - 6". ♂: Center of crown scarlet. Forehead, sides and back of head, and the underparts grayish black; mantle sky blue. Wings and tail black; central tail-feathers pointed and protruding beyond the rest. ♀: Upperparts, wings and tail bright olive green. Throat grayish green, breast olive green, rest of underparts pale yellowish green. Central tail-feathers protruding as in ♂.

Range. Coiba and Margarita Islands. Panama and northern Venezuela.

Colombia. Forest. Tropical zone. Caribbean coast, eastward to the Zulia Valley.

16. BLUE-BACKED MANAKIN
(Chiroxiphia pareola)

Description. 4¾ - 5". ♂: Differs from No. 15 by darker blue back, deep black underparts and normal tail. Flight-feathers narrower and more pointed. ♀ differs from No. 15 by greener upperparts and wings; tail normal. *Immature:* ♂ of both species resembles ♀ but have a scarlet crown patch.

Range. Venezuela and the Guianas southward to Bolivia and southeastern Brazil. Tobago and Trinidad.

Colombia. Forest. Tropical zone east of the Andes from Caquetá southward to Amazonas *(napensis).*

17. WHITE-RUFFED MANAKIN
(Corapipo leucorrhoa)

Description. 4". ♂: Shiny blue-black, blacker on under surface. Throat and under tail-coverts white, the feathers on sides of throat lengthened, forming a ruff. ♀: Upperparts, wings and tail olive green; throat and sides of head gray. Underparts olive green, yellowish on center of abdomen, and under tail-coverts.

Range. Nicaragua southward to Panama. Western Venezuela.

Colombia. Forest. Tropical and lower subtropical zone. Northwestern Colombia south to the Baudó Mts. *(altera).* East of the Andes in Arauca. West slope of the Eastern Andes in Santander and Cundinamarca westward to the Cauca Valley and on the west slope of the Western Andes in the Dagua Valley *(leucorrhoa).*

18. WHITE-BEARDED MANAKIN
(Manacus manacus)

Description. 5". ♂: Mostly black and white. Crown, nape, mantle, wings and tail black, rest of back gray. Sides of head, collar and hindneck, throat, breast and lesser wing-coverts white; feathers of the throat lengthened (or crown black, mantle yellowish white, lower back black, rump gray, 1). ♀: Upperparts bright olive green; underparts pale olive green, paler on abdomen, grayish on throat. Feet orange-yellow.

Range. Venezuela and the Guianas, Ecuador, Peru, Brazil, Paraguay and Argentina. Western Ecuador and northern Peru. Trinidad.

Colombia. Forest. Tropical zone. The Santa Marta region, the lower and middle Magdalena Valley south to eastern Antioquia and the lower Cauca Valley *(abditivus).* Upper Magdalena Valley northward on the eastern side of the middle Magdalena Valley to Santander (1, *flaveolus).* Pacific slope of Nariño *(bangsi).* East of the Andes in Santander, Meta, Vichada and Caquetá *(interior).*

19. GOLDEN-COLLARED MANAKIN
(Manacus vitellinus) Plate XIII

Description. 4½ - 5". ♂: Mostly black and yellow. Above black. A broad collar on hindneck, sides of head, throat and upper breast golden yellow, the throat feathers lengthened; rest of underparts olive green (or pale greenish yellow, 1). Rump and upper tail-coverts dark olive green. Feet orange-yellow, bill black. ♀ differs from the White-bearded Manakin by having the upper surface more olivaceous, the under surface dark yellowish olive without the gray tint on the throat, and the tail slightly longer. Feet orange-yellow.

Range. Costa Rica to eastern Panama.

Colombia. Forest. Tropical zone. Shores of the Gulf of Urabá *(vitellinus).* Middle Magdalena, the lower Cauca and Sinú Valleys (1, *milleri).* West coast southward to the río Dagua and eastward to the upper Cauca Valley *(viridiventris).*

20. CINNAMON MANAKIN
(Neopipo cinnamomea)

Description. 4". ♂: Top and sides of head dark grayish, a line down center of crown reddish chestnut or yellow. Mantle grayish turning to rufous on lower back and rump. Throat fulvous white, rest of underparts cinnamon. Wings and tail rufous. ♀ similar to ♂ but crown patch cinnamon.

Range. Southern Venezuela and the Guianas to northwestern Brazil, Ecuador, and Peru.

Colombia. Tropical zone. Extreme eastern Colombia in Vaupés *(cinnamomea).*

21. THRUSH-LIKE MANAKIN
(Schiffornis turdinus) Plate XVIII

Description. 7 - 7½ ". Upperparts, wings and tail dull olive brown (or bronze brown, 1), crown tinged reddish brown. Area before eye rather pale. Underparts uniform olive to olive gray (or throat and breast bronzy brown, rest of underparts contrasting pale grayish olive, 1). Bill rather high and narrow.

Range. Mexico southward through Central America to Venezuela, the Guianas, eastern Brazil, eastern and western Ecuador, Peru and Bolivia.

Colombia. Forest. Tropical zone. The Santa Marta region southward to Boyacá. The western foothills of the Eastern Andes in the Magdalena Valley southward to western Cundinamarca (1, *stenorhyn-chus*). Western Colombia from the Panama border eastward to the upper Sinú Valley (1, *panamensis*). The Upper Atrato Valley and western slope of the Western Andes southward to the río Munchique *(furvus)*. Pacific sope of Nariño *(rosenbergi)*. East of the Eastern Andes in Meta *(subsp.?)*; in Vaupés *(amazonus)*.

22. BROAD-BILLED MANAKIN
(Sapayoa aenigma) Plate XVIII

Description. 6¼ - 6½ ". Bill broad, flat, flycatcher-like. Semi-concealed golden yellow patch in center of crown (or without crown patch, ♀). Upperparts, wings and tail dark olive green; below paler and more yellowish, particularly on throat and center of abdomen.

Range. Eastern Panama and northwestern Ecuador.

Colombia. Forest. Tropical zone from the upper Sinú Valley westward to the Pacific coast, southward to Nariño.

23. SAFFRON-CRESTED TYRANT-MANAKIN
(Neopelma chrysocephalum)

Description. 5¼ - 5½". Sides of crown grayish olive, center of crown with a broad, silky golden yellow crest. Back, wings and tail dull olive. Throat grayish white, breast grayish olive, belly and under tail-coverts pale yellow.

Range. Tropical zone. The Guianas, southern Venezuela, northwestern Brazil.
Colombia. Known only from Vaupés.

24. YELLOW-CROWNED MANAKIN
(Heterocercus flavivertex)

Description. 6 - 6¼ ". ♂ : Upperparts olive green. Center of crown golden yellow. Throat silky white, the feathers at sides of throat elongated. Sides of head and narrow band below white throat, grayish, rest of underparts chestnut. Wings and very much rounded tail, grayish brown. ♀ similar to ♂ but duller and without yellow crown patch.

Range. Southern Venezuela to north central Brazil.

Colombia. Tropical zone. Eastern Colombia in Vichada and Vaupés.

COCKS-OF-THE-ROCK (Rupicolidae)

Fig. 65. Guianan Cock-of-the-Rock
(Rupicola rupicola)

Cocks-of-the-Rock form a small group of birds remarkable both in appearance and habits. They are found only in South America.

They live in damp forests in the vicinity of rocky streams. During courtship they assemble on an area of ground which they have cleared and the males dance to attract the females. Their nests are shallow saucers, made of mud and placed on ledges either in caves or on the face of cliffs. They live on fruit and insects. (2 Col.; 2 S.A.; 2 N.&S.A.; 2 wld.)

GUIANAN COCK-OF-THE-ROCK
(Rupicola rupicola)

Description. 12½ - 14". ♂ : Mostly bright orange. A broad, rounded compressed fan-shaped crest, bordered by a narrow band of maroon, springing forward from in front of the eyes and partially hiding the bill. Wings mostly black, the primaries with a prominent white speculum. Inner remiges very broad, truncate, edged orange, the outer webs orange extended into long filaments. Tail dark chocolate brown, edged and tipped with pale orange. ♀ : Dark olive gray with a much reduced crest; wings and tail browner. Under wing-coverts pale orange. Outer webs of inner remiges extended into filaments like ♂ .

Range. The Guianas, southern Venezuela on the rio Negro region of Brazil.

Colombia. Forest. Tropical zone. Extreme eastern Colombia in Vichada and Vaupés.

ANDEAN COCK-OF-THE-ROCK
(Rupicola peruviana) Plate XIII

Description. 14 - 15". ♂ : Mostly brilliant scarlet (or bright deep orange, 1). Ample, flat crest springing forward from the forehead and covering the bill. Innermost secondaries very broad, silvery gray; rest of wings and tail black. ♀ : Dark maroon red (or orange-brown, 1). Wings grayish olive brown, tail dull maroon brown (or dull orange-brown, 1).

Range. Western Venezuela, southward through the Andes to Ecuador, Peru and northern Bolivia.

Colombia. Forest. Subtropical zone of the Central Andes in Caldas, Tolima and Huila and the Eastern Andes in Norte de Santander, Santander and Huila; sometimes in the upper tropical zone of the east slope in Meta (1, *aequatorialis*). Both slopes of the Western Andes from Antioquia southward to Nariño in the upper tropical and subtropical zones *(sanguinolenta)*.

255

PLATE XIII

BLUE COTINGA
(*Cotinga n. nattererii*)
Page 259

POMPADOUR COTINGA
(*Xipholena punicea*)
Page 259

LANCE-TAILED
MANAKIN
(*Chiroxiphia lanceolata*)
Page 252

CLUB-WINGED
MANAKIN
(*Allocotopterus
deliciosus*)
Page 251

ANDEAN
COCK-OF-THE ROCK
(*Rupicola peru-
viana sanguinolenta*)
Page 255

BLACK-NECKED
RED COTINGA
(*Phoenicircus nigricollis*)
Page 258

CHESTNUT-CRESTED
COTINGA
(*Ampelion rufax-
illa antioquiae*)
Page 258

ORANGE-BREASTED
FRUITEATER
(*Pipreola jucunda*)
Page 260

STRIPED MANAKIN
(*Machaeropterus reg-
ulus striolatus*)
Page 251

WIRE-TAILED MANAKIN
(*Teleonema f. fil'cauda*)
Page 251

GOLDEN-COLLARED
MANAKIN
(*Manacus vitel-
linus viridiventris*)
Page 253

GOLDEN-HEADED
MANAKIN
(*Pipra e. erythro-
cephala*)
Page 250

E.L.Poole

COTINGAS, BECARDS AND FRUITCROWS (Cotingidae)

Fig. 66. Umbrellabird
(Cephalopterus ornatus) p. 266

Cotingas are a comparatively large family of birds practically confined to the American tropics. They live in the forest, usually high up in the trees, and feed on fruit. Included among them are some of the most beautiful as well as the most peculiar of South American birds. They range in size from the wren-sized purpletufts to the crow-like umbrellabird. In addition to their brilliant colors some are remarkable for their large crests, enamel-like plumage or bare heads and necks. Their peculiarities are not confined to their plumage for the voices of some are more than remarkable. The note of the bellbird resembles the striking of an anvil and can be heard a mile away. Well-named is the screaming piha whose deafening lash-like three-syllable call, "cri-cri-ó" rings through the forest and carries for a great distance. (46 Col.; 71 S.A.; 79 N.&S.A.; 79 wld.)

AID TO IDENTIFICATION

With crimson or blue or purple in plumage 1E, 5E, 6E, 7, 8E, 9E, 10E, 42.

Body plumage white or grayish white 11, 39E, 40, 41, 46.

Bright grass green above 12, 13, 14, 15.

Olive green above (over 7″) 1E, 2E, 16, 17, 19, 28, 46; (under 6″) 30, 34, 35E, 36.

Cinnamon, chestnut, or rufous above 19, 20, 22, 25, 29, 31, 32E, 33, 37, 38E.

Plain gray or grayish brown above 3, 4, 10E, 11, 18E, 21E, 23E, 24E, 26, 27E, 37.

Brown, feathers speckled or edged whitish 5E, 6E, 7, 8E, 9E.

Gray and black above 30, 31, 34, 35E, 36, 39E, 40, 41, 45E.

Black, or mostly black 34, 38E, 42, 43, 44.

257

1. BLACK-NECKED RED COTINGA
(Phoenicircus nigricollis) Plate XIII

Description. 9 - 10". ♂ : Forehead, crown and short silky crest crimson. Chin and center of throat dull brownish pink mixed with black. Lower throat, sides of head, neck and the mantle deep velvety black. Wings brownish black, the greater coverts and secondaries edged maroon. Entire under surface, rump and upper tail-coverts crimson; tail crimson, tipped black. ♀ : Crown, ear-coverts, upper tail-coverts and tail maroon red, tail narrowly tipped black. Throat, sides of neck, back and wings olive green; underparts scarlet.

Range. Southwestern Venezuela, northern and central Brazil westward to eastern Ecuador and eastern Peru.

Colombia. Forest. Tropical zone. Putumayo southward to the Amazon.

2. SHRIKE-LIKE COTINGA
(Laniisoma elegans)

Description. 6¾ - 7". ♂ : Lores, crown and nape black. Back and tail olive green. Underparts bright yellow tinged orange at sides of throat, tinged olive on sides of body with a few black bars on flanks. Under tail-coverts pale yellow with dusky bars. ♀ resembles ♂ , but lores, crown and nape green like back. Throat with a few small black spots.

Range. Southeastern Brazil. Northern Bolivia. Eastern Ecuador. Northwestern Venezuela.

Colombia. Known only from northern Boyacá (venezuelensis).

3. RED-CRESTED COTINGA
(Ampelion rubro-cristatus)

Description. 8¾ - 9½". Crown, ear-coverts and wings sooty gray. Long, flat crest springing from center of crown chestnut maroon. Feathers of rump, belly and under tail-coverts mixed white and gray, rest of plumage ashy gray. Tail black with a large subterminal white spot on the inner web of all tail-feathers except central pair. Young birds lack the crest. The upperparts are gray streaked paler; the under surface yellowish white, streaked gray. Tail as in adult.

Range. Venezuela southward through the Andes to Bolivia.

Colombia. Forest. Upper subtropical and temperate zone of the mountains throughout.

4. CHESTNUT-CRESTED COTINGA
(Ampelion rufaxilla) Plate XIII

Description. 8¾ - 9½". Forehead and sides of crown dark gray. Broad, recumbent crest dark chestnut red bordered on each side by broad black line. Throat and sides of head bright reddish chestnut. Upper surface and wings olive gray, the feathers dark centered; wing-coverts chestnut red. Band across chest plain olive gray, rest of underparts pale yellow streaked with black, particularly on chest and sides of body. Tail black.

Range. Northern and central Peru.

Colombia. Forest. Subtropical zone of the Central and Western Andes (antioquiae).

5. PURPLE-THROATED COTINGA
(Porphyrolaema porphyrolaema)

Description. 7½ - 8". ♂ : Upper surface, wings and tail black, the feathers of the back margined with white; middle wing-coverts tipped white. Throat plum purple; entire under surface white, upper breast just below throat stained with plum purple. ♀ : Dull blackish, speckled and barred with light brown. Below ferruginous brown, narrowly barred with black.

Range. Western Brazil, eastern Ecuador and northeastern Peru.

Colombia. Forest. Tropical zone. Caquetá southward (porphyrolaema).

6. PURPLE-BREASTED COTINGA
(Cotinga cotinga)

Description. 7½ - 8". ♂ : Top and sides of head, entire upperparts, flanks and under tail-coverts shining cornflower blue, the black bases of the feathers of the upperparts showing through. Throat, breast and belly deep purple. Wings and tail black, the wing-coverts edged cornflower blue. ♀ : Upperparts dark brown, all the feathers edged fulvous and obscurely tinged blue. Throat fulvous; rest of underparts dark brown, the feathers broadly edged with fulvous giving a scaled appearance. Under wing-coverts buff. Wings and tail dark brown.

Range. Southern Venezuela, the Guianas and northern Brazil, the south bank of the Amazon from the rio Tapajóz to Belém.

Colombia. Forest. Tropical zone. Vaupés.

7. BLUE COTINGA
(Cotinga nattererii) Plate XIII

Description. 7½ - 7¾ ". ♂ : Throat dark purple, center of abdomen paler purple. Rest of plumage brilliant shining turquoise blue, deeper on crown. Wings and tail black; wing-coverts and tertials edged with blue. ♀ : Upperparts, wings and tail dark brown with bluish reflections, the feathers everywhere edged with pale fulvous. Below paler, mostly uniform tawny buff, the feathers of the breast broadly centered with dark brown. Under wing-coverts cinnamon.

Range. Mexico southward to Mérida, Venezuela and western Ecuador.

Colombia. Forest and scrub. Tropical zone of the entire Pacific coast eastward through the upper Atrato, upper Sinú, and lower Cauca Valleys to the middle Magdalena Valley *(nattererii)*.

8. PLUM-THROATED COTINGA
(Cotinga maynana)

Description. 7½ - 7¾ ". ♂ : Throat plum purple; rest of plumage brilliant shining turquoise blue, the feathers of the crown and lores narrow, pointed and rather stiff. All the body feathers basally white with a subterminal purple band which shows through here and there. Wings and tail black, the wing-coverts, inner remiges and tail-feathers broadly edged with blue. ♀ differs from No. 6 only in being somewhat paler above, the feathers with a greenish gloss, below darker and more uniform on breast. Under wing-coverts cinnamon.

Range. Upper Amazonia southward to northern Bolivia.

Colombia. Forest. Tropical zone east of the Andes from Caquetá and Vaupés southward to Amazonas.

9. SPANGLED COTINGA
(Cotinga cayana)

Description. 8½ - 9". ♂ : Entire throat and extreme upper breast purple. Above brilliant, shining turquoise blue, the feathers basally black, the black showing through and giving a spotted appearance. Below more uniform turquoise blue. Wings and tail black, the feathers narrowly edged with turquoise blue. ♀ : Above blackish brown, the feathers narrowly edged with whitish. Below similar but paler becoming buffy on abdomen and upper tail-coverts. Inner remiges and wing-coverts edged buffy brown; tail-feathers dark brown, with rusty tips and inner webs. Under wing-coverts buff.

Range. Southern Venezuela, the Guianas, northern Brazil westward to eastern Ecuador, eastern Peru and northern Bolivia.

Colombia. Forest. Tropical zone east of the Andes from Arauca southward to Caquetá and Vaupés.

10. POMPADOUR COTINGA
(Xipholena punicea) Plate XIII

Description. 8 - 8½ ". ♂ : Shining purplered, the feathers somewhat hair-like, upper wing-coverts lengthened with stiffened white shafts. Wings white, the outer primaries tipped black. Tail pale purplered, white basally. ♀ : Above mostly uniform dark grayish, paler below. Wings and tail like back, wing-coverts and secondaries broadly edged white.

Range. Southern Venezuela, the Guianas and northwestern Brazil.

Colombia. Forest. Extreme eastern Colombia along the upper río Guainía in Vaupés.

11. WHITE COTINGA
(Carpodectes hopkei) Plate VIII

Description. ♂ 10 - 10½"; ♀ 9 - 9½ ". ♂ : Entirely white with small black tips to the remiges and central rectrices. Iris orange; bill black. ♀ : Ashy gray; wing-coverts, secondaries and tertials edged white. Belly and under tail-coverts white. Tail grayish black.

Range. Northwestern Ecuador.

Colombia. Forest and scrub. Tropical zone of the entire Pacific coast.

12. GREEN-AND-BLACK FRUITEATER
(Pipreola riefferii)

Description. 7½ - 8″. ♂ : Crown and sides of head glossy greenish black. Back, wings and tail grass green. Throat and breast dark moss green, a yellow band extending from behind the ear-coverts and surrounding the green of the breast. Rest of underparts mixed grass green and yellow, center of abdomen almost unmarked. Bill red, feet and legs orange. ♀ like ♂ but head uniform with back and breast grass green.

Range. Northern and western Venezuela southward through the Andes to Bolivia.

Colombia. Forest. Upper tropical to subtropical zone. West slope of the Eastern Andes and both slopes of the Central Andes. East of the Andes in Cundinamarca and southeastern Nariño (riefferii). Western Andes and western Nariño (occidentalis).

13. BLACK-BREASTED FRUITEATER
(Pipreola lubomirskii)

Description. 7½ - 8″. ♂ : Entire head, throat and center of breast shiny black. Back, wings and tail and sides of breast grass green; flanks mixed grass green and yellow, rest of underparts lemon yellow. ♀ : Very similar to ♀ of No. 12 but tertials with pale yellow edges; feet and legs grayish green instead of orange.

Range. Eastern Ecuador and northeastern Peru.

Colombia. Forest. Subtropical zone at the head of the Magdalena Valley; east of the Andes in eastern Nariño.

14. ORANGE-BREASTED FRUITEATER
(Pipreola jucunda) Plate XIII

Description. 7½-8″. ♂ : Entire head shiny black. Upper breast orange, this color continued around sides of neck, somewhat yellower at juncture with black of throat, the orange of breast outlined below with black, lower breast and rest of underparts yellow. Back, wings and tail and sides of breast grass green. Sides of body mixed green and yellow. Bill orange; feet and legs grayish green. ♀ : Similar to ♀ of No. 13 but breast green streaked with yellow instead of uniform green.

Range. Western Ecuador.

Colombia. Forest. Upper tropical zone. The Pacific coast from the lower río San Juan southward.

15. GOLDEN-BREASTED FRUITEATER
(Pipreola aureopectus)

Description. 7½ - 8″. ♂ : Upperparts and sides of head grass green; the feathers of the center of the hindcrown, center of back and tail-coverts strongly tinged blue. Chin and lores blackish; throat and breast golden yellow (or the yellow continued up sides of neck, 1); center of abdomen and under tail-coverts lemon yellow; flanks green mixed with yellow. ♀ differs from ♀ of No. 14 by having the throat yellow streaked with green instead of plain green.

Range. Northwestern and western Venezuela.

Colombia. Forest. Subtropical zone of the Eastern Andes in Magdalena (aureopectus). Santa Marta Mts. (1, decora).

16. BARRED FRUITEATER
(Pipreola arcuata)

Description. 9¾ - 10½″. ♂ : Entire head, throat and upper breast glossy blue-black. Upper surface olive green, the upper tail-coverts with a subterminal black bar and dull yellow tip. Wing-feathers black edged exteriorly with olive; greater coverts and inner secondaries with a yellowish white mark on outer web. Outer tail-feathers black, central tail-feathers olive green with a black terminal band, all feathers tipped white. Under surface yellow regularly barred with black. Bill crimson, feet scarlet. ♀ differs from ♂ by having the head green like back and throat and upper breast banded like rest of underparts.

Range. Northern Venezuela southward through the Andes to Bolivia.

Colombia. Forest. Upper tropical to temperate zone of the Eastern and Central and Western Andes. Recorded definitely from Tolima, Caldas and Cauca (arcuata).

17. SCALED FRUITEATER
(Ampelioides tschudii)

Description. 8¼ - 8¾". ♂ : Crown, to below eye and the nape glossy blue-black; lores and stripe from gape continuing along sides of head yellowish white, the latter joining a yellow collar on hindneck, the yellow collar narrowly bordered posteriorly with black. Rest of upperparts black, the feathers widely bordered with olive yellow giving a scaled appearance. Upper tail-coverts olive green with a broad subterminal black band and yellow tip. Greater wing-coverts olive yellow forming a broad band; lesser wing-coverts and rest of wing black, the primaries bordered with pale yellow, the tertials tipped olive. Throat and sides of neck dirty white, mottled with dusky, rest of underparts pale greenish yellow, the feathers edged olive green giving a scaled appearance. Upper tail-coverts olive, distally black with a broad yellow fringe. Central tail-feathers olive, others mostly black, all but central ones with pale yellowish tip. ♀ like ♂ but without black cap and feathers of mantle more broadly edged green, giving the back a greener appearance.

Range. Mountains of Ecuador and Peru.

Colombia. Forest. Upper tropical and subtropical zones. East of the Andes in the Macarena Mts. The west slope of the Eastern Andes in Huila and the west slope of the Western Andes in Antioquia, Caldas, Valle and Cauca.

18. WHITE-BROWED PURPLETUFT
(Iodopleura isabellae) Plate XVIII

Description. 4¾ - 5". ♂ : Upperparts dark brown, the crown glossed with blue-black, wings and tail darker. Lores, stripe behind eye, spot at gape, throat, center of breast, abdomen, under tail-coverts, under wing-coverts and bar across rump white. Malar streak, sides of head and neck, and sides of breast, dark brown. Large tuft of partly concealed silky violet feathers springing from the sides of breast. Sides of body barred dark brown and white. ♀ like ♂ but tuft at sides of breast smaller composed of silky white feathers. The smallest Colombian cotinga.

Range. Southern Venezuela. The Amazon Valley eastward to Ecuador, Peru and northern Bolivia.

Colombia. Forest. Tropical zone east of the Eastern Andes from Meta southward to Vaupés (isabellae).

19. BRIGHT-RUMPED ATTILA
(Attila spadiceus)

Description. 7½ - 8½". Bill shrike-like and strongly hooked. Variable in color, varying from mostly bright cinnamon to olive green. The rump usually pale yellow but sometimes buff. Below paler, either uniform pale cinnamon, often darker on the breast, to greenish on the breast, striped with dull yellow, abdomen whitish; or entire underparts whitish streaked with brown on breast. Under tail-coverts usually yellow but sometimes pale cinnamon. Wing-coverts edged with grayish olive to cinnamon-rufous.

Range. Mexico southward to Venezuela, the Guianas, southeastern Brazil, Ecuador, Peru and Bolivia. Trinidad.

Colombia. Forest. Tropical and subtropical zone. Santa Marta region (parvirostris). Middle Magdalena and lower Sinú Valleys (caniceps). From west of the Gulf of Urabá to the upper Sinú Valley (sclateri). Upper Atrato Valley and west slope of the Western Andes southward to Nariño (parambae). East of the Eastern Andes from Meta southward to Caquetá (spadiceus).

20. CINNAMON ATTILA
(Attila cinnamomeus) Plate XVIII

Description. 8¼ - 8¾" (or 8½ - 9", 1). Bill shrike-like, strongly hooked. Upperparts orange-rufous, (or tawny cinnamon, 1) paler on rump. Remiges and wing-coverts blackish margined with cinnamon-rufous. Throat and breast cinnamon, belly ochraceous-cinnamon (or tawny yellow, 1). Tail rufous.

Range. Venezuela, the Guianas southward through the Amazon Valley to Maranhão. Eastern Ecuador, Peru and Bolivia. Western Ecuador.

Colombia. Mangroves, coffee plantations, forest. Tropical zone east of the Eastern Andes in Meta (cinnamomeus). Southwestern Nariño (1, torridus).

21. CINEREOUS MOURNER
(Laniocera hypopyrrha)

Description. 8½ - 9". ♂: Upperparts, throat and breast ashy gray. Lesser inner wing-coverts, patch on sides of breast orange-rufous or yellow. Wing-coverts and inner secondaries with broad ochraceous tips bordered below by black. Lower breast and abdomen gray faintly tinged yellowish, obscurely barred, sometimes some of the feathers on center of breast and under tail-coverts cinnamon-orange, tipped black. Wings and tail ashy gray, the tail tipped ochraceous. ♀ like ♂ but spots on wing-coverts smaller and paler. Tuft at sides of breast lemon yellow or ochraceous. No cinnamon-orange feathers on center of breast, and under tail-coverts like the belly.

Range. Venezuela and the Guianas southward to the Amazon Valley, eastern Ecuador, Peru and Bolivia.

Colombia. Forest. Tropical zone east of the Eastern Andes in Boyacá and Meta.

22. SPECKLED MOURNER
(Laniocera rufescens)

Description. 8½ - 9". ♂: Uniform rufous-brown, paler below (or obsolete dusky barring on the chest and gray cast on throat, 1). Tuft of lemon yellow feathers at sides of breast. Wing-coverts brownish black with broad rufous tips. Tail like back. ♀ similar to ♂ but tuft at sides of breast orange-rufous instead of yellow.

Range. Guatemala to western Ecuador.

Colombia. Forest. Tropical zone. Pacific coast from the Panama border to the Baudó Mts. and the lower Atrato Valley (1, rufescens). Upper Sinú and the lower Cauca Valleys, the middle Magdalena in Santander (1, griseigula). Western Nariño (tertia).

23. GRAYISH MOURNER
(Rhytipterna simplex)

Description. 8¾ - 9". Entire plumage including wings and tail gray with a greenish cast; belly palest with a definite yellowish green cast. Head slightly crested.

Range. The Guianas and southern Venezuela southward to Bolivia and southeastern Brazil.

Colombia. Open forest. Tropical zone east of the Eastern Andes from Meta south to Putumayo and Vaupés (frederici).

24. PALE-BELLIED MOURNER
(Rhytipterna immunda)

Description. 8". ♂: Above dark ashy gray; throat and breast pale gray, rest of underparts pale yellowish. Wings and tail blackish, wing-coverts grayish, forming not very distinct wing-bars. Remiges and outer retrices edged rusty. ♀ like ♂, wings and tail edged whitish.

This species resembles very closely the flycatcher Myiarchus cephalotes and it is very difficult to tell the two apart in the field. The hind tarsus is serrated in Rhytipterna, smooth in Myiarchus.

Range. Southern Venezuela; French and Dutch Guiana; northern Brazil.

Colombia. Forest. Tropical zone. Eastern Colombia in Vaupés.

25. RUFOUS MOURNER
(Rhytipterna holerythra)

Description. 8 - 8½". Very similar to No. 22 but without pectoral tufts. Further distinguishable by more uniform wing-coverts; lower belly and under tail-coverts definitely paler than rest of underparts (or purer rufous above with the sides of the head, throat and breast dark rufous without gray cast, 1).

Range. Guatemala southward to western Ecuador.

Colombia. Forest. Tropical zone. Lower Atrato, lower Cauca and middle Magdalena Valleys (holerythra). West of the Western Andes from the upper Atrato southward to Nariño (1, rosenbergi).

26. DUSKY PIHA
(Lipaugus fusco-cinereus)

Description. 12½ - 13½". Entirely ashy gray, purer gray on throat and tinged with brown on breast, belly and especially under tail-coverts. Tail rather long, 7".

Range. Ecuador.

Colombia. Forest. Subtropical and temperate zone of the Eastern and Central Andes and the northern portion of the Western Andes.

27. GRAY SCREAMING PIHA
(Lipaugus vociferans) Plate VIII

Description. 10½ - 11". Very similar to No. 26 but considerably smaller and under tail-coverts pale grayish with no brown shade.

Range. The Guianas and Venezuela southward to Bahia in eastern Brazil and Bolivia.

Colombia. Forest. Tropical zone east of the Eastern Andes, from Meta southward to Amazonas.

28. OLIVACEOUS PIHA
(Lipaugus cryptolophus)

Description. 9¾ - 10¼". Upperparts including wings olive green. Tail ashy green. Throat and breast like back, center of abdomen yellow to olive yellow. Somewhat concealed flat crest black, the feathers basally chestnut (or white, 1).

Range. Ecuador and Peru.

Colombia. Forest. The upper tropical and subtropical zone. The head of the Magdalena Valley *(cryptolophus);* the western slope of the Western Andes in Cauca and Nariño (1, *mindoensis).*

29. RUFOUS PIHA
(Lipaugus unirufus)

Description. 9½ - 10". Very similar to No. 25 but larger, and throat definitely paler than rest of underparts instead of uniform.

Range. Mexico southward to western Ecuador.

Colombia. Forest. Tropical zone. Northwestern Colombia eastward to the Sinú and lower Cauca Valleys *(unirufus).* The Baudó Mts. and the upper Atrato Valley southward to Nariño *(castaneotinctus).*

30. BARRED BECARD
(Pachyramphus versicolor)

Description. 4½ - 5¼". ♂ : Crown and nape and upper back glossy black; lower back and tail ashy gray. Wings black, wing-coverts, scapulars and secondaries edged white. Lores white, sides of head and neck, throat and upper breast greenish yellow, inconspicuously banded with

dusky, rest of underparts white, banded with black. ♀ : Crown and nape gray; sides of head, neck and back olive. Inner wing-coverts chestnut, outer wing-coverts black. Inner remiges black, margined with ochraceous. Underparts yellow, barred with broken olive bars on breast. Tail ashy.

Range. Costa Rica and western Panama. Western Venezuela southward to Ecuador, Peru and Bolivia.

Colombia. Trees bordering pastures and open woods. Subtropical zone. The western slope of the Eastern Andes westward to the Western Andes and west of them southward to western Nariño. East of the Andes in southeastern Nariño *(versicolor).*

31. CINEREOUS BECARD
(Pachyramphus rufus)

Description. 5½ - 6". ♂ : Forehead and lores white; crown and nape glossy black. Back, wings and tail ashy gray, wing-coverts and inner remiges margined with white. Underparts white, strongly shaded with gray on sides of breast and neck. ♀ : Above cinnamon; below rufescent buff, darkest on breast.

Range. Eastern Panama, Venezuela and the Guianas, northern Brazil, eastern Ecuador and Peru.

Colombia. Scrub. Tropical zone. Santa Marta region; lower and middle Magdalena Valley; lower and middle Cauca Valley.

32. CHESTNUT-CROWNED BECARD
(Pachyramphus castaneus)

Description. 5½ - 6". Crown chestnut, margined all around by gray; a white line above the lores. Back, wings and tail chestnut-rufous. Underparts pale cinnamon.

Range. Venezuela, southward to Ecuador, Peru, Brazil, Bolivia, Argentina and Paraguay.

Colombia. Forest. Tropical zone east of the Eastern Andes from Meta southward to Caquetá, Putumayo and undoubtedly eastern Nariño *(saturatus).*

33. CINNAMON BECARD
(Pachyramphus cinnamomeus)

Description. 5½ - 6". Upperparts, wings and tail chestnut-rufous. Line above lores whitish. Below pale cinnamon, palest on throat (or white, washed cinnamon, 1).

Range. Mexico southward to western Ecuador. Western Venezuela.

Colombia. Forest. Entire Pacific coast eastward to the Atrato and upper Sinú Valleys *(cinnamomeus)*. The Caribbean coast region from the lower Sinú eastward to the lower Cauca and lower and middle Magdalena Valleys, and the Catatumbo lowlands (1, *magdalenae*).

34. WHITE-WINGED BECARD
(Pachyramphus polychopterus)
Plate VIII

Description. 6 - 6½". Crown black, the feathers tipped with shiny blue-black. Back shiny black (or with collar around hindneck, rump and upper tail-coverts gray, 1; or only rump and upper tail-coverts gray, 2). Wings black, wing-coverts and inner remiges broadly edged white. Tail much rounded, black with broad white tips. Under surface black (or pale gray, 1, 2; or dark gray, 3). ♀: Upper surface olive to olive brown; under surface pale yellow. Wings and tail dark brown. Wing-coverts and inner remiges broadly edged buff to ochraceous; tail with a subterminal black bar and ochraceous tip, broadest on outer tail-feathers.

Range. Guatemala southward to Venezuela, the Guianas, Brazil, Argentina and Bolivia. Trinidad and Tobago.

Colombia. Forest and forest edge. Tropical and subtropical zones. Caribbean coast from the western and southern Santa Marta region to the lower Magdalena and río Sinú regions (2, *cinereiventris*). Western slope of the Eastern Andes in Cundinamarca westward through the Central and Western Andes to the Pacific slope of Nariño (1, *dorsalis*). East of the Eastern Andes in Meta southeastward to Vaupés *(niger);* in Caquetá *(tenebrosus);* in Norte de Santander, Boyacá and Vichada, (3, *tristis*).

35. BLACK-CAPPED BECARD
(Pachyramphus marginatus)

Description. 5½ - 5¾". ♂: Crown black, the feathers tipped with shiny blue-black. Mantle mixed gray and black; rump and upper tail-coverts gray. Wings black, the wing-coverts and inner remiges margined white. Below pale gray. Tail black, tipped white. ♀: Forecrown rufous, hindcrown blackish, the feathers broadly tipped with rufous. Back, sides of head and neck, and breast olive. Throat and center of underparts pale yellow. Wings black, wing-coverts and inner remiges margined ochraceous. Central tail-feathers olive brown, outer ones black, all tipped ochraceous.

Range. The Guianas and Venezuela southward to southeastern Brazil, Ecuador, Peru and Bolivia.

Colombia. Forest. Tropical zone east of the Eastern Andes from southern Meta southward and eastward *(nanus).*

36. BLACK-AND-WHITE BECARD
(Pachyramphus albogriseus)

Description. 5¾ - 6¼". ♂: Crown and nape glossy blue-black, eyebrow white. Back, sides of head and neck gray. Breast pale gray; belly and under tail-coverts white. Wings black, wing-coverts and inner remiges margined with white. Central tail-feathers gray with a broad subterminal black band and white tip, rest black tipped white, the outermost feathers with the basal portion of the outer web white. ♀: Crown dull chestnut brown surrounded by black. Lores and eye-ring white, sides of head gray; throat whitish, otherwise like No. 34.

Range. Nicaragua to western Ecuador, northern Venezuela, eastern Ecuador, northern Peru.

Colombia. Forest. Tropical zone. East slope of the Eastern Andes *(albogriseus).* Santa Marta Mts. *(coronatus).* Eastern base of the Andes in Nariño *(salvini).*

37. ONE-COLORED BECARD
(Platypsaris homochrous)

Description. 7¼ - 7¾". ♂: Upperparts, wings and tail gray, crown darker; base of scapulars white. Below uniform gray much paler than back. ♀: Upperparts, wings and tail cinnamon-rufous; lower parts cinnamon buff.

Range. Eastern Panama. Northwestern Venezuela, western Ecuador, northwestern Peru.

Colombia. Scrub. Tropical zone. Caribbean coast and the lower Magdalena Valley *(canescens)*. From the Gulf of Urabá and the Sinú Valley southward to Remedios and eastward to the west bank of the middle Magdalena *(quimarinus)*. Atrato Valley and Pacific coast south to the lower río San Juan *(homochrous)*.

38. LESSER BECARD
(Platypsaris minor)

Description. 7½ - 8". ♂: Upperparts, wings and tail glossy black; remiges and scapulars white basally. A rose red patch on the lower throat, rest of underparts dark gray. ♀: Crown, nape and back gray, becoming rufous-chestnut on lower back; underparts dark cinnamon buff. Upper tail-coverts, tail and wings chestnut.

Range. Venezuela and the Guianas southward to eastern Brazil and westward to Ecuador, Peru and Bolivia.

Colombia. Forest. Tropical zone east of the Eastern Andes from Meta southward to Caquetá.

39. BLACK-TAILED TITYRA
(Tityra cayana)

Description. 8½ - 9". ♂: Top and sides of head, chin, wings and tail black. Rest of plumage pale pearl gray (or white tinged gray, 1). Bare skin around eye pink. Basal half of bill pale flesh, distal half black. ♀ like ♂ but back darker gray, with back, throat and chest streaked black.

Range. The Guianas and Venezuela southward through Brazil, to Argentina, Paraguay, Bolivia, Peru and Ecuador.

Colombia. Forest. Tropical zone along the eastern base of the Eastern Andes from Arauca southward to Putumayo (1, *candida*). Vichada and Vaupés to Amazonas *(cayana)*.

40. MASKED TITYRA
(Tityra semifasciata) Plate VIII

Description. 8 - 8¼ " (or 9 - 9½ ", 1). ♂: Forecrown, region round eye, and the chin black. Upperparts pearl gray (or white, 2), lowerparts pale pearl gray to white. Wings black. Tail gray, with a broad subterminal black band (or mostly black, only tip and extreme base gray, 3). Bill dark violet with black tip, bare skin around eye pink. ♀: Top and sides of head brownish gray. Back brownish gray (or brown, 4), upper tail-coverts gray. Below like ♂. Base and tip of tail gray, central portion of tail black.

Range. Mexico southward to western Ecuador. Venezuela and the Guianas southward to southern Brazil, Paraguay, Ecuador, Peru and Bolivia.

Colombia. Forest. Tropical zone. West of the Eastern Andes including Santa Marta but not the upper Magdalena Valley or Nariño (4, *columbiana*). Upper tropical and lower subtropical zones on the east base of the Andes in Meta. The upper Magdalena Valley (1, *fortis*). Tropical zone of western Nariño (2, 3, *nigriceps*).

41. BLACK-CROWNED TITYRA
(Tityra inquisitor)

Description. 7½ - 8". ♂: Lores, crown and nape black. Ear-coverts and below eye white (or black, 1). Back pearl gray, a white band bordering the black of the nape. Below white shaded with pearl gray on breast. Remiges black, basally white on inner webs. Tail grayish white with a broad subterminal black band (or black, the extreme base only gray, 2). Upper mandible black, lower blue-gray. ♀: Forehead and lores rusty white, crown black, cheeks rufous. Back brownish gray slightly streaked dusky on mantle. Wings and tail as in ♂.

Range. Mexico southward to western Ecuador. Venezuela, Dutch and French Guiana, Brazil, Ecuador, Peru, Bolivia, Paraguay and Argentina.

Colombia. Forest. Tropical zone. The Santa Marta region and the Magdalena Valley westward to the Pacific coast *(albi-*

torques). East of the Andes from Arauca and Meta eastward to Vichada (1, 2, *erythrogenys*). Caquetá (2 *buckleyi*).

42. PURPLE-THROATED FRUITCROW
(Querula purpurata)

Description. 11½ - 12¼ ". ♂ : Entirely glossy black except for a broad dark crimson patch on throat. ♀ : Entirely black.

Range. Costa Rica southward to Venezuela, the Guianas, the Amazon Valley, Ecuador, Peru and Bolivia.

Colombia. Forest. Tropical zone. Throughout Colombia in wooded regions, sometimes in the company of toucans.

43. RED-RUFFED FRUITCROW
(Pyroderus scutatus)

Description. 17 - 17½ ". ♂ : Throat, breast and sides of neck reddish orange, the feathers somewhat crimped, shiny and edged with orange-scarlet. Chin and rest of plumage glossy black; breast sometimes with a few spots of chestnut (or breast and upper belly solid chestnut, 1); under wing-coverts chestnut. Feathers of forecrown and lores plush-like. Feathers of nape somewhat elongated. ♀ similar to ♂ but nape feathers shorter.

Range. British Guiana, Venezuela, eastern Ecuador and eastern Peru. Southeastern Brazil, adjacent Paraguay and Argentina.

Colombia. Forest. Upper tropical and subtropical zone. Eastern Andes to the east slope of the Central Andes; in Norte de Santander, Santander, Cundinamarca, Tolima and Huila *(granadensis)*. The Cauca Valley in Antioquia and Valle and the west slope of the Western Andes southward to Nariño (1, *occidentalis*).

44. UMBRELLABIRD
(Cephalopterus ornatus) Fig. 66

Description. 18¾ - 20". ♂ : General plumage black glossed with blue. A tall upstanding crest of silky hair-like feathers springing from the forecrown and overhanging the bill, the shafts basally white (or black, 1). A flat, wide, feathered wattle 3 or 4" long (or round and narrow and up to 11" long, 1), hanging from the lower throat. Feathers of crest, hindneck

and wattle strongly glossed with blue, those of the mantle margined with glossy blue-black. ♀ similar but duller, with smaller crest and wattle.

Range. Southern Venezuela, British Guiana, western Brazil, western and eastern Ecuador, Peru and northern Bolivia.

Colombia. Tall forest trees. The eastern form often on islands in the larger rivers. Tropical zone. East of the Andes from Boyacá southward to Amazonas *(ornatus)*. Upper tropical and subtropical zone of the west slope of the Western Andes from the lower río San Juan southward (1, *penduliger*, probably specifically distinct).

45. BARE-NECKED FRUITCROW
(Gymnoderus foetidus)

Description. 13¾ - 14½ ". ♂ : Crown, hindneck and chin covered by short, dense, plush-like feathers. Neck very sparsely feathered, the bare skin black tinged with blue. Back and under surface black with a grayish powdery bloom. Lesser wing-coverts, outer margins of secondaries and primaries pale silvery gray; greater and median wing-coverts dark silvery gray. Central tail-feathers black, rest grayish. ♀ like ♂, but wings uniform with rest of plumage.

Range. The Guianas, southern Venezuela, Brazil, eastern Ecuador, Peru and Bolivia.

Colombia. Forest. Tropical zone east of the Eastern Andes from Meta and Vichada south to Amazonas.

46. BEARDED BELLBIRD
(Procnias averano)

Description. 10¾ - 11½ ". ♂ : Crown and ear-coverts coffee brown; wings black; rest of plumage grayish white. Throat bare covered with very numerous, string-like black wattles. ♀ : Above olive green. Throat grayish with narrow pale streaks, rest of underparts pale yellow streaked with green, under tail-coverts pale yellow.

Range. Northern Venezuela. British Guiana. Northeastern Brazil. Trinidad.

Colombia. Forest. Tropical zone. Extreme northeastern Colombia in the Sierra de Perijá; possibly the middle Magdalena Valley in Santander *(carnobarba)*.

TYRANT FLYCATCHERS (Tyrannidae)

Fig 67. White-headed Marsh-Tyrant
(Arundinicola leucocephala) p. 271

A very large number of species of flycatcher inhabit Colombia. They represent in the New World the flycatchers *(Muscicapidae)* of the Old. They are found in every type of country from tropical deserts and jungles to the snow-capped peaks of the Andes. Most species are resident but some migrate to Colombia from either North America or southern South America.

In habits they are generally similar to North American flycatchers. The ground-tyrants however, as their name implies, are terrestrial, living at high altitudes on the open, rocky slopes of the Andes; others, such as the water and marsh tyrants, live in swamps and along the banks of streams.

Many flycatchers are dull-colored, nondescript little birds, showing shades of gray, olive or brown. A yellow, orange or red crown patch is characteristic of many species; bright yellow underparts are frequent in the group. Wing-bars are often prominent and crests are not unusual, the latter reaching their greatest development in the royal flycatchers. Bills are often flat and very wide but also may be narrow and pointed. In a few species tails are very long, and among flycatchers the habit of flicking the tail is well known. In most species the sexes are similar.

Song is insignificant in the group, but some species such as the kiskadees produce a loud short call. Flycatchers feed chiefly on insects which they often catch on the wing, the bristles found at the base of the bill helping to guide prey into their mouths. Many of the smaller species search the leaves for insects, much in the manner of vireos and warblers. Fruits are eaten by a number of species. In a family as large and varied as this, nests assume many forms: some are open, cup-shaped and woven with grass; others are domed with side entrances; still others are placed in cavities or woodpeckers' old holes. (154 Col.; 343 S.A.; 365 N.&S.A.; 365 wld.)

267

AID TO IDENTIFICATION

Over 6":

Outer tail-feathers all or mostly white, cinnamon, rufous or chestnut 1, 4, 5, 7, 15, 42, 43, 69E.

Above mostly gray, sandy or brown (with wing-bars) 8, 28, 56; (without wing-bars) 2, 3, 6, 25, 49, 52, 75, 121aE.

Above all or mostly black 13, 14, 22.

Above olive green, below pale yellow, bill flat and wide 76, 80, 81, 83; (chest tawny) 82, 84.

Tail very long, or with a fan-shaped red crest, or with scarlet or pink underparts 14, 18, 21, 70E, 71.

Underparts bright yellow 23, 24, 27, 32, 34, 36, 37, 38E, 39E, 40, 41; (with white throat) 20, 33, 34, 35.

Underparts streaked 26, 29, 30, 31, 124E, 148.

Nondescript: dull olive above, pale grayish to yellowish below (with wing-bars) 53, 56, 76, 115, 121aE, (without wing-bars) 44, 45, 46, 47, 48, 50, 119, 120, 121, 122E, 123, 125, 126, 128.

Under 6":

Above black, or black and white 10, 14, 16, 17, 90E.

Nondescript: above brown, grayish, olive or sandy (with wing-bars) 12, 51, 53, 54, 55E, 68aE, 77, 78E, 88E, 91, 92E, 113, 115, 129, 130, 131, 132, 135, 137, 138, 139; (without wing-bars) 11, 17, 19E, 93, 107, 121, 125, 128, 150.

With a band across breast, or band across rump in contrast to rest of upperparts 9, 58, 59, 60, 61, 62, 63, 64, 101.

Underparts partly or all bright yellow 65, 66, 67, 79, 84, 86E, 103, 106, 108, 114, 118, 129, 147.

Underparts streaked or spotted 68, 85, 94, 99, 148, 149.

Very small with flat, broad stubby bill and short tail 71a, 72, 72a, 73, 74.

Crested 57, 96, 97E, 98E, 109, 110, 111, 133, 141.

Head or cap in contrast to rest of plumage 17, 85, 86E, 87, 89, 90E, 95, 100, 102, 104, 105, 112, 116, 117, 127, 129, 134, 136, 140, 142E, 143E, 144, 145, 146.

1. MOUNTAIN GROUND-TYRANT
(Agriornis montana) Plate XIV

Description. 9¾ - 10". Mostly dark smoky gray, the inner remiges edged paler. Lores and throat white, the latter streaked with blackish. Center of belly and under tail-coverts buffy white. Central tail-feathers like back, the rest white. Thrush-like in appearance. Its loud notes are said to resemble exactly the notes of the North American Olive-sided Flycatcher.

Range. Upper level of the Andes from Ecuador to Patagonia.

Colombia. Open country of the temperate and páramo zones of Nariño (solitaria).

2. ALPINE GROUND-TYRANT
(Muscisaxicola alpina) Plate XIV

Description. 7½ - 8". Forehead, broad supercilium and spot below eye white. Upperparts and wings smoky brown, tinged rufous on crown. Under surface pale gray, lightest on abdomen. Upper tail-coverts and tail blackish brown, the outer tail-feathers narrowly edged white.

Range. The Andes from Ecuador to Bolivia and Chile.

Colombia. Páramo zone. Eastern Andes in Boyacá and Cundinamarca (quesadae). The Central Andes in Tolima and Caldas (columbiana).

3. SPOT-BILLED GROUND-TYRANT
(Muscisaxicola maculirostris)

Description. 6 - 6¼ ". Bill black, base of lower mandible yellow. Eyebrow buffy white. Upperparts and wings pale sandy brown, the wing-coverts edged with cinnamon-buff. Below isabelline. Upper tail-coverts and tail blackish brown, the outer web of the outermost tail-feather white or buff.

Range. The Andes from Ecuador to Bolivia and western Argentina.

Colombia. Temperate zone of the Eastern Andes in Cundinamarca and Boyacá *(niceforoi)*.

4. STREAK-THROATED GROUND-TYRANT
(Myiotheretes striaticollis)

Description. 9¾ - 10". Upperparts dark smoky brown, the feathers obscurely dark centered. Upper tail-coverts edged with rufous. Central tail-feathers blackish brown; rest of tail-feathers cinnamon for ¾ of their length on the inner web with a broad subterminal band of blackish brown; outermost tail-feathers cinnamon also on the outer web. Throat and upper breast white, broadly streaked with black, rest of underparts and under wing-coverts rufous. Remiges brownish black on the outer web, the inner webs for the most part cinnamon, tipped with blackish brown; wing-coverts edged grayish cinnamon.

Range. Western Venezuela southward through the Andes to Bolivia and Argentina.

Colombia. Scrub and open slopes. Temperate, rarely subtropical zone of the Andes and Santa Marta Mts. *(striaticollis)*.

5. RED-RUMPED GROUND-TYRANT
(Cnemarchus erythropygius)

Description. 9¼ - 9¾ ". Forehead white, crown and nape ashy gray, forecrown streaked white. Back dark smoky gray with an olive tinge. Wings black with a large white patch on outer web of innermost feathers. Throat white, streaked with gray. Breast smoky gray, lower breast and abdomen, rump, upper and under tail-coverts orange-rufous. Central tail-feathers black, outer tail-feathers orange-rufous with a broad terminal black band.

Range. The Colombian Andes southward to Bolivia.

Colombia. Scrubby open slopes. Páramo zone of the Santa Marta Mts. *(orinomus)*. Andes of Nariño *(erythropygius)*.

6. SMOKY GROUND-TYRANT
(Ochthodiaeta fumigata)

Description. 8¼ - 8½ ". Dark smoky brown (or dark smoky brown with an olive tinge, 1); lores and inconspicuous eyebrow whitish, throat whitish obscurely streaked. Closed wing like back, wing-coverts pale edged, basal portion of inner webs of remiges and under wing-coverts orange-rufous. Tail dusky brown, the outer web of the outer tail-feathers whitish.

Range. The Andes from northern Venezuela southward to Bolivia.

Colombia. Forest. Temperate, rarely subtropical, zone of the Andes, not Santa Marta *(fumigata)*. The northern extremity of the Perijá Mts. *(1, olivacea)*.

7. SANTA MARTA GROUND-TYRANT
(Ochthodiaeta pernix)

Description. 7¼ - 7½ ". Upperparts dark smoky brown, browner in middle of back. Wings black, wing-coverts, edges of inner remiges and inner webs of remiges ferruginous. Tail blackish, outer rectrix ferruginous. Lores, below eye and throat white, the throat streaked with olive. Breast olive, the feathers dark at center, light at edges, some with ferruginous borders producing a clouded effect; rest of underparts ferruginous.

Range. Colombia.

Colombia. Forest edge and scrub. Temperate zone of the Santa Marta Mts.

8. SMOKE-BROWN CHAT-TYRANT
(Ochthoeca fumicolor)

Description. 6¼ - 6½ ". Upperparts reddish brown. Broad eyebrow white to buffy white. Throat grayish; breast and underparts pale ferruginous (or cinnamon, 1). Wings and tail black, the wing-coverts with a broad double bar of chestnut.

Range. The temperate zone of the Andes from northern and western Venezuela southward to Bolivia.

Colombia. Forest and scrub. Temperate zone. Eastern Andes from Norte de Santander to Cundinamarca (fumicolor). Northern end of the Central and Western Andes in Antioquia (1, ferruginea). Southern portion of the Central and Western Andes and both slopes of the Eastern Andes in Nariño (brunneifrons).

9. RUFOUS-BREASTED CHAT-TYRANT
(Ochthoeca rufipectoralis)

Description. 5¾ - 6". Crown and nape dark smoky brown; broad eyebrow white. Throat grayish, broad band across breast orange-rufous; rest of underparts white (or grayish, 2). Back reddish brown (or crown and nape dark slaty brown, back dark grayish brown, 1). Wings blackish, the wing-coverts broadly edged with rufous, inner remiges narrowly edged with buffy. Tail dark brown, the outer web of the outer rectrix white.

Range. Ecuador southward to Bolivia.

Colombia. Forest edge and scrubby slopes. Upper subtropical and temperate zone. Perijá Mts. at their northern end (rubicundulus). Santa Marta Mts. (2, poliogastra). Eastern Andes from Norte de Santander to Cundinamarca (1, rufopectus). Central and Western Andes including Nariño where it occurs on both slopes (1, obfuscata).

10. SLATY-BACKED CHAT-TYRANT
(Ochthoeca cinnamomeiventris)
Plate XVI

Description. 5¼ - 5½". Slaty black. Line above lores and under wing-coverts white. Lower breast and belly deep chestnut. ♀ differs only in having black portions of the plumage slightly grayer.

Range. The Andes from northern and western Venezuela southward to Bolivia.

Colombia. Forest. Subtropical zone to temperate zone of the three Andes ranges and Nariño (cinnamomeiventris).

11. CROWNED CHAT-TYRANT
(Ochthoeca frontalis)

Description. 5¼ - 5½". Forehead, joining long eyebrow, white (or forehead yellow, eyebrow white, 1). Lores and around the eye black. Crown dark smoky brown. Back, wings and tail earthy brown. Underparts pale gray; under tail-coverts deep buff.

Range. The Andes from Ecuador southward to Bolivia.

Colombia. Temperate zone. Eastern Andes in Cundinamarca (albidiadema). Central Andes southward to Nariño (1, frontalis).

12. YELLOW-BELLIED CHAT-TYRANT
(Ochthoeca diadema)

Description. 4¾ - 5". Forehead and long eyebrow yellow. Lores black. Crown and nape blackish; hindneck olive; back olive brown, becoming tinged with rufescent on lower back, rump and upper tail-coverts (or becoming reddish brown on these parts, 1). Wings and tail dusky, the wing-coverts and inner remiges edged with rusty rufous. Throat and breast olive, more yellowish on throat; abdomen yellow.

Range. The Andes from western Venezuela to northern Peru.

Colombia. Forest and clearings. Subtropical to temperate zone. Santa Marta Mts. (jesupi). Sierra de Perijá (1, rubellula). Eastern Andes from Norte de Santander to Cundinamarca (diadema). Central and Western Andes and Nariño where it occurs on both slopes (gratiosa).

13. BLACK PHOEBE
(Sayornis nigricans)

Description. 7¼ - 7½" Sooty black, grayer on lower back and upper and under tail-coverts. Wing-coverts and remiges margined with white. Tail sooty black, outer web of outermost tail-feathers and center of abdomen white. Flicks tail.

Range. Western United States southward to Panama. Northern Venezuela southward to Ecuador, Peru, Bolivia and Argentina.

Colombia. Forest and scrub, usually near water. Tropical and subtropical zones, rarely lower temperate zones of the Andes and Santa Marta Mts. Not recorded from Nariño (angustirostris).

14. LONG-TAILED TYRANT
(Colonia colonus) Plate XIV

Description. 5½ - 5¾ " (including tail, up to 10¾"). Central tail-feathers narrow, very long, protruding up to 5" beyond rest of the tail. General plumage black, (or with a white band down the back, 1). Forehead, lores and eyebrow white, crown and nape gray, the feathers with dark centers (or crown and nape smoky brown margined posteriorly by gray, 1). Small patch on rump grayish white.

Range. Honduras southward to western Ecuador. Eastern Venezuela, and the Guianas. Ecuador, Peru, Bolivia, Paraguay, western and southern Brazil, Argentina.

Colombia. Forest and scrub. Likes tall, dead trees. Eastern base of the Eastern Andes from Meta southward to Putumayo *(fuscicapilla)*. Tropical, occasionally subtropical, zone west of the Eastern Andes except Santa Marta (1, *leuconota*).

15. RUFOUS-TAILED TYRANT
(Knipolegus poecilurus)

Description. 6 - 6¼". Upperparts smoky gray, wing-coverts like back, pale edged forming a double bar; inner webs of remiges rusty buff. Throat and breast grayish, patch on lower throat, abdomen and under tail-coverts fawn. Central tail-feathers dusky, remainder with most of the inner web cinnamon. Iris red.

Range. British Guiana, Venezuela southward through the Andes to Bolivia,

Colombia. Forest border. Subtropical and temperate zone of the Andes including Nariño. Not Santa Marta *(poecilurus)*.

16. PIED WATER-TYRANT
(Fluvicola pica) Plate XIV

Description. 5½ - 5¾". White. Hindcrown, nape, middle of back, wings and tail black. Inner remiges margined and tail tipped with white. Young birds have the back brown. Bill black.

Range. Eastern Panama. The Guianas, Venezuela, Brazil, Ecuador, Peru, Bolivia, Paraguay and Argentina. Trinidad.

Colombia. Marshes and streams of the tropical zone throughout the country except the Pacific coast and Nariño *(pica)*.

17. WHITE-HEADED MARSH-TYRANT
(Arundinicola leucocephala) Fig. 67

Description. 5¼ - 5½". ♂: Whole head white, rest of plumage black. ♀: Forehead, lores, forecrown, sides of head and underparts white. Upperparts and wings pale grayish brown. Tail black. Upper mandible black, lower mandible yellow. Rather like the young of No. 16 but bill differently colored, lower mandible yellow instead of black.

Range. Venezuela, the Guianas, central and southern Brazil, eastern Bolivia, Paraguay and northern Argentina. Trinidad.

Colombia. Scrub. Swampy portions of the Caribbean coast. The Magdalena Valley and llanos del Meta.

18. VERMILION FLYCATCHER
(Pyrocephalus rubinus)

Description. 5½ - 5¾". ♂: Crown and underparts scarlet. Lores, ear-coverts, back, wings and tail dark smoky brown (or blackish brown, 1). Margins of inner remiges and wing-coverts and outer web of outer tail-feathers white. ♀: Above pale smoky brown. Underparts white, breast and upper belly streaked with grayish brown (or crown tinged scarlet, throat and upper breast white, the latter streaked with grayish brown; lower breast and rest of under surface pinkish scarlet, 1; or throat, breast and center of abdomen white, the breast finely streaked with grayish brown; rest of underparts salmon pink, 2).

Range. Southwestern United States, southward throughout Mexico to Nicaragua. Western Ecuador, western Peru and Chile. Southern Venezuela, British Guiana and northern Brazil. Eastern Ecuador, eastern Peru, southern Brazil, Uruguay, Paraguay, northern Argentina and eastern Bolivia.

Colombia. Open dry scrub and woodland clearings. Tropical zone. Eastern base of the Santa Marta Mts., the extreme northern tip of the Department of Magdalena southward to Norte de Santander (1, *saturatus*). The rest of Colombia west of the Andes (2, *piurae*). East of the Andes in Caquetá *(rubinus)*.

PLATE XIV

TORRENT TYRANNULET
(*Serpophaga c. cinerea*)
Page 291

TUFTED TIT-LIKE
TYRANT
(*Anairetes parulus
aequatorialis*)
Page 290

APICAL FLYCATCHER
(*Myiarchus apicalis*)
Page 278

WHITE-CRESTED
ELAENIA
(*Elaenia albiceps
griseogularis*)
Page 292

YELLOW-THROATED
SPADEBILL
(*Platyrinchus
f. flavigularis*)
Page 282

FORK-TAILED
FLYCATCHER
(*Muscivora tyran-
nus monachus*)
Page 273

STREAKED FLYCATCHER
(*Myiodynastes macu-
latus solitarius*)
Page 275

SIRYSTES
(*Sirystes sibi-
lator albogriseus*)
Page 274

LONG-TAILED TYRANT
(*Colonia colonus
fuscicapilla*)
Page 271

MOUNTAIN
GROUND-TYRANT
(*Agriornis montana*)
Page 268

PIED WATER-TYRANT
(*Fluvicola p. pica*)
Page 271

ALPINE
GROUND-TYRANT
(*Muscisaxicola
alpina quesadae*)
Page 268

E.L.Poole

19. DRAB WATER-TYRANT
(Ochthornis littoralis)

Description. 5½ - 6″. General plumage pale sandy brown, wings and tail darker; throat whitish. Lores, eyebrow and narrow line below eye white.

Range. The Guianas and Venezuela southward to central Brazil, eastern Ecuador, Peru and Bolivia.

Colombia. River banks. Tropical zone east of the Andes from Meta southward.

20. FIRE-CROWNED TYRANT
(Machetornis rixosa) Plate XV

Description. 7¾ - 8¼″. ♂: Above pale sandy grayish with a greenish cast becoming rufescent on rump and upper tail-coverts; wings and tail somewhat darker. A concealed crown patch fiery orange. Below bright yellow, clouded on breast with sandy; under wing-coverts bright yellow. Tail pale tipped. ♀ differs by lacking the crown spot.

Range. Venezuela. Southern Brazil, Paraguay, Uruguay, Argentina and Bolivia.

Colombia. Open woods, pasturelands. Tropical zone. Sinú Valley eastward to the Guajira Peninsula. Lower Magdalena Valley and east of the Andes southward to the llanos del Meta *(flavigularis)*.

21. FORK-TAILED FLYCATCHER
(Muscivora tyrannus) Plate XIV

Description. Whole length up to 16″. Tail very long, 11″, much graduated, longer in ♂ than in ♀. Crown, nape and sides of head black with a concealed bright yellow crest. Back pale gray, rump and upper tail-coverts and tail black, the outer tail-feathers white on the outer web for the basal half. Wings dusky, inner remiges edged with gray. Entire underparts white.

The various races are distinguishable chiefly by the emargination of the outer primaries. Outer primaries notched near tip (1); nearly normal (2); deeply notched (3).

Range. Mexico southward through Central America over virtually all of South America, south to Patagonia and the

Falkland Islands. Trinidad. Accidental in North America. Birds from southern South America migrate to northern South America.

Colombia. Savanna and scrub. Tropical to temperate zone. Summer visitor, March to October in most of Colombia east of the Andes and west of them in Magdalena, Norte de Santander and Cundinamarca (1, *tyrannus*). Resident on the Caribbean coast from Bolívar to Magdalena (2, *sanctaemartae*). Resident in tropical and lower subtropical zones south of the range of *sanctaemartae* and east of the Andes in Meta (3, *monachus*).

22. EASTERN KINGBIRD
(Tyrannus tyrannus)

Description. 8 - 8¾″. Crown, nape, sides of head blackish with a concealed fiery orange crest. Back dark gray. Upper tail-coverts black margined with white. Wings including wing-coverts blackish, the feathers pale edged. Below snowy white, clouded on breast with gray. Tail black conspicuously tipped white.

Range. Breeds in North America. Winters from southern Mexico south to Bolivia.

Colombia. Migrant. Recorded both east and west of the Andes in March, April, May and September, October.

23. SNOWY-THROATED KINGBIRD
(Tyrannus niveigularis)

Description. 7¾ - 8″. Crown and nape pale gray with a large semi-concealed yellow patch on center of crown; sides of head blackish. Back gray, strongly shaded with olive. Wings brownish black, the wing-coverts and inner remiges margined with pale ashy. Throat white, shading to gray on breast, rest of underparts clear yellow. Upper tail-coverts and tail black.

Range. Western Ecuador, northwest Peru.

Colombia. Tropical zone of southwestern Nariño.

24. TROPICAL KINGBIRD
(Tyrannus melancholicus) Plate XV

Description. 8½ - 9½″. Upperparts, wing and tail much as in No. 23, but crest orange instead of yellow. Throat gray becoming olive green on breast, rest of underparts deep golden yellow. Tail slightly forked.

Range. Texas southward to Venezuela and the Guianas, southeastern Brazil, Bolivia, Argentina, Paraguay and Uruguay. Grenada, Tobago, Trinidad, Margarita Island, the Dutch West Indies.

Colombia. Open woods, plantations, gardens. Tropical to temperate zone. Caribbean coast region, lower Magdalena Valley and the Santa Marta Mts. (chloronotus). Rest of Colombia east and west of the Andes (melancholicus).

25. GRAY KINGBIRD
(Tyrannus dominicensis)

Description. 9 - 9½". Above gray; a concealed orange yellow patch on crown. Wings and tail sepia brown, the wing-coverts and inner remiges margined with whitish. Below white, the breast slightly clouded with gray. Tail slightly forked.

Range. Southern United States southward through Central America and the islands of the Caribbean to Venezuela. Trinidad.

Colombia. Open woods. Winter visitor (October-May), but some may breed. Tropical zone. Northern and western Colombia southward on the east to Meta and on the west to the río San Juan (dominicensis).

26. VARIEGATED FLYCATCHER
(Empidonomus varius) Plate XV

Description. 7½ - 8". Crown and nape brown encircled by a broad white line and with a concealed golden yellow patch in center. Broad stripe through eye blackish, bordered below by a broad whitish line. Back dark brown, the feathers margined with whitish giving a streaked appearance. Wings dark brown, the greater wing-coverts and inner remiges broadly margined with white, the lesser wing-coverts margined with rufous. Sides of throat and breast dusky, center of throat whitish. Breast and underparts creamy yellow, the breast and flanks streaked with blackish. Tail and upper tail-coverts blackish, the feathers margined with chestnut.

Range. The Guianas and Venezuela. Eastern and southern Brazil, Paraguay, Bolivia and Argentina. Eastern Peru. Trinidad.

Colombia. Open woodlands and clearings. Probably a migrant (April to August) from the south. Tropical zone east of the Andes from Boyacá southward (varius).

27. PIRATIC FLYCATCHER
(Legatus leucophaius) Plate XV

Description. 6 - 6¾". Bill broad and stubby. Crown dark brown surrounded by a broad white line; concealed spot in center of crown pale yellow to orange yellow. Stripe through eye blackish, bordered below by a white line, the white line narrowly bordered below by dusky. Back dark olive brown, the feathers inconspicuously edged paler. Wings dark brown, wing-coverts and inner remiges edged paler. Throat white, breast yellowish white becoming yellow on sides of body, abdomen and under tail-coverts, streaked and clouded on breast, and streaked on sides with dusky. Upper tail-coverts and tail-feathers olive brown edged reddish brown.

Range. Mexico southward to Venezuela, the Guianas, Paraguay, Bolivia and Argentina. Trinidad.

Colombia. Llanos, open woodland, often near small streams; tall isolated trees. Tropical and lower subtropical zones including Nariño (leucophaius).

28. SIRYSTES
(Sirystes sibilator) Plate XIV

Description. 7¾ - 8¼". Crown and nape black. Back pale gray with a faint greenish yellow wash (or pale gray, 1). Rump white; upper tail-coverts gray (or blackish, 1) margined paler. Wings black, wing-coverts broadly edged with greenish white, inner remiges with white (or wing-coverts narrowly edged cinereous, 1). Underparts white, the throat and breast washed with gray. Tail black, the feathers tipped with white (or uniform black, 1). Young birds have the back white and the wing-coverts margined with cinnamon.

Range. Eastern Panama. East of the Andes from western Venezuela and eastern Ecuador southward to western and southeastern Brazil, Paraguay and Argentina.

Colombia. Forest. Tropical zone. Extreme northwestern Colombia (albogriseus). East of the Andes in Meta (1, albocinereus).

29. SULPHUR-BELLIED FLYCATCHER
(Myiodynastes luteiventris)

Description. 8¾ - 9¼ ". Forehead and eyebrow white, streaked with black; crown brown, narrowly streaked black, with a concealed yellow patch. Stripe through eye black, bordered below by a broad white line. Back sandy brown broadly streaked dusky, upper tail-coverts and tail chestnut, the tail-feathers with central dark shaft stripes. Sides of throat blackish, center of throat white finely streaked black. Underparts yellow, the breast and flanks broadly streaked blackish.

Range. Breeds from southern Arizona to Costa Rica. Winters in western South America, mostly in Peru and Bolivia.

Colombia. Forest edge, plantations, clearings. Transient (October) in the tropical zone both east and west of the Andes *(luteiventris.)*

30. STREAKED FLYCATCHER
(Myiodynastes maculatus) Plate XIV

Description. 8¾ - 9¼ " (or 9¼ - 9½ ", 1). Very like No. 29. Differs by not having a pale forehead; lores and streak through eye blacker, crown more rufescent and lower parts much whiter, less yellow (or quite different. Above blackish streaked white. Throat white, rest of underparts pale yellow, boldly streaked with black. Upper tail-coverts margined with rufous. Tail dusky narrowly edged rufous, 1).

Range. Mexico southward to Venezuela, the Guianas, Argentina, Brazil, Paraguay, Uruguay and Bolivia. Trinidad and Tobago.

Colombia. Pastures, clearings, thin woodland. Tropical zone. West slope of the Perijá Mts., Santa Marta region, extreme lower Magdalena Valley and the Caribbean coastal region *(nobilis)*. Pacific coast north of the Baudó Mts. *(difficilis)*. South of the Baudó Mts. *(chapmani)*. Migrant from the south (April, May, July, December) ; recorded from the temperate zone of the Central Andes and east of the Andes from Meta southward and eastward (1, *solitarius*).

31. GOLDEN-CROWNED FLYCATCHER
(Myiodynastes chrysocephalus)

Description. 8¼ - 9". Crown and nape dark gray, crown with a concealed golden yellow patch. Eyebrow white, stripe through eye dusky, bordered below by a buffy white line, this bordered below by a dusky line. Back olive, upper tail-coverts edged with rufous. Wings dark brown, wing-coverts and outer remiges edged with rufous, the inner remiges with white. Chin white, throat pale fawn, dusky at sides; rest of underparts yellow, tinged on breast with fawn and obscurely streaked on breast with dusky. Tail dark brown, edged with rufous.

Range. Costa Rica southward to western Venezuela, Ecuador, Peru and Bolivia.

Colombia. Dense forest. Upper tropical and subtropical zone. Santa Marta Mts. *(intermedius)*. Eastern, Central and Western Andes and Nariño. East of the Andes in Meta and Nariño *(minor)*.

32. BOAT-BILLED FLYCATCHER
(Megarynchus pitangua) Plate XVI

Description. 9¼ - 9¾ ". Bill broad, flat. Crown blackish surrounded by a broad white line and with a concealed yellow orange central patch. Upperparts olive. Remiges brown, edged rufescent; wing-coverts plain olive brown (or edged rufescent, 1). Throat white, rest of underparts bright yellow. Tail olive brown (or olive brown, feathers edged rufescent, 1).

Range. Mexico south through Central America to Venezuela, the Guianas, Brazil, Ecuador, Peru, Bolivia, Paraguay and Argentina. Trinidad.

Colombia. Clearings, forest edge. Extreme northwestern Colombia *(mexicanus)*. Caribbean coast and Magdalena Valley south to Huila. East of the Andes from their base to Vichada and Amazonas (1, *pitangua*).

33. LEMON-BROWED FLYCATCHER
(Conopias cinchoneti) Plate XV

Description. 7 - 7½ ". Upperparts, sides of head, wings and tail olive green. Forehead, long broad eyebrow and entire underparts yellow.

Range. Ecuador and Peru.

Colombia. Forest. Upper tropical and subtropical zone of the Andes, not Santa Marta (icterophrys).

34. WHITE-RINGED FLYCATCHER
(Coryphotriccus parvus) Plate XV

Description. 6½ - 7". Crown dark brown, with a central yellow patch, the crown encircled by a very broad white band, sides of head and neck blackish. Back dull olive. Throat white (or yellow, 1), rest of underparts yellow. Wings and tail dark brown, innermost remiges pale edged.

Range. Eastern Costa Rica to western Ecuador. British and French Guiana, southern Venezuela and northern Brazil.

Colombia. Forest. Tropical zone of the Pacific coast southward to Nariño (albovittatus). East of the Andes in Vaupés (1, parvus).

35. RUSTY-MARGINED FLYCATCHER
(Myiozetetes cayanensis) Plate XVI

Description. 6 ¾ - 7½". Bill relatively small for this type of flycatcher. Forehead, long eyebrow and throat white. Long central crown patch orange to yellow, bordered on each side by a broad blackish band; sides of head blackish. Back dull olive. Underparts bright yellow. Wings and tail hair brown, the feathers inconspicuously (or conspicuously, 1) margined with rufous.

Range. Eastern Panama to western Ecuador. Venezuela, the Guianas, eastern and southern Brazil and northeastern Bolivia.

Colombia. Clearings and edges of woodland; sometimes wooded shores of streams and lakes. Tropical and lower subtropical zone. West of the Andes (hellmayri). East of the Andes from Norte de Santander to Meta and eastward to Vichada and Vaupés (1, rufipennis).

36. VERMILION-CROWNED FLYCATCHER
(Myiozetetes similis)

Description. 7 - 7½". Rather similar to No. 35 but differs by having the crown and sides of head dark ashy gray; central crown patch vermilion; the wings without any rufous and wing-coverts pale edged.

Range. Mexico southward to Bolivia and southeastern Brazil.

Colombia. Open country; sometimes banks of wooded streams. Tropical zone. Caribbean coast and Magdalena Valley (columbianus). East of the Andes from Norte de Santander southward to Putumayo and eastward to Vichada (similis).

37. GRAY-CAPPED FLYCATCHER
(Myiozetetes granadensis)

Description. 7 - 7½". Very similar to No. 36. ♂: Differs principally by lacking the white eyebrow. ♀: Lacks white eyebrow and the orange crown patch.

Range. Nicaragua to western Eucador. Southern Venezuela, eastern Ecuador, western Brazil, Peru and northern Bolivia.

Colombia. Pasturelands. Tropical zone. Pacific coast eastward to northern Bolívar and Atlántico (occidentalis). East of the Eastern Andes in Meta (obscurior).

38. DUSKY-CHESTED FLYCATCHER
(Myiozetetes luteiventris)

Description. 6 - 6½". ♂: Upperparts, wings and tail dark olive brown. Forehead dark gray, concealed crown patch orange. Throat grayish white. Underparts yellow, the breast clouded with olive. Wings and tail hair brown. Bill very short and stubby. ♀ similar to ♂, but lacking the crown patch.

Range. Southern Venezuela, eastern Ecuador, northeastern Peru and northwestern Brazil. Dutch Guiana.

Colombia. Tropical zone in Putumayo (luteiventris).

39. SULPHURY FLYCATCHER
(Tyrannopsis sulphurea) Plate XV

Description. 7½ - 7¾". Crown, nape, sides of head and neck dark ashy gray; a concealed yellow crown patch. Back dull olive. Wings and tail hair brown. Throat and upper breast soiled white, sides of breast gray, rest of lower parts bright yellow. Sides of neck and breast clouded with olive gray. Bill broad and short.

Range. Southern Venezuela, Ecuador, northern Brazil and Peru. Trinidad.

Colombia. Forest. Tropical zone east of the Andes in Meta.

40. GREAT KISKADEE
(Pitangus sulphuratus) Plate XV

Description. 9 - 9½". Crown and sides of head black, the crown encircled by a broad white band. A large, somewhat concealed yellow crest. Back earthy brown (or rufous-brown, 1). Throat white, rest of underparts bright yellow. Wings and tail dark brown, the outer webs of remiges rufous (or wing-coverts and remiges broadly edged rufous, tail-feathers edged with rufous, 2).

Range. Texas southward to northwestern Panama. Venezuela, and the Guianas southward through Brazil to eastern Ecuador, Peru, Bolivia, Paraguay, Uruguay and Argentina. Trinidad.

Colombia. City parks, banks of streams and ponds, open woodland and scrub. Tropical zone. Eastern Caribbean coast and lower Magdalena Valley (1, 2, *rufipennis*). Western Caribbean coast, Cauca and middle and upper Magdalena Valleys (2, *caucensis*). East of the Andes in Meta *(trinitatis)*. In Caquetá *(sulphuratus)*.

41. LESSER KISKADEE
(Pitangus lictor)

Description. 7½ - 8 " (or 8-8¼", 1). Very similar in color to the brown-backed forms of No. 40, but much smaller, and with a much narrower bill, and the back slightly tinged olive.

Range. Panama to Venezuela, the Guianas, Brazil, eastern Ecuador, Peru and Bolivia.

Colombia. Open woodlands near streams and lakes. Tropical zone. Caribbean coast region from the Panama border to Santa Marta *(panamensis)*. Eastern base of the Andes from Norte de Santander southward to the Amazon *(1, lictor)*.

Myiarchus

The genus *Myiarchus* is composed of a group of flycatchers very similar to each other in appearance and difficult to tell apart. The head is more or less crested, the throat and breast is pale gray, the abdomen and under tail-coverts pale yellow. The upperparts are usually uniform dull olive brown to olive, the wing-coverts pale edged. The tail in most Colombian species is dusky olive brown. In the following descriptions only the distinguishing characters will be given.

42. GREAT CRESTED FLYCATCHER
(Myiarchus crinitus)

Description. 8 - 9". Edges to primaries and inner webs of all but central rectrices orange-rufous.

Range. Breeds in Canada and the United States. Winters from Florida and Mexico southward to Colombia.

Colombia. Winter resident, November to May, west of the Eastern Andes *(crinitus and boreus)*.

43. BROWN-CRESTED FLYCATCHER
(Myiarchus tyrannulus)

Description. 8½ - 9¼". Very similar to No. 42 but with much less rufous in the tail.

Range. Southwestern United States to Costa Rica. The Lesser Antilles and islands of the southern Caribbean. Venezuela and the Guianas southward to south-central Brazil, Paraguay, and Argentina. Trinidad and Tobago.

Colombia. Pastures, thickets and clearings. Tropical zone. Caribbean coast from southwestern Bolívar eastward. The eastern base of the Andes from Norte de Santander to Meta *(tyrannulus)*.

44. SWAINSON'S FLYCATCHER
(Myiarchus swainsoni)

Description. 7¾ - 8½". Distinguished from other species by the rather pale instead of black bill. Dark (or light, 1) olive brown above, paler on throat and breast; crown sooty (or brownish olive, 1); no rufous in tail or wings.

Range. Venezuela and British Guiana southward to Paraguay, Argentina, Uruguay, and southern Brazil. Birds breeding in the southern parts of the range migrate to northern South America. Trinidad.

Colombia. Forest. Migrant from the south. Recorded in June from the Caquetá region *(1, ferocior)*. Recorded from Bogotá in May *(swainsoni)*.

45. SHORT-CRESTED FLYCATCHER
(Myiarchus ferox)

Description. 7¾-8¼". Very similar to No. 44 but bill black.

Range. Costa Rica southward to Venezuela, the Guianas, and through eastern Brazil to Paraguay, Argentina and westward to eastern Bolivia. Trinidad and Tobago.

Colombia. Open woods, savannas. Tropical zone. West of the Andes on the Pacific coast *(audens)*. The Caribbean coast *(panamensis.)* The Guajira Peninsula *(venezuelensis)*. East of the Andes in Arauca *(brunnescens)*; in Meta *(australis)*; in Caquetá and Vaupés *(ferox)*.

46. PALE-EDGED FLYCATCHER
(Myiarchus cephalotes)

Description. 7¾ - 8½". Distinguishable from the other species by the pale outer web (but not tip) of the outermost tailfeathers and broader, whitish wing edgings. Resembles closely the cotinga *Rhytipterna immunda* (See page 262, No. 24).

Range. Northern Venezuela. Ecuador, Peru and Bolivia.

Colombia. Forest. Subtropical zone. Slopes above the middle and upper Cauca of the middle and upper Magdalena Valleys *(caucae)*. East of the Andes in southeastern Nariño *(cephalotes)*.

47. APICAL FLYCATCHER
(Myiarchus apicalis) Plate XIV

Description. 8¼ - 8¾". Distinguishable from the other species by having the rectrices, except the central pair, broadly tipped with whitish.

Range. Colombia.

Colombia. Scrub. Arid tropical and subtropical zones of the upper Patía and Dagua Valleys eastward to western slope of the Eastern Andes.

48. DUSKY-CAPPED FLYCATCHER
(Myiarchus tuberculifer)

Description. 6¼ - 7". Distinguishable by its small size and black (or mouse gray, 1; or dusky brown, 2) crown, contrasting with the olive green back. Margins of remiges rufescent.

Range. Mexico southward through Central America to western Ecuador.

Colombia. Plantations and woodland in arid or moist regions. Tropical and subtropical zones. Caribbean coast from northern Córdoba to the Santa Marta region (1, *pallidus*). Northwest coast from the Darién Mts., lower Atrato and Sinú Valleys to the upper Cauca Valley (2, *brunneiceps*). West coast from Baudó Mts. and upper Atrato southward to Nariño *(nigriceps)*. East slope of the Eastern Andes from Meta south to Caquetá. Perhaps the upper Magdalena Valley *(tuberculifer)*.

49. OLIVE-SIDED FLYCATCHER
(Nuttallornis borealis)

Description. 7¼ - 8". Above olive gray somewhat crested, darkest on crown. Eyering white. Wings and tail dark brown, wing-coverts pale edged, inner remiges edged white. Throat, center of abdomen white, sharply defined, center of breast streaked dusky. Sides of breast and body olive gray, somewhat streaked dusky. Maxilla black, mandible pale brownish. A rather chunky species with large bill.

Range. Breeds in northern North America. Winters from Colombia and Venezuela southward to Peru. Trinidad.

Colombia. Pasturelands and woods. Winter resident, late August to May. Tropical to temperate zone.

50. WOOD PEWEE
(Contopus virens)

Description. 6 - 6½". Eye-ring whitish. Above grayish olive, to brownish gray, wings and tail darker, the wing-coverts, edged with grayish forming two wingbars, inner remiges with whitish. Throat white, abdomen yellowish white, breast and sides of body pale brownish gray.

Range. Breeds in North America. Winters southward to Venezuela, Ecuador Peru and Bolivia.

Colombia. Forest. Winter resident from tropical to temperate zone, September to the end of April *(virens, veliei, peninsulae* and probably *amplus)*. Recorded as breeding in Chocó *(sordidulus)*.

51. TROPICAL PEWEE
(Contopus cinereus)

Description. 5 - 5½". Very similar to No. 50 but smaller. Wing-bars usually whiter. A rather conspicuous whitish spot before the eye.

Range. Mexico southward to Venezuela, the Guianas, southern Brazil, Ecuador, Peru, Argentina and Bolivia. Trinidad.

Colombia. Brushland. Tropical, occasionally to lower temperature zone of eastern Colombia from Santa Marta Mts. southward through the Eastern Andes to Caquetá (bogotensis).

52. GREATER PEWEE
(Contopus fumigatus) Plate XV

Description. 7 - 7½". Uniform dark slaty gray, somewhat paler below. Crown blackish, somewhat crested. Wings and tail dusky brown, the wing-coverts edged dark gray.

Range. Southwestern United States southward through Central America to Venezuela southward through the Andes to Bolivia and Argentina. The form breeding in the United States (Coues' Flycatcher) winters from Mexico to Guatemala.

Colombia. Forest border. Upper tropical to temperate zones of the Andes, not Santa Marta (ardosiacus). Pacific slope of Nariño (zarumae).

53. ACADIAN FLYCATCHER
(Empidonax virescens)

Description. 5½ - 6¼". Eye-ring white. Upperparts dull olive green. Wings and tail dark brown; wing-coverts with two conspicuous yellowish white to buffy white wing-bars; inner remiges conspicuously margined with yellowish white. Throat and center of lower breast white, upper breast clouded with gray; sides of body pale greenish yellow.

Range. Breeds in southern Canada and United States. Winters from Costa Rica to western Venezuela and Ecuador.

Colombia. Forest. Winter resident, October to end of March. Tropical to temperate zone.

54. TRAILL'S FLYCATCHER
(Empidonax traillii)

Description. 5¼ - 6". Differs from No. 53 by brownish back.

Range. Breeds in North America. Winters from Mexico to Venezuela, Ecuador, Peru, Argentina and Bolivia.

Colombia. Thickets and wet brushland. Winter resident, August to end of April. Tropical to temperate zone recorded chiefly west of the Eastern Andes (traillii and brewsteri).

55. EULER'S FLYCATCHER
(Empidonax euleri) Plate XV

Description. 5 - 5¼". Eye-ring white. Above dark olive (or olive brown, 1); wings and tail darker, the wing-coverts with two conspicuous buffy bars, inner remiges margined with buffy white (or buff, 1). Throat and chest olive, throat paler. Lower breast and belly sulphur yellow. Under wing-coverts sulphur yellow (or buff, 1).

Range. Venezuela and the Guianas, Brazil, Ecuador, Peru, Bolivia, Paraguay, Uruguay and Argentina. Grenada, Trinidad.

Colombia. Open woods and clearings. Southern Meta southward to Caquetá (lawrencei). Probably migrant from the south. The Zulia Valley in Norte de Santander (1, bolivianus).

56. FUSCOUS FLYCATCHER
(Cnemotriccus fuscatus)

Description. 6 - 6½". Upperparts, wings and tail dark grayish brown. Double wing-bar clay-color. Lores and narrow eyebrow white. Throat whitish, breast gray, rest of underparts white. There is a color phase in which the upperparts are decidedly brown, the belly sulphur yellow.

Range. The Guianas and Venezuela southward to southeastern Brazil and northern Peru. Trinidad.

Colombia. Open scrub. Tropical zone from Cartagena eastward to Norte de Santander and southward in the Magdalena Valley to Tolima (cabanisi).

57. TUFTED FLYCATCHER
(Mitrephanes phaeocercus)

Description. 5 - 5¼ ". Head crested. Eye-ring pale. Upperparts and sides of head olive green; wings and tail brown, wing-coverts and inner remiges edged pale grayish. Underparts buffy olive, bright canary yellow in center of abdomen.

Range. Mexico south to Central America and northwestern Ecuador. Eastern Peru, northern Bolivia.

Colombia. Forest. Tropical zone of northern Chocó, undoubtedly southward into Nariño *(berlepschi)*. East slope of Mt. Tacarcuna *(eminulus)*.

58. RUDDY-TAILED FLYCATCHER
(Terenotriccus erythrurus) Plate XV

Description. 4 - 4¼ ". Lores and cheeks grayish white. Crown olive gray gradually shading down the back to rufous on the upper tail-coverts. Below tawny ochraceous, throat paler, chin white. Tail orange-rufous. Wings dark brown, inner and under wing-coverts and margins of remiges chestnut-rufous. Bill short.

Range. Guatemala southward through tropical Central America to Venezuela, the Guianas, Brazil, Ecuador, Peru and Bolivia.

Colombia. Forest. Tropical zone. The northwest coast eastward to the Santa Marta region *(fulvigularis)*. The eastern base of the Eastern Andes from Meta southward to Putumayo *(signatus)*. Vaupés *(venezuelensis)*.

59. BLACK-BILLED FLYCATCHER
(Aphanotriccus audax) Plate XVII

Description. 5¼ - 5½ ". Upperparts, wings and tail dull olive green, margins of inner remiges and double wing-bar grayish white. Sides of head grayish, lores and eye-ring white. Chin and throat white, lower breast and belly sulphur yellow. Sides of neck and broad band across breast dull olive.

Range. Eastern Panama.

Colombia. Forest. Tropical zone. Northwestern Colombia in Córdoba. Undoubtedly also occurs in northernmost Chocó.

60. SULPHUR-RUMPED FLYCATCHER
(Myiobius barbatus)

Description. 5 - 5¼ ". Semi-concealed crown patch bright yellow. Upperparts and wings olive. Rump and belly sulphur yellow. Throat white, chest pale olive (or breast and sides of body tawny buff, 1). Under tail-coverts olive brown. Tail black.

Range. Mexico southward through Central America to Venezuela, the Guianas, Ecuador, Peru, Brazil and Bolivia.

Colombia. Forest. Tropical zone. West of the Western Andes (1, *aureatus*). The Lebrija Valley *(semiflavus)*. East of the Eastern Andes in Caquetá, Putumayo and Vaupés *(barbatus)*.

61. TAWNY-BREASTED FLYCATCHER
(Myiobius villosus)

Description. 5¾ - 6". Conceaied golden yellow patch in center of crown. Upper surface dark moss green; rump sulphur yellow. Wings dusky, the feathers edged olive brown. Throat whitish, breast and sides of body dark tawny olive. Center of abdomen pale yellow. Tail black. Rather like No. 60 (1) but considerably larger, duller and darker in color.

Range. East and west Ecuador, eastern Peru, western Bolivia.

Colombia. Forest. Upper tropical and subtropical zones of the Andes from Boyacá westward to Antioquia and southward down the Pacific coast to Nariño *(villosus)*.

62. BLACK-TAILED FLYCATCHER
(Myiobius atricaudus) Plate XVI

Description. 5¼ - 5¾ ". Very similar to No. 60 from east of the Andes but rump and belly bright yellow instead of creamy yellow, and chest washed with brownish olive instead of greenish olive. Yellow of rump reaching the lower back.

Range. Costa Rica southward to Venezuela, the Guianas, northeastern Brazil. Western Ecuador and northern Peru.

Colombia. Forest. Tropical zone west of the Eastern Andes from the lower and middle Magdalena Valley westward to the Pacific coast and southward to the río Dagua *(atricaudus)*.

63. ORNATE FLYCATCHER
(Myiotriccus ornatus) Plate XVI

Description. 5 - 5¼ " (or 4¾ - 5", 1). Crown black with a large concealed yellow patch. A conspicuous white spot before eye. Back dark green, rump and upper tail-coverts golden yellow. Tail blackish, basally rufous (or all rufous, 2). Wings blackish, the inner remiges margined rufescent. Throat and sides of head gray, breast dark green, belly golden yellow.

Range. The Andes of Ecuador and Peru.

Colombia. Forest. Upper tropical and subtropical zone. The western slope of the Eastern Andes and the northern portion of the Central Andes *(ornatus).* Pacific slope of the Western Andes from the upper Atrato southward (1, *stellatus).* Eastern slope of the Eastern Andes in Caquetá (2, *phoenicurus).*

64. CINNAMON FLYCATCHER
(Pyrrhomyias cinnamomea)

Description. 5¼ - 5½ ". Crown and back moss green (or rufous-chestnut, 1), the crown with a large central yellow patch. A band across rump fulvous (or pale rufous, 1), upper tail-coverts and tail black (or rufous-chestnut with an indefinite blackish subterminal band, 1) with pale tips. Remiges blackish, the inner webs of the outer feathers, the outer webs of the inner feathers and a double bar across wing-coverts chestnut. Lower surface rufous, paler on ventral surface.

Range. Northern Venezuela, Peru, Bolivia and northern Argentina.

Colombia. Forest clearings and borders. Subtropical to temperate zone of the Andes, on the east slope from Boyacá southward to eastern Nariño *(pyrrhoptera).* Santa Marta Mts. (1, *assimilis).*

65. FLAVESCENT FLYCATCHER
(Myiophobus flavicans)

Description. 5¼ - 5½ ". ♂ : Above olive green. A concealed yellow or orange crown patch. Stripe above lores dull yellow. Throat pale greenish; breast olive, flammulated with yellow; belly dull yellow. Wing-coverts dusky edged with buff, remiges dusky, the inner ones edged with yellowish buff. Tail dusky, edged with olive. ♀ : Lacks crown patch.

Range. Northern Venezuela. Eastern Ecuador and Peru.

Colombia. Forest. Upper tropical to lower temperate zone of the Andes including southeastern Nariño. *(flavicans).*

66. ORANGE-CRESTED FLYCATCHER
(Myiophobus phoenicomitra)

Description. 5¼ - 5½ ". Differs from No. 65 in being darker green above, much paler yellow below, the crown patch cinnamon-orange often broadly yellow basally, in both sexes.

Range. Eastern and western Ecuador.

Colombia. Tropical zone. Western slope of the Western Andes in Chocó and undoubtedly southward *(litae).*

67. HANDSOME FLYCATCHER
(Myiophobus pulcher) Plate XV

Description. 4¾ - 5". Crown olive tinged gray with a semi-concealed orange patch. Back and tail olive green (or olive brown, 1). Wings dusky, wing-coverts with double band of yellowish buff (or cinnamon-buff, 1). Throat and breast ochre yellow merging into yellow on abdomen (or throat whitish, breast buffy ochraceous, sharply defined from yellow abdomen, 1).

Range. Andes of Ecuador and Peru.

Colombia. Forest. Subtropical zone. Eastern and Central Andes in Cundinamarca, Huila and Tolima (1, *bellus).* Western slope of the Western Andes from the mountains west of Popayán probably southward to Nariño *(pulcher).*

68. BRAN-COLORED FLYCATCHER
(Myiophobus fasciatus)

Description. 5¼ - 5¾ ". Entire upperparts reddish brown (or mouse brown, 1). Line above lores white. A large semi-concealed orange crown patch. Wings and tail dusky, wing-coverts with two pale buff bands. Below white (or buffy, 1), streaked on breast with dusky lines.

Range. From Costa Rica to the Canal Zone. Venezuela, the Guianas, Ecuador,

Peru, Bolivia, Brazil south of the Amazon, Paraguay, Uruguay and northern Argentina. Trinidad.

Colombia. Scrub and clearings. Tropical and subtropical zone. Pacific slope of Nariño (1, *crypterythrus);* the rest of Colombia west of the Eastern Andes *(fasciatus).*

69. CLIFF FLYCATCHER
(Hirundinea ferruginea) Plate XV

Description. 7¾ - 8¼ ". Forehead, forecrown, sides of head and chin mottled dusky and white. Hindcrown, upperparts and central tail-feathers blackish brown. Entire under surface chestnut. Wings long, the feathers mainly chestnut, bordered on outer webs and tip with black. Closed wing black, inner remiges chestnut at base forming a conspicuous wing patch. All but central tail-feathers with the inner web largely chestnut (or tail black, 1).

Range. The Guianas and southern Venezuela southwestward to northern Brazil, Ecuador and Peru.

Colombia. Precipitous ravines, rock faces, canyons. Upper tropical zone on the eastern slope of the Eastern Andes in Meta *(sclateri).* Extreme eastern Colombia in Vaupés (1, *ferruginea).*

70. AMAZONIAN ROYAL FLYCATCHER
(Onychorhynchus coronatus)

Description. 6½ - 7″. Bill flat, rather long. ♂: Remarkably large fan-shaped crest crimson, the feathers tipped with steel blue. Back and wings dull olivaceous brown, the wing-coverts pale tipped, the upper tail-coverts fawn. Throat whitish, rest of underparts fawn, lightly barred on chest with dusky. Tail pale rufous at base and darkening toward tip ♀: Similar but crest deep orange edged with steel blue.

Range. Venezuela and the Guianas, northern Brazil, Ecuador, Peru and Bolivia.

Colombia. Forest. Tropical zone. East of the Eastern Andes from Meta to Vaupés *(castelnaui).*

71. NORTHERN ROYAL FLYCATCHER
(Onychorhynchus mexicanus)
Plate XVI

Description. 6½ - 7″. ♂: Very similar to No. 70 but bill considerably larger, underparts paler with less barring and tail proportionately much longer. ♀: Similar to No. 70 but with the crest yellow instead of deep orange.

Range. Mexico southward through Central America to Colombia.

Colombia. Forest. Tropical zone of northern Colombia from Córdoba eastward to the western base of the Perijá Mts. *(fraterculus)* .

Platyrinchus

The Spadebills *(Platyrinchus)* are very small flycatchers characterized by a very broad, flat, stubby bill and short tail.

72. YELLOW-THROATED SPADEBILL
(Platyrinchus flavigularis) Plate XIV

Description. 3½″. Bill flat, broad and stubby. Tail short. Crown and nape fulvous-brown. A large semi-concealed patch of white feathers with a subterminal black bar and brown tip in center of crown. Spot before eye white. Back dull olive. Wings and tail dusky, the feathers margined with olive. Below pale yellow, the breast flammulated with olive.

Range. Northwestern Venezuela southward through the Andes to Peru.

Colombia. Forest. Subtropical zone in the upper and middle Magdalena Valley *(flavigularis).*

73. WHITE-THROATED SPADEBILL
(Platyrinchus mystaceus)

Description. 3¾ - 4″. Bill flat, broad and stubby. ♂: A broad semi-concealed yellow patch in center of crown. Line above lores and eye-ring buffy white, lores, region below eye and moustacial streak blackish. Tail short. Upperparts, wings and tail olive brown. Throat white, rest of underparts pale yellow, strongly shaded with brown on breast and sides of body. ♀: Similar, but without coronal spot.

[Species 68a, 71a, and 72a, see Page 410.]

Range. Costa Rica southward to southeastern Venezuela, the Guianas, Ecuador, Peru, Brazil, Paraguay, Bolivia, and Argentina.

Colombia. Forest. Upper tropical and lower subtropical zone. Northern Colombia from the Panama border eastward across the Cauca Valley to the Santa Marta region; east of the Andes in southern Meta (*neglectus*). Western slope of the Western Andes from the río San Juan southward, and the upper Cauca Valley (*albogularis*).

74. GOLDEN-CROWNED SPADEBILL
(*Platyrinchus coronatus*)

Description. 3¾ - 4". Bill broad, flat and stubby. Tail short. ♂ : Center of crown chestnut, the feathers basally golden yellow. Line at sides of crown, patch behind eye and malar streak black. Broad circle around eye, eyebrow and ear-coverts pale yellow. Back, wings and tail olive. Throat and underparts yellow, tinged with olive. ♀ : Similar but feathers of crown without yellow bases.

Range. Nicaragua to western Ecuador, Venezuela, the Guianas and the upper and middle Amazon Valley, Ecuador, Peru and Bolivia.

Colombia. Forest. Tropical zone. Southeastern Córdoba and the entire Pacific coast (*superciliaris*). East of the Andes in Caquetá (*coronatus*).

75. BROWNISH FLYCATCHER
(*Cnipodectes subbrunneus*) Plate XV

Description. 7¾ - 8¼ ". Upperparts dark brown; throat and breast paler, obscurely streaked dusky on throat; lower breast and sides of body pale grayish, center of abdomen pale yellow (or center of abdomen white, 1). Wings dark brown, the wing-coverts and inner remiges margined with rufescent-buff. Tail dark reddish brown. Young birds are chocolate brown above, wing-coverts, inner remiges and tail-feathers margined with chestnut. In this species the wing is very peculiar, for some of the feathers are twisted and the shafts are very thick.

Range. Panama southward to western Ecuador. Eastern Ecuador, Peru and

western Brazil.

Colombia. Forest and scrub. Tropical zone. Northwestern Colombia from the Panama border to the middle Magdalena Valley (*panamensis*). Pacific coast from the Baudó Mts. southward (*subbrunneus*). East of the Eastern Andes from southern Meta southward to Putumayo (1, *minor*).

Tolmomyias

The following group of small flycatchers (*Tolmomyias*) is composed of species which resemble each other closely and are very difficult to tell apart even in the hand. Their heads are large; their bills are flat and rather broad. Above they are olive green, the crown usually gray or grayish; the throat and breast usually pale olive green, the belly yellow, and the wing-coverts and remiges margined with pale yellow.

76. YELLOW-OLIVE FLYCATCHER
(*Tolmomyias sulphurescens*) Plate XV

Description. 6 - 6½ ". Lores white; crown and nape grayish green (or green, 1). Best distinguishable from other species by its large size.

Range. Southern Mexico southward to Venezuela, the Guianas, southeastern Brazil and Bolivia. Trinidad.

Colombia. Forest. Tropical and subtropical zones. The Santa Marta region (1, *exortivus*). Both slopes of the Eastern Andes from Norte de Santander southward to Cundinamarca and Meta (*confusus*). The Atrato Valley and the Pacific coast south to the río Dagua. Upper Cauca Valley and the head of the Magdalena Valley (*asemus*).

77. YELLOW-MARGINED FLYCATCHER
(*Tolmomyias assimilis*)

Description. 5½ - 5¾ ". Very much like No. 76 but smaller, cap grayer.

Range. Costa Rica southward to Venezuela, the Guianas, the lower Amazon, Ecuador, Peru, and Bolivia.

Colombia. Forest. Tropical zone. The lower Cauca Valley and Córdoba, thence southward down the Pacific coast to Nariño *(flavotectus)*. Southern Meta and Caquetá *(obscuriceps)*. Vichada and Vaupeś *(neglectus)*.

78. GRAY-CROWNED FLYCATCHER
(Tolmomyias poliocephalus)

Description. 4¾ - 5¼ ". Similar to No. 77 but smaller.

Range. Venezuela and the Guianas southward to Bahia. Ecuador, Peru and Bolivia.

Colombia. Forest. Tropical zone. East of the Eastern Andes in Meta, Vichada, Vaupés, Caquetá and Putumayo *(poliocephalus)*.

79. YELLOW-BREASTED FLYCATCHER
(Tolmomyias flaviventris)

Description. 5 - 5½ ". Differs from other species by having the crown green like the back, the breast gamboge yellow the belly bright yellow and the upperparts much more yellowish olive green (or chest with a brownish olive wash, belly pale yellow, back olive, crown grayish green, 1).

Range. Venezuela, British and Dutch Guiana southward to Bolivia and southeastern Brazil. Trinidad.

Colombia. Open woodland. Tropical zone. Semi-arid Caribbean coast region from the Guajira Peninsula westward to Córdoba *(aurulentus)*. East of the Eastern Andes from Norte de Santander and Meta eastward to the Orinoco; probably the Sinú Valley *(collingwoodi)*. Caquetá (1, *viridiceps*).

80. OLIVACEOUS FLATBILL
(Rhynchocyclus olivaceus)

Description. 6¼ - 6½ ". Bill very broad and flat. Above olive green; eye-ring white; remiges margined with yellowish olive (or buffy olive, 1). Throat and breast obscurely streaked olive and yellow; abdomen clear pale yellow. Tail olive green (or olive brown, 1).

Range. Eastern Panama southward to Venezuela, British and French Guiana, Bolivia and southeastern Brazil.

Colombia. Forest. Tropical zone. From the Pacific coast inland to the lower

Atrato Valley (1, *mirus*). From the Panama border eastward to northern Córdoba *(bardus)*. East side of the Magdalena Valley in Santander *(tamborensis)*. East of the Eastern Andes from Meta southward to Putumayo *(aequinoctialis)*. The Santa Marta region and the eastern base of the Andes in Meta *(flavus)*.

81. EYE-RINGED FLATBILL
(Rhynchocyclus brevirostris)

Description. 6 - 6½ ". Very similar to No. 80 but much darker olive green; throat and breast more uniform; wing-coverts edged pale olive green (or tawny olive, 1).

Range. Southern Mexico to western Ecuador.

Colombia. Forest. Tropical zone. Region around the Gulf of Urabá *(hellmayri)*. The Atrato Valley and the entire Pacific coast (1, *pacificus*).

82. FULVOUS-BREASTED FLATBILL
(Rhynchocyclus fulvipectus) Plate XVI

Description. 6½ - 6¾ ". Bill broad and flat. Upperparts olive green. Chin grayish, throat and breast ochraceous tawny, rest of underparts yellow. Wings blackish, the inner remiges and wing-coverts broadly margined with tawny ochre. Tail brown margined with olive.

Range. Western Venezuela. Ecuador, Peru and Bolivia.

Colombia. Forest. Tropical and subtropical zones. West of the Eastern Andes in Cundinamarca, Huila, Antioquia, Caldas, Cauca and Nariño.

83. RUFOUS-TAILED FLATBILL
(Ramphotrigon ruficauda)

Description. 6½ - 6¾ ". Bill flat, moderately broad. Upperparts dull olive, upper tail-coverts and tail and broad margins to wing-coverts and remiges bright rufous. Throat streaked grayish olive and whitish; breast streaked olive and yellow. Center of abdomen pale yellow; under tail-coverts buffy rufous.

Range. The Guianas and southern Venezuela southward through Brazil to western Mato Grosso and Peru.

Colombia. Forest. Tropical zone east of the Eastern Andes in Meta, Caquetá and Vaupés.

84. LARGE-HEADED FLATBILL
(Ramphotrigon megacephala)

Description. 5¾ - 6¼". Bill flat, moderately broad. Eye-ring white. Upperparts dull olive, crown darker. Wings blackish with two buffy ochraceous wing-bars, inner remiges margined yellowish olive. Throat and breast pale olive, tinged ochraceous on breast, rest of underparts clear yellow. Tail brownish, edged olive.

Range. Southern Venezuela. Southeastern Brazil, Argentina, Paraguay and Bolivia.

Colombia. Forest. Tropical zone east of the Eastern Andes in Meta and Putumayo (pectoralis).

Todirostrum

The Tody - Flycatchers (Todirostrum) form a group of very small, gnatcatcher-like birds, with very flat, rather wide and long bills.

85. BLACK-HEADED
TODY-FLYCATCHER
(Todirostrum chrysocrotaphum)
Plate XVI

Description. 3¼ - 3¾". Crown, nape and sides of head glossy blue-black. Back bright citron green. Wings black edged yellow, the wing-coverts edged with yellow forming a double bar. Throat white, rest of underparts bright yellow (or crown, nape and sides of head black, lores white, line from behind eye yellow. Back olive green, chin white, throat and underparts bright yellow, the sides of throat and the breast spotted with black, 1). Tail blackish edged citron.

Range. Costa Rica to western Ecuador. Southern Venezuela southward to Maranhão and westward through Amazonia to eastern Peru and Bolivia.

Colombia. Forest and scrub. Tropical zone. From the lower Atrato Valley eastward to the Santa Marta region, the lower and middle Magdalena Valley, and probably the Pacific coast (nigriceps). East of the Eastern Andes from Meta southward to Caquetá and Vaupés (1, guttatum).

86. GOLDEN-WINGED
TODY-FLYCATCHER
(Todirostrum calopterum)

Description. 4 - 4¼". Crown, nape and sides of head black. Back olive. Shoulders deep chestnut, median wing-coverts golden yellow, remiges black, the inner ones edged with yellowish white. Throat white, rest of underparts golden yellow. Tail black.

Range. Eastern Ecuador and Peru.

Colombia. Forest and scrub. Tropical zone east of the Eastern Andes in Putumayo (calopterum).

87. COMMON TODY-FLYCATCHER
(Todirostrum cinereum)

Description. 4 - 4¼". Forecrown and sides of head black, hindcrown, nape and upper back gray, shading to olive on rump and upper tail-coverts. Wings and wing-coverts black, edged yellow. Throat and underparts bright yellow (or throat white, rest of underparts yellow, 1). Tail black.

Range. Southern Mexico southward to Central America, western Ecuador and northwestern Peru. Venezuela, the Guianas, eastern and central Brazil, eastern Ecuador, Peru and Bolivia.

Colombia. Open woodland, plantations and thickets. Tropical and lower subtropical zones. Western Nariño (1, sclateri); the rest of Colombia west of the Andes and east of them as far south as Putumayo (cinereum).

88. RUSTY-FACED
TODY-FLYCATCHER
(Todirostrum latirostre)

Description. 4½ - 4¾". Lores, forehead and ocular region rusty buff; crown and nape grayish green; back olive green. Throat and center of abdomen whitish; breast and sides of body pale grayish, flanks olive. Remiges and rectrices dusky edged olive, wing-coverts broadly margined ochraceous.

Range. Ecuador, Peru and Bolivia eastward to the interior of Brazil.

Colombia. Scrub. Tropical zone in Caquetá and Putumayo (caniceps).

89. SLATE-HEADED TODY-FLYCATCHER
(Todirostrum sylvia)

Description. 4 - 4½ ". Lores dusky, line above lores and eye-ring white; crown and nape gray. Back olive green. Wing-coverts black, broadly edged olive yellow forming a double wing-bar; remiges and rectrices dusky broadly edged olive yellow. Sides of neck and breast pale grayish (or more definitely grayish, 1); throat and belly white; flanks and under tail-coverts olive yellow.

Range. Southern Mexico southward to Panama. Venezuela, British and French Guiana and eastern Brazil.

Colombia. Open woodland, thickets. Tropical zone. East of the Andes southward to Meta and west of them south to the Dagua Valley (superciliare). Extreme eastern Colombia in Vichada (1, griseolum).

90. BLACK-AND-WHITE TODY-FLYCATCHER
(Todirostrum capitale)

Description. 4 - 4¼ ". ♂ : Entire upperparts, sides of head, neck and breast, wings and tail glossy black. Lores, eyering and rest of underparts white. Under wing-coverts, margins of inner remiges and flanks pale yellow. ♀ : Crown chestnut; sides of head and breast gray; throat and abdomen white, flanks and under wing-coverts pale yellow. Back, wings and tail olive green; inner remiges margined with yellowish white.

Range. Eastern Ecuador, northeastern Peru.

Colombia. Forest. Tropical zone of Putumayo.

91. BENTBILL
(Oncostoma cinereigulare) Plate XV

Description. 4¼ - 4½ ". Bill thick, bent downward. Upperparts, wings and tail olive green, the wing-coverts edged yellowish olive, forming a double wing-bar. Throat and breast olive yellow, slightly tinged brownish. Sides of body olive, center of abdomen yellow.

Range. Mexico and Central America.

Colombia. Forest, plantations. Tropical zone of western and northern Colombia, eastward to the Santa Marta region and southward to the upper Atrato (olivaceum).

Idioptilon

In general shape Idioptilon is rather like Todirostrum but the bill is narrower.

92. WHITE-EYED TODY-TYRANT
(Idioptilon zosterops)

Description. 4 - 4¼ ". Forehead, ocular region and throat gray somewhat mottled with whitish. Upperparts, wings and tail olive green; wing-coverts with two prominent olive yellow bands. Breast olive obscurely streaked with yellow; abdomen pale yellow.

Range. Dutch and French Guiana westward through southern Venezuela to eastern Ecuador, the middle Amazon, Peru and Bolivia.

Colombia. Forest. Tropical zone in Caquetá (zosterops).

93. BLACK-THROATED TODY-TYRANT
(Idioptilon granadensis) Plate XVI

Description. 4¼ - 4¾ ". Lores and ocular region pure white (or buff, 1; or buffy white, 2). Upperparts, wings and tail olive green. Throat black, breast gray (or brownish gray, 1); patch at base of throat and center of abdomen white.

Range. Northern and western Venezuela to southern Ecuador and Peru.

Colombia. Forest. Subtropical and temperate zone. The Santa Marta Mts. (1, lehmanni). West slope of the Eastern Andes in Santander and Norte de Santander (2, andinus). Eastern Andes from Bogotá southward to southeastern Nariño. Central and Western Andes (granadensis).

94. PEARLY-VENTED TODY-TYRANT
(Idioptilon margaritaceiventris)

Description. 4¾ - 5¼ ". Pre-ocular region and eye-ring white, sides of head pale brown. Crown dark brown, back pale brown (or grayish olive, 1). Throat and breast white, streaked pale brown; abdomen silky white. Wings and tail dark brown; wing-coverts with two white bars, inner remiges edged white, outer remiges and tail-feathers edged olive yellow.

Range. Venezuela southward through Brazil to Paraguay, Argentina and Bolivia. Margarita Island.

Colombia. Sparsely wooded lands and scrub. Arid tropical zone of the Caribbean coast and the Magdalena Valley to Santander *(impiger)*. Forest. Middle Magdalena Valley in Tolima (1, *septentrionalis)*.

95. RUFOUS-CROWNED TODY-TYRANT
(Poecilotriccus ruficeps)

Description. 4 - 4¼″. Bill and general shape much as in *Todirostrum*. Crown rufous-chestnut, bordered by a black line posteriorly, this followed by a gray band. Ear-coverts pale rufous, margined below by a broad black line (or white with a black moustacial streak, 1; or without black, 2). Upperparts bright olive green. Wings and tail black, edged olive yellow, the wing-coverts with two prominent yellow bars. Throat and breast white, the throat tinged rufous (or throat rufous, 2). Lower breast and abdomen bright yellow, separated from the white breast by a diffused black band.

Range. Northwestern Venezuela, Ecuador, and Peru.

Colombia. Forest. Subtropical zone. Northern portion of the Eastern Andes from Norte de Santander and western Cundinamarca southward to the east slope of the Eastern Andes in southeastern Nariño *(ruficeps)*. Central Andes and the upper Cauca Valley (1, *melanomystax)*. Andes of western Nariño (2, *rufigenis)*.

96. SCALE-CRESTED PYGMY-TYRANT
(Lophotriccus pileatus) Plate XVII

Description. 4 - 4½″. Crown black with a wide crest, the feathers broadly edged with rufous; eye-ring buff. Back bright olive green. Throat and breast white (or yellow, 1) broadly streaked with gray, sides of neck and of breast brownish

olive, flanks yellow, center of abdomen yellowish white (or yellow, 1). Wings and tail dusky edged olive, the wing-coverts with a double band of yellowish olive.

Range. Costa Rica southward to Venezuela, Ecuador and Peru.

Colombia. Forest and scrub. Tropical and subtropical zone of the Eastern Andes *(squamaecrista)*. Western and Central Andes and western Nariño *(hesperius)*. The northern end of the Perijá Mts. (1, *santaluciae)*.

97. DOUBLE-BANDED PYGMY-TYRANT
(Lophotriccus vitiosus)

Description. 4¼ - 4½″. Rather similar to No. 96 but crest edged with gray; no buff eye-ring.

Range. French and Dutch Guiana, northern Brazil westward to Ecuador and Peru.

Colombia. Forest. Tropical zone east of the Andes in Caquetá and Putumayo *(affinis)*. Meta and Vaupés *(guianensis)*.

98. HELMETED PYGMY-TYRANT
(Colopteryx galeatus)

Description. 4¼ - 4½″. Crest black, edged gray, not as full as in the preceding two species, the feathers narrow and pointed rather than broad and rounded. Upperparts, wings and tail olive green. Throat whitish streaked with gray, rest of underparts yellowish white, obscurely streaked on breast with dusky. No wing-bars.

Range. Southern Venezuela and the Guianas southward to Maranhão and westward to the rio Negro, Brazil.

Colombia. Forest. Tropical zone. Extreme eastern Colombia in Vichada and undoubtedly Vaupés.

99. PALE-EYED PYGMY-TYRANT
(Atalotriccus pilaris)

Description. 4 - 4¼″. Lores whitish, ocular region pale smoky brown. Crown and upperparts, wings and tail bright yellowish olive green (or crown smoky gray contrasting with back, 1); wing-coverts, remiges pale margined. Underparts dirty white, throat mottled with blackish,

PLATE XV

FIRE-CROWNED TYRANT
(*Machetornis rix-*
osa flavigularis)
Page 273

TROPICAL KINGBIRD
(*Tyrannus m. melancholicus*)
Page 273

VARIEGATED
FLYCATCHER
(*Empidonomus*
v. varius)
Page 274

PIRATIC FLYCATCHER
(*Legatus l. leucophaius*)
Page 274

LEMON-BROWED
FLYCATCHER
(*Conopias cin-*
choneti icterophrys)
Page 275

WHITE-RINGED
FLYCATCHER
(*Coryphotriccus*
parvus albovittatus)
Page 276

SULPHURY FLYCATCHER
(*Tyrannopsis sulphurea*)
Page 276

GREAT KISKADEE
(*Pitangus sulphur-*
atus rufipennis)
Page 277

GREATER PEWEE
(*Contopus fumi-*
gatus zarumae)
Page 279

EULER'S FLYCATCHER
(*Empidonax euleri*
lawrencei)
Page 279

RUDDY-TAILED
FLYCATCHER
(*Terenotriccus eryth-*
rurus fulvigularis)
Page 280

HANDSOME
FLYCATCHER
(*Myiophobus p. pulcher*)
Page 281

CLIFF FLYCATCHER
(*Hirundinea f. ferruginea*)
Page 282

BROWNISH
FLYCATCHER
Cnipodectes s. subbrunneus)
Page 283

YELLOW-OLIVE
FLYCATCHER
(*Tolmomyias sulphur-*
escens exortivus)
Page 283

BENTBILL
(*Oncostoma cinerei-*
gulare olivaceum)
Page 286

SHORT-TAILED
PYGMY-TYRANT
(*Myiornis ecaud-*
atus miserabilis)
Page 289

MARBLED-FACED
BRISTLE-TYRANT
(*Pogonotriccus*
o. ophthalmicus)
Page 289

SLENDER-BILLED
TYRANNULET
(*Inezia tenuirostris*)
Page 291

PLUMBEOUS-CROWNED
TYRANNULET
(*Oreotriccus plumbeiceps*)
Page 296

YELLOW-BELLIED
TYRANNULET
(*Ornithion semi-*
flavum dilutum)
Page 296

288

breast obscurely streaked with pale brown. Under tail-coverts and flanks yellow.

Range. Panama eastward through Venezuela to British Guiana.

Colombia. Forest, scrub, often along streams. Tropical zone. Semi-arid Caribbean coast from the Guajira Peninsula westward to Córdoba. The Magdalena Valley south to Huila. East of the Andes in the Zulia Valley and southern Meta (*pilaris*). Extreme eastern Colombia along the Orinoco (1, *griseiceps*).

100. SHORT-TAILED PYGMY-TYRANT
(Myiornis ecaudatus) Plate XV

Description. 3 - 3¼ ". Tail exceedingly short. Crown black (or gray, 1), sides of head gray; spot above lores and eye-ring white. Back bright yellowish olive green. Throat and breast white, rest of underparts sulphur yellow (or eyebrow and underparts white, sides of body and under tail-coverts yellow, 1). Wings and tail black, feathers edged greenish yellow.

Range. Costa Rica southward to western Ecuador. Venezuela southward to Mato Grosso and westward through Amazonia to Ecuador, Peru and Bolivia. Trinidad.

Colombia. Forest. Tropical zone. Atrato Valley and the Pacific coast (*atricapillus*). East of the Andes in Meta (1, *miserabilis*).

101. BRONZE-OLIVE PYGMY-TYRANT
(Pseudotriccus pelzelni)

Description. 4¾ - 5¼ ". Crown dusky olive. Upperparts, breast and sides of body dark reddish brown (or olive brown, 1; or olive, 2). Throat whitish, center of abdomen buffy yellow (or pale yellow, 2). Wings and tail brown, margined rufescent (or dark olive, 2).

Range. Eastern Panama. Ecuador.

Colombia. Forest. Tropical zone. Northwestern Colombia (*berlepschi*). Western Colombia from the region about Munchique southward (1, *annectens*).* Eastern

---

*Not *connectens* as usually given.

base of the Eastern Andes from Meta southward (2, *pelzelni*).

102. RUFOUS-HEADED PYGMY-TYRANT
(Pseudotriccus ruficeps) Plate XVII

Description. 4½ - 5 ". Entire head orange-rufous. Back, breast and sides of body olive green, center of abdomen primrose yellow. Wings and tail rufous.

Range. The Andes of Ecuador, Peru and Bolivia.

Colombia. Forest. Subtropical and temperate zones of the Central and Western Andes in Caldas, Tolima and Cauca. Both slopes of the Andes in Nariño.

103. MARBLED-FACED BRISTLE-TYRANT
(Pogonotriccus ophthalmicus)
Plate XV

Description. 5 - 5½ ". Crown and nape dark gray. Sides of head, region around eye and forehead marbled black and white. Anterior part of ear-coverts white, posterior part black, edged behind with a crescentic white mark. Throat grayish white. Back and wings olive green, the wing-coverts edged yellow forming two bars. Breast olive yellow, abdomen bright yellow. Tail brown edged olive green.

Range. Northwestern Venezuela, Ecuador, Peru and Bolivia.

Colombia. Forest. Upper tropical and subtropical zone of the Central and Western Andes and perhaps the Eastern Andes in Tolima, Caldas, Huila, Valle, Cauca, the west slope of the mountains of western Nariño. Recorded from "Bogotá" but subsequently not found on either slope of the Eastern Andes (*ophthalmicus*).

104. VARIEGATED BRISTLE-TYRANT
(Pogonotriccus poecilotis)

Description. 4¾ - 5¼ ". Very similar to No. 103 but distinguishable by the very broad ochraceous edges to the wing-coverts forming a double bar and by the yellow instead of blue-gray lower mandible.

Range. Venezuela. Ecuador.

Colombia. Forest. Subtropical zone of the Andes from the west slope of the Eastern

Andes westward in Cundinamarca, Tolima, Antioquia, Huila, Caldas, Valle and Cauca. *(poecilotis)*. The Perijá Mts. *(pitanoi)*.

105. RUFOUS-BROWED TYRANNULET
(Phylloscartes superciliaris)

Description. 4¾ - 5¼ ". Crown grayish black; short eyebrow rufous; sides of head freckled gray and white. Back olive green; wings and tail dusky, feathers edged with olive green. Throat and breast gray, belly lemon yellow.

Range. Costa Rica and Panama. Western Venezuela. British Guiana.

Colombia. Tropical zone. Known only from "Bogotá", but probably occurs in humid forest west of the Gulf of Urabá and perhaps eastward *(palloris)*.

106. YELLOW TYRANNULET
(Capsiempis flaveola)

Description. 4¾ - 5¼ ". Short eyebrow yellow (or white, 1). Upperparts, wings and tail yellowish olive, the wing-coverts edged with pale buff forming a double wing-bar. Underparts yellow.

Range. Nicaragua southward to Venezuela, British and French Guiana. Bolivia and eastern Brazil and Paraguay. Southwestern Ecuador.

Colombia. Open woods and scrub. Tropical zone of the western lowlands of the Santa Marta region and the Magdalena Valley south to Tolima (1, *leucophrys*). Extreme eastern Colombia in Vaupés and the eastern slope of the Andes of Nariño *(cerula)*.

107. TAWNY-CROWNED PYGMY-TYRANT
(Euscarthmus meloryphus)

Description. 4 - 4½ ". Crown tawny, sides of head buff. Upperparts, wings and tail pale brown; below white, becoming somewhat yellowish on abdomen.

Range. Venezuela. Southern Brazil, Paraguay and eastern Bolivia. Western Ecuador and western Peru.

Colombia. Open or sparsely wooded country. Tropical zone. Santa Marta region and lower Magdalena Valley southward to Tolima *(paulus)*.

108. SHARP-WINGED TYRANNULET
(Pseudocolopteryx acutipennis)

Description. 4¾ - 5". Upperparts yellowish olive; underparts golden yellow. Wing and tail brownish edged olive. Inner primaries attenuated.

Range. Ecuador, Peru, Bolivia and northwestern Argentina.

Colombia. Subtropical zone of the Central Andes in Antioquia and Caldas, and perhaps the Eastern Andes.

109. NARROW-TAILED TYRANNULET
(Polystictus pectoralis)

Description. 4¼ - 4½ ". ♂ : Head crested. Crown slaty, bases of feathers white. Lores dusky surmounted by a conspicuous white mark. Eye-ring white, post-ocular region and upper throat dusky, streaked white. Dorsal surface brown becoming rufous on rump. Lower throat and center of abdomen buffy white, sides of breast and body rufescent. Wings and tail dark brown, the feathers edged fulvous, the wing-coverts edged fulvous forming a double bar. ♀ differs from ♂ in having top and sides of head brown; throat buff, underparts more strongly rufescent.

Range. Southern Venezuela and British Guiana. Southwestern Brazil, Uruguay, northern Argentina, Paraguay and eastern Bolivia.

Colombia. Marshes. Subtropical and temperate zone of the Eastern Andes in Cundinamarca. The west slope of the Western Andes in Valle in the upper tropical zone *(bogotensis)*.

110. TUFTED TIT-LIKE TYRANT
(Anairetes parulus) Plate XIV

Description. 4½ - 4¾ ". A long, narrow black crest. Crown blackish, streaked with white. Supra-loral streak white, sides of head black, lower edge of eye white. Cheeks, throat and breast white, conspicuously streaked black; belly pale yellow. Back ashy. Wings and tail blackish, wing-coverts edged with white forming two bars; outer web of outer tail-feather white.

Range. The Andes from Ecuador southward to the Straits of Magellan.

Colombia. Forest and páramo. Subtropical to páramo zone at the southern end of the Central Andes in Cauca and in western Nariño *(aequatorialis)*.

111. AGILE TIT-LIKE TYRANT
(Uromyias agilis)

Description. 5″. A broad black crest occupying center of crown, margined on sides by a broad white line, lores speckled blackish and white. Back and wings brown, the back with dark streaks. Chin and throat whitish, rest of underparts pale yellowish, streaked with dusky on throat and breast. Tail brown, the outer tail-feathers shorter than the rest with the outer web white.

Range. Western Venezuela. Ecuador.

Colombia. Forest. Subtropical and temperate zones of the Eastern Andes in Cundinamarca and the head of the Magdalena Valley.

112. TORRENT TYRANNULET
(Serpophaga cinerea) Plate XIV

Description. 4¾ - 5¼″. Crown and sides of head black, concealed crest white. Upper and lower parts pale gray, center of abdomen white. Wings and tail black, edges of wing-coverts, inner remiges and narrow tip to tail-feathers white.

Range. Costa Rica to western Venezuela. Ecuador, Peru and Bolivia.

Colombia. Rocky streams and torrents. Rarely tropical, more usually subtropical and temperate zones west of the Eastern Andes and the Santa Marta Mts. East of the Andes in Norte de Santander and Cundinamarca *(cinerea)*.

113. SLENDER-BILLED TYRANNULET
(Inezia tenuirostris) Plate XV

Description. 4″. Above mouse brown. Eye-ring, lores and throat white, breast and belly pale yellow. Two conspicuous white wing-bars. Tail brown, outer web of outer tail-feather pale.

Range. Western Venezuela.

Colombia. Forest and arid scrub. Caribbean coast region from the eastern shore of the Ciénaga Grande in Magdalena to La Guajira Peninsula. In many works this species is referred to the genus *Phaeomyias*.

114. PALE-TIPPED TYRANNULET
(Inezia subflava)

Description. 5″. Above olivaceous brown (or brown, 1). Line from nostrils to above eye and eye-ring white. Wings like back, tips to wing-coverts white forming a double bar, inner remiges bordered with white. Chin white, rest of underparts yellow (or yellow flammulated with olive on breast and flanks, 1). Tail like back, graduated, tipped white.

Range. Venezuela, British and Dutch Guiana. The south bank of the middle Amazon.

Colombia. Forest, wooded savanna, mangroves. Tropical zone. Santa Marta region and the lower Magdalena Valley *(intermedia)*. Extreme eastern Colombia in Vaupés (1, *obscura*).

115. WHITE-THROATED TYRANNULET
(Mecocerculus leucophrys)
Plate XVII

Description. 5¾ - 6¼″. Tail rather long. Narrow eyebrow white. Upperparts, wings and tail olivaceous brown (or brown, 1); wing-coverts and tertials broadly edged with white (or buffy ochraceous, 1); secondaries edged with yellowish (or rufous, 1). Throat white; breast grayish (or brownish, 1); abdomen pale yellow.

Range. Mountains of British Guiana and Venezuela. The Andes of Ecuador southward to Bolivia and western Argentina.

Colombia. Forest, scrub at forest edge. Subtropical and temperate zone. Santa Marta Mts. *(montensis)*. Eastern Andes *(setophagoides)*. Central and Western Andes (1, *notatus*). West slope at the extreme southern end of the Central Andes and Andes of Nariño (1, *rufomarginatus*).

116. WHITE-BANDED TYRANNULET
(Mecocerculus stictopterus)

Description. 5 - 5½". Crown gray; broad eyebrow white, feathers below eye mixed gray and white. Back olive, wings dusky; wing-coverts broadly tipped white forming a double bar; inner remiges edged with yellowish. Throat and breast pale gray; center of belly white, sides of body and flanks pale yellow. Tail gray, edged olive.

Range. Northern and western Venezuela. Ecuador, Peru and Bolivia.

Colombia. Forest. Subtropical and temperate zone of the Andes in Boyacá, Caldas, Cauca and Nariño *(stictopterus)*.

117. WHITE-TAILED TYRANNULET
(Mecocerculus poecilocercus)

Description. 4½ - 5". Very similar to No. 116 but smaller, back greener, less olive, the wing-coverts tipped buffy white; upper tail-coverts yellowish white; inner webs of four outer tail-feathers white.

Range. Andes of Ecuador and Peru.

Colombia. Forest. Subtropical to temperate zone of the Andes in Santander, Cundinamarca, Huila, Caldas, Tolima, Cauca and Nariño.

118. SULPHUR-BELLIED TYRANNULET
(Mecocerculus minor)

Description. 4¾ - 5". Crown slaty. Broad eyebrow white. Back olive green. Wings brown, wing-coverts edged ochraceous forming a double bar, inner remiges edged yellowish. Throat white; breast olive flammulated with yellow, rest of underparts clear yellow. Tail brown, edged olive.

Range. Western Venezuela. Northwestern Peru.

Colombia. Forest. Subtropical zone. East of the Eastern Andes in Norte de Santander and Boyacá. The head of the Magdalena Valley in Huila.

Elaenia

The many species belonging to the genus *Elaenia* are notorious for being very difficult to tell apart. In Colombia eight species occur. Above they are olive to olive brown, the wing-coverts edged white to yellowish white forming a double bar, the remiges pale edged. Often a concealed white crown patch is present and the head is crested, in some conspicuously so. The breast is usually gray, the rest of underparts white to pale yellow. The bill is rather short, often flesh-color basally. Only the characters which may help to distinguish them are given.

119. YELLOW-BELLIED ELAENIA
(Elaenia flavogaster)

Description. 6½ - 7". Conspicuously crested; center of crown with a concealed white patch. Throat whitish, breast gray, rather sharply defined from the pale yellow abdomen.

Range. Mexico and Central America. Venezuela and the Guianas southward to Brazil, Ecuador, Peru, Bolivia and Argentina. The Lesser Antilles; Trinidad and Tobago.

Colombia. Open woods, clearings and savanna. Tropical and subtropical zones throughout the country *(flavogaster)*.

120. WHITE-CRESTED ELAENIA
(Elaenia albiceps) Plate XIV

Description. 6¼ - 6¾". Crested. Concealed crown patch white. Below dull grayish, strongly tinged with green on sides of body. Outer margin of outermost tail-feathers rather pale.

Range. Ecuador southward through the Andes to Tierra del Fuego. Eastern and southeastern Brazil.

Colombia. Open woodland, savanna, cultivated lands. Subtropical to páramo zones of the mountains of Nariño *(griseogularis)*.

121. SMALL-BILLED ELAENIA
(Elaenia parvirostris)

Description. 5¾ - 6½". Below whiter than any other *Elaenia* found in Colombia, the belly virtually white. Throat and breast very pale grayish; flanks pale yellowish.

Range. Venezuela and the Guianas southward to Argentina and Bolivia, Paraguay and Uruguay. Trinidad.

Colombia. Open country and thin woods. Summer resident, March to May. Breeds in southern South America. Found mostly east of the Andes from Meta to Vaupés and Caquetá. Recorded also in the Santa Marta region, and on the west slope of the Eastern Andes in Cundinamarca.

122. GIANT ELAENIA
(Elaenia gigas)

Description. 7¼ - 8″. A large, white, concealed crown patch. Throat white, breast yellow washed with brown. Rest of underparts yellow, slightly streaked with brown. The white throat and brownish breast are the best characters of this species.

Range. Ecuador, Peru and Bolivia.

Colombia. Forest and scrub. Tropical zone east of the Eastern Andes from Meta to Vaupés.

123. LESSER ELAENIA
(Elaenia chiriquensis)

Description. 6 - 6¼ ″. A concealed white crown patch. Rather like No. 119, particularly brachyptera, but smaller.

Range. Costa Rica southward to western Ecuador. Venezuela, the Guianas, Brazil, Peru, Paraguay and Bolivia. Trinidad. The island of Fernando de Noronha off the coast of Brazil.

Colombia. Scrub, savanna, open woodland, cultivated lands. Tropical and subtropical zones virtually throughout (albivertex). Mountains of western Nariño (brachyptera).

124. RUFOUS-CROWNED ELAENIA
(Elaenia ruficeps)

Description. 6¼ - 6¾ ″. Differs from all other Colombian species by having the concealed crown patch rufous and by being browner above. Throat whitish, streaked with dusky and breast grayish, streaked with yellowish.

Range. The Guianas, southern Venezuela and northwestern Brazil.

Colombia. Forest. Meta and Vaupés.

[Species 121a, see Page 410.]

125. DUSKY ELAENIA
(Elaenia obscura)

Description. 7 - 7½ ″ (or 5¾ - 6¼ ″, 1). Not distinguishable in the field from E. c. albivertex (or not distinguishable in the field from brachyptera, 1). Both differ slightly in size.

Range. Guatemala southward to Venezuela, Ecuador, southern Brazil, Argentina and Bolivia.

Colombia. Forest clearings and edge of woods. Upper tropical to temperate zones. Santa Marta Mts. (browni); rest of Colombia except Nariño (1, pudica).

126. SIERRAN ELAENIA
(Elaenia pallatangae)

Description. 6 - 6½ ″. Best distinguishable from other species in Colombia by its yellower underparts, the breast somewhat clouded with brownish.

Range. Southern Venezuela, Ecuador and Peru.

Colombia. Forest clearings and pastureland. Subtropical zone. West slope of the Central Andes in Caldas and Huila; head of the Magdalena Valley; southern portion of Western Andes in Cauca; western Nariño (pallatangae).

127. FOREST ELAENIA
(Myiopagis gaimardii)

Description. 5¼ - 6″. Crown dark gray with a concealed white (or yellow, 1) patch; eye-ring white. Upperparts, wings and tail olive, the inner remiges and wing-coverts broadly edged with yellowish white, forming two conspicuous wing-bars. Throat whitish, breast grayish streaked inconspicuously with yellow, lower breast and belly clear pale yellow.

Range. Panama to Venezuela and the Guianas, northern Brazil, eastern Ecuador, Peru and Bolivia. Trinidad.

Colombia. Humid forest. Tropical zone. The north side of the Santa Marta Mts. (bogotensis). The Caribbean coast from Córdoba eastward to the western and southern base of the Santa Marta Mts. (1, macilvainii). East of the Andes in Meta (gaimardii); Vichada and Vaupés (guianensis).

128. GREENISH ELAENIA
(Myiopagis viridicata)

Description. 5½ - 6¼ ". Concealed crown patch yellow. Differs from No. 127 by having no wing-bars and the crown green.

Range. Mexico southward through Central America to western Venezuela and southward to Bolivia.

Colombia. Forest near streams. Tropical zone. The northern end of the Perijá Mts. *(zuliae)*. The Santa Marta region and the tropical upper Magdalena Valley *(pallens)*. The lower Cauca Valley westward and south on the Pacific coast to the Dagua Valley *(accola)*. The Patía Valley southward to Nariño *(implacens)*. The eastern base of the Andes in Nariño *(subsp.?)*.

129. GRAY ELAENIA
(Myiopagis caniceps)

Description. 5½ - 5¾ " (or 4¾ - 5¼ "). ♂ : Above bluish gray with a concealed white coronal patch; throat and breast gray, rest of underparts white. Wings and tail blackish, the inner remiges and wing-coverts broadly edged with white. ♀ : Crown like ♂ , back olive green, edges to wing-coverts, remiges and underparts pale greenish, and under tail-coverts yellow. (or like ♂ , 1). *Immature:* Crown and nape gray, crown patch white; throat and upper breast gray, rest of underparts yellow.

Range. Western and southern Venezuela, northern Brazil, Ecuador, Peru, Bolivia, Paraguay and Argentina.

Colombia. Scrub. Tropical zone. Extreme eastern Colombia in Vaupés *(cinerea)*. Pacific coast from the Baudó Mts. southward (1, *parambae)*.

130. SCRUB FLYCATCHER
(Sublegatus arenarum)

Description. 5½ - 6¼ ". Head somewhat crested. Lores and eye-ring whitish. Above, including wings and tail, ashy brown; wing-coverts and inner remiges pale-edged forming a rather inconspicuous double wing-bar. Throat and breast grayish white (or gray, 1); lower breast and belly pale sulphur yellow, sharply defined from the gray (or not sharply defined, 1; or underparts ashy gray, white in center of belly

only, 2). Bill broader and flatter than in *Elaenia*.

Range. Costa Rica, southward to Venezuela, the Guianas and southward to Peru, the Amazon Valley and northern Bolivia. Trinidad, Tortuga, and the Dutch West Indies.

Colombia. Dry open forest, woodlands near streams and mangroves. Tropical zone of the Caribbean coast and lower Magdalena Valley *(atrirostris)*. East of the Andes in Meta (1, *glaber)*. Meta (accidental?), Vaupés and Putumayo (2, *sordidus)*.

131. MOUSE-COLORED TYRANNULET
(Phaeomyias murina)

Description. 5 - 5½ ". Rather like No. 130 *(atrirostris)* but at once distinguished by much more conspicuous buff to whitish wing-bars, pale eyebrow and much browner back.

Range. Venezuela southward through eastern and western Ecuador and Peru to Bolivia on the west, and the Guianas to Paraguay and Argentina on the east. Trinidad, Ronda Island.

Colombia. Open woods; roadside scrub. Tropical and lower subtropical zone throughout the country particularly in arid regions *(incomta)*.

132. SOUTHERN BEARDLESS TYRANNULET
(Camptostoma obsoletum)

Description. 4½ - 5". Crown dusky (or like back, 1) eye-ring white; back grayish olive (or brownish olive, 1; or olive 2). Throat whitish (or yellowish, 2); rest of underparts pale yellow (or yellow, 2). Wings dusky with two white wing-bars. Tail like back, pale tipped.

Range. Costa Rica southward to western Ecuador, Venezuela, the Guianas, Ecuador, Peru, Bolivia, southeastern Brazil, Paraguay and northern Argentina. Trinidad; the Pearl Islands.

Colombia. Plantations and bushy pastures. Tropical zone. Caribbean coast from the Atrato Valley to La Guajira Peninsula. The lower and middle Magdalena Valley, the Cauca Valley and the west slope of the Western Andes. The Pacific slope of Nariño *(caucae)*. Eastern base of the Andes in

Meta (1, *bogotensis*). East of the Andes in Arauca and Boyacá *(napaeum)*. Base of the Andes in Caquetá (2, *olivaceum*).

133. SOOTY-HEADED TYRANNULET
(Phyllomyias griseiceps)

Description. 4½ - 4¾″. Crown grayish olive (or crested, crown and nape blackish, 1), streak in front of eye and eye-ring white. Back, wings and tail olive (or dark olive, 1). Throat whitish, breast olive, rest of underparts pale yellow. No wing-bars.

Range. Eastern Panama, Venezuela, British Guiana, northern Brazil, Ecuador and eastern Peru.

Colombia. Dry forest. Tropical zone. The Santa Marta region and Magdalena Valley (1, *cristatus*). Upper Cauca Valley (1, *caucae*). The Pacific coast *(griseiceps)*.

134. BLACK-CAPPED TYRANNULET
(Tyranniscus nigro-capillus)

Description. 5 - 5¼″. Short crest, crown and nape black, eyebrow white (or greenish yellow, 1). Back and tail olive. Wings blackish with two conspicuous yellowish white wing-bars, inner remiges margined with yellow. Throat grayish, breast washed olivaceous, rest of underparts yellow (or entire underparts yellow, 1).

Range. Venezuela to Ecuador and Peru.

Colombia. Heavy forest. Subtropical to temperate zone of the Andes in Cundinamarca, Huila, Tolima, Caldas and Cauca *(nigro-capillus)*. Santa Marta Mts. (1, *flavimentum*).

135. TAWNY-RUMPED TYRANNULET
(Tyranniscus uropygialis)

Description. 4½ - 4¾″. Upper surface brown, darkest on crown and becoming tawny on rump and upper tail-coverts. Eyebrow white, sides of head, throat and upper breast grayish white, lower breast isabelline; rest of underparts yellowish white. Wings and tail dark brown, wing-coverts edged with pinkish buff forming a double wing-bar; remiges edged buffy white.

Range. Northern Venezuela. The Andes of Ecuador, Peru and Bolivia.

Colombia. Forest. Subtropical zone of

the Andes. Recorded from Cundinamarca, Cauca and Nariño.

136. ASHY-HEADED TYRANNULET
(Tyranniscus cinereiceps) Plate XVI

Description. 4½ - 4¾″. Lores and ring around eye white. Ear-coverts yellowish green, edged posteriorly with black forming a crescentic mark. Crown gray. Back olive green. Wings and tail dark brown, wing-coverts with yellowish white tips forming wing-bars, remiges edged olive. Chin and upper throat whitish, rest of underparts bright yellow, flammulated on breast with olive.

Range. Northern Venezuela. Ecuador and Peru.

Colombia. Spottily distributed in the subtropical zone of the Andes in Huila, Cundinamarca, Antioquia, Tolima, Caldas and Cauca. Not Santa Marta.

137. PALTRY TYRANNULET
(Tyranniscus vilissimus)

Description. 5 - 5¼″ (or 3¾ - 4¼″, 1). Upper surface, wings and tail olive. Inner remiges and wing-coverts edged with bright yellow. Eyebrow, throat and breast grayish white, becoming yellow on abdomen and under tail-coverts.

Range. Guatemala southward to northern Venezuela.

Colombia. Humid open forest and forest edge. Subtropical zone of the Santa Marta Mts., and the northern end of the Eastern Andes *(tamae)*. Extreme northwestern Colombia (1, *parvus*).

138. GOLDEN-FACED TYRANNULET
(Tyranniscus chrysops)

Description. 5 - 5¼″. Differs chiefly from No. 137 in color by having the lores and eyebrow yellow and the tail-feathers pale tipped.

Range. Venezuela, eastern and western Ecuador and Peru.

Colombia. Forest and scrub. Upper tropical and subtropical zones. Santa Marta Mts. *(minimus)*. Pacific slope of Nariño *(albigularis)*. Rest of Colombia except the Caribbean coast and the Amazonian region *(chrysops)*.

139. SLENDER-FOOTED TYRANNULET
(Tyranniscus gracilipes)

Description. 4¼ - 4¾ ". Lores and eyering yellowish white. Above olive green, grayer on crown. Wings dusky brown, the feathers margined with yellow. Below yellow, clouded on chest with olive. Tail olive brown, margined olive.

Range. Southern Venezuela, the Guianas, northern Brazil, Ecuador, Peru and Bolivia.

Colombia. Forest. Tropical zone. East of the Andes in Vichada, Vaupés and Putumayo *(gracilipes)*.

140. PLUMBEOUS-CROWNED TYRANNULET
(Oreotriccus plumbeiceps) Plate XV

Description. 4¾ - 5¼ ". Crown and nape leaden gray. Eyebrow and sides of head whitish, a dusky streak behind eye. Back, wings and tail olive green, wing-coverts and inner remiges margined with yellow forming a double wing-bar. Throat white; rest of underparts bright yellow, clouded with olive on breast. Tail rather long (2.5"), brownish margined with olive.

Range. Ecuador and Peru.

Colombia. Forest. Subtropical zone of the Andes in Cundinamarca, Huila, Valle, Caldas and Cauca.

141. YELLOW-CROWNED TYRANNULET
(Tyrannulus elatus)

Description. 4 - 4¼ ". Crested. Crown black or blackish olive with a long bright yellow median line. Sides of head and nape gray. Back grayish olive, wings brown, wing-coverts edged with white forming a double wing-bar. Throat grayish white, rest of underparts yellowish olive becoming bright yellow on center of abdomen. Tail brown, edged olive.

Range. Panama southward to Venezuela, the Guianas, northern Brazil, Ecuador, Peru and Bolivia.

Colombia. Thickets and open woods. Tropical zone. West of the Eastern Andes and east of them south to Arauca *(panamensis)*. Southeastern Colombia *(elatus)*.

142. WHITE-FRONTED TYRANNULET
(Acrochordopus zeledoni)

Description. 4¼ - 4½ ". Forehead and ocular region whitish, crown dark gray. Upperparts olive; wings blackish, wing-coverts and inner remiges narrowly margined with yellow. Below yellow, throat and breast tinged with gray. Tail brown margined olive. Upper mandible dark, the lower one flesh color, bill rather thick.

Range. Costa Rica, Western Panama. Southwestern Venezuela, Ecuador and Peru.

Colombia. Forest. Tropical zone. Eastern slope of the Andes in Meta *(leucogonys)*. By some considered a cotinga.

143. WHITE-LORED TYRANNULET
(Ornithion inerme)

Description. 3¾ ". Crown and sides of head plumbeous with a narrow, short, but very distinct white eyebrow and mark at lower edge of eye. Upperparts dark olivaceous. Wings and tail blackish, wing-coverts with a double bar, yellowish white. Chin and upper throat whitish, rest of underparts yellowish green, becoming yellow on center of abdomen.

Range. The Guianas, southern Venezuela, northern Brazil, northeastern Peru and eastern Brazil.

Colombia. Forest. Tropical zone. Vichada and Putumayo.

144. YELLOW-BELLIED TYRANNULET
(Ornithion semiflavum) Plate XV

Description. 3¼ - 3½ ". Crown brown, eyebrow white. Back, wings and tail olive, no wing-bars. Under surface uniform bright yellow. Tail rather short; bill arched and thick.

Range. Mexico southward through Central America to western Ecuador and northern Venezuela.

Colombia. Forest and scrub. Tropical zone. Santa Marta region *(dilutum)*. Pacific coast eastward to the middle Magdalena Valley *(brunneicapillum)*.

145. SLATY-CAPPED FLYCATCHER
(Leptopogon superciliaris)

Description. 5½ - 6". Crown slaty gray. Sides of head and sides of throat mottled grayish and white, the ear-coverts blackish posteriorly. Back olive green. Wing-coverts edged with yellowish (or ochraceous buff, 1), forming a double wing-bar, inner remiges broadly margined pale yellowish. Throat grayish white, breast olivaceous, rest of underparts pale yellow.

Range. Panama southward to Venezuela, Ecuador, Peru and Bolivia. Trinidad.

Colombia. Tropical and lower subtropical zones. The Eastern, Central and Western Andes and the Macarena Mts. (poliocephalus). Western Andes from the region of Cerro Munchique southward (1, transandinus). Caquetá (1, superciliaris).

146. SEPIA-CAPPED FLYCATCHER
(Leptopogon amaurocephalus)
Plate XVI

Description. 5½ - 6". Very similar to No. 145 but crown and nape sepia brown instead of gray.

Range. Guatemala southward to Venezuela, British Guiana, southeastern Brazil, Peru, Bolivia, Paraguay and Argentina.

Colombia. Forest. Tropical zone. Santa Marta region and lower and middle Magdalena Valley (diversus). Southwestern Córdoba (faustus). East of the Eastern Andes from Norte de Santander southward to Caquetá (peruvianus).

147. RUFOUS-BREASTED FLYCATCHER
(Leptopogon rufipectus)

Description. 5½ - 6". Crown and nape leaden gray. Sides of head, throat and breast rufous, lower breast and belly pale yellow. Back olive green. Wings dusky, wing-coverts and remiges edged brown. Tail reddish brown.

Range. Northwestern Venezuela; eastern Ecuador.

Colombia. Forest. Subtropical zone of the west slope of the Eastern Andes in Cundinamarca and Huila and both slopes of the Central Andes in Antioquia, Tolima and Huila.

148. STREAK-NECKED FLYCATCHER
(Mionectes striaticollis)

Description. 5½ - 6¼". Crown and nape gray (or green, 1). Back, wings and tail olive green. Throat and upper breast gray, narrowly streaked with white (or green streaked with yellowish white, 2). Lower breast olive green, pale streaked, rest of underparts yellow streaked on sides with olive.

Range. The Andes of Ecuador, Peru and northern Bolivia.

Colombia. Thick forest. Subtropical zone of the Eastern Andes in Cundinamarca and Huila and the Central Andes in Antioquia, Tolima, Caldas, Valle and Cauca (columbianus). West slope of the Western Andes in Caldas (2, selvae). Pacific slope of Nariño (1, 2, viridiceps).

149. OLIVE-STRIPED FLYCATCHER
(Mionectes olivaceus) Plate XVI

Description. 5¼ - 5¾". Very similar to the Nariño form of No. 148 but breast much more broadly streaked with yellow and wing-coverts with pale, dull ochraceous tips (or differing from other races of No. 148 by throat freckled and breast streaked with yellow, 1).

Range. Costa Rica southward to Venezuela, Ecuador and Peru. Trinidad.

Colombia. Forest. Tropical and subtropical zones. Santa Marta region (1, galbinus). The Eastern Andes, west slope in Magdalena and east slope in Meta (pallidus). East slope of the Andes in Norte de Santander (meridae). The rest of Colombia (hederaceus).

150. OCHRE-BELLIED FLYCATCHER
(Pipromorpha oleaginea)

Description. 5 - 5½". Upperparts olive green; wings dusky, wing-coverts edged with pale (or deep, 1) buff. Throat grayish olivaceous becoming more olivaceous on breast and turning to pale (or deep, 1) ochre on lower breast and belly. Tail brownish edged olive.

Range. Mexico southward through Central America to Venezuela, British Guiana, Brazil, Peru, Bolivia, Trinidad, Tobago.

Colombia. Forest and scrub. Tropical zone from the Panama border eastward to the middle Magdalena and Santa Marta regions (parca). Southwestern Nariño (pacifica). East of the Andes from eastern Cundinamarca and Meta south to Putumayo and Vaupés (1, chloronota).

LARKS (Alaudidae)

Fig. 68. Horned Lark
(Eremophila alpestris)

Of this typically Old World family, only one has succeeded in establishing itself in the New World. The Horned Lark, a holarctic species, is found throughout North America south as far as southern Mexico. It is unknown in Central America, but reappears high up in the Eastern Andes of Colombia!

Horned Larks live on the ground in open country and often are found in swampy meadows. They walk rather than hop. (1 Col.; 1 S.A.; 1 N.&S.A.; 76 wld.)

HORNED LARK
(Eremophila alpestris)

Description. 6½ - 7¼ ". ♂ : Forehead and eyebrow yellowish white. Forecrown and sides of crown black, prolonged backward into two "horns" (absent in winter). Lores and broad stripe below eye and crescentic mark on breast black. Hindcrown, nape, upper mantle, sides of breast, wing-coverts and upper tail-coverts rufous; rest of back and wings brown, the back dark streaked. Throat yellowish, underparts white. Tail black, outer margins of outer tail-feathers white. ♀ : Similar to ♂ but crown, nape and mantle streaked brown and dusky. No "horns." Streak below eye not well marked.

Range. Temperate zone of Europe, north Africa, Asia and North America. Northwestern South America.

Colombia. Open lands and marshy meadows. Temperate zone. Savanna of Bogotá and adjacent plateaus of Cundinamarca and Boyacá *(peregrina)*.

SWALLOWS (Hirundinidae)

Fig. 69. Barn Swallow
(Hirundo rustica) p. 302

Swallows are found virtually throughout the world, look more or less alike and are similar in habits everywhere. In Colombia most of the species are found in the tropical zone and are resident, but a few migrate from elsewhere. (17 Col.; 22 S.A.; 28 N.&S.A.; 78 wld.)

AID TO IDENTIFICATION

Above glossy dark blue (all blue below) 4, 6, (ashy or buff below) 4, 5, 6, 16, (all or mostly white below) 8, 9, 17, (band across breast) 10E, 11E.
Above glossy green (white below) 1, 2, (ashy below), 7.
Above brown or ashy (below white or yellowish) 3, 14, (below ashy) 12, 13E, (banded across breast) 15.

1. TREE SWALLOW
(Tachycineta bicolor)

Description. 5 - 6". ♂ : Above shining bronzy green to blue-green. Entire underparts white. Wings and tail sooty black. Tail slightly forked. ♀ like ♂ but duller above. *Immature:* Sooty brown above, throat and underparts white.

Range. Breeds in North America from Alaska and Newfoundland southward to the middle Atlantic States and California. Winters from southern California and Virginia south to Cuba and Honduras. Recorded rarely as far south as Panama.

Colombia. Accidental. Recorded once (February) on the east slope of the Andes in Nariño.

2. WHITE-WINGED SWALLOW
(Tachycineta albiventer)

Description. 5¼ - 5¾". Upperparts shiny bronzy green to blue-green, feathers in center of mantle basally white. Inner wing-coverts and inner remiges extensively white, forming a white wing patch. Rump and entire underparts white. Tail slightly forked.

Range. Venezuela and the Guianas southward to Brazil, Ecuador, Peru, Bolivia and Argentina. Trinidad.

Colombia. River courses and lagoons. Tropical zone. The Caribbean coast west to the Atrato, the Magdalena Valley and all of Colombia east of the Andes.

299

3. BROWN-CHESTED MARTIN
(Progne tapera)

Description. 6¾ - 7¼ ". Upperparts ashy brown. Throat and abdomen white, breast and sides of body pale ashy brown (or with dusky tear-shaped spots in center of lower breast, 1). Wings and tail brown, tail only slightly forked.

Range. Venezuela and the Guianas, southward to Bolivia and Argentina. Southern birds migrate north to Panama.

Colombia. Savanna, often near water. Tropical, rarely subtropical zones. From the Sinú Valley eastward to the Magdalena Valley and east of the Andes from Norte de Santander eastward and southward *(tapera)*. Migrants from southern South America are found in Colombia during the summer months. (1, *fusca*).

4. PURPLE MARTIN
(Progne subis)

Description. 7½ - 8". ♂ : Uniform glossy steel blue, the wings and tail black, tail forked. ♀ : Above like ♂ but duller. Forehead grayish, throat and breast ashy brown, rest of lower parts soiled white lightly streaked dusky.

Range. Canada south through the United States to lower California, Mexico and the West Indies. In winter, south through Central America to Venezuela, British and Dutch Guiana, southern Brazil and northern Bolivia.

Colombia. Transient, possibly winter resident. Recorded from late August to early December in the temperate zone of the Eastern Andes *(subis)*.

5. GRAY-BREASTED MARTIN
(Progne chalybea)

Description. 6¾ - 7½". ♂ : Above uniform glossy steel blue, wings and tail blacker. Throat and breast ashy brown, rest of underparts white. Tail forked. ♀ : Very similar to No. 4 but smaller and no gray on forehead.

Range. Southern Texas south through Mexico and Central America to Venezuela, the Guianas, Argentina and Bolivia. Trinidad.

Colombia. Mangroves, forest clearings, towns. Tropical zone, probably throughout the country *(chalybea)*.

6. SOUTHERN MARTIN
(Progne modesta)

Description. 6¼ - 6¾ ". ♂ : Entirely glossy steel blue. Very like No. 4, but smaller, with a longer and somewhat more deeply forked tail, lacking the concealed white patch on the flanks, though retaining them on the sides of the lower back. ♀ : Very similar to Nos. 4 and 5 but distinguishable from both by the dark instead of white belly and under tail-coverts. Below entirely dark sooty brown, the feathers edged paler, the edgings paler and wider on the lower abdomen.

Range. Breeds from Bolivia and Argentina southwards. Migrates chiefly to northwestern Brazil. Accidental (?) in eastern Panama and Key West, Florida. The coast of Peru and northern Chile. The Galápagos Islands.

Colombia. While no specimens have been taken, the bird is found commonly in July on the Brazilian side of the río Vaupés. A specimen collected at Obaldía (July) just across the border of eastern Panama must have crossed Colombia to get there *(elegans)*.

7. BROWN-BELLIED SWALLOW
(Notiochelidon murina)

Description. 5¼ - 5¾ ". Upperparts and sides of head glossy, oily green, wings and tail dusky. Underparts dark ashy. Tail forked.

Range. From Venezuela southward through the Andes to Ecuador, Peru and Bolivia.

Colombia. Open slopes. Upper subtropical to temperate zone of the mountains throughout *(murina)*.

8. BLUE-AND-WHITE SWALLOW
(Notiochelidon cyanoleuca)

Description. 5 - 5½". Upperparts, sides of head and sides of breast and under tail-coverts glossy blue-black. Wings, under wing-coverts and tail dusky blackish (or under wing-coverts pale ashy gray, 1). Underparts white. Tail forked. Young birds are ashy brown above, usually with a few glossy blue feathers; the throat and breast mottled with ashy brown, the throat sometimes with a pinkish wash.

Range. Costa Rica southward over South America to Tierra del Fuego. Trinidad. Southern birds migrate northward in the austral winter.

Colombia. Forest edge and pasturelands, towns. Upper tropical to lower temperate zones throughout the country *(cyanoleuca)*. Summer resident recorded from the end of April to early October (1, *patagonica*).

9. PALE-FOOTED SWALLOW
(Notiochelidon flavipes)

Description. 4¾ - 5¼ ". Entire upperparts silky, deep ultramarine blue. Wings, tail, under tail-coverts and sides of body brownish black. Sides of head, throat and upper breast pinkish buff, center of breast and center of abdomen white. Feet pale flesh color. Tail forked.

Range. Southern Peru (one specimen).

Colombia. Forest. Temperate zone of the Central Andes in Caldas and Tolima (two specimens).

10. WHITE-BANDED SWALLOW
(Atticora fasciata)

Description. 5¾ - 6¼ ". Entirely glossy blue-black except for a broad white band across lower breast. Tail rather deeply forked.

Range. The Guianas and southern Venezuela southward to Mato Grosso, Ecuador, Peru and Bolivia.

Colombia. Forested river courses. Tropical zone east of the Eastern Andes from Meta southward to Putumayo and Vaupés.

11. BLACK-COLLARED SWALLOW
(Atticora melanoleuca)

Description. 5½ - 6". Entire upperparts glossy deep blue; below white with a broad blue band across breast; under tail-coverts blue-black. Tail deeply forked.

Range. Southern Venezuela and British Guiana southward through eastern Brazil to Mato Grosso.

Colombia. Forested rivers. Recorded only from Vaupés.

12. WHITE-THIGHED SWALLOW
(Neochelidon tibialis)

Description. 4½ - 4¾ " (or 5 - 5½ ", 1). Crown and back dark brown glossed with greenish black, rump dark brown without gloss (or rump ashy brown in contrast to back, 1). Underparts dark smoky brown (or ashy brown, much paler than back, 1). Wings and tail blackish (or dark brown, 1). Thighs white. Tail forked. *Immature:* Much browner above than adults with no blackish gloss. (Underparts pale ashy, 1). Tail forked.

Range. Panama to western Ecuador. Eastern Ecuador and Peru. Southeastern Brazil.

Colombia. Forest and scrub. Tropical zone. Pacific coast in Valle and Chocó and the middle Magdalena Valley in Antioquia and Santander *(minima)*. East of the Andes in Caquetá (1, *griseiventris)*.

13. TAWNY-HEADED SWALLOW
(Alopochelidon fucata)

Description. 5¼ - 5½". Crown blackish, feathers edged with tawny. Sides of head and collar around hindneck pale rufous. Upperparts, wings and tail pale ashy brown, wings and tail darkest. Throat and breast pinkish buff, rest of underparts white. Tail slightly forked.

Range. British Guiana, Venezuela, Brazil, Paraguay, Uruguay, northern Argentina and Bolivia and Peru.

Colombia. Foothills. The llanos east of the Andes in Boyacá (April). Perhaps a migrant from the south.

14. ROUGH-WINGED SWALLOW
(Stelgidopteryx ruficollis)

Description. 5¼ - 5¾". Upperparts dark brown, ashy (or whitish, 1) on rump. Throat cinnamon buff; breast and sides of body ashy, center of abdomen and under tail-coverts yellowish white. Wings and tail blackish, the inner remiges margined with white. Tail square.

Range. Southern Canada and United States southward through Mexico and Central America to Venezuela, the Guianas, Bolivia and Argentina. Trinidad.

Colombia. River courses, lagoons and clearings. Tropical and subtropical zones. Northern Colombia from the lower Atrato eastward to the Santa Marta region, and east of the Andes south to Meta (1, *aequalis*). The Pacific slope, the upper Cauca Valley and both slopes of the Central Andes in Antioquia, Caldas and Tolima (1, *uropygialis*). East of the Andes in Meta southward to Caquetá (*ruficollis*). All are resident.

15. BANK SWALLOW
(Riparia riparia)

Description. 5 - 5¼ ". Upperparts, wings and tail, band across breast ashy brown; throat and rest of underparts white. Tail slightly forked.

Range. Breeds in North America, Europe, northern Africa and northern Asia. In winter southward to South America, southern Africa and southern Asia.

Colombia. Rivers, coastal marshes. Winter resident. Recorded in September, February and April *(riparia)*.

16. BARN SWALLOW
(Hirundo rustica) Fig. 69

Description. 6¾ - 7". Entire upperparts, sides of head, neck and breast glossy steel blue. Wings blackish. Forehead, throat and center of breast chestnut. Rest of underparts pale buffy white to deep cinnamon-buff. Tail forked, outer tail-feathers lengthened and narrow, inner webs of all but central feathers with a white patch.

Range. Breeds in North America, Europe, northern Africa and Asia. Winters in South America, southern Africa, India, the East Indies and Australia.

Colombia. Open country. Winter resident from end of August to the middle of May *(erythrogaster)*.

17. CLIFF SWALLOW
(Petrochelidon pyrrhonota)

Description. 5¾ - 6". Frontal band buffy white; crown and patch on lower throat glossy blue-black; upper throat, sides of neck, sides of head, prolonged around hindcrown chestnut. Band on hindneck ashy. Back glossy blue-black streaked with white, rump cinnamon. Breast ashy buff, rest of underparts white, upper and under tail-coverts ashy fringed white. Wings and tail blackish, tail square.

Range. Breeds in Canada, United States and Mexico. Winters in Brazil, Argentina and Paraguay.

Colombia. Transient. Recorded in northern Colombia in September and October and Caquetá in April *(pyrrhonota)*.

CROWS, JAYS AND MAGPIES (Corvidae)

Fig. 70. Green Jay
(*Cyanocorax yncas*) p. 305

The phrase "as black as a crow" hardly applies to the Colombian members of this family. They are among the most beautiful of birds, exhibiting mostly shades of blue. True crows, the black ones, do not occur in Colombia, all the members of the family being more properly called jays. (7 Col.; 15 S.A.; 43 N.&S.A.; 100 wld.)

AID TO IDENTIFICATION

Blue above (a black crescent across breast) 1, 2, (head and breast black) 4E, 5E.
Back green 7.
Back dark violet-brown (belly white) 6, (belly violet-blue) 3.

1. COLLARED JAY
(Cyanolyca viridicyana)

Description. 13¼ - 14″. Tail rather long, about 7″. Forehead, sides of head, chin, sides of neck connecting with a narrow band across the breast, black. Crown, nape pale violet-blue shading to violet-blue on back. Throat blue, rest of lower parts deep violet-blue. Wings and tail blue (or similar but bluer, less violet, 1).

Range. Western Venezuela. Northeastern Ecuador.

Colombia. Forest. Subtropical and temperate zone of the Eastern Andes *(armillata)*. Both slopes of the Central Andes in Caldas, and Tolima southward to the head of the Magdalena Valley. The east slope of the Andes in Putumayo and Nariño (1, *quindiuna*).

2. TURQUOISE JAY
(Cyanolyca turcosa)

Description. 13 - 13½″. In pattern exactly similar to No. 1 but tail shorter. Forecrown bluish white shading to bright blue on hindcrown. Throat bright cornflower blue; rest of plumage turquoise blue.

Range. Ecuador and northern Peru.

Colombia. Forest. Temperate zone of the Andes of Nariño, both slopes.

3. BEAUTIFUL JAY
(Cyanolyca pulchra)

Description. 11 - 11½″. Forehead, lores, chin, sides of head, black. Forecrown milky blue shading to violet-blue on upper mantle. Back and breast dusky violet-brown. Rump, upper tail-coverts and ab-

PLATE XVI

FULVOUS-BREASTED
FLATBILL
(*Rhynchocyclus fulvipectus*)
Page 284

NORTHERN ROYAL
FLYCATCHER
(*Onychorhynchus mexi-
canus fraterculus*)
Page 282

BLACK-HEADED
TODY-FLYCATCHER
(*Todirostrum chryso-
crotaphum nigriceps*)
Page 285

BOAT-BILLED
FLYCATCHER
(*Megarynchus p. pitangua*)
Page 275

OLIVE-STRIPED
FLYCATCHER
(*Mionectes oliv-
aceus hederaceus*)
Page 297

SEPIA-CAPPED
FLYCATCHER
(*Leptopogon amauro-
cephalus faustus*)
Page 297

RUSTY-MARGINED
FLYCATCHER
(*Myiozetetes caya-
nensis hellmayri*)
Page 276

ORNATE FLYCATCHER
(*Myiotriccus
ornatus stellatus*)
Page 281

ASHY-HEADED
TYRANNULET
(*Tyranniscus cinereiceps*)
Page 295

BLACK-THROATED
TODY-TYRANT
(*Idioptilon grana-
densis lehmanni*)
Page 286

SLATY-BACKED
CHAT-TYRANT
(*Ochthoeca c. cin-
namomeiventris*)
Page 270

BLACK-TAILED
FLYCATCHER
(*Myiobius a. atricaudus*)
Page 280

E.L.Poole

domen dark violet. Wings and tail violet-blue.

Range. Northwestern Ecuador.

Colombia. Thick forest. Upper tropical and subtropical zone of the west slope of the Western Andes from the upper río San Juan southward to Nariño.

4. VIOLACEOUS JAY
(Cyanocorax violaceus)

Description. 14¾ - 15¼ ″. Mostly violet-blue. Top and sides of head, throat and breast black, head with a short crest. Narrow band across nape extending to behind ear-coverts whitish.

Range. Southern Venezuela and British Guiana southward to northern Brazil, Ecuador and Peru.

Colombia. Open woods and forest. Tropical zone east of the Eastern Andes from Meta southward to Caquetá *(violaceus).*

5. AZURE-NAPED JAY
(Cyanocorax heilprini)

Description. 14 - 15″. Forehead, forecrown, sides of head, throat and upper breast black, the feathers of forehead and forecrown stiff and upstanding. Short moustacial streak pale blue. Hindcrown and nape milky blue, rest of plumage violet-blue. Under tail-coverts and tips of tail-feathers white.

Range. Northwestern Brazil; southern Venezuela.

Colombia. Forest. Vaupés.

6. BLACK-CHESTED JAY
(Cyanocorax affinis)

Description. 14 - 15″. Crown, sides of head, throat and breast black. Ring around eye and moustacial streak cobalt blue. Nape pale violet-blue; back violet-brown. Wings and tail dark blue. Underparts and tips of tail-feathers white.

Range. Costa Rica to western Venezuela.

Colombia. Woodland and scrub. Tropical and subtropical zones. Eastern Andes southward to the latitude of Bogotá *(affinis).* Santa Marta region westward to northern Chocó *(sclateri).* Birds from near the Panama border are yellowish white below and approach the Panamanian race *zeledoni.*

7. GREEN JAY
(Cyanocorax yncas) Fig. 70

Description. 12½ - 13½ ″. Frontal feathers stiff, directed forward (much lengthened, 1). Frontal feathers, line above eye and cheeks cobalt blue. Crown and nape white tinged blue (or blue, 2). Sides of head, throat and breast black. Back, wings and central tail-feathers bright green (or bluish green, 2); underparts and rest of tail-feathers bright yellow.

Range. Southern Texas through Mexico to Honduras. Northern Venezuela, eastern Ecuador, Peru and Bolivia.

Colombia. Forest and scrub. Subtropical zone. West slope of the Eastern Andes westward to the Pacific coast and southward to the upper río San Juan (1, *galeata).* Upper Cauca and Patía Valleys and the east slope of the Andes in Nariño *(yncas).* Eastern slope of the Eastern Andes from Norte de Santander southward to the Bogotá region (2, *cyanodorsalis).*

DIPPERS (Cinclidae)

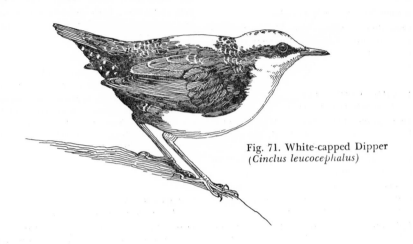

Fig. 71. White-capped Dipper
(*Cinclus leucocephalus*)

Dippers are long-legged, short-tailed birds which rather resemble large wrens. They live along the banks and among the rocks of fast-flowing mountain streams, swim and dive expertly, and walk submerged along the bottom. They are restless birds and fly swiftly, close over the water. They live on mollusks, small fish, worms and some vegetable matter.

Not differing in habits, dippers are found in North and South America, Europe and Asia. The name dipper is derived from the habit of bobbing up and down. They build large domed nests with the entrance at the side which is placed just above the water. (1 Col.; 1 S.A.; 2 N.&S.A.; 4 wld.)

WHITE-CAPPED DIPPER
(Cinclus leucocephalus)

Description. 5½ - 6". Crown and throat white, sides of head dark gray, rest of plumage deep mouse gray (or above blackish brown with crown patch, middle of back and entire underparts white, 1).

Range. Venezuela, southward in the Andes to Ecuador, Peru and Bolivia.

Colombia. Subtropical and temperate, occasionally upper tropical zones. The Santa Marta Mts. *(rivularis)*. All three Andean ranges (1, *leuconotus*).

306

WRENS (Troglodytidae)

Fig. 72. Gray-breasted Wood-Wren
(Henicorhina leucophrys) p. 312

All of the known species of wren occur in the Americas; only one, the Winter Wren, has spread elsewhere and is widely distributed in Europe, Asia and North Africa.

Most wrens are excellent songsters, and many are familiar and tame. The many Colombian species are inhabitants of forest and second growth but some are found in xerophytic vegetation, and others in marshes high up in the Andes.

Wrens are soberly colored, shades of brown prevailing, alleviated in some species by white or rufous; some are streaked or barred. Mostly solitary, they live on insects and are usually non-migratory. (27 Col.; 38 S.A.; 61 N.&S.A.; 61 wld.)

AID TO IDENTIFICATION

Spotted or barred below:
  Spotted below 2, 3, 4, 12, 15.
  Barred below 11, 15, 16, 25.
Neither barred nor spotted below:
  White below 1, 2, 5, 18, 19, 23, 25.
  Brown or rufous 6, 7, 10, 17, 26, 27.
  Gray below 13, 14E, 24.
  Buff below 20, 21, 22, (back striped) 8, 9.

1. BICOLORED WREN
(Campylorhynchus griseus)

Description. 7½ - 8″ (or 9 - 10″, 1) . Entire underparts and broad eyebrow white. Crown, nape, upper mantle and stripe through eye blackish brown; lower back, rump and upper tail-coverts reddish brown, (or entire back blackish brown, 1; or entire back reddish brown, 2). Wings dark brown the coverts edged reddish brown (or uniform, 1). Tail blackish brown (or wings and tail with obscure dark bars, 2). All but central tail-feathers with a wide subterminal white band.

Range. Venezuela, British Guiana and northern Brazil.

Colombia. Semi-arid savanna, brushlands, open woods. Tropical zone. The Guajira Peninsula westward to the upper Sinú Valley *(albicilius)*. West slope of the Eastern Andes in Santander and Boyacá (1, *bicolor)*. Arid part of the upper Magdalena Valley in Huila and Tolima (1, *zimmeri)*. Eastern base of the Eastern Andes in Meta (2, *minor)*. Southern Meta and probably Vaupés *(pallidus)*.

307

2. THRUSH-LIKE WREN
(or, WHITE-HEADED WREN, 1)
(Campylorhynchus turdinus)

Description. 8 - 8¼". Above dark brown, feathers pale edged giving a scaled appearance. Wings dark brown, outer remiges notched paler on outer web. Below white, heavily spotted everywhere, except throat, with dusky. Tail uniform dark brown (or head and underparts white; back, wings and tail chocolate brown, 1; or showing various stages of intermediacy between the above two, 2).

Range. Panama southward to Ecuador, Peru, Bolivia and eastern, central and southeastern Brazil.

Colombia. Forest, scrub. Tropical zone east of the Eastern Andes *(hypostictus)*. The Gulf of Urabá and the Pacific coast south to the lower río San Juan (1, *harterti)*. Southwestern Nariño (2, *aenigmaticus)*.

3. STRIPE-BACKED WREN
(Campylorhynchus nuchalis)

Description. 7¼ - 8". Crown ashy white, feathers with black centers; eyebrow white. Slightly marked nuchal collar pale cinnamon-buff. Back, wings and tail black, the back striped and spotted with white; wings and tail notched with white. Below white, spotted everywhere, except throat, with black.

Range. Northern and central Venezuela.

Colombia. Forest. Tropical zone. Caribbean coast from the Sinú Valley eastward. The Magdalena Valley south to 8° N. *(pardus)*.

4. BAND-BACKED WREN
(Campylorhynchus zonatus)

Description. 7¾ - 8¼". Crown ashy, feathers with dark centers. Back, wings and tail regularly barred brownish black and buffy white. Throat and breast white, profusely spotted with blackish. Abdomen cinnamon-buff (or pale pinkish buff, 1), barred on sides with blackish.

Range. Mexico southward to western Panama. Western Ecuador.

Colombia. Open woodland and scrub. Tropical zone. Southern base of the Santa Marta Mts. *(curvirostris)*. Eastern Atlántico *(brevirostris)*. Western Atlántico westward to Córdoba (1, *imparilis)*.

5. GRAY-MANTLED WREN
(Odontorchilus branickii)

Description. 4¾ - 5¼". Crown and nape dull ashy brown brighter on forehead; sides of head and eyebrow streaked dark gray and white. Back and wings ashy gray. Tail ashy gray, banded white; under tail-coverts barred black and white.

Range. Northwestern and eastern Ecuador and Peru.

Colombia. Subtropical zone at the head of the Magdalena Valley *(branickii)*.

6. RUFOUS WREN
(Cinnycerthia unirufa)

Description. 6¾ - 7¼" (or 7¼ - 7¾", 1). Lores dusky, otherwise uniform cinnamon-rufous, the wings obscurely barred with black (or uniform reddish brown, wings and tail obscurely barred with black, 1). Iris red or dark brown (or iris white or gray, 2). Young birds have the forecrown and sides of head whitish.

Range. Western Venezuela and Ecuador.

Colombia. Forest. Subtropical and tropical zone. The Perijá Mts. (2, *chakei)*. Eastern Andes from Cundinamarca northward to the Sierra de Perijá *(1, unirufa)*. Central and probably Western Andes and Nariño *(unibrunnea)*.

7. SEPIA-BROWN WREN
(Cinnycerthia peruana)

Description. 6 - 6¼". Upperparts reddish brown; lower parts sepia brown. Wings and tail sharply barred with black. Often a white spot or patch is present on forehead or forecrown. Young birds have the throat gray.

Range. Ecuador, Peru and Bolivia.

Colombia. Forest. Subtropical to temperate zone on the west slope of the Eastern Andes in Cundinamarca and Huila; the east slope in Nariño *(bogotensis)*. Central and Western Andes and western Nariño *(olivascens)*.

8. SHORT-BILLED MARSH WREN
(Cistothorus platensis)

Description. 4¼ - 4½". Crown uniform brown (or feathers tipped ashy, 1). Mantle blackish streaked with buffy white. Under surface mostly buffy (or white, 1). Wings and tail brown, barred with dusky.

Range. Eastern North America southward through Mexico to western Panama. British Guiana, northern and western Venezuela southward through the Andes to Tierra del Fuego. Falkland Islands. Birds breeding in North America winter in Florida and on the Gulf coast.

Colombia. Grassy swamps. Upper tropical to lower temperate zone of the Santa Marta Mts. (1, alticola). Temperate and páramo zones of the Eastern Andes from Norte de Santander to Cundinamarca (tamae). Central Andes at their northern end (tolimae). Subtropical to temperate zone of the southern end of the Central and Western Andes and the mountains of Nariño (aequatorialis).

9. APOLINAR'S MARSH WREN
(Cistothorus apolinari)

Description. 5¼ - 5½". A large replica of No. 8 with whitish underparts.

Range. Colombia.

Colombia. Marshes. Temperate and páramo zone. The Bogotá savanna and Páramo de Sumapaz.

10. SOOTY-HEADED WREN
(Thryothorus spadix)

Description. 6¼ - 6½". Crown sooty black; sides of head and throat deep black; stripe behind eye white, ear-coverts striped with white. Back chestnut. Breast rufous-chestnut, center of abdomen buffy, obscurely barred with black. Tail black regularly barred with rufous-brown.

Range. Eastern Panama.

Colombia. Upper tropical and lower subtropical zones of the Pacific coast from the upper río San Juan south to Cerro Munchique.

11. BAND-BELLIED WREN
(Thryothorus fasciato-ventris)

Description. 6¼ - 6¾". Upperparts and wings reddish brown. Eyebrow white, sides of head sooty gray (or lower part of ear-coverts white, 1). Throat and breast white, the breast margined with black; rest of underparts black, barred with white on lower breast and center of abdomen and with reddish brown on flanks.

Range. Costa Rica and Panama.

Colombia. Forest. Tropical zone. Santa Marta region southward to the middle Magdalena Valley and westward to the Sinú and lower Cauca Valleys (fasciato-ventris). The lower Atrato Valley and the west coast south to the río San Juan (1, albigularis).

12. SPOTTED-CHESTED WREN
(Thryothorus euophrys)

Description. 6½ - 7". Crown olive brown somewhat mottled with black; rest of upperparts, wings and tail cinnamon-rufous. Eyebrow white, stripe through eye black, ear-coverts streaked black and white. Upper breast white heavily spotted with black; center of underparts grayish obscurely spotted with black, sides of body and under tail-coverts rufescent.

Range. Ecuador, northern Peru.

Colombia. Forest. Upper subtropical zone of the west slope of the Andes in Nariño (euophrys).

13. MOUSTACHED WREN
(Thryothorus genibarbis)

Description. 6¼ - 7". Lores, eyebrow and eye-ring white, cheeks and ear-coverts streaked black and white bordered below by a white band, this in turn bordered by a broad black moustacial band. Top of head, nape and upper mantle, sides of neck ashy gray; rest of back and wings chestnut. Throat white, breast gray, belly and flanks tawny brown to olive brown (or pale grayish brown, 1). Tail chestnut (or olive, 2) barred with black.

Range. Northern Venezuela, eastern Ecuador, Peru, Brazil and northern Bolivia.

Colombia. Tangled thickets. Upper tropical and subtropical zone. West slope of the Eastern Andes from Santander to Huila and east slope of the Central Andes from Antioquia southward to the head of the

Magdalena Valley (2, *macrurus*). West slope of the Western Andes from Valle to Cauca and the upper Cauca Valley (1, *saltuensis*). Interior of western Nariño *(yananchae)*. East slope of the Eastern Andes from Santander southward to Meta, the west slope in Norte de Santander *(amaurogaster)*.

14. CORAYA WREN
(Thryothorus coraya)

Description. 6½ - 6¾ ". Crown and nape dusky brown gradually turning to chestnut brown on back and rump. Wings reddish brown. Sides of head streaked black and white, a broad black moustacial streak and narrow white eyebrow. Throat white, breast gray, sides of body reddish brown (or only slightly shaded with paler reddish brown, 1). Tail black barred with brown.

Range. The Guianas, Venezuela and the middle and upper Amazon Valley to eastern Ecuador and eastern Peru.

Colombia. Forest. Tropical zone east of the Andes from southern Meta southward to Putumayo and Amazonas *(griseipectus)*. Vaupés (1, *caurensis*).

15. SPECKLED WREN
(Thryothorus rutilus)

Description. 5¾ - 6". Upperparts and wings dull grayish brown, tinged rufous on head. Tail gray barred with blackish. Sides of head, neck and throat white, spotted with black. Breast orange-rufous (or orange-rufous spotted with black, 1), center of abdomen white, sides of body rufous-brown (or sandy brown, 2; or entire underparts white regularly banded all over with black, 3).

Range. Costa Rica southward to western Ecuador and western Peru. Northern Venezuela. Trinidad and Tobago.

Colombia. Tangled undergrowth in woodlands. Tropical zone. East slope of the Andes in Norte de Santander *(rutilus)*. East slope of the Andes in Boyacá and Meta (2, *hypospodius*). The foothills of the Santa Marta Mts. (1, *laetus*). West slope of the Eastern Andes in Magdalena, Norte de Santander and Santander

(interior). Subtropical zone of the west slope of the Central Andes in Valle and possibly the west slope of the Eastern Andes in Tolima (3, *columbianus*).

16. BLACK-CAPPED WREN
(Thryothorus nigricapillus)

Description. 6 - 6¼ ". Crown, nape and sides of head deep black, eyebrow, lores, hind portion of ear-coverts and moustacial streak white. Above chestnut, wings and tail barred black. Throat, breast and center of abdomen white banded with black (or throat white, breast and center of abdomen banded with black, 1). Flanks, under tail-coverts reddish brown, banded with black.

Range. Nicaragua southward to southwestern Ecuador.

Colombia. Forest, scrub. Tropical and lower subtropical zone. West shore of Gulf of Urabá and the Pacific coast south to the Baudó Mts. *(schottii)*. The lower río San Juan southward to Nariño (1, *connectens*) .

17. STRIPE-THROATED WREN
(Thryothorus thoracicus)

Description. 5 - 5¼ ". Upperparts, wings and tail dark earthy brown (or grayish brown, 1), wings and tail banded with black. Eyebrow white. Throat and sides of head streaked black and white. Underparts like back but paler.

Range. Nicaragua southward to western Ecuador.

Colombia. Forest. Tropical zone. Córdoba; the Pacific coast southward to Nariño *(leucopogon)*. The west shore of the Gulf of Urabá (1, *grisescens*).

18. RUFOUS-AND-WHITE WREN
(Thryothorus rufalbus)

Description. 6¼ - 6¾ ". Long eyebrow white, stripe behind eye rufous-chestnut, ear-coverts and cheeks streaked black and white. Upperparts bright rufous-chestnut, wings and tail barred with black, feathers of rump with concealed white spots (or upper surface rufous-brown, the crown dusky brown, 1). Lowerparts white, flanks reddish brown, under tail-coverts barred black and white.

Range. Southern Mexico southward to western Panama. Western Venezuela. Colombia. Brushy plains and woods. Tropical zone. Caribbean coast as far west as Cartagena (cumanensis). East of the Andes in Magdalena, Norte de Santander and Boyacá southward to the Macarena Mts. (1, minlosi).

19. NICEFORO'S WREN
(Thryothorus nicefori)

Description. 6½ - 6¾". Upperparts, wings and tail olive brown, somewhat more rufescent on lower back and rump where obsoletely barred with black, feathers of lower back with large concealed round white spots which are margined with black. Wings and tail olive brown barred with black. Lores and eyebrow white, streak behind eye olive brown, cheeks and ear-coverts and sides of neck streaked black and white. Throat and underparts white, sides of breast and body pale olive brown, under tail-coverts barred black and white.

Range. Colombia.

Colombia. Woods, coffee plantations. Upper tropical zone. West slope of the Eastern Andes in Santander.

20. BUFF-BREASTED WREN
(Thryothorus leucotis)

Description. 5¼ - 5¾". Eyebrow white, sides of head white streaked dusky. Upperparts reddish brown. Throat white becoming buffy on breast and deepening to deep cinnamon-buff on belly and sides of body (or white in center of abdomen, buff on sides only, 1). Wings and tail reddish brown barred with black.

Range. Pearl Islands and Panama. Venezuela, the Guianas, Brazil, Ecuador and Peru.

Colombia. Woods and thickets. Tropical zone. Northeastern Chocó and northern Antioquia (galbraithii). From the west side of the Santa Marta Mts. westward to the Sinú Valley. The Magdalena Valley (leucotis). North and east of the Santa Marta Mts. (1, venezuelanus). The Macuira Mts. on the Guajira Peninsula (collinus). East of the Andes in Norte de Santander

(zuliensis). East of the Andes in Meta and Vichada (bogotensis). Caquetá (peruanus).

21. HOUSE WREN
(Troglodytes aëdon)

Description. 5 - 5¾". Upperparts, brown to grayish brown, the mantle sometimes with a few black bars, rump with concealed white spots. Lores and eyebrow buffy white. Below more or less uniform pinkish buff (or throat and abdomen white, breast and sides of body pinkish buff, 1). Wings and tail like back barred with dusky. Under tail-coverts cinnamon-buff (or pale buff barred with dusky, 2).

Range. Canada and the United States to Mexico southward through Central America to Venezuela, the Guianas and Tierra del Fuego. West Indies; Trinidad and Tobago; Falkland Islands.

Colombia. Gardens, scrub and pastureland. Tropical to temperate zone. The Guajira Peninsula; the lower and middle Ranchería Valley in extreme northeastern Magdalena (effutitus). The Caribbean coast region from Atlántico eastward to the Guajira Peninsula; lower Magdalena Valley south to about 7°N. East of the Andes in the Zulia lowlands (atopus). Both slopes of the Eastern Andes in the subtropical zones from Norte de Santander to Cundinamarca (columbae). Upper Magdalena and middle and upper Cauca Valleys, upper Sinú Valley westward and down the Pacific coast to the río Dagua (1, 2, striatulus). Shores of the Gulf of Urabá (inquietus). Tropical zone east of the Eastern Andes from Norte de Santander southward to Meta and Vaupés. Pacific slope of Nariño (1, albicans).

22. MOUNTAIN WREN
(Troglodytes solstitialis)

Description. 4½ - 4¾". Above reddish brown, wings and tail like back barred with black. Eyebrow, sides of head, throat and breast tawny buff (or pale buff, 1; or clay color, 2). Sides of body reddish brown, under tail-coverts barred black and white.

Range. Southern Mexico to Panama. Northern Venezuela southward through the Andes to southern Bolivia and western Argentina.

Colombia. Forest and thick undergrowth. Subtropical to páramo zone. Eastern and Central Andes and eastern slope of the Western Andes (1, *solitarius*). The Santa Marta Mts. (2, *monticola*). Head of the Magdalena Valley and both slopes of the Andes of Nariño (*solstitialis*).

23. WHITE-BREASTED WOOD-WREN
(Henicorhina leucosticta)

Description. 4¼ - 4½″. Crown and nape blackish brown or black (or rufous-brown margined at sides with black, 1). Long eyebrow white, postocular streak black, lower part of cheeks and sides of neck streaked black and white. Back rufous, wings and tail rufous-brown barred with black, wing-coverts with a few white spots. Throat, breast and center of abdomen white, sides of breast gray, flanks rufous-brown. Young birds have the breast grayish.

Range. Mexico southward through Central America to Venezuela, northern Brazil, Ecuador and Peru.

Colombia. Forest and scrub. Upper tropical and subtropical zones. From the Sinú Valley westward to the Panama border and southward to the Baudó Mts. *(darienensis)*. Lower and middle Cauca Valley eastward to the middle Magdalena Valley *(albilateralis)*. Western slope of the Western Andes at the headwaters of the río Dagua *(eucharis)*. From the lower río San Juan southward to Nariño (1, *inornata*). East of the Andes from Meta southward to Caquetá *(hauxwelli)*.

24. GRAY-BREASTED WOOD-WREN
(Henicorhina leucophrys) Fig. 72

Description. 4¾ - 5″. Crown brown, margined at sides with black, otherwise very similar to No. 23 but adults at once distinguishable by gray instead of white breast, (or grayish white breast, 1) and less richly colored flanks. The crown olive brown, in slight contrast to back, not black or rufous (except rufous-brown in 2).

Range. Mexico southward through Central America to western Panama. Northern and western Venezuela southward through the Andes to Bolivia.

Colombia. Forest and thick undergrowth. Upper tropical and subtropical zone of the Santa Marta Mts. *(bangsi)*. Upper subtropical and temperate zones of the Santa Marta Mts. (1, *anachoreta*). Subtropical zone. East slope of the Eastern Andes from Norte de Santander to southern Meta *(tamae)*. Subtropical and temperate zones. West slope of the Eastern Andes from Magdalena southward to Cundinamarca, the eastern slope in Nariño. The Central Andes from Antioquia and east slope of the Western Andes from Valle south to Nariño *(leucophrys)*. Upper tropical zone. Upper Atrato Valley *(subsp.)*. Upper tropical and subtropical zones. The west slope of the Western Andes from the headwaters of the río San Juan southward to Nariño (2, *brunneiceps)*.

25. NIGHTINGALE WREN
(Microcerculus marginatus)

Description. 5 - 5¼″. Bill long. Above deep reddish brown. Lores and sides of head grayish. Below white, sides of body reddish brown. Very young birds are uniform dark brown below, the throat whitish. Older ones have the throat, breast and abdomen white barred with black; as the birds mature, the bars on the under surface disappear.

Range. Southern Mexico to Honduras. Costa Rica southward to western Ecuador. Northwestern Venezuela, northwestern and western Brazil, Ecuador and Peru eastward south of the Amazon to Pará and southward to Bolivia.

Colombia. Forest. Tropical zone. Extreme northwestern Colombia in Chocó *(philomela)*. Córdoba and Antioquia southward down the Pacific coast to Nariño *(taeniatus)*. The Santa Marta region *(corrasus)*. East of the Andes in Norte de Santander and the west slope in Magdalena *(squamulatus)*. Meta southward to Caquetá *(marginatus)*.

26. CHESTNUT-BREASTED WREN
(Cyphorhinus thoracicus)

Description. 6¼ - 6¾″. Bill somewhat elevated at base; feathers of forehead and lores stiff and erect. Crown, lores and eye-ring blackish brown, ear-coverts, sides of neck, throat and breast orange-chestnut, belly dark brown. Back deep wood brown, wings and tail darker.

Range. Ecuador and Peru.

Colombia. Forest undergrowth. Upper tropical and subtropical zones of the Central and Western Andes in Antioquia, Tolima, Valle and Cauca *(dichrous)*.

27. MUSICIAN WREN
(Cyphorhinus aradus) Plate XVIII

Description. 5¼ - 5½ ". Forehead, forecrown, eyebrow, throat and upper breast orange-rufous (or forehead dark reddish brown like back, no eyebrow, throat and breast chestnut, 1). Back, wings and tail, sides of body and belly dark reddish brown (upper belly grayish, 2) , wings and tail barred with black.

Range. Honduras southward to western Ecuador. Venezuela and the Guianas southward to the middle and upper Amazon, Ecuador, Peru and Bolivia.

Colombia. Forest. Tropical zone. The Sinú and lower Cauca Valleys eastward to the Magdalena and Lebrija Valleys (1, *propinquus*). Region about the mouth of the Atrato south to Murindó in Antioquia (1, 2, *lawrencii):* a certain amount of albinism is present in these two races, the throat and sometimes even the breast appearing as white instead of chestnut. The Pacific coast from the Panama border southward to the Baudó Mts. (1, *chocoanus*). Lower río San Juan southward to Nariño (1, *phaeocephalus*). East of the Andes in Caquetá *(transfluvialis);* Putumayo and eastern Nariño *(salvini)*.

CATBIRDS AND MOCKINGBIRDS (Mimidae)

Fig. 73. Tropical Mockingbird
(Mimus gilvus)

Members of this family are found only in the New World. They are bold and inquisitive birds and make their presence known by their loud and often beautiful song. They can, however, make very unpleasant sounds and skillfully imitate the sounds made by other birds.

In appearance they differ from thrushes by their much longer tails and long and somewhat curved bills. Mostly clothed in shades of gray and brown they live near the ground and eat insects and small fruits. They build open, cup-shaped nests which are placed in low bushes: the Black-capped Mockingthrush, however, builds a large globular nest. (3 Col.; 10 S.A.; 30 N.&S.A.; 30 wld.)

COMMON CATBIRD
(Dumetella carolinensis)

Description. 8½ - 9¼″. General plumage leaden gray; cap black; under tail-coverts chestnut.

Range. Breeds in North America. Winters in the southern United States, the Bahamas, West Indies, Mexico and Central America to western Panama.

Colombia. Accidental. Recorded once from Magdalena (March 23).

TROPICAL MOCKINGBIRD
(Mimus gilvus)

Description. 10 - 10½″. Above pale gray. Stripe through eye blackish, eyebrow and entire underparts dirty white. Wings and tail dark brownish black, the wing-coverts and remiges margined with white, tail-feathers with broad white tips.

Range. Lesser Antilles, the islands in the southern Caribbean. Mexico southward to Panama. Locally in Venezeula, the Gui-

314

anas, extreme northern Brazil. Pará southward coastally to Rio de Janeiro. Trinidad and Tobago. The lesser Antilles. San Andres and the Dutch and Venezuelan islands of the southern Caribbean.

Colombia. Tropical and subtropical zones. East of the Andes from Meta northward. Caribbean coast westward to Atlántico and up the Magdalena Valley to 6°N. *(melanopterus);* the rest of Colombia excepting Nariño *(tolimensis).*

BLACK-CAPPED MOCKINGTHRUSH
(Donacobius atricapillus)

Description. 9 - 9¼". Crown, nape, sides of head and neck, and extreme upper mantle black, rest of back seal brown (or blackish brown, 1), becoming rufescent on rump and upper tail-coverts, a buff band across rump. Entire underparts ochraceous, more or less barred on sides of body with black. Wings and tail blackish brown, remiges basally white, rectrices much graduated, outer ones mostly white, rest broadly tipped white, central pair with a very narrow white tip.

Range. Panama southward to Venezuela, the Guianas, Brazil, Ecuador, Peru, Bolivia, Paraguay and Argentina.

Colombia. Scrub, marshes and flooded forest. Tropical zone. The Santa Marta region. The Magdalena Valley westward to the lower Atrato *(brachypterus).* East of the Andes from Meta northward *(atricapillus).* Putumayo and Caquetá (1, *nigrodorsalis).*

THRUSHES (Turdidae)

Fig. 74. Great Thrush
(*Turdus fuscater*) p. 318

Thrushes form a large family of smallish to medium-sized birds, widely distributed throughout the temperate and tropical parts of the world, many tropical varieties inhabiting mountainous country. Many northern species migrate southward in winter, forming loose flocks. They feed on fruit, snails, worms and other invertebrates. Among the foremost of songbirds, the most famous of all is probably the nightingale of the Old World.

Thrushes are usually dull-colored but sometimes attractively patterned birds: black, gray, chestnut, cinnamon, brown and olive, and combinations thereof predominating. Only a few species, among which are the North American bluebirds and two species of aberrant Asiatic thrushes, exhibit shades of bright blue, green and purple.

Colombian thrushes vary in size from the foot-long Great Thrush to the nightingale-thrushes, less than half as big. They are largely terrestrial and run, rather than hop, along the ground. The solitaires, however, differ from typical thrushes by having short legs and live a strictly arboreal life. (21 Col.; 35 S.A.; 58 N.&S.A.; 319 wld.)

AID TO IDENTIFICATION

Size very large, over 12 inches.
  Mostly sooty gray to olive gray 11.
Size smaller, under 11 inches.
  Above rufous-brown to olive brown, throat unstreaked, breast gray or soiled white
      unspotted 1, 3, 4, (spotted) 5, 6, 7, 8,
  Above brown or olive, throat streaked (under wing-coverts not in contrast to lower
      parts) 16, 18E, 19, 20, 21, (under wing-coverts orange-rufous) 13, 15, 17.
  All or mostly black 10, 12, (cheeks and outer tail-feathers white) 2.
  Above gray or olive, head all or mostly black 4, 5, 9, 13, 14,

316

1. ANDEAN SOLITAIRE
(Myadestes ralloides)

Description. 7¼ - 7¾". Forehead, forecrown, sides of head and underparts plumbeous gray. Hindcrown, back, wings reddish brown (or chestnut brown, 1). Base of primaries white. Tail dull brown, outer tail-feathers tipped with white. In the solitaires the bill is short and broad at the base, more like that of a flycatcher than a thrush.

Range. Costa Rica, Panama. Northern Venezuela, Ecuador, Peru and Bolivia.

Colombia. Forest. Subtropical zone. Both slopes of the Eastern Andes in Norte de Santander. East of the Andes in Boyacá and the Macarena Mts. *(venezuelensis).* Head of the Magdalena Valley (1, *candelae).* Central and Western Andes from Antioquia southward to Nariño *(plumbeiceps).*

2. BLACK SOLITAIRE
(Entomodestes coracinus) Plate XVIII

Description. 9¼ - 9¾". Mainly lustrous black. Malar region, cheeks, pectoral tufts white. Basal portion of inner web of primaries white; under wing-coverts black and white. Central tail-feathers black, outer ones broadly tipped white. Mandible orange.

Range. Western Ecuador.

Colombia. Upper branches of tall forest trees. Upper tropical and subtropical zone of the Western Andes from Antioquia southward to Nariño.

3. ORANGE-BILLED NIGHTINGALE-THRUSH
(Catharus aurantiirostris)

Description. 6¾ - 7¼". Upperparts, sides of head, wings and tail cinnamon brown (or olive brown, 1; or crown, sides of head and nape ashy gray, rest of upperparts olive brown, 2). Throat and abdomen white. Breast and sides of body pale gray (or dark gray, 2). Eye-ring and bill orange, legs yellow.

Range. Mexico to western Panama. Venezuela. Trinidad.

Colombia. Dense second growth, forest edge. Upper tropical and lower subtropical zone. Santa Marta Mts. *(sierrae).* East of the Andes in Norte de Santander *(aurantiirostris).* West slope of the Eastern Andes in Santander (1, *inornatus).* Upper Magdalena Valley *(insignis).* Upper Cauca and upper Patía Valleys southward into Nariño (2, *phaeopleurus).*

4. SLATY-BACKED NIGHTINGALE-THRUSH
(Catharus fuscater)

Description. 7½ - 8". Upperparts, sides of head, wings and tail dark slaty gray (or top and sides of head and chin slaty black, 1). Underparts mostly pale gray, abdomen white (or throat, breast and sides of body dark gray, center of abdomen white, 1; or upperparts, wings and tail brownish gray; throat, lower breast and abdomen whitish, upper breast and sides of body brownish gray, 2). Bill and feet orange-yellow.

Range. Costa Rica southward to the mountains of Bolivia.

Colombia. Forest. Upper tropical and subtropical zones. Santa Marta Mts. (1, *sanctae-martae).* Eastern Andes from Magdalena, southward to Boyacá and Santander *(fuscater).* Western Andes at their northern end (2, *opertaneus).*

5. SPOTTED NIGHTINGALE-THRUSH
(Catharus dryas)

Description. 7¼ - 7¾". Top and sides of head black; back, wings and tail dark ashy gray. Throat, breast and rest of underparts creamy white, spotted with dusky, sides of body gray. Bill and feet orange-red.

Range. The mountains of southern Mexico, Guatemala and Honduras. Venezuela southward through the Andes to Ecuador, Peru and Bolivia.

Colombia. Forest. Upper tropical and lower subtropical zone. Eastern slope of the Eastern Andes in Boyacá, the Macarena Mts. and the head of the Magdalena Valley *(maculatus).*

6. VEERY
(Catharus fuscescens)
Description. 6½ - 7½ ". Upperparts, wings and tail dull cinnamon brown. Throat white, breast buffy with small somewhat diffused spots, rest of underparts white.
Range. Breeds in southern Canada and the United States. In winter southward to Venezuela, British Guiana and northern Brazil.
Colombia. Tropical and subtropical zone and probably higher. Probably winter resident, but so far recorded only in October (fuscescens and salicicola).

7. GRAY-CHEEKED THRUSH
(Catharus minimus)
Description. 6¼ - 7". Best distinguishable from No. 8 by having no buff on lores and sides of head, throat white and sides of body grayer.
Range. Breeds in Alaska, Canada and United States. Winters southward to Venezuela, the Guianas and Peru.
Colombia. Tropical to temperate zones. Winter residents from October to the beginning of May (minimus).

8. SWAINSON'S THRUSH
(Catharus ustulatus)
Description. 6½ - 7½ ". Upperparts, flanks, wings and tail olive brown (or grayish olive, 1); eye-ring, sides of head and upper breast buff, breast spotted with dusky, lower breast and abdomen white.
Range. Breeds in Alaska, Canada and the United States. South in winter to Central America, Venezuela, Bolivia and Argentina.
Colombia. Tropical to temperate zone. Winter resident from October to the end of April (swainsoni and 1, almae).

9. YELLOW-LEGGED THRUSH
(Turdus flavipes)
Description. 8¾ - 9¼ ". ♂ : Entire head, breast, wings and tail lustrous black; back and belly blue-gray. Bill and feet yellow; iris brown. ♀ : Upperparts, wings and tail pale gray-brown. Throat whitish streaked with dark brown, breast pale ashy brown,

belly grayish white; under tail-coverts pale ashy brown edged with white. Bill blackish, ridge yellow; feet yellow. Iris brown.
Range. Venezuela and British Guiana. Southwestern Brazil and Paraguay. Trinidad and Tobago. Margarita Island.
Colombia. Forest. Tropical and subtropical zones. Northern slopes of the Santa Marta Mts. and east slope of Eastern Andes in Norte de Santander (venezuelensis).

10. PALE-EYED THRUSH
(Turdus leucops)
Description. 8¼ - 8¾ ". ♂ : Entirely glossy deep blue-black. Iris white or yellowish; bill and feet yellow. ♀ : Upperparts, wings and tail dark olivaceous brown, sides of head, neck, breast and sides of body somewhat paler and browner, lower breast and abdomen pale gray. Bill black; feet yellowish brown. Iris brown.
Range. British Guiana, Venezuela, northern Brazil, Ecuador and Peru.
Colombia. Forest. Subtropical zone of the Eastern, Central and Western Andes in Meta, Huila and Valle.

11. GREAT THRUSH
(Turdus fuscater) Fig. 74
Description. 13½ - 15". Uniform dark sooty gray, wings and tail darker (or uniform olive gray above and below, 1; or olive brown below, 2; or lower breast whitish, abdomen white, 3).
Range. Northern Venezuela, Ecuador, Peru and Bolivia.
Colombia. Open slopes, scrub. Subtropical to temperate zones. Santa Marta Mts. (2, cacozelus). The Perijá Mts. (clarus). Eastern Andes from Norte de Santander southward to Cundinamarca (1, gigas). Central and Western Andes southward to Nariño, the east slope of the Andes in Putumayo and Nariño (quindio). The northern portion of the Western Andes in Antioquia (3, opertaneus).

12. GLOSSY-BLACK THRUSH
(Turdus serranus)
Description. 10¾ - 11¼ ". ♂ : Entirely deep lustrous black. Ring around eye, bill and feet yellow (black in young birds),

iris brown. ♀: Upperparts, wings and tail uniform olive brown, paler, somewhat rufescent below (or dark olive above, olivaceous below, center of belly gray, 1).

Range. Northern Venezuela. Ecuador, Peru and Bolivia.

Colombia. Forest. Subtropical to temperate zone of the Andes except in Norte de Santander (1, *fuscobrunneus*). East slope of the Andes in Norte de Santander (*atrosericeus*).

13. BLACK-HOODED THRUSH
(*Turdus olivater*)

Description. 9¾ - 10¼ ". ♂: Entire head and upper breast black (or throat grayish streaked with black, upper breast sandy gray, 1). Lower breast and abdomen pale sandy (or sandy gray, 1), under tail-coverts darker. Above, including wings, olivaceous (or olivaceous gray, 1). Tail blackish. Bill dusky (or bright yellow, 1). ♀: Above uniform olivaceous; underparts uniform drab buff, throat slightly streaked. Under wing-coverts dull cinnamon.

Range. Venezuela, British Guiana.

Colombia. Forest. Upper tropical and subtropical zones. Santa Marta Mts. (*sanctae-martae*). East of the Andes in Norte de Santander (*olivater*). West slope of the Central Andes at their southern end (1, *caucae*).

14. CHESTNUT-BELLIED ROBIN
(*Turdus fulviventris*)

Description. 9¾ - 10½ ". Head black, throat more or less streaked with grayish. Back, wings and under tail-coverts dark gray; upper breast pale gray, lower breast and belly orange-rufous. Tail black.

Range. Western Venezuela, eastern Ecuador and northern Peru.

Colombia. Forest. Upper tropical and subtropical zones. Both slopes of the Eastern Andes from Norte de Santander and Magdalena southward to Huila on the west and Putumayo on the east.

15. PALE-BREASTED ROBIN
(*Turdus leucomelas*)

Description. 9½ - 10 ". Above pale olive brown, grayer on head and upper mantle.

Throat white streaked with dusky; breast and sides of body light sandy gray, center of abdomen and under tail-coverts white. Under wing-coverts and inner margins of remiges orange-rufous. Wings and tail like back.

Range. Venezuela and the Guianas, Brazil, Paraguay. Peru.

Colombia. Gardens, plantations and savanna. Tropical and subtropical zones. Upper Magdalena Valley, the Santa Marta region, Perijá Mts., west slope of the Eastern Andes in Santander and east of the Andes from Boyacá to Meta and eastward to Vichada (*albiventer*). Guajira Peninsula (*cautor*).

16. BLACK-BILLED ROBIN
(*Turdus ignobilis*)

Description. 8½ - 9". General plumage dull olive brown, wings and tail darker. Throat whitish, streaked with dusky, merging into olive brown on breast (or throat sharply defined from olive on breast, 1), center of underparts and under tail-coverts white.

Range. Venezuela, British and French Guiana, northern Brazil, eastern Ecuador, Peru and Bolivia.

Colombia. Forest border and brushlands. Tropical and subtropical zones. Slopes of the Eastern and Central Andes above the Magdalena Valley and the west slope of the Central Andes at their northernmost end (*ignobilis*). Middle and upper Cauca Valley and west slope of the Western Andes in the region of the río San Juan and río Dagua (*goodfellowi*). East of the Eastern Andes from Boyacá southward to Putumayo (1, *debilis*).

17. PALE-VENTED ROBIN
(*Turdus fumigatus*)

Description. 9 - 9½ ". General color reddish brown (or browner, less reddish, 1), below paler, center of abdomen white, throat lightly streaked with dusky. Under wing-coverts bright cinnamon-rufous. Wings and tail like back.

Range. Costa Rica southward to western Ecuador. Venezuela, the Guianas, Brazil, Peru and Bolivia.

PLATE XVII

**RED-LEGGED
HONEYCREEPER**
(*Cyanerpes cyaneus eximius*)
Page 348

BANANAQUIT
(*Coereba flaveola intermedia*)
Page 345

**RUSSET-CROWNED
WARBLER**
(*Basileuterus coron-
atus elatus*)
Page 342

**GOLDEN-FRONTED
REDSTART**
(*Myioborus o. ornatus*)
Page 340

**SCARLET-BREASTED
DACNIS**
(*Dacnis berlepschi*)
Page 349

**SCALE-CRESTED
PYGMY-TYRANT**
(*Lophotriccus pil-
eatus hesperius*)
Page 287

BLUE-BACKED CONEBILL
(*Conirostrum s. sitticolor*)
Page 345

**INDIGO FLOWER-
PIERCER**
(*Diglossa indigotica*)
Page 347

**BLACK-BILLED
FLYCATCHER**
(*Aphanotriccus audax*)
Page 280

**WHITE-THROATED
TYRANNULET**
(*Mecocerculus leuco-
phrys rufomarginatus*)
Page 291

**RUFOUS-HEADED
PYGMY-TYRANT**
(*Pseudotriccus ruficeps*)
Page 289

**OLIVE-CROWNED
YELLOWTHROAT**
(*Geothlypis s. semiflava*)
Page 339

E.L.Poole

Colombia. Forest. Tropical and subtropical zones. West shores of the Gulf of Urabá (obsoletus). West of the Andes in Valle (1, parambanus). The upper Cauca Valley and upper río Patía (colombianus). East of the Andes in Norte de Santander (aquilonalis). The Macarena Mts. eastward to Vichada (orinocensis).

18. BARE-EYED ROBIN
(Turdus nudigenis)

Description. 9½ - 10″. Bare skin about eye orange-yellow. General color olive brown, paler below. Throat white, streaked dusky, center of abdomen white. Tail dark brown, under tail-coverts white. In worn plumage the coloration is much grayer.

Range. Venezuela and the Guianas southward to northeastern Brazil. Western Ecuador, northwestern Peru. The southern Lesser Antilles, Trinidad and Tobago.

Colombia. Gardens, plantations, savanna and forest clearings. Tropical zone east of the Andes from Boyacá to Meta, eastern Cundinamarca and Vichada (nudigenis).

19. CLAY-COLORED ROBIN
(Turdus grayi)

Description. 9½ - 10″. Above pale olive brown; below clay color (or pale brownish, 1), the throat palest and inconspicuously streaked with brownish. Bill yellowish olive.

Range. Mexico southward to northern Colombia.

Colombia. Open woodland. Tropical zone of the Santa Marta region westward to

Atlántico (incomptus). Gulf of Urabá (1, casius).

20. WHITE-NECKED ROBIN
(Turdus albicollis)

Description. 8 - 8½″. Upperparts and wings russet brown. Rump, upper tail-coverts and tail dark gray (or upper tail-coverts like back, tail brownish, 1). Throat white boldly streaked with brown, a crescentic white patch at base, lower breast and sides of body pale ashy gray, the breast tinged with brownish. Center of abdomen and under tail-coverts white.

Range. Venezuela and the Guianas, Ecuador, Peru, Bolivia, Paraguay and Argentina. Trinidad and Tobago.

Colombia. Forest. Tropical zone. Santa Marta Mts., and the eastern slope of the Eastern Andes in Boyacá (1, minusculus). East of the Andes from Meta southward to Putumayo (berlepschi). Extreme eastern Colombia in Vichada and Vaupés (phaeopygus).

21. WHITE-THROATED ROBIN
(Turdus assimilis)

Description. 8 - 8½″. Mostly dark olive brown. Throat white boldly streaked with black; a sharply defined crescentic white patch at base of throat, lower breast and abdomen paler olive brown than back, under tail-coverts white. Tail like back.

Range. Mexico southward to northwestern Ecuador.

Colombia. Forest. Tropical zone west of the Western Andes from the lower Atrato to Nariño (daguae).

OLD WORLD WARBLERS (Sylviidae)

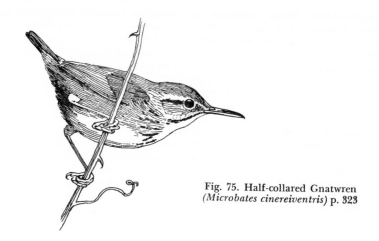

Fig. 75. Half-collared Gnatwren
(Microbates cinereiventris) p. 323

Old World Warblers form the largest of all bird families. They are found in great variety in Europe, Asia, Africa and Australia but in the Americas are represented by a mere handful of species.

In South America there are two groups, the gnatcatchers, small, active, gray-black-and-white birds inhabiting semi-arid country and open woodland, and the long-billed gnatwrens, small inhabitants of the undergrowth of forest and jungle. The latter are very reminiscent of antbirds, and indeed, until recently were classed among them.

Because some aberrant species of warblers resemble thrushes and others Old World flycatchers some ornithologists would combine the three families into one, the *Muscicapidae*. This would result in a most unwieldy group of over 1000 species and the individuality of the typical members representing the three families would be sacrificed in deference to the few aberrant species of each group. (5 Col.; 10 S.A.; 17 N.&S.A. 398 wld.)

SLATE-THROATED GNATCATCHER
(Polioptila schistaceigula)

Description. 4 - 4½". General plumage dark slaty gray; abdomen and under tail-coverts white. Tail black.

Range. Eastern Panama; northwestern Ecuador in the province of Esmeraldas.

Colombia. Tropical zone from the Pacific slope of the Western Andes in Valle eastward through the Cauca Valley in Antioquia to the middle Magdalena Valley in Santander.

TROPICAL GNATCATCHER
(Polioptila plumbea)

Description. 4¼ - 4¾". Tail rather long, 2". ♂ : Crown and nape glossy black (with white eyebrow, 1). Upperparts blue-gray; wings black, the outer remiges margined with gray, the inner ones with white. Tail black, outermost feathers mostly white, the succeeding pair tipped white. Throat and center of abdomen white, rest of underparts pale gray. ♀ similar but crown gray, slightly darker than back.

Range. Southern Mexico southward to western Ecuador, northwestern Peru. Venezuela, the Guianas, eastern and northern Brazil.

Colombia. Arid scrub, open woodland, brushland, mangroves. Tropical zone. East side of the Santa Marta Mts., the Guajira Peninsula and the eastern base of the Andes in Norte de Santander (*plumbiceps*). Western base of the Santa Marta Mts. westward along the Caribbean coast to the Pacific thence southward to Nariño (1, *bilineata*). Arid parts of the Magdalena Valley (*anteocularis*). West slope of the Western Andes in the upper río Dagua and upper río Patía Valleys (*daguae*). Extreme eastern Colombia in Vichada (*innotata*).

LONG-BILLED GNATWREN
(*Ramphocaenus melanurus*)

Description. 5 - 5½ ". Bill long, 1". Crown and nape dull buffy brown. Back and wings sandy grayish brown. Throat white, sides of head and neck and rest of underparts cinnamon-buff, flank-feathers long and silky. Tail black, outer feathers tipped white.

Range. Mexico southward through Central America to western Ecuador. Venezuela, the Guianas, Brazil, eastern Ecuador and eastern Peru. Trinidad.

Colombia. Forest and tangled undergrowth. Tropical zone. Caribbean coast from the río Sinú eastward (*sanctaemartae*). Córdoba westward (*rufiventris*). Upper tropical to lower temperate zones of the west slope of the Eastern Andes in Cundinamarca westward to the Western

Andes in Antioquia (*griseodorsalis*). East of the Andes in the Zulia Valley (*pallidus*). In Meta (*trinitatis*).

COLLARED GNATWREN
(*Microbates collaris*)

Description. 4½ - 4¾ ". Bill long, .8". Upperparts, wings and tail olive brown. Eyebrow, sides of head white with a black stripe through eye and another below cheeks and ear-coverts. Below white, a black band across the breast.

Range. French Guiana; southern Venezuela; northern and western Brazil.

Colombia. Forest. Tropical zone in Caquetá and Putumayo (*collaris*). In Amazonas *M. c. perlatus* undoubtedly occurs.

HALF-COLLARED GNATWREN
(*Microbates cinereiventris*) Fig. 75

Description. 4¼ - 4½ ". Bill .7". Tail short. Upperparts, wings and tail rufescent brown. Eye-ring white, cheeks and ear-coverts cinnamon (with a black postocular streak, 1). Throat white with a black line dividing it from the cinnamon of the cheeks, rest of underparts gray (or grayish white, 2) with a series of black spots across upper breast forming a broken collar.

Range. Nicaragua southward to eastern and western Ecuador and Peru.

Colombia. Forest. Tropical zone. The Atrato Valley and entire Pacific coast (1, *cinereiventris*). The lower Cauca and middle Magdalena Valleys and the eastern base of the Eastern Andes in Cundinamarca (2, *magdalenae*). East of the Andes in Putumayo and eastern Nariño (*peruvianus*).

PIPITS AND WAGTAILS (Motacillidae)

Fig. 76. Páramo Pipit
(Anthus bogotensis)

Pipits are small, brown, streaked, terrestrial birds. They run rather than hop and inhabit open country, some species preferring moist sites, and live chiefly on insects. Most species are found in the Old World and except for wagtails, which do not occur in South America, almost all species are brown above, whitish or yellowish below, the lower parts sometimes streaked. (2 Col.; 9 S.A.; 11 N.&S.A.; 48 wld.)

YELLOWISH PIPIT
(Anthus lutescens)

Description. 5¼ - 5¾ ". Crown, back, wings and tail sparrow-like, fulvous-brown streaked with black. Eyebrow, eye-ring, throat and underparts yellowish white, the breast streaked with blackish. Outer tail-feathers white.

Range. Western Panama. South America east of the Andes from Venezuela and the Guianas south to Bolivia and Argentina; west of them on the coast of northern Chile and southern Peru.

Colombia. Llanos east of the Eastern Andes from Boyacá to the southern Meta *(lutescens).*

PARAMO PIPIT
(Anthus bogotensis)

Description. 6¼ - 6¾ ". Upperparts cinnamon brown streaked with black. Wings and tail dark brown, the feathers pale edged, the outer tail-feathers with a wedge-shaped buffy white mark. Below buff with a few dusky spots on breast and flanks.

Range. Western Venezuela. Ecuador, Peru, Bolivia and Argentina.

Colombia. Open slopes. Temperate and páramo zones. The Eastern Andes from Norte de Santander southward to the mountains of Nariño. Possibly the northern portions of the Central Andes *(bogotensis).*

WAXWINGS (Bombycillidae)

Fig. 77. Cedar Waxwing
(*Bombycilla cedrorum*)

These birds, characteristic of northern coniferous and birch forests, only reach northernmost South America as stragglers in winter. They are gregarious and fly in rather compact flocks, uttering a soft, carrying, lisping note. They feed on berries and insects. (1 Col.; 1 S.A.; 2 N.&S.A.; 3 wld.)

CEDAR WAXWING
(*Bombycilla cedrorum*)

Description. 6½ - 7½ ". Head with a long crest. Plumage mostly dull cinnamon brown. Stripe through eye black, outlined by a narrow white line. Rump, wings and tail gray; tips of the inner remiges sometimes terminating with a bright red sealing-wax-like appendage; tail tipped bright yellow. Throat blackish, breast dull cinnamon brown, abdomen dull lemon yellow; under tail-coverts white. *Immature:* Generally like adult but back indistinctly streaked white; breast and sides brown streaked white, abdomen and under tail-coverts white.

Range. Breeds in eastern Canada and the United States. Winters southward to central Panama and the West Indies. Accidental in Venezuela.

Colombia. Accidental winter visitor to northern Colombia. It has been recorded once (Chocó, February).

PEPPERSHRIKES (Cyclarhidae)

Fig. 78. Rufous-browed Peppershrike
(Cyclarhis gujanensis)

Although closely related to vireos and sometimes included in that family, peppershrikes are very unlike them in outward appearance. The chief distinguishing character is the curiously-formed bill which is high, arched, hooked, laterally compressed. It almost could be described as parrot-like.

Peppershrikes live along the forest edge, in clearings and brushlands. Their movements are slow and deliberate, the song vireo-like, and the nest, woven like that of the vireos, is placed in a forked branch. They live on insects and fruit. (2 Col.; 2 S.A.; 2 N.&S.A.; 2 wld.)

RUFOUS-BROWED PEPPERSHRIKE
(Cyclarhis gujanensis)

Description. 6¼ - 6½". Forehead and broad eyebrow chestnut, crown, nape and sides of head gray; rest of upperparts, wings and tail olive green. Throat white, breast yellow (or lemon green, 1), rest of underparts buffy white (or white, 1). Bill brown.

Range. Mexico southward through Central America to Bolivia, Argentina and southeastern Brazil. Trinidad.

Colombia. Tropical zone. Caribbean coast region and the Magdalena Valley southward to Huila *(canticus)*. East slope of the Andes from the Zulia Valley southward to Meta and eastward to Vichada (1, *parvus*). Extreme eastern Colombia in Vaupés *(gujanensis)*. Western Nariño *(subsp.)*.

BLACK-BILLED PEPPERSHRIKE
(Cyclarhis nigrirostris)

Description. 6¼ - 6½". Forehead and short eyebrow dark chestnut; forecrown, ocular region and throat gray; rest of crown, upperparts, wings and tail, sides of neck and narrow breast-band olive green. Lower breast and sides of body gray, center of abdomen strongly tinged buff (or gray, like rest of underparts, 1). Bill black.

Range. Ecuador.

Colombia. Upper tropical and subtropical zone. Western Nariño (1, *atrirostris*). West of the Eastern Andes, excepting the Santa Marta region. No record from east of the Eastern Andes but it may occur as it is found in eastern Ecuador *(nigrirostris)*.

SHRIKE-VIREOS (Vireolaniidae)

Fig. 79. Gray-capped Shrike-Vireo
(Smaragdolanius leucotis)

Little is known about the members of this small family of rather rare birds. Like the peppershrikes they are closely related to vireos and are sometimes included in that family. They live in the treetops in the forest and are difficult to observe which may account for their apparent scarcity. Much more brightly colored than vireos, they differ from them by their larger size and in having a heavier bill. (2 Col.; 2 S.A.; 4 N.&S.A.; 4 wld.)

GREEN SHRIKE-VIREO
(Smaragdolanius eximius)

Description. 5½ - 6". Crown and nape bright blue (or strongly tinged green on forecrown, 1). Eyebrow and spot below eye bright yellow; sides of head and neck, back, wings and tail grass green, wing-coverts green (or olive, 1). Throat yellow shading gradually into olive yellow on rest of underparts (or under tail-coverts canary yellow, 1).

Range. Mexico southward through Central America to western Venezuela and western Ecuador.

Colombia. Forest. Tropical zone. From the west slope of the Eastern Andes in Boyacá and Santander westward to Bolívar *(eximius)*. Córdoba and Antioquia (1, *mutabilis)*.

GRAY-CAPPED SHRIKE-VIREO
(Smaragdolanius leucotis)

Description. 6 - 6½". Crown, nape and sides of head blue-gray, forehead, stripe above the eye and spot below it bright yellow, lower part of ear-coverts white (or similar, but ear-coverts gray, extreme forecrown and line above it yellow, eyebrow black, 1). Back, wings and tail, sides of breast and body olive green. Throat, center of breast and abdomen and under tail-coverts bright golden yellow.

Range. The Guianas and Venezuela, Ecuador, western Brazil, Peru and Bolivia.

Colombia. Forest. Tropical zone. East of the Andes in Nariño *(leucotis)*. Subtropical zone of the western slope of the Western Andes from the río San Juan southward to Nariño (1, *mikettae)*.

327

VIREOS AND GREENLETS (Vireonidae)

Fig. 80. Yellow-throated Vireo
(Vireo flavifrons)

Vireos are a family of small dull-colored forest birds found only in the Americas. Species nesting in North America and temperate South America migrate to the tropics, but for the most part they are resident. Two main groups occur: the typical vireos — nondescript little olive green birds with thick, somewhat hooked bills, pale underparts and difficult to tell apart — and the greenlets, smaller, warbler-like, with rather thin, sharply pointed bills. Vireos subsist on insects and fruit. Their movements are rather deliberate, and their song loud and pleasant. They construct prettily woven nests which they attach to the fork of a small branch. (13 Col.; 21 S.A.; 39 N.&S.A.; 39 wld.)

AID TO IDENTIFICATION

Above olive to olive brown:
   With two white wing-bars 1
   Without wing-bars, lower parts whitish 2, 3, 4, 5, below creamy yellow, 11.
Above bright olive green:
   Chest lemon yellow 6E, below white 13.
Above brown:
   Crown bright chestnut or tawny 8, 12; crown dull brown 5, 7E, 9, 10E.

1. YELLOW-THROATED VIREO
(Vireo flavifrons)

Description. 5 - 6". Top and sides of head and upper back bright olive green gradually turning to gray on lower back, rump and upper tail-coverts. Forehead and conspicuous eye-ring, throat and breast bright yellow; abdomen white, sharply defined. Wings and tail dusky, wing-coverts gray with a wide double white bar; inner remiges broadly edged white. Outer webs of outer tail-feathers white.

Range. Breeds in eastern Canada and the eastern United States. Winters in Central America, the West Indies and Venezuela. **Colombia.** Woodland borders. Tropical and subtropical zones. Winter resident, December to March. Santa Marta Mts.; Eastern, Central and Western Andes.

2. RED-EYED VIREO
(Vireo olivaceus)

Description. 5½ - 6½". Crown gray, eyebrow dingy white edged above by a black line (or black line absent, 1). Above dull olive green; below white, sides of body grayish olive (or greenish yellow, 1). Under tail-coverts pale yellow (or bright greenish yellow, 1).

328

Range. Canada and United States southward through Mexico and Central America to Venezuela, the Guianas, Argentina, Paraguay and Bolivia. The Trés Marías and Pearl Islands; Trinidad and Tobago. Northern and Central American birds migrate southward, those from southern South America migrate northward.

Colombia. Forest. Tropical to temperate zones. Migrant from the north, winter resident, September to May *(olivaceus)*. Migrant from the south, summer resident, recorded in April and May in Meta and in August from Vaupés *(chivi)*. Breeds on the Trés Marías Islands, winter resident recorded in western Colombia and the Caquetá region in November *(1, forreri)*. Transient in the tropical zone, recorded in April, July, August and October *(1, flavoviridis)*. Resident, tropical zone. Caribbean coast in the Santa Marta region and east of the Eastern Andes in the Zulia Valley and at the base of the Macarena Mts. *(vividior)*. Resident, upper Patía and the Cauca Valleys and the west slope of the Western Andes in the Dagua Valley and the northern Pacific coast *(caucae)*.

Vireo flavoviridis (Yellow-green Vireo) including the subspecies *forreri* and *vividior* sometimes are considered to form a distinct species, as is *Vireo chivi* (Chiví Vireo) with the subspecies *caucae*.

3. BLACK-WHISKERED VIREO
(Vireo altiloquus)

Description. 6½" (or 5¾", 1). Upperparts dull olive green, grayish on top of head; sides of head buffy olive; eyebrow prominent, grayish white; streak through eye and malar streak dusky. Underparts dirty white tinged greenish yellow, particularly on under tail-coverts.

Range. Breeds in southern Florida, the West Indies, Old Providence and St. Andrew's Islands. Migrates in winter to Panama, Venezuela, British Guiana and northern Brazil. Trinidad. Venezuelan islands.

Colombia. Winter resident. Recorded from August to April in the Santa Marta region and Eastern Andes *(altiloquus; 1, barbatulus)*.

4. PHILADELPHIA VIREO
(Vireo philadelphicus)

Description. 4½-5". Forehead, lores and eyebrow whitish, crown dull grayish, eye-stripe dusky. Above grayish olive; below light yellowish becoming whitish on abdomen. Wings and tail brownish olive.

Range. Breeds in Canada southward to the northern United States. Winters from Guatemala to Colombia.

Colombia. Tropical zone. Winter resident. Recorded from the extreme northwest and the vicinity of Bogotá in October and November.

5. WARBLING VIREO
(Vireo gilvus)

Description. 5-6". Lores and eyebrow white; crown and nape sepia brown; back, wings and tail olive brown (or olive, 1). Sides of head, neck and breast pale brown, throat whitish; rest of underparts pale yellow.

Range. Southern Canada southward through the United States and Central America to western Panama. Western Venezuela, Ecuador, Peru and Bolivia.

Colombia. Forest-clearings and plantations. Upper tropical to subtropical zone. Eastern Andes and the head of the Magdalena Valley *(leucophrys)*. Santa Marta Mts. *(mirandae)*. Eastern slope of the Central Andes at their northern end *(disjunctus)*. Western Andes in their central and southern portions. The Central Andes from Caldas and Tolima southward to western Nariño *(dissors)*. The temperate zone of the east slope of the Andes of Nariño *(1, josephae)*.

By some the North American *Vireo gilvus* group is regarded as specifically distinct from the Central and South American *V. leucophrys* (Brown-capped Vireo).

6. LEMON-CHESTED GREENLET
(Hylophilus thoracicus)

Description. 5-5½". Upperparts, sides of head, wings and tail bright olive green; nape and hindcrown slightly tinged with gray. Throat and belly grayish white, breast bright lemon green. Iris white, bill and feet pale.

Range. The Guianas, southern Venezuela, upper Amazonia, southward along the eastern base of the Andes to Bolivia. Southeastern Brazil.

Colombia. Forest. Tropical zone. The base of the Eastern Andes, no definite localities *(aemulus).*

7. BROWN-HEADED GREENLET
(Hylophilus brunneiceps)

Description. 5¼ - 5½ ". Crown and nape pale brown; back, wings and tail olive, lighter on lower back. Sides of head, throat and breast pale brownish gray, abdomen white; sides of body and under tail-coverts pale olive yellowish.

Range. Southern Venezuela and northern Brazil.

Colombia. Forest. Tropical zone. Vaupés *(brunneiceps).*

8. RUFOUS-NAPED GREENLET
(Hylophilus semi-brunneus)

Description. 5¼ - 5½ ". Crown and nape rufous. Back, wings and tail olive, the upper back tinged rufous. Ocular region, throat and abdomen white. Band across breast pale brownish olive, sides of body and under tail-coverts pale olive yellow.

Range. Western Venezuela, eastern Ecuador.

Colombia. Forest. Upper tropical and subtropical zone except Santa Marta and Nariño.

9. GOLDEN-FRONTED GREENLET
(Hylophilus aurantiifrons)

Description. 4½ - 5". Forecrown dull ochraceous-orange (or forehead only, yellowish, 1), rest of crown, back, wings and tail light olive green. Eyebrow and sides of head whitish, throat white; rest of underparts pale yellow more or less tinged ochraceous on breast, under tail-coverts canary yellow.

Range. Eastern Panama, eastward to Venezuela and Trinidad.

Colombia. Clearings and thin woods, plantations. Tropical zone. Caribbean coast region *(aurantiifrons).* Eastern base of the Eastern Andes in Boyacá and Arauca (1, *saturatus).*

10. SEPIA-CAPPED GREENLET
(Hylophilus hypoxanthus)

Description. 4¾ - 5½ ". Crown and nape dull sepia brown turning to olive on lower back, and brighter olive green on rump and upper tail-coverts. Throat grayish white, rest of underparts bright olive yellow, tinged ochraceous on breast (or without ochraceous tinge, 1) and becoming bright yellow on center of abdomen. Wings and tail olive.

Range. The Amazon Valley from the río Xingú westward to Peru and northward to southern Venezuela.

Colombia. Forest. Tropical zone. Eastern base of the Eastern Andes in Putumayo (1, *fuscicapillus).* Extreme eastern Colombia in Vaupés *(hypoxanthus).*

11. SCRUB GREENLET
(Hylophilus flavipes)

Description. 4¾ - 5". Lores and throat whitish. Upperparts pale brownish olive becoming olive on rump and upper tail-coverts. Wings and tail pale olive. Lower breast, belly and under tail-coverts pale buffy yellowish. Feet flesh color.

Range. Costa Rica southward to Panama and across northern South America to Trinidad. Margarita Island.

Colombia. Scrub; open woodland. Tropical zone. Caribbean coast region from the Santa Marta region westward to the Gulf of Urabá; southward in the Magdalena Valley to Huila *(flavipes).* The Guajira Peninsula southward through the río Ranchería to the Zulia Valley and Meta *(galbanus).* Foothills of the Macuira Mts. at the eastern tip of the Guajira Peninsula *(melleus).*

12. TAWNY-CROWNED GREENLET
(Hylophilus ochraceiceps) Plate XIX

Description. 4¾ - 5". Forecrown dull rufous (or ochraceous-tawny, 1); hindcrown, back and wings olive. Throat and center of abdomen grayish white; breast and sides of body dull olive (or olive yellow, 1). Tail reddish olive brown.

Range. Mexico southward through Central America to western Ecuador. Eastern and southern Venezuela, the Guianas, the Amazon Valley westward to Peru and Ecuador.

Colombia. Forest. Tropical zone. East of the Eastern Andes from southern Meta south to Putumayo and Vaupés *(ferrugineifrons)*. West of the Western Andes (1, *bulunensis*).

13. LESSER GREENLET
(Hylophilus minor)

Description. 3¾ - 4″. Upperparts, sides of body, wings and tail bright yellowish olive green; below white.

Range. Central Panama to western Ecuador.

Colombia. Forest. Tropical zone in the Pacific coast south to the Dagua Valley. The upper Sinú and middle Magdalena Valleys *(darienensis)*. Nariño *(minor)*.

WOOD-WARBLERS (Parulidae)

Fig. 81. Slate-throated Redstart
(*Myioborus miniatus*) p. 340

This large family of small and often brightly-colored birds is found only in the New World. Most breed in North America and migrate southward to spend the winter in the West Indies, Central and South America; others are resident in the tropics. Of the species migrating to Colombia from North America, only the ones nesting in the eastern part of the continent are known definitely from Colombia as winter visitors.

For the most part they are birds of the tree-tops, but a few live near the ground, and some are even terrestrial. Warblers, in spite of their name, are not notable for their song.

They feed on insects, plant scales and berries, and live in coniferous and deciduous forests, swamps and scrub country. Some of the tropical species inhabit mangroves along the coast.

The breeding plumage of males of the northern breeding species is very different from the winter plumage. In autumn the migrant males arrive in South America in their winter plumage, but assume breeding plumage before their departure for the north. As the winter plumage of the males is often very similar to that of females, only those in breeding plumage will be described.

Colored figures of the North American migrants can be found in virtually all fields guides to North American birds; therefore none is reproduced in this book. (44 Col.; 54 S.A.; 108 N.&S.A.; 108 wld.)

AID TO IDENTIFICATION

No wing bars or wingpatch

Below bright yellow, lower surface or sides, unstreaked

Back green, head or cap not in contrast to back 7, 20, 21, 24, 33, 34, 35; (tail bar white) 2, 8.

Back green, crown patch on head in contrast to back (crown yellow) 31, 42; (crown chestnut) 40.

Back green, black stripes at sides of crown (throat yellow) 36; (throat white) 37; (throat gray) 41, 43.

Back green (crown or sides of head black) 23, 24, 25, 32; (head gray) 22.

Back yellow-green, head yellow 2.

Back gray (crown chestnut, outer tail-feathers white) 28, 30; (crown yellow or orange, outer tail-feathers white) 28; (outer tail-feathers not white) 39.

Below not bright yellow

Back olive (crown gray, eyebrow white) 5; (crown black, eyebrow and coronal streak whitish) 38.

Back brown, base of tail fawn 44.

Lower surface all or partially streaked (under surface bright yellow) 26; (under surface and eyebrow whitish) 18; (or yellowish) 19; (center of crown orange) 17.

Wing bars or wingpatch present. Tail-feathers marked with yellow, orange or white.

Underparts all or partially yellow.

Entire back olive to olive yellow, 4, 7.

Back black and white or gray and olive, 6, 13.

Underparts without yellow.

Back streaked (crown yellow or partly so) 10, 14, (crown black or black and white) 1, 16, (crown chestnut) 15, (crown blue) 12, (crown streaked) 16.

Back uniform (throat or throat and breast black) 3, 9, 11, 27; (throat and breast not black, olive-green above) 4, 11, 14, 15; (above brownish or bluish) 9, 12, 27.

1. BLACK-AND-WHITE WARBLER

(Mniotilta varia)

Description. 5 - 5½". ♂ : Striped black and white; sides of crown, ear-coverts, throat and rump black. Center of breast and abdomen white. Wings black with two white wing-bars. Outer tail-feathers with white tips on inner webs. ♀ like ♂ but underparts white with little black streaking. Differs from other warblers by climbing on trees like a treecreeper.

Range. Breeds in southern Canada and Newfoundland south to Texas and Georgia. Winters from Florida and Texas southward through the West Indies and Central America to western Ecuador and northern Venezuela.

Colombia. Forest and woodland. Winter resident, except in the Amazonian region, from the end of August to the middle of March.

2. PROTHONOTARY WARBLER
(Protonotaria citrea)

Description. 5¼ - 5½ ". ♂: Head and underparts deep golden yellow. Back olive yellow; wings, rump, upper tail-coverts, and tail feathers blue-gray; tail feathers, except central ones, with white on inner web except at tip. ♀ similar to ♂ but duller; throat gray instead of black.

Range. Breeds in the central and eastern United States south to Texas and Florida. Winters from southern Mexico to northern Venezuela. Trinidad.

Colombia. Wooded swamps. Winter resident in northern Colombia along the Caribbean coast and lower Magdalena Valley, from the end of August to early April.

3. GOLDEN-WINGED WARBLER
(Vermivora chrysoptera)

Description. 4¾ - 5¼ ". ♂: Crown to behind eyes golden yellow, broad stripe through eye, throat and upper breast black, eyebrow and malar streak white. Lower breast and belly grayish white, sides of body blue-gray. Back and wings gray, the wing-coverts yellow. Tail blue-gray, outer feathers with a white patch on inner webs. ♀: Crown olive yellow, broad streak through eye dark gray, eyebrow, chin and moustacial streak white. Inner wing-coverts tipped with golden yellow. Back gray, tinged in center with olive. Throat and upper breast and sides of body gray, tail like ♂.

Range. Breeds in southeastern Canada to Iowa and Georgia. Winters from Guatemala south to northern Venezuela.

Colombia. Winter resident. The Santa Marta region, the Western and Central Andes and east of the Andes in Meta from early September to the end of March.

4. BLUE-WINGED WARBLER
(Vermivora pinus)

Description. 4½ - 5 ". ♂: Crown to behind eyes and entire underparts bright yellow, narrow stripe through eye black. Upper surface bright olive yellow. Wings, tail and upper tail-coverts blue-gray, wing-coverts tipped white, forming a double bar. Outer tail-feathers with white inner webs. ♀ similar but duller.

Range. Breeds from Minnesota and Massachusetts southward to Missouri, Kentucky, and Delaware. Winters from southern Mexico to Nicaragua and rarely Panama.

Colombia. Accidental. Recorded once from the Santa Marta Mts. in March.

5. TENNESSEE WARBLER
(Vermivora peregrina)

Description. 4½ - 5 ". ♂: Crown gray, nape and extreme upper back gray with an olive tinge. Eye-ring and short eyebrow white. Below soiled white. Back, wings and tail olive green; no wing-bars or tail patches. ♀: Conspicuous eyebrow yellowish. Above olive green; below white washed with olive. Wings and tail like ♂ except for a narrow and inconspicuous white wing-bar.

Range. Breeds in Alaska and Canada southward to Minnesota and New York. Winters from Mexico southward to northern Venezuela.

Colombia. Winter resident, from the east slope of the Andes in Meta westward from October to early May.

6. TROPICAL PARULA
(Parula pitiayumi)

Description. 4¼ - 4½ " (or 3¾ - 4", 1). ♂: Forehead and ocular region black. Center of back olive green, rest of upperparts, wings and tail grayish blue, the wing-coverts tipped with white forming a double wing-bar, the outer tail-feathers with a white patch on inner webs. Throat and breast burnt orange, lower breast and belly bright yellow, under tail-coverts white. ♀ similar but throat and breast only, tinged with burnt orange.

Range. Southern Texas south through Mexico and Central America to Venezuela, southward to southern Brazil, Uruguay, Argentina, and Bolivia. Trinidad and Tobago. Margarita Island.

Colombia. Forest, forest edge and thickets. Tropical and subtropical zone. Santa Marta region and the three Andean ranges (elegans). Northwestern Colombia in Córdoba (1, nana). Pacific slope of Nariño (pacifica).

7. YELLOW WARBLER
(Dendroica petechia)

Description. 4½ - 5". ♂ : Crown and entire underparts bright golden yellow, sometimes tinged orange on crown, breast lightly streaked with chestnut (or crown chestnut, breast heavily streaked with chestnut, 1; or entire head and upper breast chestnut, rest of underparts golden yellow streaked with chestnut, 2). Upperparts olive to golden olive, wings and tail dusky brown, the wing-coverts and inner remiges broadly margined with canary yellow. Inner margins of all but central tail feathers canary yellow. ♀ like ♂ but duller. The females of the chestnut-headed forms differ from males in lacking chestnut on head or crown.

Range. Alaska and Canada southward through Central America to Peru. West Indies. Trinidad, Galápagos Islands. Northern races are migratory.

Colombia. Winter resident throughout, from the end of August to the beginning of May *(aestiva, morcomi, sonorana, amnicola)*. Resident in mangroves. The Guajira Peninsula *(2, chrysendeta)*. The Caribbean coast *(2, erithachorides)*. Pacific coast of Nariño *(1, peruviana)*.

8. MAGNOLIA WARBLER
(Dendroica magnolia)

Description. 4½ - 5". ♂ : Crown and nape blue-gray, streak behind eye white. Cheeks and back black. Underparts yellow, patch on lower throat and sides of body streaked black. Rump yellow. Wings and tail black; wing-coverts white, central tail-feathers black, the rest black crossed by a broad white band. ♀ : Crown, nape and extreme upper back gray, rest of upperparts olive, band across rump yellow. Wings and tail gray, the wing-coverts narrowly edged white, forming a double wing-band. Under surface yellow, streaked on sides with black. Tail as in ♂ .

Range. Breeds in Canada southward to the central and eastern United States. Winters from southern Mexico to Panama and the Greater Antilles.

Colombia. Accidental. Recorded once in December from Boyacá.

9. BLACK-THROATED BLUE WARBLER
(Dendroica caerulescens)

Description. 5 - 5½". ♂ : Above dark blue gray. Sides of head, throat, upper breast and sides of body black, rest of underparts white. Wings black, base of inner remiges white forming a conspicuous wing-patch. Tail black with a white patch near tip of outer feathers. ♀ : Above dull pale olive, wings like back, the primaries with a small white patch at base just below the greater wing-coverts forming a wing patch. Sides of head brownish, line above lores and eyebrow and lower part of eyelid white. Underparts dirty white, tinged olive on sides. Tail grayish.

Range. Breeds from eastern Canada southward to Michigan and Georgia. Winters from Florida and the Bahamas southward to the West Indies and Mexico; rarely to Guatemala. Accidental in Venezuela (sight records).

Colombia. Accidental. Recorded once from Santa Marta in December *(caerulescens)*.

10. MYRTLE WARBLER
(Dendroica coronata)

Description. 5 - 6". ♂ : Center of crown, patch on sides of breast and the rump bright yellow. Eyebrow white, cheeks black. Back gray streaked black. Underparts white, breast and sides of body heavily streaked with black. Wings and tail dark gray, wing with a double white bar, large patch on inner web of outer tail-feathers white. ♀ : Upper surface grayish brown streaked with black. Somewhat concealed coronal patch, small patch at sides of breast and band across rump yellow. Eyebrow and lower lid white, lores, cheeks and ear-coverts dusky. Under surface white, streaked on breast with black. Wings and tail as in ♂ .

Range. Breeds in Alaska and Canada south to Minnesota and New York. Winters southward to the southern United States, Mexico and Panama. The Bahamas and West Indies.

Colombia. Accidental. Recorded once from Magdalena in March *(coronata)*.

PLATE XVIII

(All birds shown are males unless otherwise noted)

WHITE-BROWED PURPLETUFT (*Iodopleura i. isabellae*) Page 261	**CINNAMON ATTILA** (*Attila cinnamomeus torridus*) Page 261	**THRUSH-LIKE MANAKIN** (*Schiffornis turdinus furvus*) Page 254
BROAD-BILLED MANAKIN (*Sapayoa aenigma*) Page 254	**MUSICIAN WREN** (*Cyphorhinus aradus phaeocephalus*) Page 313	**BLACK SOLITAIRE** (*Entomodestes coracinus*) Page 317
GIANT CONEBILL (*Oreomanes f. fraseri*) Page 346	**FULVOUS SHRIKE-TANAGER** (*Lanio fulvus peruvianus*) Page 370	**TAWNY-CRESTED TANAGER** (*Tachyphonus d. delattrii*) Page 371
SCARLET-BROWED TANAGER (*Heterospingus xanthopygius*) Page 371	**RUFOUS-CRESTED TANAGER** (*Creurgops verticalis*) Page 371	**COMMON BUSH-TANAGER** (*Chlorospingus ophthalmicus jacqueti*) Page 373
BLACK-FACED TANAGER (*Schistochlamys melanopis aterrima*) Page 375	**BLACK CACIQUE** (*Archiplanus solitarius*) Page 379	**VELVETY-FRONTED GRACKLE** (*Lampropsar t. tanagrinus*) Page 380
LARGE-BILLED SEED-FINCH (*Oryzoborus crassirostris occidentalis*) Page 393	**BLUE-BLACK GRASSQUIT** (*Volatinia jacarina splendens*) Page 394	**SOUTHERN SISKIN** (*Spinus magellanicus capitalis*) Page 394
PLUMBEOUS FINCH (*Phrygilus unicolor geospizopsis*, ♀) Page 396	**SLATY FINCH** (*Haplospiza r. rustica*) Page 396	**YELLOW-FRONTED SPARROW** (*Myospiza a. aurifrons*) Page 400

11. BLACK-THROATED GREEN WARBLER
(Dendroica virens)

Description. 4½ - 5¼". ♂: Sides of head bright yellow, ear-coverts somewhat greener. Entire upperparts bright yellowish olive green, spotted with black on center of back. Center of throat, breast and sides of body black, center of abdomen and lower breast white. Wings and tail black, the wing-coverts tipped white forming a double bar and the outer tail-feathers largely white. ♀ like ♂ except throat pale yellow, breast and sides of body white, streaked and spotted with black.

Range. Breeds in eastern North America from Canada southward to Alabama. Winters south from southern Texas to central Panama. The Greater Antilles.

Colombia. Accidental. Recorded once from the Santa Marta region in the middle of April (virens).

12. CERULEAN WARBLER
(Dendroica cerulea)

Description. 4 - 5". ♂: Above cerulean blue, brightest and deepest on crown, back somewhat mottled with black. Below white, a narrow band across breast and streak on sides of body blackish blue. Wings and tail dusky, the remiges edged with gray and the wing-coverts with white, forming a double wing-bar, outer rectrices with a white patch on inner web. ♀ differs from ♂ in having the upperparts shaded with green, eyebrow white and plain white below shaded with yellowish on breast.

Range. Breeds in eastern North America south to Georgia. Winters in western South America from Venezuela southward to Bolivia.

Colombia. Winter resident. Recorded from the Western Andes eastward to the east slope of the Eastern Andes in November, December, January and March.

13. BLACKBURNIAN WARBLER
(Dendroica fusca)

Description. 5 - 5½". ♂: Crown black, patch in center, stripe from nostril produced backward over eye to surround ear-coverts, eye-ring, throat and upper breast orange yellow. Back black streaked white. Lower breast and belly pale yellow streaked black. Wings and tail black. Double wing-bar and large part of outer tail-feathers white. ♀: Above brown or grayish brown streaked with black. Pattern of head and underparts as in ♂ but much paler and duller. Wings and tail dusky, wings with a double wing-bar, outer tail-feathers largely white.

Range. Breeds from eastern Canada to Minnesota and Georgia. Winters from Guatemala to northern Venezuela, Ecuador and Peru. The Bahamas and Cuba.

Colombia. Winter resident throughout the mountains from early September to early May.

14. CHESTNUT-SIDED WARBLER
(Dendroica pensylvanica)

Description. 5 - 5½". ♂: Crown bright yellow, forehead and ear-coverts and sides of neck white, moustacial streak and stripe through eye black. Underparts white, sides of body chestnut. Upper mantle streaked black and white; back and rump streaked black and lemon yellow, upper tail-coverts black fringed with gray. Wings dusky, inner wing-coverts broadly edged with yellowish white forming two wing-bars. Tail black, outer feathers largely white on inner webs. ♀: above bright lemon-green, upper tail-coverts gray. Sides of head and breast grayish, eye-ring white. Underparts white, wings and tail as in ♂.

Range. Breeds from eastern Canada southward to Nebraska, Ohio and Georgia. Winters from Nicaragua to central Panama. The Greater Antilles. Accidental in Venezuela.

Colombia. Casual. Recorded twice from Tolima and Santander in October and November.

15. BAY-BREASTED WARBLER
(Dendroica castanea)

Description. 5 - 6". ♂: Forehead and sides of head black. Crown and nape, throat and upper breast, sides of body chestnut, rest of underparts dull white. Large patch at sides of neck buff. Back olive gray, streaked with black. Wings and tail dusky, wing-coverts with a double white wing-bar; outer tail-feathers with a large white patch on inner webs. ♀: Upperparts yellowish green, inconspicuously streaked with dusky, wing-coverts with two white bars. Sides of head and breast buffy greenish, flanks pale chestnut, center of abdomen white. Tail like ♂.

Range. Breeds in eastern Canada southward to New York. Winters from eastern Panama to northern and western Venezuela. Tortuga Island.

Colombia. Winter resident, west of the Eastern Andes from early November to early May.

16. BLACK-POLL WARBLER
(*Dendroica striata*)

Description. 5 - 5½ ". ♂: Crown solid black; sides of head and underparts white. A black V-shaped mark on sides of neck coming to a point on chin and prolonged in the form of spots down the sides, rest of underparts white. Above gray streaked with black. Wing-coverts black with two white bars; primaries edged with olive, inner remiges with white. Tail black, outer feathers with a white patch on inner webs. ♀ very similar to ♀ of No. 15 but back more conspicuously streaked, underparts more greenish yellow, and flanks without chestnut.

Range. Breeds in Alaska and Canada southward to Michigan and New York. Winters in Venezuela and east of the Andes in Ecuador, Peru, western Brazil and Chile.

Colombia. Winter resident chiefly east of the Eastern Andes. Recorded once from Atlántico and once from the Cauca Valley. Early September to end of April.

17. OVENBIRD
(*Seiurus aurocapillus*)

Description. 5½ - 6½ ". Center of crown orange-rufous bordered on each side by a black line which springs from above the nostrils. Lores and eye-ring white. Sides of crown, ear-coverts, back, wings and tail olive brown. Throat and underparts white, moustacial streak, spots on breast and sides of body dusky.

Range. Breeds in southern Canada and southward to Colorado and Georgia. Winters from the southern United States to Panama, northern Venezuela. The Bahamas and West Indies.

Colombia. Casual. Terrestrial. Recorded once from the Santa Marta region in October (*aurocapillus*).

18. LOUISIANA WATERTHRUSH
(*Seiurus motacilla*)

Description. 5½ - 6¼ ". Upperparts, wings and tail dark brown. Long eyebrow and lower parts white, tinged fulvous on flanks and under tail-coverts. Moustacial streak, spots on breast and sides of body dusky.

Range. Breeds in the plains states, eastward to the Atlantic coast. Winters from Mexico southward to Panama and western Venezuela. Trinidad.

Colombia. Winter resident. Terrestrial. Recorded from the Santa Marta region from early November to the end of January.

19. NORTHERN WATERTHRUSH
(*Seiurus noveboracensis*)

Description. 5 - 6 ". Above similar to No. 18. Underparts yellowish white, the throat with small spots and breast and flanks more heavily spotted than in No. 18; flanks and under tail-coverts with no fulvous tinge.

Range. Breeds in Alaska and Canada southward to the northwestern states and eastward to Pennsylvania. Winters from lower California and Mexico southward to Panama, Venezuela, the Guianas, Ecuador and Peru. Trinidad.

Colombia. Terrestrial. Winter resident from early September to the end of April throughout the country (*noveboracensis, notabilis, limnaeus*).

20. KENTUCKY WARBLER
(*Oporornis formosus*)

Description. 5½ - 6 ". ♂: Forecrown black becoming spotted with gray on center of crown and turning to gray on hindcrown.

Eyebrow yellow; lores, cheeks, ear-coverts and sides of neck black. Upperparts, wings and tail dull olive green; underparts bright yellow. ♀: Crown brownish, back, wings and tail olivaceous. Eyebrow yellow, sides of head as in ♂ but grayish instead of black, underparts bright yellow.

Range. Breeds from Canada southward to northern Florida and Texas. Winters from Mexico southward through Central America to Panama and northwestern Venezuela.

Colombia. Winter resident. Forest undergrowth. Recorded from the Santa Marta region in October and January.

21. CONNECTICUT WARBLER
(Oporornis agilis)

Description. 5¼ - 6". ♂: Crown grayish, throat and breast pale gray, eye-ring white. Back, wings, tail and sides of body dull olive, rest of underparts dull yellow. ♀: Top and sides of head brown, eye-ring white. Throat and breast pale grayish brown, rest of underparts dull yellow. Back, wings and tail brownish olive.

Range. Breeds from southern Canada to Minnesota and Michigan. Winters from Venezuela southward to northwestern and central Brazil.

Colombia. Transient. Recorded from the Santa Marta and Orinoco regions in October and at the end of April.

22. MOURNING WARBLER
(Oporornis philadelphia)

Description. 5 - 5¾". ♂: Whole head, throat and breast gray, the lower breast heavily mottled with black, forming a black patch. Upperparts, wings, tail and sides of body dull olive, rest of underparts bright yellow. ♀: Crown grayish olive, sides of head gray, throat whitish becoming grayish on breast. Otherwise like ♂.

Range. Breeds from southern Canada southward to Minnesota and Virginia. Winters from Nicaragua southward to western Venezuela and Ecuador.

Colombia. Winter resident throughout the country, from the middle October to the early May.

Note. MacGillivray's Warbler (*Oporornis tolmiei*) reaches Panama in winter and has been reported from Colombia. The records, however, are not satisfactory as they are based on sight records or young birds; if it does reach Colombia it is the only warbler nesting west of the Rocky Mts. to do so. Adult males resemble No. 22 but can easily be distinguished by the black ocular region and white bar on upper and lower eyelid. Females are virtually indistinguishable.

23. COMMON YELLOWTHROAT
(Geothlypis trichas)

Description. 4½ - 5½". ♂: Forecrown, sides of head and neck black, margined posteriorly with grayish white. Back, wings and tail olive brown. Throat, breast and under tail-coverts yellow; flanks olive brown, center of abdomen yellowish white. ♀ similar, but without the black mask.

Range. Breeds in Alaska, Canada and the United States southward to Mexico. Winters from the southern United States southward to the Canal Zone and Puerto Rico. Accidental in Venezuela.

Colombia. Accidental. Recorded once from Chocó in the middle of June and from the Santa Marta region in April *(trichas)*.

24. MASKED YELLOWTHROAT
(Geothlypis aequinoctialis)

Description. 5¼ - 5½". ♂: Forehead, ocular region and ear-coverts black, crown blue-gray. Back, wings and tail bright olive green. Sides of body olive, underparts bright yellow. ♀ similar but without black mask, and crown like back.

Range. Western Panama. Venezuela and the Guianas southward to eastern Peru, Brazil, Argentina, Uruguay, Paraguay and Bolivia. Southwest Ecuador and western Peru.

Colombia. Tropical zone. The middle and upper Magdalena Valley, east of the Andes south to Meta *(aequinoctialis)*.

25. OLIVE-CROWNED
YELLOWTHROAT
(Geothlypis semiflava) Plate XVII

Description. 4¾ - 5¼". ♂: Front half of crown and sides of head and neck black.

Hind half of crown, back, wings, tail and sides of body olive green, rest of underparts bright yellow. ♀ similar but without black mask.

Range. Honduras to northwestern Panama. Western Ecuador.

Colombia. Tropical zone of the Pacific slope and the upper Cauca Valley *(semiflava)*.

26. CANADA WARBLER
(Wilsonia canadensis)

Description. 5 - 5¾ ". ♂ : Crown black, the feathers edged with gray, supra-loral streak and eye-ring yellow or white. Streak below eye continued down sides of neck and joining broad band of spots on breast black. Underparts bright golden yellow, under tail-coverts white. Upperparts, wings and tail gray. ♀ like ♂ but with forecrown yellowish gray and streak at sides of neck and spots grayish and inconspicuous.

Range. Breeds from Canada south to Minnesota and Georgia. Winters from Venezuela southward to Ecuador and Peru.

Colombia. Winter resident. Recorded throughout, excepting the Caribbean coast, from end of September to early May.

27. AMERICAN REDSTART
(Setophaga ruticilla)

Description. 4½ - 5½ ". ♂ : Head, breast, back, wings and tail black, the basal portion of the remiges and basal ¾ of outer tail-feathers and sides of breast and under wing-coverts orange-red. Lower breast and rest of underparts white. ♀ : Top and sides of head grayish. Back wings and tail olive brown, patches on sides of breast and tail, reduced on wings orange yellow. Underparts and lores and eyebrow whitish.

Range. Breeds from Alaska and Canada southward to Colorado, Louisiana and Georgia. Winters from Mexico southward to Venezuela, British and Dutch Guiana, and northern Brazil.

Colombia. Winter resident. Recorded throughout the country from the end of August to early May *(ruticilla, tricolora)*.

28. SLATE-THROATED REDSTART
(Myioborus miniatus) Fig. 81

Description. 5½ - 5¾ ". Center of crown chestnut surrounded by slaty black. Back, sides of head, neck, breast and wings dark gray. Throat slaty black, upper breast ochraceous yellow, lower breast and abdomen golden yellow (or without ochraceous wash on chest, 1). Tail black, outer feathers and under tail-coverts largely white.

Range. Mexico southward to Venezuela, British Guiana, northern Brazil, Ecuador, Peru and Bolivia.

Colombia. Upper tropical and subtropical zones throughout the Andes *(ballux);* the Santa Marta Mts. (1, *sanctaemartae*).

29. GOLDEN-FRONTED REDSTART
(Myioborus ornatus) Plate XVII

Description. 5½-6". Crown bright yellow, forehead, chin, sides of head and streaks behind ear-coverts white; ear-coverts, nape, sides of neck black. Upperparts, wings and tail olive gray, upper tail-coverts and tail black, the outer tail-feathers and under tail-coverts white. Underparts bright yellow (or similar but forehead, sides of head and chin and underparts orange yellow, 1).

Range. Western Venezuela.

Colombia. Subtropical zone. Both slopes of the Eastern Andes south to the latitude of Bogotá *(ornatus)*. Subtropical to temperate zone of the Central and Western Andes southward to Cauca and Huila *(1, chrysops)*.

30. SPECTACLED REDSTART
(Myioborus melanocephalus)

Description. 5¾ - 6". Head pattern variable, either with forecrown and ocular region yellow, center of crown chestnut or forehead and eye-ring yellow, forecrown and sides of crown and head black, rest of crown chestnut or any intermediate stage. A broad band across nape black, or no black band. Upperparts dark gray, lower parts bright yellow. Tail black, the outer feathers and under tail-coverts white.

Range. Ecuador, Peru and Bolivia.

Colombia. Subtropical to temperate zone of both slopes of the Andes of Nariño. Possibly the east slope of the Western Andes in Valle (*ruficoronatus*).

31. YELLOW-CROWNED REDSTART
(Myioborus flavivertex)

Description. 5½ - 5¾". Large patch in center of crown yellow surrounded by black, forehead buff, sides of head black. Back olive green. Below yellow, tinged ochre on throat and upper breast. Wings and tail slaty, outer tail-feathers largely white.

Range. Colombia.

Colombia. Subtropical to temperate zones of the Santa Marta Mts.

32. BLACK-CRESTED WARBLER
(Basileuterus nigro-cristatus)

Description. 5¾ - 6¼". Broad line from nostrils extending backwards to eye yellow. Lores, forehead and center of crown black. Sides of hindcrown, back, wings, tail and sides of body olive green. Underparts bright yellow, more or less clouded on breast with olive.

Range. Western Venezuela, Ecuador, Peru and Bolivia.

Colombia. Upper tropical to temperate zones of the Eastern Andes from Santander and Central Andes from Antioquia to the Andes of Nariño.

33. CITRINE WARBLER
(Basileuterus luteoviridis)

Description. 5¾ - 6". Bill black. Entire upper surface, sides of head, wings and tail olive green. Lores blackish, eyebrow dull yellow (or yellowish white, 1). Chin white (or chin and throat whitish, 2), rest of underparts yellow, clouded with olive on breast and sides.

Range. Western Venezuela. Ecuador, Peru and Bolivia.

Colombia. Subtropical and temperate zones of the Eastern Andes from Norte de Santander southward to eastern Nariño (*luteoviridis*). Both slopes of the Central Andes in Tolima and Caldas (1, *quindianus*). Southern end of the Western Andes in Cauca (2, *richardsoni*).

34. YELLOW-GREEN WARBLER
(Basileuterus signatus)

Description. 5½ - 5¾". Bill black. Very similar to the Citrine Warbler from the Eastern Andes but eyebrow less conspicuous and underparts brighter yellow. Eyelids yellow. Legs yellow or flesh instead of brownish.

Range. Peru and Bolivia.

Colombia. Subtropical zone of the Eastern Andes in Cundinamarca (*subsp.?*).

35. FLAVESCENT WARBLER
(Basileuterus flaveolus)

Description. 5¾ - 6". Bill dark and slender. Differs from No. 34 by having the lores yellow, no eyebrow and the underparts brighter yellow with little or no olive clouding. Above brighter olive green. Legs yellow.

Range. Coastal regions of Venezuela. Southern Brazil, Paraguay and Bolivia.

Colombia. Tropical zone. The Zulia Valley and possibly the Cauca Valley.

36. GOLDEN-BELLIED WARBLER
(Basileuterus chrysogaster)

Description. 5 - 5¼". Center of crown orange yellow broadly bordered on each side with black, the black lines continuing on the nape. Sides of head, sides of body, upperparts, wings and tail olive green. Throat and center of underparts golden yellow.

Range. Western Ecuador; southern Peru.

Colombia. Tropical zone of the Pacific slope of the Western Andes in Cauca southward to Nariño (*chlorophrys*).

37. SANTA MARTA WARBLER
(Basileuterus basilicus)

Description. 6¼ - 6½". Top, sides of head, neck and throat black. Coronal streak, eyebrow, continued backwards to surround ear-coverts, patch below eye and throat white. Back, wings and tail olive. Lower throat and rest of underparts bright yellow.

Range. Colombia.

Colombia. Forest, in undergrowth and on the ground. Lower temperate zone of the Santa Marta Mts.

38. THREE-STRIPED WARBLER
(Basileuterus tristriatus)

Description. 5½ - 5¾ ". Sides of crown and ear-coverts black; central crown stripe, eyebrow, spot below eye and line behind ear-coverts buffy white (or similar, but crown stripe ochraceous orange, auriculars olive, 1). Upperparts, flanks, wings, and tail olive. Underparts dull wax yellow, somewhat clouded with olive.

Range. Costa Rica southward to western Ecuador. Venezuela. Eastern Ecuador, Peru and Bolivia.

Colombia. Forest and second growth. Upper tropical and subtropical zones of the Andes from Norte de Santander and Antioquia southward to Nariño *(auricularis)*. Northernmost Chocó on Mt. Tacarcuna (1, *tacarcunae).*

39. GOLDEN-CROWNED WARBLER
(Basileuterus culicivorus)

Description. 5 - 5¼ ". Center of crown yellow to orange, bordered laterally by black, eyebrow grayish white, stripe through eye blackish; sides of head, back, wings and tail gray. Underparts bright yellow.

Range. Northern Mexico to western Panama. Venezuela, British Guiana, Brazil, Argentina, Uruguay, Paraguay and Bolivia. Trinidad.

Colombia. Forest. Upper tropical and subtropical zone. The Santa Marta Mts. *(indignus).* The east slope of the Andes in Norte de Santander *(cabanisi).* The eastern slope of the Eastern Andes from Boyacá to Meta *(austerus).* From the western slope of the Eastern Andes in Santander and southern Magdalena westward through Antioquia to the Western Andes in Valle and the upper río Patía *(occultus).*

40. CHESTNUT-CAPPED WARBLER
(Basileuterus delattrii)

Description. 5 - 5¼ ". Crown and ear-coverts chestnut, stripe through eye dusky, eyebrow, chin, patch below eye white. Nape grayish olive, back, wings and tail olive green. Underparts bright yellow.

Range. Guatemala southward to Panama.

Colombia. Dry forest. Tropical zone. Santa Marta region and the Magdalena Valley southward to Tolima and Huila *(mesochrysus).*

41. WHITE-LORED WARBLER
(Basileuterus conspicillatus)

Description. 5½ - 6". Crown patch orange, bordered laterally by two black bands which continue down over nape. Center of nape and sides of head gray. Supraloral stripe and eye-ring white, stripe through eye dusky. Throat grayish white; breast and rest of underparts yellow, shaded with olive on flanks. Back, wings and tail olive green.

Range. Colombia.

Colombia. Forest. Upper tropical and lower subtropical zones of the Santa Marta Mts.

42. GRAY-THROATED WARBLER
(Basileuterus cinereicollis)

Description. 5¾ - 6¼ ". Top and sides of head and the nape dark gray, supra-loral streak pale gray, crown patch bright yellow, bordered by two blackish bands, throat and upper breast grayish white, lower breast and center of abdomen yellow. Back, flanks, wings and tail dark olive green.

Range. Western Venezuela.

Colombia. Forest. Upper tropical and lower subtropical zones. The northern portion of the Sierra de Perijá *(pallidulus).* Both slopes of the Eastern Andes from Norte de Santander southward to Meta *(cinereicollis).*

43. RUSSET-CROWNED WARBLER
(Basileuterus coronatus) Plate XVII

Description. 6¼ - 6½ ". Rather similar to No. 41 but larger, the orange crown patch darker and more extensive; no white eye-ring or supraloral streak but a more or less prominent black streak extending back from the eye.

Range. Western Venezuela, Ecuador, Peru and Bolivia.

Colombia. Forest undergrowth. Subtropical to temperate zone of the Andes from Cundinamarca and Antioquia southward to Huila and Cauca *(regulus).* Subtropical zone of the Pacific slope of Nariño *(elatus).*

44. RIVER WARBLER
(Basileuterus rivularis)

Description. 5½ - 5¾″. Crown dark grayish, back and wings dark olive brown. Upper tail-coverts and tail fawn, the distal third dark olive brown. Underparts mostly cinnamon buff to pale fawn, whiter on throat and center of abdomen.

Range. Honduras southward to western Ecuador. Venezuela, British and French Guiana, Brazil, Ecuador, Peru, Paraguay to southern Bolivia.

Colombia. Stream banks in woodlands. Tropical zone west of the Andes except Santa Marta and the upper Magdalena Valley *(semicervinus).* The upper Magdalena Valley *(motacilla).* East of the Andes from Meta southward to Nariño *(fulvicauda).*

HONEYCREEPERS (Coerebidae)

Fig. 82. Slaty Flower-Piercer
(Diglossa baritula) p. 347

Honeycreepers form a rather ill-assorted group of small, often brilliantly colored birds confined to the New World. Some species closely approach the tanagers, while others resemble wood-warblers. Some ornithologists would suppress the family of honeycreepers entirely and distribute the members among the wood-warblers and tanagers.

The flower-piercers have curiously upturned and sharply hooked bills, which they use in piercing the base of the corolla of tubular flowers so that the nectar can be removed with the tongue. They are all birds of the mountains and are found up to the páramo zone of the Andes.

The honeycreepers *(Cyanerpes)* have long down-curved bills. They feed on fruit, insects and the nectar of flowers, which they visit as they creep about vines and branches, never in the hovering manner of hummingbirds. Their plumage is usually purplish blue. They are found in second growth and forest borders of the tropical zones.

The tanager-like *Chlorophanes, Dacnis* and *Iridophanes* have sharply pointed, straight bills, resemble the honeycreepers in habits, but are more partial to forest. They are brilliantly colored and are found only in the tropical zone.

The conebills, as their name implies, have straight conical bills. They live at high altitudes in the Andes, except for the small, gray, warbler-like species, and are partial to forest and scrubby slopes. They are rather dull colored.

The bananaquit is a small active bird with a rather long, decurved bill. It is found in gardens, plantations, forest edge and clearings and is widespread throughout tropical America and the islands of the Caribbean. Bananaquits have the curious habit of building individual nests to sleep in, quite distinct from those that are built for egg-laying. They are closest to warblers. (30 Col.; 35 S. A.; 35 N.&S.A.; 35 wld.)

344

AID TO IDENTIFICATION

Below blue or mostly blue (bill upturned, hooked) 10, 11, 12E, 13, (bill long, decurved) 18, 19, 20E, 21, (bill straight, pointed) 22, 23, 28E, 29.

Below green or mostly green (bill straight) 23, 24, 29, (bill decurved, streaked below) 18, 19, 20E, 21.

Below black (bill upcurved, hooked) 14, 15, 16, (bill straight) 5, 25.

Below all or partially bright to greenish yellow (bill straight) 22, 27E, 30, (bill decurved) 1.

Below partially scarlet 26.

Below whitish, yellowish or buffy (back green, blue or gray) 7E, 8, 10, 24, 25, 28E, (back olive brown) 2, 5, 16, 17, 22, 27E, (back mostly black) 30.

Below all or partially blue-gray 5, 6, 7, 8.

Below chestnut to cinnamon (bill straight) 3, 4, 9, (bill upturned, hooked) 14, 15, 17.

1. BANANAQUIT
(Coereba flaveola) Plate XVII

Description. 3¾ - 4¼". Bill .4 - .5", distinctly curved. Upperparts, sides of head, wings and tail sooty gray, (or soot‐ brown, 1) darkest on pileum. Long eyebrow, wing speculum and under tail-coverts white. Throat pale gray, rest of underparts and rump bright yellow.

Range. The Bahamas and most of the Caribbean islands. Mexico southward to western Ecuador. Venezuela, the Guianas southward to Paraguay Argentina and Bolivia. Trinidad, Tobago. Accidental in Florida.

Colombia. Gardens, plantations, woodland. Tropical zone. The Caribbean coast from the east shore of the Gulf of Urabá to the lower Magdalena Valley and the Santa Marta region. East of the Andes in Norte de Santander (1, *luteola*). West shore of the Gulf of Urabá to northwestern Antioquia and eastward to the Magdalena Valley from Santander to Huila. The eastern base of the Andes in Meta *(columbiana)*. The upper Atrato Valley southward west of the Western Andes to Cerro Munchique. The upper Cauca Valley *(caucae)*. Both slopes of the Andes of Nariño, eastward to the río Guainía south to the Casiquiare junction *(intermedia)*. The río Guainía south of the Casiquiare (1, *minima*). Gorgona Island. (1, *gorgonae*).

2. CINEREOUS CONEBILL
(Conirostrum cinereum)

Description. 4¾ - 5¼". ♂: Forehead and eyebrow pale buff, crown blackish; back dark olivaceous gray tinged with brown on rump. Under surface rusty buff. Wings and tail slaty black, greater wing-coverts and conspicuous wing speculum white. ♀ similar but paler and browner above; wing speculum smaller.

Range. The Andes southward from Ecuador to northern Chile and Bolivia.

Colombia. Forest edge and open scrubby slopes. Temperate zone of the mountains of Nariño northward to the mountains at the head of the Magdalena Valley *(fraseri)*.

3. RUFOUS-BROWED CONEBILL
(Conirostrum rufum)

Description. 5¼ - 5½". Above dark gray. Forehead and forecrown, eyebrow and entire underparts chestnut-rufous. Wings and tail slaty black, inner remiges edged with whitish.

Range. Colombia.

Colombia. Scrubby woods. Upper subtropical and temperate zones. The Santa Marta region and the Eastern Andes south to the region about Bogotá.

4. BLUE-BACKED CONEBILL
(Conirostrum sitticolor) Plate XVII

Description. 5¼ - 5½". Head and upper breast, wings and tail black; back blue. Underparts cinnamon-rufous.

Range. Western Venezuela. Ecuador, Peru and Bolivia.

Colombia. Forest. Subtropical and temperate zones of the Andes. Not Santa Marta *(sitticolor)*.

5. CAPPED CONEBILL
(Conirostrum albifrons)

Description. 5¼ - 5½". ♂ : Mainly sooty, purplish black below (or bluish black, 1); mantle purplish blue becoming brighter and bluer on lower back, rump and inner wing-coverts. Lores and crown white (or crown ultramarine blue, 2). ♀ : Crown blue, hindneck, sides of neck, throat and breast gray. Back, wings and tail yellowish olive green. Lower breast, belly and under tail-coverts greenish yellow.

Range. Northern and western Venezuela, Ecuador, Peru and Bolivia.

Colombia. Forest. Subtropical and temperate zones. The Eastern Andes from Norte de Santander to Cundinamarca (albifrons). The Central Andes from Antioquia southward to Cauca (1, central-andium). The Western Andes from Valle southward to western Nariño (2, atrocy-aneum).

6. BICOLORED CONEBILL
(Conirostrum bicolor)

Description. 4¼ - 4¾". Above blue-gray, below pale grayish with a buffy wash. Bill and feet pale. Young birds are grayish green above, yellow below.

Range. Venezuela and the Guianas southward to southeastern Brazil and Argentina. Trinidad.

Colombia. Mangroves in the delta of the Magdalena River and the Ciénaga Grande (bicolor).

7. CHESTNUT-VENTED CONEBILL
(Conirostrum speciosum)

Description. 4½ - 4¾". Bill very pointed, .3". ♂ : Blue-gray, paler below, white in center of abdomen. Wing speculum white. Under tail-coverts chestnut. ♀ : Top of head bluish green, rest of upper surface green. Wings and tail yellowish green. Below whitish, buff on breast and under tail-coverts.

Range. Venezuela. British and French Guiana, southward to Brazil, Ecuador, Peru, Bolivia and Argentina.

Colombia. Open woodland. Tropical zone east of the Andes. Recorded only from "Bogotá" but probably found in the southeast (amazonum).

8. WHITE-EARED CONEBILL
(Conirostrum leucogenys)

Description. 3¾ - 4". ♂ : Crown and nape black; ring around eye and patch extending from below eye backward over ear-coverts white. Back dark blue-gray, rump white. Underparts blue-gray, white on center of abdomen; under tail-coverts chestnut, the longest ones white. Wings and tail black, the wings with a small white speculum. ♀ : Above blue-gray, patch on rump white. Lores, sides of head and underparts yellowish, brightest on center of abdomen, grayish on sides of body.

Range. Eastern Panama to western and northern Venezuela.

Colombia. Forest and scrub. Tropical zone. Caribbean coast in the Sinú Valley (panamensis). The Santa Marta region and southward up the Magdalena Valley to Huila (leucogenys).

9. GIANT CONEBILL
(Oreomanes fraseri) Plate XVIII

Description. 6¾ - 7¼". Bill pointed, straight, .6 - .7". Above gray, below chestnut. Forecrown whitish; eyebrow chestnut; cheeks and ear-coverts white, malar streak black.

Range. Ecuador, Peru and northern Bolivia.

Colombia. Polylepis woodland exclusively. Temperate zone of the Andes of Nariño (fraseri).

10. MASKED FLOWER-PIERCER
(Diglossa cyanea)

Description. 6 - 6½". Dark blue. Forecrown, sides of head, chin and upper throat deep black. ♀ similar but duller.

Range. Northern and western Venezuela, Ecuador, Peru and northern Bolivia.

Colombia. Forest. Subtropical to temperate zone throughout excepting the Santa Marta Mts. (cyanea).

11. BLUISH FLOWER-PIERCER
(Diglossa caerulescens)

Description. 5¾ - 6". ♂: Grayish blue above, paler below, center of abdomen pale gray. Lores and forehead narrowly black. ♀ similar but a trifle duller and grayer, particularly below. Bill black but less upturned than in other members of the genus; young birds have the basal half of the mandible yellow.

Range. Northern and western Ecuador, Peru and Bolivia.

Colombia. Forest. Subtropical and temperate zone, occasionally upper tropical zone. The Eastern, Central and Western Andes from Norte de Santander and Antioquia southward to Nariño *(saturata).*

12. DEEP-BLUE FLOWER-PIERCER
(Diglossa glauca)

Description. 4¾ - 5". ♂: Very dark dull blue. Lores and forehead narrowly black. ♀ similar but duller. Iris brown or yellow.

Range. Eastern Ecuador, Peru and northern Bolivia.

Colombia. Subtropical zone. Eastern Nariño *(tyrianthina).*

13. INDIGO FLOWER-PIERCER
(Diglossa indigotica) Plate XVII

Description. 4¼ - 4½". ♂: Entirely shiny indigo blue, margins of remiges greenish blue. Lores black. ♀ similar but duller. Iris red.

Range. Western Ecuador.

Colombia. Upper tropical and subtropical zone of the western slope of the Western Andes, from the headwaters of the río San Juan southward to southern Cauca, and undoubtedly Nariño.

14. COAL-BLACK FLOWER-PIERCER
(Diglossa carbonaria)

Description. 5½ - 6" (or 5 - 5½", 1). Glossy black; shoulder patch blue-gray (or without shoulder patch, 1), rump dark gray (or sides of throat and entire underparts chestnut, 2; or entirely black without gray shoulder or rump, 3).

Range. Western Venezuela, Ecuador, Peru and Bolivia.

Colombia. Open scrubby slopes. Subtropical to temperate zones. The Santa Marta Mts. (1, *nocticolor).* Both slopes of the Eastern Andes from Norte de Santander to Cundinamarca *(humeralis).* Isolated colonies in the temperate zone at the northern end of the Central and Western Andes in Antioquia (2, *brunneiventris).* The Central Andes from Caldas and Tolima southward; the southern end of the Western Andes in Cauca and the mountains of Nariño (3, *aterrima).*

15. GLOSSY FLOWER-PIERCER
(Diglossa lafresnayi)

Description. 6 - 6¼". Deep, lustrous black; shoulder patch blue-gray (or breast and belly rufous; rump suffused with slate gray, 1).

Range. Western Venezuela, Ecuador, Peru and Bolivia.

Colombia. Forest edge, open brushy slopes. Upper subtropical to temperate zones. The Eastern and Central Andes from Norte de Santander, Tolima and Caldas south to the mountains of Nariño *(lafresnayi).* Temperate zone of the Western Andes from Antioquia south to the latitude of Popayán (1, *gloriosissima).*

16. WHITE-SIDED FLOWER-PIERCER
(Diglossa albilatera)

Description. 5 - 5½". ♂: Slaty gray; a white patch at sides of body. ♀: Olive brown above; rufescent brown below, center of abdomen buffy white, patch at sides of body white.

Range. Northern and western Venezuela, Ecuador and northern Peru.

Colombia. Forest edge, scrub. Subtropical to temperate zones throughout *(albilatera).*

17. SLATY FLOWER-PIERCER
(Diglossa baritula) Fig. 82

Description. 4¾ - 5¼". ♂: Top and sides of head, upperparts, wings and tail bluish gray (or forehead and sides of head slaty gray, 1); below cinnamon. ♀: Above olive brown; below soiled buffy white.

Range. Mexico southward to western Panama. Northern and western Venezuela,

Ecuador, Peru, Bolivia and western Argentina.

Colombia. Forest clearings, bushy slopes. Subtropical, occasionally upper tropical zone. Santa Marta Mts. *(hyperythra).* The Eastern Andes from Boyacá to Cundinamarca, the Central Andes and east slope of the Western Andes from Antioquia south to Nariño where it is found up to the temperate zone (1, *d'orbignyi*).

18. PURPLE HONEYCREEPER
(Cyanerpes caeruleus)

Description. 4¼ - 4½ ". Bill rather long, .6 - .7", conspicuously curved. ♂ : Legs bright yellow. Uniform purple-blue, forecrown and sides of head brighter and purer blue. Forehead, lores and stripe through eye, chin, throat, wings and tail black. ♀ : Forehead, lores and ocular region tawny buff. Upperparts, wings and tail grass green, the forecrown narrowly streaked with buffy. Throat buff, malar streak blue; rest of underparts green streaked with pale yellowish, center of abdomen and under tail-coverts plain yellowish.

Range. Venezuela, the Guianas, eastern and central Brazil. Ecuador, Peru and Bolivia. Trinidad.

Colombia. Forest. Tropical zone. The Santa Marta region *(caeruleus).* From the upper Sinú Valley eastward to the middle Magdalena. East of the Andes from Meta eastward and southward to Vaupés *(microrhynchus).* The Pacific coast from the Panama border to Nariño *(chocoanus).*

19. SHINING HONEYCREEPER
(Cyanerpes lucidus)

Description. 4½ - 4¾". Bill rather long, .6 - .7". ♂ : Very similar to the Pacific form of the Purple Honeycreeper but larger, the general plumage bluer with lighter almost azure blue sides of head, and feet and legs pale yellow instead of bright yellow. ♀ differs from the ♀ of No. 18 by lacking the tawny forehead and lores, and feathers of breast blue streaked with whitish instead of green streaked with pale yellowish, throat paler, buffy white.

Range. Southern Mexico to northwestern Colombia.

Colombia. Forest. Tropical zone. Extreme northwest Pacific coast *(isthmicus).*

20. SHORT-BILLED HONEYCREEPER
(Cyanerpes nitidus)

Description. 4 - 4¼", Bill rather short, .4". Legs yellow. Mainly cornflower blue. ♂ : Resembles No. 18 but black of throat extends to upper breast. ♀ : Upperparts and sides of head grass green. Forehead, eye-ring and malar streak blue. Breast and sides of body grass green, streaked with whitish. Throat and center of abdomen buffy white.

Range. Southern Venezuela, northern and western Brazil, eastern Ecuador and eastern Peru.

Colombia. Forest. Tropical zone. Base of the Andes in Caquetá *(caquetae);* in Vaupés *(nitidus).*

21. RED-LEGGED HONEYCREEPER
(Cyanerpes cyaneus) Plate XVII

Description. 5¼ - 5¾". Bill rather long, .6 - .8", somewhat curved. ♂ : Forehead, ocular region, mantle, wings, tail and under tail-coverts black. Inner margins of remiges canary yellow. Feathers of crown enamel-like, brilliant turquoise blue. Sides of head, nape, narrow line surrounding crown patch, lower back, scapulars, upper tail-coverts and under surface purple-blue. ♀ : Entire upper surface dull grass green. Throat and eyebrow yellowish white; breast and sides of body dull grass green, the breast streaked with yellowish; center of abdomen pale yellow. Wings and tail dusky, the wing-coverts, remiges and rectrices margined with olive green. Legs bright red (♂), dull reddish (♀).

Range. Mexico southward through Central America to western Ecuador. Northern Venezuela and the Guianas southward to Bolivia and southeastern Brazil. Trinidad and Tobago. Cuba where probably introduced.

Colombia. Plantations, forest edge. Tropical zone. Humid forest belt of the

Macuira Mts. in the Guajira Peninsula (*gemmeus*). Santa Marta region and the west slope of the Eastern Andes southward to Santander (*eximius*). East of the Eastern Andes from the Catatumbo Valley southward to Meta (*dispar*). Northwestern Colombia in Bolívar (*carneipes*). Pacific coast from the Baudó Mts. southward to Nariño (*pacificus*). Gorgona Island (*gigas*).

22. BLACK-FACED DACNIS
(*Dacnis lineata*)

Description. 4¾ - 5". ♂ : Glossy sky blue (or verditer blue, 1). Forehead, sides of head and neck, mantle, wings and tail glossy blue-black. Center of abdomen, under wing- and tail-coverts white (or golden yellow, 1). ♀ : Upperparts pale olive brown (or with a bluish cast, 1). Below pale greenish, whiter on center of abdomen (or center of abdomen and under tail-coverts bright yellow, 1). Wings and tail brown.

Range. Venezuela and the Guianas, southward to the Amazon Valley; westward to Ecuador, Peru and Bolivia.

Colombia. Forest. Tropical zone. East of the Andes from Meta southward to Putumayo and Vaupés (*lineata*). Upper and middle Magdalena Valley and the lower Cauca Valley (1, *egregia*).

23. BLUE DACNIS
(*Dacnis cayana*)

Description. 5¼ - 5½". Bill short, .4", straight and very pointed. ♂ : Mainly turquoise blue (or light or dark purple-blue, 1). Forehead and lores, throat, center of back, wings and tail black, remiges margined with turquoise blue. ♀ : Grass green. Top and sides of head blue; throat gray.

Range. Nicaragua to western Ecuador. Venezuela and the Guianas southward to Argentina and Bolivia. Trinidad.

Colombia. Forest. Tropical zone. Santa Marta region westward to the east side of the Gulf of Urabá (1, *napaea*). Lower Cauca and upper and middle Magdalena Valleys (1, *coerebicolor*). Extreme northwest Pacific coast and the west shore of the Gulf of Urabá (1, *ultramarina*). The

Baudó Mts. southward to Nariño (1, *baudoana*). East of the Eastern Andes from Meta eastward to Vichada and Vaupés (*cayana*). Eastern base of the Andes in Caquetá and Putumayo (*glaucogularis*).

24. VIRIDIAN DACNIS
(*Dacnis viguieri*)

Description. 4¾ - 5" ♂ : Mainly shining verditer blue, bluer on rump and underparts, becoming sky blue on upper tail-coverts. Forehead, lores, triangular patch on mantle, outer wing-coverts, primaries and rectrices black. Inner remiges and inner wing-coverts shining bright olive green shot with verditer blue. ♀ : Above pale olive, wings and tail brown, the feathers edged olive. Underparts pale greenish, center of abdomen pale buff.

Range. Eastern Panama.

Colombia. Forest and scrub. Extreme northwestern Chocó eastward to Córdoba.

25. SCARLET-THIGHED DACNIS
(*Dacnis venusta*)

Description. 5 - 5¼". ♂ : Crown, nape, ear-coverts, cheeks and sides of neck, scapulars, line down center of mantle, lower back and rump turquoise blue, cornflower blue when seen against the light. Forecrown, lores, eye-ring, center of throat, underparts, mantle, wings and tail and upper tail-coverts black, lower parts with a greenish gloss in certain lights. Thighs scarlet. ♀ : Crown, sides of head, mantle dull greenish blue, much lighter and brighter on lower back and rump. Wings and tail dusky. Cheeks greenish blue. Throat, breast, sides of body pale buffy brown, center of breast and abdomen fawn, under tail-coverts cinnamon buff.

Range. Costa Rica to northern Ecuador.

Colombia. Forest and scrub. Tropical zone of the Pacific coast from the Panama border to Nariño and eastward to the lower Cauca and middle Magdalena Valleys (*fuliginata*).

26. SCARLET-BREASTED DACNIS
(*Dacnis berlepschi*) Plate XVII

Description. 4¾ - 5". ♂ : Crown and nape dark blue, back bright blue, streaked with glistening silvery blue, lower back brilliant pale blue. Throat and breast bright blue, lower breast brilliant flame scarlet; abdomen golden buff, under tail-coverts white. Wings and tail black, wing-coverts edged blue. ♀: Above brown; throat and breast pale brown; band across lower breast orange-scarlet, rest of underparts mainly golden buff, browner on sides.

Range. Northwest Ecuador.

Colombia. Forest. Tropical zone. Southwestern Nariño.

27. YELLOW-BELLIED DACNIS
(Dacnis flaviventer)

Description. 5 - 5¼". ♂: Forehead, lores, sides of head, throat, mantle, wings and tail black. Crown and nape bluish olive green. Scapulars, lower back and rump, underparts and malar streak golden yellow, the black bases of the feathers of the breast showing through, giving a somewhat mottled appearance. ♀: Above dull olivaceous brown, wings and tail brown. Below pale grayish buff, buff slightly mottled with brown on the breast, center of abdomen and under tail-coverts buff.

Range. Southern Venezuela, western Brazil, Ecuador, Peru and Bolivia.

Colombia. Forest. Tropical zone east of the Andes in Caquetá and Putumayo.

28. WHITE-BELLIED DACNIS
(Dacnis albiventris)

Description. 4¾ - 5". ♂: Mostly shiny purple-blue. Forehead, lores, ocular region, ear-coverts, wings and tail black, the wing-coverts and remiges edged with purple-blue. Lower breast, belly and under tail-coverts white, sides of body dull blue. ♀: Above green, brighter on the rump. Underparts greenish yellow becoming yellower on the center of belly. Wings and tail black, edged green.

Range. Eastern Ecuador, northeastern Peru. Northeastern Brazil in the state of Pará.

Colombia. Forest. Tropical zone at the eastern base of the Eastern Andes from Meta to Putumayo.

29. GREEN HONEYCREEPER
(Chlorophanes spiza)

Description. 5¼ - 6". Bill .5", slightly curved. ♂: Generally shining emerald green (or shining blue-green, 1). Top and sides of head and sides of neck black. Mandible yellow. ♀: Grass green with more or less yellow on throat and center of abdomen. Mandible greenish yellow.

Range. Southern Mexico southward to western Ecuador. Venezuela, the Guianas southward to northern and southeastern Brazil. Trinidad.

Colombia. Flowering trees in forest clearings. Tropical zone. Northwestern Colombia and the Pacific coast southward to the Baudó Mts. (arguta). From the headwaters of the río San Juan southward to the Dagua Valley and eastward to the west slope of the Eastern Andes and east probably to the Perijá Mts. (1, subtropicalis). West coast from the vicinity of Cerro Munchique to Nariño (exsul). East of the Eastern Andes from Arauca southward (1, caerulescens). Extreme eastern Colombia in Vaupés (spiza).

30. YELLOW-COLLARED HONEYCREEPER
(Iridophanes pulcherrima)

Description. 5 - 5¼". Tanager-like in appearance. Entire head, upper mantle, sides of upper back and upper tail-coverts black; a golden yellow collar around sides and back of neck. Center of back shiny, opalescent, pale greenish straw color. Breast and sides of body greenish straw color, lower breast and abdomen whitish. Wing-coverts shiny blue; remiges and rectrices black edged with blue, the outer rectrices sometimes with a white patch on inner web.

Range. Western Ecuador. Eastern Ecuador to southeastern Peru.

Colombia. Known in Colombia from trade skins but probably occurs in the forests of the subtropical zone on the east slope of the Eastern Andes (pulcherrima) and possibly southwestern Nariño (aureinucha).

SWALLOW-TANAGERS (Tersinidae)

Fig. 83. Swallow-Tanager
(Tersina viridis)

Swallow-Tanagers are so-called because of their long swallow-like wings and short tarsi. Their flat, wide bills are well adapted to catching insects on the wing. In addition to insects they also eat fruit. They nest in holes in banks or trees and even walls of houses. They are gregarious and live in open woodland, and are partially migratory. (1 Col.; 1 S.A.; 1 N.&S.A.; 1 wld.)

SWALLOW-TANAGER
(Tersina viridis)

Description. 5½ - 5¾ ″. ♂ : Mainly purple-blue when seen against the light, bluish green when seen away from it. Forehead, lores, ocular region and throat black. Center of belly and under tail-coverts white. Wings and tail black, the feathers broadly margined with blue. Flanks barred with black. ♀ : Mainly grass green (or grayish green, 1). Black facial area replaced by gray. Center of abdomen and bars on flanks pale yellow. Wings and tail black broadly margined green.

Range. Eastern Panama, Venezuela, British and French Guiana, eastern and western Ecuador, Peru, Brazil, Paraguay, Bolivia and northern Argentina. Trinidad.

Colombia. Clearings and semi-arid country. Tropical and lower subtropical zones. Santa Marta Mts. (1, *grisescens);* the rest of Colombia both east and west of the Andes *(occidentalis).*

351

TANAGERS (Thraupidae)

Fig. 84. White-winged Tanager
(Piranga leucoptera) p. 369

Tanagers comprise a large, exclusively American family of small to medium-sized birds, varied in appearance and habits, and notable for their brilliant colors, sometimes shared by both sexes.

Somewhat gregarious, some species travel through the canopy of the tropical forest or in second growth in mixed bands of tanagers and other small birds. Others live in the thickets of the arid lowlands, while still others inhabit the subtropical and temperate zone of the Andes. Their food consists of fruit and insects.

The family is of neotropical origin: only four species occur north of Mexico. For the most part tanagers are non-migratory. They are closely related to the finches and it is difficult to draw the line between the two where they approach each other. A few are very like warblers.

Tanagers usually construct a cup-shaped nest placed in a tree or bush, but the chlorophonias and euphonias build a domed structure. (123 Col.; 186 S.A.; 222 N.&S.A.; 222 wld.)

AID TO IDENTIFICATION

No red in plumage:
    Underparts spotted 28, 29, 30, 48E, 110.
    Underparts all or partly bright yellow or tawny yellow.
        Above dark blue or purplish blue 4, 5, 6, 7, 8, 9, 10E, 11, 13, 14E, 55, 56, 57, 59, 63.
        Above all or mostly bright green 1, 2, 3, 15, 16, 25, 29E, 32, 58, 61, 62, 65.
        Above mostly yellow, olive or black; (yellow) 31, 32, 88, (olive) 12, 66, 77, 78, 79, 80, 93, 97, 101, 102, 113, 115, 123, (black) 41E, 60, 64, 65, 75.
    Not bright yellow or tawny yellow below.
        Above all or mostly olive yellow, buffy, gray or ochraceous (bill thick, short, hooked) 1, 5, 6, 7, 8, 9, 10E, 11, 13, 14E, 15, 16E, 123, (bill normal) 23, 82E, 83E, 84, 91, 92E, 101, 106, 108, 109, 110, 111, 112, 113, 116, (cap blue in contrast to back) 3, 4, 70E.
        Above mostly dark blue (below mostly blue) 48, 52, 53, (below ochraceous) 12, 14.

Above and below mostly black, or black and white; (black) 89, 90, 93, 94, 118, 119, (with rump yellow or buff) 75, 91E, 95, (black and white) 122E.

Above all or mostly black, not black below, (below blue) 17E, 18E, 22, 23, 24E, 36, 38, 39, (below opalescent) 35, (below olive) 98.

Bright grass green or bluish green 19, 20, 21, 26, 44, 45, 120.

All or mostly pale silvery green or silvery olive or silvery blue; back usually streaked black 27, 33, 34, 37, 40, 46, 47, 50E, 51, 69.

All mostly rufous to earthy brown 85, 86, 88E, 89, 90E, 94, 103, 105, 117, 121E.

With red or scarlet in the plumage: 44, 45, 54, 71E, 72E, 73, 74, 76E, 77, 78, 79, 80, 81, 85, 86, 87, 92, 95, 99, 103, 107.

Supplementary category: head of a solid color (black, red, green, etc.) in sharp contrast to body color 23, 38, 39, 44, 45, 51, 57, 81, 88E, 97, 102, 104, 106, 111, 120, 122E.

1. BLUE-NAPED CHLOROPHONIA
(Chlorophonia cyanea)

Description. 4½ - 5". ♂ : Head, throat and upper breast bright yellowish green, eye-ring blue. Underparts bright yellow. Back bright blue, outer remiges and tail black edged green, inner remiges grass green (or similar but forehead yellow, back green with narrow blue collar on hindneck, 1). ♀ very like ♂ but duller. Back green, lower breast and belly olive yellow.

Range. Venezuela, British Guiana, eastern Ecuador, Peru, Bolivia, Paraguay, southern Brazil and northern Argentina.

Colombia. Forest, coffee plantations. Upper tropical and subtropical zones. Santa Marta region (1, *psittacina*). Upper Magdalena Valley *(longipennis)*. Western slope of the Western Andes in Caldas and Valle *(intensa)*.

2. GREEN-AND-YELLOW CHLOROPHONIA
(Chlorophonia flavirostris)

Description. 4". ♀ : Bright grass green, center of breast, abdomen and the under tail-coverts bright yellow. Bill reddish brown, feet and legs reddish yellow. Iris white. ♂ from Colombia unknown. The following description of a ♂ is based on a specimen from Ecuador without precise locality and which possibly belongs to a different subspecies. ♂ : Head, throat, chest and sides of body, back, wings and tail bright green, upper back crossed by a broad yellow collar.

Lower breast and belly yellow, separated from the green of the breast by a narrow chestnut band. Iris white. Bill yellow or salmon. Legs salmon.

Range. Eastern (?) Ecuador.

Colombia. Tropical zone of southwestern Nariño *(minima)*.

3. CHESTNUT-BELLIED CHLOROPHONIA
(Chlorophonia pyrrhophrys) Plate XIX

Description. 4¾ - 5¼". ♂ : Crown and nape purple-blue margined, except at back, by black. Forehead, sides of head, back, wings and tail grass green; rump bright yellow. Throat and breast grass green; margined below by a narrow black band. Center of underparts chestnut, sides of body bright yellow. ♀ like ♂ but forehead and sides of crown margined by maroon; rump and underparts olive yellow.

Range. Western Venezuela and eastern Ecuador.

Colombia. Forest. Subtropical and temperate zones of Eastern, Central and east slope of the Western Andes and the Pacific slope of the Andes of Nariño.

4. BLUE-HOODED EUPHONIA
(Tanagra musica)

Description. 4¾ - 5¼". ♂ : Crown and nape pale blue. Upperparts and throat deep ultramarine (or deep purple, 1). Rump and underparts golden yellow (or tawny yellow, 1). ♀ : Mainly olive, yellower below. Forehead rufous-chestnut (or yellow), crown and nape blue.

Range. Mexico southward through Central America. Venezuela, British and Dutch Guiana, Brazil, Paraguay, Uruguay, Argentina, Bolivia, Peru, eastern and western Ecuador. The West Indies.

Colombia. Open forest often in trees with mistletoe. Upper tropical and subtropical zone. Eastern slope of the Eastern Andes from Norte de Santander to Meta (1, *intermedia*). The Central and Western Andes from Antioquia south to Cauca where birds are intermediate between *intermedia* and *pelzelni*. In Nariño birds are probably typical of *pelzelni*. As yet it has not been taken there.

Euphonia

The males of the following 8 species of euphonia resemble each other closely in their glossy dark blue or purplish blue upperparts and throat, bright yellow underparts, small size and thick, blunt bills and are difficult to tell apart. On the other hand the females are quite distinctive; if pairs are seen, identification is more easily made through the female.

5. ORANGE-BELLIED EUPHONIA
(Tanagra xanthogaster) Plate XIX

Description. 4¼ - 4½ ". ♂ : Crown to behind eyes, breast and rest of underparts yellow, washed ochraceous. Nape, throat, sides of head glossy purplish blue. Back and wings glossy steel blue; basal portion of inner remiges white. Tail blue-black, the outer tail-feathers with a large white subterminal patch on inner web. ♀ : Forehead and short eyebrow dull dark yellow; nuchal patch gray. Crown and rest of upperparts, wings and tail and sides of head olive. Throat and breast grayish buff becoming cinnamon-buff on center of abdomen; sides of breast and body olive yellow.

Range. Eastern Panama, Venezuela, British Guiana, Brazil, Ecuador, Peru and Bolivia.

Colombia. Forest. Tropical and subtropical zones. Northern extremity of the Sierra de Perijá and Boyacá *(exsul)*. East of the Eastern Andes from Norte de Santander to Meta and the slopes of the Eastern and Central Andes above the Magdalena Valley *(brevirostris)*. West slope of the Central Andes westward to the Pacific coast southward to Nariño *(chocoensis)*. Amazonas *(dilutior)*.

6. TAWNY-CAPPED EUPHONIA
(Tanagra anneae)

Description. 4¼ - 4¾ ". ♂ : Crown to behind eyes rufous-chestnut. Upper parts glossy purple. Underparts tawny yellow, under tail-coverts white. Outer tail-feather with a large, white subterminal patch on the inner web. Base of inner remiges white. ♀ : Forecrown rufous. Upperparts, wings and tail dark olive. Below yellowish olive, the throat, breast and center of abdomen gray, yellowish on flanks.

Range. Costa Rica southward through Panama.

Colombia. Tropical zone. Shores of the Gulf of Urabá *(rufivertex)*.

7. FULVOUS-VENTED EUPHONIA
(Tanagra fulvicrissa)

Description. 4¼ - 4½ ". ♂ : Forecrown lemon yellow; hindcrown, sides of head, throat, back, wings and tail steel blue (or purplish blue, 1) . Sides of body bright yellow; center of underparts and under tail-coverts tawny rufous. Outer tail-feathers with white on inner webs. ♀ : Forecrown rufous, hindcrown and upper back bronzy olive green, somewhat glossed with blue; lower back and tail yellowish olive, wings edged olive yellow. Center of abdomen and under tail-coverts tawny ochraceous; rest of underparts olive yellow, brightest on sides of abdomen.

Range. Costa Rica to northwestern Ecuador.

Colombia. Forest and scrub. Tropical zone. Extreme northwestern Chocó *(fulvicrissa)*. The rest of Colombia west of the Eastern Andes, not Santa Marta or Nariño *(omissa)*. The Pacific slope of Nariño (1, *purpurascens*) .

8. WHITE-VENTED EUPHONIA
(*Tanagra minuta*)

Description. 4 - 4¼ ". ♂ : Forecrown bright yellow; hindcrown, sides of head, throat, upperparts, wings and tail glossy steel blue, glossed purplish on head. Underparts bright yellow; under tail-coverts white and three outer tail-feathers with white on the inner web. ♀ : Upperparts, wings and tail olive. Chin yellowish, throat, center of abdomen and under tail-coverts grayish white, breast and sides of body olive yellow.

Range. Costa Rica and Panama southward to western Ecuador. Venezuela and the Guianas southward to the middle and upper Amazon Valley and eastern Peru.

Colombia. Scrub. Tropical zone. East of the Eastern Andes from Meta southward to southeastern Nariño (*minuta*). From the middle Magdalena Valley westward to Chocó and southward to western Nariño (*humilis*).

9. TRINIDAD EUPHONIA
(*Tanagra trinitatis*)

Description. 4¼ - 4½ ". ♂ : Very like No. 8 but yellow cap extending to behind eyes and only two instead of three outer tail-feathers with white markings. Under tail-coverts yellow. ♀ : Above pale olive. Throat, sides of breast and body olive yellow, center of body pale gray becoming white on abdomen. Under tail-coverts bright yellow.

Range. Northern Venezuela to the middle Orinoco. Trinidad.

Colombia. Dry, open woodland, forest, mangroves. Tropical zone. Northern Colombia from Antioquia eastward to the Santa Marta region.

10. PURPLE-THROATED EUPHONIA
(*Tanagra chlorotica*)

Description. 4½ - 4¾ ". ♂ : Rather like No. 9 but considerably larger with the throat, sides of head, nape and upper back purplish instead of steel blue, and

the white base to the inner remiges much more extensive. ♀ differs from the ♀ of No. 9 by larger size and by sometimes having a patch of white on inner web of the outer tail-feathers.

Range. Venezuela, the Guianas, Brazil, Peru, eastern Bolivia and northern Argentina.

Colombia. Forest. Tropical zone east of the Andes in Meta and Vichada (*cynophora*).

11. VELVETY-FRONTED EUPHONIA
(*Tanagra concinna*)

Description. 4 - 4¼ ". ♂ : Rather like No. 7 but forehead black instead of yellow, back more purplish and more uniformly tawny yellow below. Outer tail-feathers without white. ♀ : Upperparts olive, somewhat grayish on nape. Forehead dusky olive, forecrown and underparts dull yellow.

Range. Colombia.

Colombia. Forest. Tropical zone of the Magdalena Valley in Tolima, Cundinamarca and Huila.

12. ORANGE-CROWNED EUPHONIA
(*Tanagra saturata*)

Description. 4 - 4¼ ". ♂ : Crown extensively orange yellow. Throat, upperparts glossy purple becoming steel blue on rump, wings and tail. Underparts deep tawny orange, yellower on sides of breast. Tail without white. ♀ : Upper surface, wings and tail bright olive. Throat, breast and sides of body olive yellow, yellow in center of abdomen.

Range. Western Ecuador and northwestern Peru.

Colombia. Forest. Upper tropical zone. Both slopes of the Western Andes from Valle southward to Nariño.

13. THICK-BILLED EUPHONIA
(*Tanagra laniirostris*)

Description. 4¾ - 5¼ ". ♂ : Differs from all the preceding by not having a blue throat. Crown and entire underparts golden yellow. Upper parts, wings and tail glossy steel blue, tinged purplish on nape and upper back (or entire back glossy purple, 1). A large white patch on inner web of two outermost tail-feathers. ♀: Upperparts, wings and tail bright olive. Below greenish yellow.

Range. Costa Rica and Panama southward through western South America to western Brazil and Bolivia. Northwestern Venezuela southward to Orinoco.

Colombia. Dry forest and open woodland. Tropical and lower subtropical zone. All of Colombia west of the Eastern Andes except Nariño and east of them in Arauca and northern Boyacá (crassirostris). East of the Eastern Andes in Meta and Vichada, south to Putumayo and undoubtedly Vaupés (1, melanura).

14. RUFOUS-BELLIED EUPHONIA
(Tanagra rufiventris)

Description. 4¾ - 5¼". ♂: Upperparts, throat, center of upper breast, steel blue. Below tawny rufous, yellow at sides of breast. Wings and tail black, edged steel blue. ♀: Upperparts, wings and tail olive; chin pale yellowish. Sides of head and of breast and body olive yellow; throat, center of breast and abdomen ashy gray; under tail-coverts tawny ochraceous.

Range. Central Venezuela southward through middle and upper Amazonia to Bolivia.

Colombia. Forest. Tropical zone east of the Eastern Andes from southern Meta southward to Putumayo, Vaupés and Amazonas.

15. BRONZE-GREEN EUPHONIA
(Tanagra mesochrysa)

Description. 4 - 4½". ♂: Forehead yellow, rest of upperparts somewhat glossy bronzy green, bluer on hindcrown. Wings and tail olive green. Throat, breast, sides of head and sides of body olive green, center of abdomen and under tail-coverts orange yellow. ♀ like ♂, but lacks the yellow on

forehead. Center of breast and abdomen pale gray instead of yellow.

Range. Eastern Ecuador, eastern Peru, northern Bolivia.

Colombia. Forest. Subtropical zone at the head of the Magdalena Valley and the tropical zone at the base of the Eastern Andes in Meta (mesochrysa).

16. GOLDEN-BELLIED EUPHONIA
(Tanagra chrysopasta)

Description. 4¾ - 5". ♂: Above similar to No. 15 but forehead olive instead of yellow. Lores and chin white. Underparts bright yellow obscurely barred with olive. Wings yellowish olive, tail dusky olive. ♀ like ♂ but underparts pale gray, only flanks and under tail-coverts yellow.

Range. Southern Venezuela, British, French and Dutch Guiana, northern Brazil southward to Mato Grosso, Peru, and eastern Bolivia.

Colombia. Forest. Tropical zone east of the Andes from Meta southward to Putumayo (chrysopasta). Vichada (nitida).

17. OPAL-RUMPED TANAGER
(Tanagrella velia) Plate I

Description. 6 - 6¼". ♂. Forehead, lores, forecrown, center of throat, cheeks, ear-coverts, ocular region and sides of throat glistening violet-blue. Band below throat, extending up the sides of the neck black, spotted with purple-blue in center of throat. Underparts violet-blue, center of abdomen and crissum chestnut. Crown, mantle, upper back black, lower back and rump glistening opalescent gold, upper tail-coverts glistening blue. Wing-coverts glistening blue; remiges and rectrices black edged blue. ♀ like ♂ but cheeks and ear-coverts glistening greenish blue.

Range. British, French and Dutch Guiana, southern Venezuela, Brazil, Ecuador, Peru and Bolivia.

Colombia. Forest. Tropical zone east of the Andes from Meta southward to Putumayo and Vaupés (iridina).

18. OPAL-BROWED TANAGER
(Tanagrella callophrys) Plate I

Description. 6 - 6½". Forecrown, broad eyebrow, lower back and rump glistening opalescent gold; hindcrown and mantle black. Forehead, sides of head and the underparts cornflower blue, the center of abdomen and the crissum black. Wings and tail black, the lesser wing-coverts glistening blue, the greater coverts, remiges and rectrices edged with blue.

Range. Eastern Ecuador, western Brazil, Peru and northern Bolivia.

Colombia. Forest. Tropical zone. Caquetá and Putumayo undoubtedly southward to Amazonas.

19. GLISTENING-GREEN TANAGER
(Chlorochrysa phoenicotis) Plate I

Description. 5½ - 5¾". Glistening grass green, palest on rump. Spot below eye, auricular spot margined posteriorly by orange, wing-coverts and thighs glistening gray, somewhat yellowish when seen against the light. Wings and tail black edged with grass green.

Range. Western Ecuador.

Colombia. Forest. Upper tropical and lower subtropical zone west of the Western Andes from the upper río San Juan southward.

20. ORANGE-EARED TANAGER
(Chlorochrysa calliparea) Plate I

Description. 4½ - 5¼". ♂: General plumage shining green strongly tinged with blue on forehead, ocular region and belly. Spot on crown and the rump orange. Throat black, patch on sides of neck burnt orange. ♀ similar but much duller, the throat gray instead of black.

Range. Eastern Ecuador and northeastern Peru.

Colombia. Forest. Subtropical zone from Cundinamarca southward to the head of the Magdalena Valley (bourcieri).

21. MULTICOLORED TANAGER
(Chlorochrysa nitidissima) Plate I

Description. 4½ - 5¼". ♂: Forehead forecrown and sides of head golden yellow, patch at sides of head black with a sienna brown streak behind it. Throat glistening orange yellow; breast and sides of body glistening blue, center of abdomen and lower breast black. Hindcrown and nape grass green; mantle straw yellow; lower back and upper tail-coverts glistening blue green. Wings and tail grass green. ♀: Head like ♂ in pattern but very much duller, rest of plumage grass green.

Range. Colombia.

Colombia. Forest edge and clearings. Upper tropical and subtropical zone from the western slope of the Central Andes in Caldas westward to the Pacific slope in Antioquia and south to southwestern Cauca.

22. FAWN-BREASTED TANAGER
(Pipraeidea melanonota)

Description. 6 - 6¼". ♂: Crown, nape, lesser wing-coverts and rump bright pale blue; sides of head deep black. Back, wings and tail deep ultramarine blue. Entire under surface pale ochraceous. ♀ like ♂ but duller, the blue of head and rump not nearly so intense, and the back dull grayish blue.

Range. Venezuela, southward through western South America to Bolivia and northwestern Argentina. Eastern Brazil from Bahia southward to Mato Grosso, Uruguay, Paraguay and northeastern Argentina.

Colombia. Bushy pastures and forest edge. Subtropical to lower temperate zone of the Andes from Norte de Santander and Tolima southward to Nariño (venezuelensis).

23. TURQUOISE DACNIS-TANAGER
(Pseudodacnis hartlaubi)

Description. 4½". ♂: Forehead, sides of head, throat, mantle, wings and tail blue-black. Crown, rump, upper tail-coverts and entire underparts, except throat, turquoise blue. Above in pattern resembles the Blue Dacnis, below the Masked Dacnis, but differs from both by the shorter, thicker bill. ♀: Lores and sides of head light olive brown; upperparts dull brown the feathers edged with pale greenish. Wings and tail dusky brown, the inner remiges and wing-coverts pale edged. Underparts grayish buff, yellowish white in center.

Range. Colombia.

Colombia. Exact range uncertain. A few specimens have been found in "Bogotá" collections and a very few more on the west slope of the western Andes in Valle in the upper tropical zone.

24. PARADISE TANAGER
(Tangara chilensis) Plate I

Description. 6 - 6½″. Above velvety black, lower back and rump scarlet (or lower back orange-scarlet, rump golden yellow, 1). Forehead and eye-ring black. Top and sides of head covered with shining, scale-like, golden green feathers. Throat and upper breast, outer wing-coverts and margins of primaries violet-blue; inner wing-coverts and entire underparts shining turquoise blue or light ultramarine blue seen against the light. Center of belly, wings, tail and under tail-coverts black.

Range. Southern Venezuela, the Guianas, northern and western Brazil, Ecuador, Peru and Bolivia.

Colombia. Tropical zone east of the Eastern Andes from Meta southward and eastward to Vichada and Vaupés (1, *coelicolor*). Eastern base of the Andes from Caquetá southward to Putumayo and Amazonas. One record from the west slope of the Eastern Andes in Huila *(chilensis)*.

25. GREEN-AND-GOLD TANAGER
(Tangara schrankii)

Description. 5 - 5½″. Forehead and forecrown, sides of head and ear-coverts black; a line before eye green; center of crown golden yellow (or forehead, sides of head and the crown uniform green, patch on ear-coverts black, 1). Back streaked golden green and black; rump bright golden yellow. Wings and tail black, the wing-coverts, outer remiges and rectrices edged verditer blue. Center of breast and under-parts bright golden yellow, throat and sides of body grass green.

Range. Southern Venezuela, eastern Ecuador, western Brazil, Peru and northern Bolivia.

Colombia. Forest. Tropical zone. East of the Eastern Andes in the Amazonian drainage *(schrankii)*. West of the Western Andes in Valle (1, *anchicayae)*.

26. BLUE-WHISKERED TANAGER
(Tangara johannae)

Description. 5 - 5½″. Mostly golden green, back streaked with black; rump yellow. Forehead, lores, sides of head, throat black. Short moustacial streak, forecrown, lower margin of throat, line behind eye, edges to wing-coverts, primaries and rectrices bright blue. Center of abdomen gray, under tail-coverts pale buff.

Range. Northwestern Ecuador.

Colombia. Forest and scrub. Tropical zone of the Pacific coast from the upper Atrato Valley and the foothills of the Baudó Mts. southward to Nariño.

27. EMERALD TANAGER
(Tangara florida)

Description. 4¾ - 5¼″. Mainly golden emerald green, back streaked black. Center of crown golden yellow; lores and ear-coverts black. Center of abdomen and under tail-coverts pale dull yellow.

Range. Costa Rica and Panama.

Colombia. Forest. Tropical zone of the Pacific coast from the río San Juan southward to Nariño.

28. SPECKLED TANAGER
(Tangara chrysophrys) Plate I

Description. 5½ - 5¾″. Feathers of upperparts black, broadly edged green giving a scaled appearance. Underparts white, the feathers with black centers giving a spotted appearance (or very heavily spotted, 1) flanks and under tail-coverts green. Supraloral streak and eye-ring yellowish. Wings black edged with verditer blue; tail black, edged green.

Range. Costa Rica to Venezuela. Possibly western Ecuador. Trinidad.

Colombia. Humid forest. Subtropical zone east of the Eastern Andes from Norte de Santander southward to the Macarena Mts. (*bogotensis*). East slope of the Central Andes in northern Tolima (1, *tolimae*).

29. YELLOW-BELLIED TANAGER
(*Tangara xanthogastra*) Plate I

Description. 4¾ - 5¼ ". Differs from No. 28 by being smaller and by having the feathers of the throat and breast emerald green, centered black; center of abdomen golden yellow.

Range. Venezuela, eastern Ecuador, extreme western Brazil, Peru and Bolivia. British Guiana.

Colombia. Forest. Tropical zone east of the Eastern Andes from Meta southward to Putumayo and Vaupés (*xanthogastra*).

30. RUFOUS-THROATED TANAGER
(*Tangara rufigula*)

Description. 5 - 5¼ ". Above black, the feathers narrowly edged with coppery green giving a scaled appearance, lower back and rump silvery green. Chin and sides of throat rufous-chestnut, the center of throat paler, rest of underparts whitish, the feathers of breast and sides of body centered black and fringed silvery green, under tail-coverts buff. Wings and tail black, the feathers edged silvery green.

Range. Northwestern Ecuador.

Colombia. Forest. Upper tropical and subtropical zones of the western slope of the Western Andes from the río San Juan southward to Nariño.

31. GOLDEN TANAGER
(*Tangara arthus*)

Description. 5½ - 5¾ ". Mostly golden yellow, mantle streaked black. Lores and ear-coverts black. Underparts golden yellow (or rich dark yellow, 1; or amber brown, 2). Wings and tail black, the inner remiges and wing-coverts edged with greenish gold to orange yellow.

Range. Venezuela, Ecuador, Peru, Bolivia.

Colombia. Forest. Upper tropical and subtropical zones. Western slope of the Eastern Andes in southern Magdalena (*palmitae*). The western slope of the Andes in Santander; east of the Andes in the Macarena Mts. (2, *sclateri*). Upper Magdalena Valley from the latitude of Bogotá southward (*aurulenta*). Western slope of the Central Andes and both slopes of the Western Andes from Antioquia southward to Nariño (1, *occidentalis*).

32. SILVER-THROATED TANAGER
(*Tangara icterocephala*)

Description. 5½ - 5¾ ". ♂: Top and sides of head golden yellow; throat, sides of neck silvery green, a black line from bill extending backwards separating the yellow from the green. Lower breast and rest of underparts golden yellow somewhat tinged with green. ♀: Similar but duller and crown dull greenish yellow. Back streaked yellow and black, rump golden yellow.

Range. Costa Rica to western Panama. Northwestern Ecuador.

Colombia. Humid forest. Upper tropical and subtropical zones of the western slope of the Western Andes from Antioquia southward to Nariño (*icterocephala*).

33. YELLOW-CROWNED TANAGER
(*Tangara xanthocephala*)

Description. 5½ - 5¾ ". Crown, cheeks and ear-coverts golden yellow; forehead, lores, orbital region, throat and extreme upper back black. Back streaked blue and black, rump and upper tail-coverts shining blue. Lower throat, breast and sides of body opalescent greenish blue; center of abdomen and under tail-coverts fawn. Wings and tail black edged blue. When seen away from the light the blue portions of the plumage becomes golden green.

Range. Western Venezuela, Ecuador, Peru, Bolivia.

Colombia. Forest. Upper tropical and subtropical zones virtually throughout, with the exception of Santa Marta and the Caribbean region (*venusta*).

34. GOLDEN-EARED TANAGER
(Tangara chrysotis)

Description. 5¾ - 6". Forehead and eyebrows glistening opalescent gold, region below eye and ear-coverts glistening golden copper; lores, orbital region, broad band below cheeks and ear-coverts, center of crown and nape black. Interscapulum black streaked with glistening golden green, coppery gold when seen away from the light; lower back, rump and upper tail-coverts, throat, breast and flanks glistening, opalescent golden green; center of belly and under tail-coverts light chestnut. Wings and tail black edged with golden green.

Range. Eastern Ecuador, Peru, northern Bolivia.

Colombia. Forest. Subtropical zone at the head of the Magdalena Valley. East of the Andes in Caquetá.

35. FLAME-FACED TANAGER
(Tangara parzudakii)

Description. 6¼ - 6½". Forehead and patch behind and below eye scarlet; ocular area, throat and posterior ear-coverts black; crown and nape continued downward to behind ear-coverts golden yellow (or crown and area below eye orange yellow, 1). Mantle, wings and tail black; lower back, rump, upper tail-coverts and inner wing-coverts glistening opalescent blue or silvery depending on the light (or green depending on the light, 1); greater wing-coverts edged with blue. Breast and sides of body glistening opalescent silvery green (or golden green, 1); center of underparts cinnamon buff.

Range. Northwestern Venezuela, Ecuador and Peru.

Colombia. Forest. Upper tropical and subtropical zones. West slope of the Eastern Andes from Cundinamarca southward and the east slope in Nariño *(parzudakii)*. West slope of the Western Andes from the río San Juan southward to Nariño (1, *lunigera)*.

36. BLUE-BROWED TANAGER
(Tangara cyanotis)

Description. 5¾ - 5¼". Above mostly black; broad eyebrow, lesser wing-coverts, lower back and underparts blue tinged with golden green when seen against the light. Center of underparts fawn. Wings and tail black, greater wing-coverts narrowly edged blue.

Range. Ecuador, Peru, and northern Bolivia.

Colombia. Forest. Known only from "Bogota" and the subtropical zone at the head of the Magdalena Valley. It probably occurs also on the east slope of the Eastern Andes *(lutleyi)*.

37. METALLIC-GREEN TANAGER
(Tangara labradorides)

Description. 5 - 5¼". Mostly shining silvery greenish blue, paler and more opalescent on forecrown and sides of crown. Forehead, lores and center of hindcrown and nape black. Lesser wing-coverts glistening purplish blue, greater wing-coverts glistening green. Center of abdomen gray, under tail-coverts cinnamon. Wings and tail black edged blue.

Range. Western Ecuador, northwestern Peru.

Colombia. Forest. Upper tropical and subtropical zones. The western slope of the Eastern Andes westward through the mountains to the Pacific slope and Nariño. Recorded once from the east slope of the Eastern Andes just north of the latitude of Bogotá *(labradorides)*.

38. BLUE-NECKED TANAGER
(Tangara cyanicollis)

Description. 5¼ - 5½". Whole head turquoise blue, purplish blue in middle of throat. Back and breast black, belly shining purplish blue (or breast and belly black, 1). Wing-coverts glistening silvery green (or glistening coppery green, 1). Lower back, rump, upper tail-coverts and margins to inner remiges glistening silvery green. Tail black, edged greenish blue.

Range. Northwestern Venezuela, Ecuador, Brazil, Peru and Bolivia.

Colombia. Open forest. Upper tropical and lower subtropical zones. East slope of the Eastern Andes in Norte de Santander (1, *hannahiae*); in eastern Cundinamarca southward to eastern Nariño (*caeruleocephala*). West slope of the Eastern Andes from western Santander southward to western Cundinamarca; the Central Andes and the Western Andes southward to southwestern Cauca (*granadensis*).

39. MASKED TANAGER
(Tangara nigro-cincta)

Description. 5 - 5¼ ". ♂: Lores, chin and ocular region black, rest of head pale lavender, cheeks and ear-coverts pale green (or forecrown and malar region silvery purplish blue, rest of head glistening golden copper, 1). Breast and upper back, wings and tail black. Lower back, rump and upper tail-coverts cornflower blue. Lesser wing-coverts blue, median wing-coverts silvery green (or lesser wing-coverts purplish, median wing-coverts silvery blue, 1). Middle of abdomen white, sides of abdomen bright blue. ♀, similar but duller.

Range. Southern Mexico, southward to northwestern Ecuador. Southern Venezuela, British Guiana, Ecuador, Peru, western Brazil, northern Bolivia.

Colombia. Forest edge, open woodland. Tropical zone. East of the Eastern Andes from Meta southward to Putumayo and undoubtedly Vaupés (*nigro-cincta*). West of the Eastern Andes except Santa Marta (1, *fanny*).

40. GOLDEN-NAPED TANAGER
(Tangara ruficervix)

Description. 5 - 5½ ". ♂: Mainly turquoise blue, duller on mantle where feathers have dusky centers. Crown, lores, ocular region black, band across center of crown violet, band across hindcrown shining golden buff, nape blackish violet, ear-coverts tipped white (or gold, 1). Center of abdomen buffy white, under tail-coverts buff. Wings and tail black broadly edged blue. ♀ similar but duller, the back dull blue.

Range. Ecuador, Peru, Bolivia.
Colombia. Forest edge and pastureland. Upper tropical and subtropical zones west

of the Eastern Andes except Santa Marta (*ruficervix*). East of the Eastern Andes in Nariño (1, *taylori*).

41. TURQUOISE TANAGER
(Tangara mexicana)

Description. 5½ - 5¾ ". Lores and chin, center of crown, nape, back, wings and tail black, the primaries edged with turquoise blue. Forecrown, sides of head, throat, breast, sides of body, wing-coverts, lower back and rump purplish blue somewhat spotted with black on lower throat and sides. Tuft on sides of breast, center of belly and under tail-coverts golden yellow (or yellowish white, 1).
Range. Venezuela, the Guianas, Brazil, Peru, Bolivia. Trinidad.
Colombia. Open woodland. Tropical zone. Eastern base of the Eastern Andes from Meta southward to Amazonas (*boliviana*). Eastern Vichada (1, *media*).

42. GRAY-AND-GOLD TANAGER
(Tangara palmeri)

Description. 6 - 6½ ". Above mainly pale gray. Forehead, lores, ocular region, patch at sides of neck, and scapulars black. Black band across extreme upper back spotted with gray. Mantle pale shining silvery green shot with purplish blue. Eyebrows, sides and the underparts mainly white. Band across breast shining pale straw yellow shot with blue and golden green, this band somewhat mixed with black. Wings and tail black.
Range. Eastern Panama, northwestern Ecuador.
Colombia. Forest. Tropical zone of the entire Pacific slope.

43. PLAIN-COLORED TANAGER
(Tangara inornata)

Description. 5 - 5½ ". Mainly leaden gray, the forehead tinged blue. Lesser wing-coverts bright blue; center of underparts white. Wings and tail black.
Range. Central and eastern Panama.
Colombia. Forest and clearings. Tropical zone. Northwestern Colombia in Chocó and extreme western Antioquia (*languens*). Upper Sinú, lower Cauca and middle Magdalena Valleys (*inornata*).

44. BAY-HEADED TANAGER
(Tangara gyrola)

Description. 5½ - 6". Whole head claret red to brick red, bordered on nape and sides of neck with golden yellow (or without border, 1). Body plumage entirely intense grass green (or rump and underparts blue, under tail-coverts green, 2). Thighs chestnut. Wings yellowish green (or wing-coverts golden yellow, 2). Tail dark green.

Range. Costa Rica southward to western Ecuador. Venezuela, the Guianas, Brazil, Peru, northern Bolivia. Trinidad.

Colombia. Humid forest. Coffee plantations. Upper tropical and subtropical zones. Santa Marta region and the east slope of the Eastern Andes in Norte de Santander and Boyacá (toddi). The eastern Andes from Meta southward to Putumayo and Nariño (2, catharinae). The western slope of the Eastern Andes westward to the Pacific coast and south to the Patía Valley (1, 2, deleticia). The Pacific slope of Nariño (2, nupera). Eastern Putumayo and Vaupés (2, parva).

45. RUFOUS-WINGED TANAGER
(Tangara lavinia)

Description. 5 - 5½". Head and wing-coverts and edges of remiges brick red, rest of plumage bright grass green, except for golden yellow mantle and sky blue line down center of underparts.

Range. Guatemala to northwestern Ecuador.

Colombia. Forest. Tropical zone of the entire Pacific coast; Gorgona Island (lavinia).

46. SCRUB TANAGER
(Tangara ruficapilla)

Description. 6 - 6¼". Crown rufous, lores and sides of head blackish. Mostly silvery green, paler and grayer below. Center of abdomen buffy white becoming fawn on under tail-coverts. Wings and tail black broadly edged with pale green.

Range. Northwestern Ecuador.

Colombia. Semi-arid scrub and pastureland. Upper tropical and subtropical zones from the west slope of the Eastern Andes

westward through the mountains to the Pacific slope and Nariño.

47. RUFOUS-CROWNED TANAGER
(Tangara cayana)

Description. 6 - 6½". ♂: Above shiny golden straw. Crown rufous, lores and sides of head black, throat and upper breast shiny pale greenish blue. Lower breast and belly golden buff, becoming buff on under tail-coverts. Wings and tail verditer blue. ♀: Similar but much duller, best distinguishable from No. 46 by buffier underparts.

Range. Venezuela, the Guianas, Brazil, Paraguay, and northern Bolivia.

Colombia. Forest. Tropical zone. East of the Andes from Norte de Santander and Boyacá southward to Meta and eastward to Vichada (cayana).

48. BLACK-AND-GREEN TANAGER
(Tangara nigroviridis)

Description. 5¼ - 5½". Crown, lower back and rump shining verditer blue spotted with black. Forehead, broad stripe through eye, chin and mantle black. Underparts black profusely spotted with verditer blue. Center of abdomen white. Wings and tail black broadly edged with blue.

Range. Venezuela, Ecuador, Peru, Bolivia.

Colombia. Open forest. Tropical zone. The east slope of the Eastern Andes in Norte de Santander (cyanescens). Subtropical zone of the east slope of the Eastern Andes from Boyacá southward to Putumayo and Nariño (nigroviridis). West of the Eastern Andes (consobrina).

49. BLUE-AND-BLACK TANAGER
(Tangara vassorii)

Description. 5¼ - 5¾". Silky cornflower blue. Forehead, lores, ocular region, chin, wings and tail black, lesser wing-coverts cornflower blue, greater coverts edged blue.

Range. Venezuela, Ecuador, Peru, Bolivia.

Colombia. Forest and scrub. Subtropical to temperate zone of the Andes from Norte de Santander, Bolívar and Antioquia southward to western Nariño. In the south, east of the Andes in Nariño (vassorii).

50. BLACK-CAPPED TANAGER
(Tangara heinei)

Description. 5½ - 5¾ ". ♂ : Glistening silvery blue, wings and tail darker. Cap black, sides of head, throat and breast silvery green somewhat streaked with black. ♀. Crown bluish green. Back, flanks, wings and tail bright yellowish olive green, throat and breast somewhat like ♂. Center of abdomen gray.

Range. Western Venezuela; eastern Ecuador.

Colombia. Forest clearings. Upper tropical and subtropical zones. The Andes generally, including Santa Marta.

51. BLACK-HEADED TANAGER
(Tangara cyanoptera)

Description. 5½ - 5¾ ". ♂ : Head and tail black, wings black the feathers broadly edged blue; rest of plumage silvery straw tinged with green. ♀. Crown and sides of head greenish gray. Throat and breast pale grayish, rest of underparts pale greenish yellow. Back, wings and tail pale olive green.

Range. British Guiana; Venezuela.

Colombia. Forest. Upper tropical and subtropical zones of the Santa Marta Mts. and Norte de Santander *(cyanoptera)*.

52. GOLDEN-CROWNED TANAGER
(Iridosornis rufi-vertex) Plate XIX

Description. 7 - 7½ ". Head and upper back black, center of crown with a flat golden yellow (or orange yellow, 1) crest. Mantle and breast intense deep blue, belly and lower back dull greenish blue; crissum chestnut (or blue, 2). Wings and tail black, the feathers broadly edged with blue-green.

Range. Western Venezuela, Ecuador, Peru.

Colombia. Forest. Temperate zone. The Eastern Andes *(rufi-vertex)*. Northern end of the Western Andes and Central Andes (2, *caeruleoventris*). Southern end of the Western and Central Andes and Nariño (1, *ignicapillus)*.

53. YELLOW-THROATED TANAGER
(Iridosornis analis)

Description. 6 - 6¼ ". Mostly deep purplish blue, tinged greenish on lower back and sides of body. Forehead, lores and ocular region black, throat bright golden yellow. Center of abdomen buffy white, under tail-coverts chestnut. Wings and tail black margined greenish blue.

Range. Ecuador southward to northern Bolivia.

Colombia. Forest. Upper tropical and subtropical zones. West slope of the Central Andes in Antioquia and both slopes of the Western Andes southward to Nariño *(porphyrocephala)*.

54. SCARLET-BELLIED TANAGER
(Anisognathus igniventris)

Description. 7½ - 7¾ ". Mostly glossy black. Ear-tufts, lower breast and belly scarlet. Lower back and wing-coverts, intense blue. Under tail-coverts black and scarlet (or virtually all black, 1).

Range. Western Venezuela, Ecuador, Peru, Bolivia.

Colombia. Forest. Upper subtropical to temperate zones. Eastern Andes from the latitude of Bogotá northwards *(lunulatus)*. Central Andes in Caldas and Cauca and the mountains of Nariño (1, *erythrotus)*.

55. BLACK-CHEEKED TANAGER
(Anisognathus melanogenys)

Description. 7¾ - 8 ". Crown and nape glossy cornflower blue, sides of head black, small spot below eye yellow. Entire upperparts, wings and tail dull greenish blue. Entire underparts golden yellow. Thighs black.

Range. Colombia.

Colombia. Forest. Subtropical to temperate zone of the Santa Marta Mts.

56. LACHRYMOSE TANAGER
(Anisognathus lacrymosus)

Description. 7¾ - 8 ". Above dark slaty blue, bright blue on rump. Sides of head and neck black, spot below eye and patch behind ear-coverts yellow. Entire underparts burnt orange (or forehead, lores, sides of head and neck yellowish olive, center of crown, nape and back ashy blue, 1). Wing-coverts bright blue, wings and tail blackish the feathers edged greenish blue.

Range. Northern Venezuela, Ecuador, Peru.

Colombia. Forest. Subtropical to temperate zones. The northern end of the Perijá Mts. (1, *pallididorsalis*). Norte de Santander and Boyacá (*tamae*). Northern portion of the Central and Western Andes (*olivaceiceps*). Eastern slope of the Western Andes in Valle and Cauca (*intensus*). Southern portion of the Central Andes in Huila and Cauca; western Nariño (*palpebrosus*).

57. HOODED MOUNTAIN TANAGER
(Buthraupis montana)

Description. 9¾ - 10¼ ". Head black. Upperparts glistening violet-blue. Underparts golden yellow.

Range. Western Venezuela, Ecuador, Peru, Bolivia.

Colombia. Forest. Upper tropical to temperate zones of the Eastern Andes from Norte de Santander to Cundinamarca (*gigas*). The Central and Western Andes and both slopes in Nariño (*cucullata*).

58. BLACK-CHESTED MOUNTAIN TANAGER
(Buthraupis eximia)

Description. 8¾ - 9½ ". Crown, nape, and lesser wing-coverts, lower back and rump blue, mantle moss green (or rump and lower back green, 1). Sides of head, throat and breast black, rest of underparts bright yellow. Wings and tail black, inner remiges margined green.

Range. Western Venezuela; Ecuador.

Colombia. Forest. Upper subtropical to temperate zones. Eastern Andes from Norte de Santander to Cundinamarca (*eximia*). Northern end of the Central and Western Andes (1, *zimmeri*). East slope of the Andes in Nariño (1, *chloronota*).

59. GOLDEN-CHESTED TANAGER
(Bangsia rothschildi)

Description. 6 - 6½ ". Mainly blue-black, tinged purplish below. Band across foreneck and under wing- and under tail-coverts yellow.

Range. Northwestern Ecuador.

Colombia. Forest. Tropical zone. Western slope of the Western Andes in Chocó, Valle and Nariño.

60. BLACK-AND-GOLD TANAGER
(Bangsia melanochlamys)

Description. 6 - 6½ ". Mostly black. Patch of rather stiff, shiny feathers on breast orange yellow, rest of central underparts golden yellow. Upper wing-coverts, upper tail-coverts and edges of rectrices blue to turquoise blue.

Range. Colombia.

Colombia. Forest. Subtropical zone. The west slope of the Central Andes in Antioquia and the west slope of the Western Andes near the sources of the río San Juan.

61. MOSS-BACKED TANAGER
(Bangsia edwardsi) Plate XIX

Description. 6 - 6½ ". Crown black, sides of head cornflower blue, throat dusky green. Patch on center of breast golden yellow, rest of underparts olive yellow. Back and tail moss green. Wings slaty bluish green.

Range. Northwestern Ecuador.

Colombia. Forest. Tropical and lower subtropical zones. The west slope of the Western Andes from the río Dagua southward to Nariño.

62. GOLD-RINGED TANAGER
(Bangsia aureocincta)

Description. 6½ - 6¾ ". ♂: Crown and nape black, sides of head blue-green, a ring starting from above eye surrounding the ear-coverts and extending forward along sides of neck to base of bill golden yellow. Throat black mottled with white. Sides of chest black, patch on center of breast orange yellow, rest of underparts yellowish olive. Back and tail moss green. Wings slaty bluish green. ♀: Similar, but black areas dusky green, sides of breast moss green.

Range. Colombia

Colombia. Forest. Subtropical zone of the western slope of the Western Andes near the sources of the río San Juan.

63. BUFF-BREASTED MOUNTAIN-TANAGER
(Dubusia taeniata)

Description. 7½ - 8½″. Head and upper breast black; forehead spotted with, and long eyebrow extending to upper back, silvery blue; band across breast buffy (or throat and breast cinnamon-buff, the throat lightly streaked black, 1). Back, wings and tail dark blue, the wing-coverts edged with silvery blue. Lower breast and belly bright yellow, under tail-coverts buff.

Range. Western Venezuela, Ecuador. Southern Peru.

Colombia. Forest and open woods. Temperate zone of the Santa Marta Mts. (1, carrikeri). Subtropical to temperate zones of all three Andean ranges in Cundinamarca, Antioquia, Tolima, Caldas, Cauca and Nariño (taeniata).

64. BLACK-MASKED MOUNTAIN-TANAGER
(Tephrophilus wetmorei)

Description. 7½ - 8″. Above mostly bright yellowish olive. Mask black encircled by bright yellow. Sides of throat and breast black. Under surface, extending in a point to upper throat, bright yellow. Wings and tail black, the wing-coverts violet-blue.

Range. South-central Ecuador.

Colombia. Forest. Temperate zone on the western slope at the southern end of the Central Andes in Cauca.

65. BLUE-WINGED MOUNTAIN-TANAGER
(Compsocoma flavinucha)

Description. 7 - 7¾″. Forecrown, sides of head and neck and extreme upper back black. Center of crown to nape and entire underparts golden yellow. Back moss green (or moss green mixed with black, 1; or deep black, rump mixed olive and black, 2). Wings and tail black, the wing-coverts glistening violet-blue, the remiges and rectrices edged with turquoise blue (or violet-blue, 2).

Range. Northern Venezuela, Ecuador, Peru, Bolivia.

Colombia. Forest. Subtropical zone. The west slope of the Eastern Andes from Santander southward to the head of the Magdalena Valley (victorini). The northern part of the Central and Western Andes (1, antioquiae). The west slope of the Central Andes from the Quindio region southward, the southern portion of the Western Andes and western Nariño (2, cyanoptera). The east slope of the Eastern Andes in Nariño (baezae).

66. BLACK-CHINNED MOUNTAIN-TANAGER
(Compsocoma notabilis) Plate XIX

Description. 8½ - 9¼″. Head and sides of neck black; nuchal patch yellow. Back glistening olive yellow; under surface orange yellow, this color coming to a point on throat. Wings and tail black, wing-coverts and remiges edged with glistening violet-blue.

Range. Northwestern Eucador.

Colombia. Forest. Upper tropical and subtropical zones of the west slope of the Western Andes from the headwaters of the río San Juan southward to Nariño.

67. BLUE-GRAY TANAGER
(Thraupis virens)

Description. 6¾ - 7½″. ♂ : Generally pale blue, brighter on rump, paler and greener below. Shoulder violet-blue (or shoulder white or bluish white, 1). ♀ similar, but duller.

Range. Southern Mexico southward through Central America. Venezuela, the Guianas, Brazil, Ecuador, Peru, northern Bolivia. Trinidad, Tobago. The Pearl Islands.

Colombia. Parks, clearings, cultivated lands. Tropical and subtropical zone. East slope of the Eastern Andes in Norte de Santander and Arauca. The rest of the country west of the Eastern Andes, including Santa Marta, but excluding Nariño (cana). Western Nariño (quaesita) East of the Andes in Cundinamarca and Meta (1, leucoptera). The middle Orinoco region (nesophila). Vaupés (1, mediana). Caquetá southward to Amazonas (1, coelestis).

68. SAYACA TANAGER
(Thraupis sayaca)

Description. 6¾ - 7½". Very similar to No. 67. Best distinguishable by having the throat grayish white quite distinctly demarcated from the bluish green of the breast, and by the duller, grayer upperparts. The shoulders are greenish blue, not markedly different from the rest of the wing; the under tail-coverts are white instead of blue.

Range. Northern Venezuela. Eastern and southern Brazil, Uruguay, Paraguay, Argentina, Bolivia.

Colombia. Arid scrub. Caribbean coast from Bolívar eastward *(glaucocolpa)*.

69. PALM TANAGER
(Thraupis palmarum)

Description. 7¼ - 7½". ♂: Crown pale green; rest of plumage rather shiny grayish olive green, heavily glossed with violet on breast and mantle. Wing-coverts and base of primaries pale grayish green; wings and tail brownish black. ♀: Duller and greener with less gloss both above and below.

Range. Nicaragua southward to Panama, Venezuela, the Guianas, Ecuador, Peru, Brazil, Paraguay, Bolivia. Trinidad.

Colombia. Thick forest. Tropical, occasionally lower subtropical zones. West of the Eastern Andes, including Santa Marta, but excluding Nariño *(atripennis)*. Western Nariño *(violilavata)*. East of the Eastern Andes from Norte de Santander southward to Vichada and eastern Nariño *(melanoptera)*.

70. BLUE-CAPPED TANAGER
(Thraupis cyanocephala)

Description. 7¼ - 7¾". Top and sides of head cobalt blue; lores and forehead black. Back, wings and tail yellowish olive green. Entire underparts dull blue gray. Crissum and thighs golden yellow (or olive yellow, 1); under wing-coverts golden yellow.

Range. Western Venezuela. Western Ecuador. Eastern Peru. Eastern Bolivia. Trinidad.

Colombia. Humid forest, coffee plantations and scrub. Subtropical, occasionally

temperate zone. The Santa Marta Mts. *(margaritae)*. Both slopes of the Eastern Andes from Norte de Santander south to Meta *(auricrissa)*. Central and Western Andes from Antioquia southward to western Nariño, the east slope of the Andes in Putumayo (1, *annectens)*.

71. MASKED CRIMSON TANAGER
(Ramphocelus nigrogularis)

Description. 7¼ - 7¾". ♂: Glossy crimson. Mask and throat black. Mantle, center of lower breast and belly, glossy velvety black. Wings and tail dull black. Base of lower mandible silvery. ♀ similar but duller with black portions of plumage tinged reddish brown.

Range. Eastern Ecuador, eastern Peru and eastward to the middle Amazon.

Colombia. Forest, scrub. Tropical zone east of the Andes from Meta southward undoubtedly to Amazonas.

72. SILVER-BEAKED TANAGER
(Ramphocelus carbo)

Description. 6¾ - 7¼". ♂: Entire plumage deep velvety maroon crimson, considerably darker above (or lower breast and abdomen dark like back, 1; or intermediate, 2), wings and tail blackish. Base of lower mandible silvery. ♀: Brownish red above, clearer red on rump and upper tail-coverts. Below dull carmine red (or brownish red, 1). Bill black.

Range. Venezuela, the Guianas, Ecuador, Peru, Brazil, Paraguay, Bolivia. Trinidad.

Colombia. Brushlands, plantations, open woodland. Tropical zone east of the Andes in Arauca and Boyacá *(venezuelensis)*; in southern Meta (2, *unicolor)*; from Caquetá southward and eastward (1, *carbo)*.

73. CRIMSON-BACKED TANAGER
(Ramphocelus dimidiatus)

Description. 6¾ - 7¼". ♂: Whole head, upper breast and mantle deep maroon crimson, rest of plumage crimson scarlet. Wings, tail, thighs and center of abdomen black. Base of lower mandible silvery. ♀: Best distinguishable from No. 72 by the throat and chest being much darker than the rest of the underparts instead of only slightly so.

Range. Panama, western Venezuela. The Pearl Islands.

Colombia. Brushlands, plantations. Tropical and lower subtropical zone west of the Eastern Andes, except the upper Magdalena Valley and Nariño (*dimidiatus*). The upper Magdalena Valley from 5°N. southward (*molochinus*).

74. FLAME-RUMPED TANAGER
(*Ramphocelus flammigerus*)

Description. 7¾ - 8¼". ♂ : Deep glossy velvety black; lower back, rump and upper tail-coverts brilliant flame scarlet. ♀ : Crown and mantle, wings and tail blackish brown; lower back, rump and upper tail-coverts and band across breast, orange-scarlet. Throat and sides of head whitish, rest of underparts orange yellow.

Range. Colombia.

Colombia. Clearings, brushlands. Upper tropical and subtropical zone of the Pacific slope, from the upper río San Juan southward to Nariño and eastward into the middle Cauca Valley.

75. LEMON-RUMPED TANAGER
(*Ramphocelus icteronotus*)

Description. 7¾ - 8¼". ♂ : Deep glossy velvety black; lower back, rump and upper tail-coverts brilliant lemon yellow. ♀ : Above grayish brown, tinged olive; lower back, rump, upper tail-coverts and underparts lemon yellow. Throat and sides of head whitish.

Range. Panama. Western Ecuador.

Colombia. Clearings, brushland. Tropical and subtropical zones. The entire Pacific coast and the lower Atrato and Sinú Valleys eastward to the middle Magdalena Valley.

On the west slope of the Andes in the upper río San Juan region, the Lemon-rumped and Flame-rumped Tanager interbreed, and males with orange rumps and females with the chest tinged orange-scarlet are found.

76. MASKED VERMILION TANAGER
(*Calochaetes coccineus*)

Description. 6½ - 7". ♂ : Mainly shiny scarlet; mask, throat, wings and tail black. ♀ like ♂ but slightly less brilliant.

Range. Eastern Ecuador. Southern Peru.

Colombia. Forest. Tropical zone. East of the Andes from Caquetá southward to eastern Nariño.

77. SUMMER TANAGER
(*Piranga rubra*)

Description. 7 - 7½". Bill pale. ♂ : Entirely rosy scarlet, darkest above. ♀ : Upper parts, wings and tail yellowish olive, dull yellow below. Young males resemble females, but when assuming adult plumage are often splotched with scarlet.

Range. Breeds in the United States and northern Mexico. Winters from Mexico southward through Central America to Peru, western Brazil and Bolivia. Western British Guiana, adjacent Venezuela. Trinidad.

Colombia. Coffee plantations, open woodland. Winter resident from October to April in the tropical and subtropical zones (*rubra*).

78. HEPATIC TANAGER
(*Piranga flava*)

Description. 7 - 7½". Bill dark. ♂ : Very like No. 77 but tone of plumage less rosy, more brick red (or much darker, crimson red, 1). Further distinguishable by grayish lores. ♀ : Greener above, lighter and brighter yellow below than No. 77.

Range. From the southwestern United States southward through Central America to Bolivia, Argentina, southern Brazil. Migratory in the northern part of the range but migrants do not reach Colombia.

Colombia. Open woodland, plantations. Upper tropical and subtropical zones. The Santa Marta Mts. (*faceta*). The western slope of the Western Andes from Antioquia southward to the Patía Valley and eastward to the middle and upper Cauca Valley (1, *desidiosa*). Interior of western Nariño (*lutea*).

79. SCARLET TANAGER
(*Piranga olivacea*)

Description. 6½ - 7½". ♂ : Scarlet; wings and tail black. ♀ : Upperparts, wings and tail olive, lower parts greenish yellow. ♂ in winter like ♀, but wings and tail

PLATE XIX

ORANGE-BELLIED
EUPHONIA
(*Tanagra xantho-
gaster brevirostris*)
Page 354

GRASS-GREEN
TANAGER
(*Chlorornis r. riefferii*)
Page 375

MOSS-BACKED
TANAGER
(*Bangsia edwardsi*)
Page 364

RED-BELLIED
GRACKLE
(*Hypopyrrhus pyro-
hypogaster*)
Page 380

GOLDEN-CROWNED
TANAGER
(*Iridosornis rufi-
vertex ignicapillus*)
Page 363

CHESTNUT-BELLIED
CHLOROPHONIA
(*Chlorophonia pyrrhophrys*)
Page 353

WHITE-CAPPED
TANAGER
(*Sericossypha albo-
cristata*)
Page 373

SCARLET-AND-WHITE
TANAGER
(*Erythrothlypis salmoni*)
Page 372

BLACK-CHINNED
MOUNTAIN-TANAGER
(*Compsocoma notabil's*)
Page 365

YELLOW-BACKED
ORIOLE
(*Icterus chrysater giraudii*)
Page 381

TAWNY-CROWNED
GREENLET
(*Hylophilus ochra-
ceiceps ferrugineifrons*)
Page 330

RED-BREASTED
BLACKBIRD
(*Leistes m. militaris*)
Page 382

E.L.Poole

black, center of abdomen and under tail-coverts bright yellow. In transition plumage, splotched with scarlet.

Range. Breeds in central and eastern North America. Winters in western South America from Colombia to Bolivia.

Colombia. Winter resident, tropical to temperate zones. October to May.

80. WHITE-WINGED TANAGER
(Piranga leucoptera) Fig. 84

Description. 6 - 6¼ ". ♂: Scarlet; lores, wings and tail black, a conspicuous white double wing-bar. ♀: Above olive, yellow below. Wings and tail dark brown, a conspicuous white double wing-bar.

Range. Southern Mexico southward to western Panama. Venezuela, Ecuador, Peru, northern Bolivia.

Colombia. Forest and scrub. Upper tropical and subtropical zone. East of the Eastern Andes from Norte de Santander to Magdalena. West of the Andes from Tolima to the west slope of the Western Andes in Caldas *(venezuelae)*. Western Nariño *(ardens)*.

81. RED-HOODED TANAGER
(Piranga rubriceps)

Description. 7¾ - 8". ♂: Head, upper mantle and breast scarlet, rest of underparts bright yellow. Back yellowish olive; wing-coverts bright yellow. Wings and tail blackish, edged olive yellow. ♀ differs from ♂ by having only the head orange-scarlet.

Range. Ecuador and northern Peru.

Colombia. Forest. Subtropical to lower temperate zones of the Andes from Cundinamarca westward to the east slope of the Western Andes. Recorded east of the Eastern Andes in southern Nariño.

82. OLIVE TANAGER
(Chlorothraupis carmioli)

Description. 7 - 7¼ ". Olive, paler below, somewhat yellowish on the throat.

Range. Nicaragua southward to Panama. Central Peru to northern Bolivia.

Colombia. Forest. The eastern base of the Andes, Caquetá, Nariño *(frenata)*. A related form, *C. c. lutescens*, has been taken

in Panama just west of the border near the Gulf of Urabá and undoubtedly occurs in northwestern Colombia.

83. LEMON-BROWED TANAGER
(Chlorothraupis olivacea)

Description. 6¾ - 7¼ ". ♂: Uniform dark olive above, somewhat paler below; throat, lores and eye-ring yellow. ♀ like ♂ but a trifle lighter in color.

Range. Eastern Panama, northwestern Ecuador.

Colombia. Forest. Tropical zone. The entire Pacific coast and eastward to the lower Atrato, upper Sinú and middle Magdalena Valleys.

84. OCHRE-BREASTED TANAGER
(Chlorothraupis stolzmanni)

Description. 7¼ - 7¾ ". Upperparts, sides of body, dull brownish olive; lower parts ochraceous-buff, brightest on abdomen. Wings and tail olive green.

Range. Northwestern Ecuador.

Colombia. Forest. Upper tropical and subtropical zones of the western slope of the Western Andes from the headwaters of the río San Juan southward to Nariño *(dugandi)*.

85. RED-CROWNED ANT-TANAGER
(Habia rubica)

Description. 6½ - 7". ♂: General plumage including wings and tail dull rosy red to vinaceous red, throat brighter, tending to scarlet. Crest scarlet, bordered laterally by dusky. ♀: Brown, paler below. Wings and tail tinged rosy. Crest yellowish buff.

Range. Southern Mexico southward to eastern Panama, northern Venezuela. Eastern Ecuador, Peru, Brazil, Paraguay, northern Argentina, Bolivia. Trinidad.

Colombia. Forest, near the ground. Tropical zone. The upper Sinú Valley *(subsp ?)*. The Perijá Mts. *(perijana)*. East of the Andes in Arauca and Boyacá *(coccinea)*. From southern Meta southward to Caquetá *(rhodinolaema)*.

86. RED-THROATED ANT-TANAGER
(Habia gutturalis)

Description. 7 - 8". ♂: Above, dark, dull rose. Crest, throat and upper breast rosy scarlet, rest of lower parts dull rosy, tinged gray. Wings and tail dark gray, washed rosy (or upper surface, wings and tail gray, crest scarlet bordered laterally with blackish; chin and sides of throat blackish, throat bright rosy scarlet. Extreme upper breast dull rosy, rest of underparts dark gray faintly washed with rosy, 1). ♀: Olive brown above, throat yellowish, rest of underparts olive brown (or similar to ♂ but duller and paler, 1).

Range. Southern Mexico southward through Panama.

Colombia. Thick forest. Tropical zone of the Caribbean coast region in northern Bolívar and Atlántico (erythrolaema); the middle Magdalena in Santander and Tolima westward to southern Antioquia as far as 75°W. (1, gutturalis).

87. CRESTED ANT-TANAGER
(Habia cristata)

Description. 8 - 8½". Long, conspicuous silky scarlet crest. Upperparts dark rosy crimson, throat and upper breast scarlet, rest of lower parts grayish rose. Looks rather like a cardinal.

Range. Colombia.

Colombia. Forest. Upper tropical and subtropical zone of both slopes of the Western Andes from Antioquia southward to southern Cauca.

88. FULVOUS SHRIKE-TANAGER
(Lanio fulvus) Plate XVIII

Description. 7 - 7½". ♂: Head, wings and tail black. Back ochraceous yellow, scapulars white. Center of breast chestnut, rest of underparts tawny ochraceous. ♀: Tawny brown above, ochraceous brown below, brownest on throat and becoming rufescent on under tail-coverts. Wings and tail brown.

Range. The Guianas and southern Venezuela, northern Brazil, Ecuador and Peru.

Colombia. Forest. Tropical zone east of the Andes from Arauca southward to Putumayo (peruvianus).

89. WHITE-LINED TANAGER
(Tachyphonus rufus)

Description. 7¾ - 8". ♂: Lustrous blue-black; inner upper wing-coverts and under

wing-coverts white. ♀: Bright rufous brown, below paler.

Range. Eastern Costa Rica, western Panama. Venezuela, the Guianas, Brazil, Ecuador, Peru, Bolivia, northern Argentina, Paraguay. Trinidad and Tobago.

Colombia. Open woodland, scrub, forest edge. Virtually throughout in the tropical and subtropical zones.

90. FLAME-CRESTED TANAGER
(Tachyphonus cristatus)

Description. 6¼ - 6¾". ♂: Black, center of throat and rump buff. Flat crest scarlet (or orange, 1) bordered in front and laterally with buff. ♀: Upperparts, wings and tail rufous brown, tinged ashy on forehead and nape. Throat whitish, rest of underparts ochraceous, the breast tinged ashy.

Range. The Guianas, southern Venezuela, Ecuador, Peru and Bolivia.

Colombia. Forest and scrub. Tropical zone east of the Andes. From Meta to Putumayo and Vaupés (cristatellus), Vichada (orinocensis). In eastern Nariño (1, fallax).

91. FULVOUS-CRESTED TANAGER
(Tachyphonus surinamus)

Description. 6¼ - 6½". ♂: Blue-black, upper and under wing-coverts and tuft at sides of breast white. Center of crown and rump fulvous, flanks chestnut. ♀: Above olive. Top of head dark gray. Underparts fulvous buff.

Range. The Guianas, Venezuela, the Amazon Valley westward to Ecuador and Peru.

Colombia. Open woodland, clearings. Tropical zone, east of Eastern Andes, from Meta southward to Putumayo and Vaupés (brevipes).

92. RED-SHOULDERED TANAGER
(Tachyphonus phoenicius)

Description. 6½ - 6¾". ♂: Glossy blue-black. Outer lesser wing-coverts red, inner ones white. ♀: Above grayish brown; below dingy white, grayest on breast. Under wing-coverts white. Wings brown, tail blackish brown.

Range. The Guianas, southern Venezuela,

eastern Brazil, eastern Peru.
Colombia. Southern Meta.

93. WHITE-SHOULDERED TANAGER
(Tachyphonus luctuosus)

Description. 5¼ - 5¾". ♂: Entirely glossy blue-black. Large shoulder patch and under wing-coverts white. ♀: Above yellowish olive. Forehead and sides of head gray, throat grayish white, rest of underparts dull yellow. Under wing-coverts white.

Range. Costa Rica, Panama, Venezuela, the Guianas, Brazil, Ecuador, Peru and Bolivia.

Colombia. Forest and clearings. Tropical and subtropical zones. Virtually throughout the country; west of the Andes (*panamensis*), east of them (*luctuosus*).

94. TAWNY-CRESTED TANAGER
(Tachyphonus delattrii) Plate XVIII

Description. 5¾ - 6¼". ♂: Dull black, crest tawny orange. ♀: Uniform dark olive brown above including wings and tail, underparts paler and more brownish.

Range. Nicaragua, southward to Panama and western Ecuador.

Colombia. Forest. Tropical zone. Entire Pacific coast and eastward across the upper Sinú Valley to the middle Magdalena. Gorgona Island (*delattrii*).

95. SCARLET-BROWED TANAGER
(Heterospingus xanthopygius)
Plate XVIII

Description. 7 - 7½". ♂: Above glossy black. Line above eye white, broad line behind eye scarlet. Upper wing-coverts and rump lemon yellow. Underparts grayish black, patch at sides of breast white. ♀: Mostly grayish black above, rump lemon yellow; lower parts iron gray, a patch at side of breast white.

Range. Western Ecuador.

Colombia. Forest. Tropical zone. The entire Pacific coast eastward to the middle Magdalena Valley.

96. RUFOUS-CRESTED TANAGER
(Creurgops verticalis) Plate XVIII

Description. 6½ - 6¾". ♂: Above leaden gray; flat crest and entire underparts rufous, the crest bordered laterally with

black. ♀: Similar but without crest, and underparts buff.

Range. Northwestern Venezuela. Ecuador and eastern Peru.

Colombia. Forest. Subtropical zone. Central and Western Andes in Antioquia, Valle, Tolima and Huila, and both slopes of the Andes in Nariño.

97. GRAY-HEADED TANAGER
(Eucometis penicillata)

Description. 7 - 7¾". Head crested. Whole head gray, paler on throat. Above yellowish olive. Underparts bright yellow, tinged ochraceous on breast.

Range. From Yucatan southward to Panama. Venezuela, the Guianas, eastern Ecuador, Peru, Brazil, Bolivia, Paraguay.

Colombia. Forest. Undergrowth in humid forest, plantations. Follows army ants. Tropical zone. The Caribbean coast, the Magdalena and Cauca Valleys, westward in northern Colombia to the Panama border. East of the Andes in Arauca (*cristata*), and from Meta southward to Amazonas (*penicillata*).

98. DUSKY-FACED TANAGER
(Mitrospingus cassinii)

Description. 7 - 7½". Forehead and sides of head blackish, throat ashy gray; crown and underparts olive. Upperparts dark gray, upper tail-coverts tinged with olive; under tail-coverts rufescent.

Range. Costa Rica to western Ecuador.

Colombia. Forest, scrub. Tropical zone. The entire Pacific coast eastward to the middle Cauca Valley in Antioquia (*cassinii*).

99. ROSE-BREASTED THRUSH-TANAGER
(Rhodinocichla rosea)

Description. 8 - 8½". ♂: Mostly dark grayish brown. Eyebrow rose red (or rose red in front of eye, pale pinkish white behind it, 1). Most of underparts rose red. ♀ like ♂, but eyebrow buff in front of eye, white behind it, and center of underparts orange-rufous.

Range. Southern Mexico; southern Costa Rica and western Panama; northern Venezuela.

Colombia. Forest floor and undergrowth. Upper tropical and lower subtropical zone. The northern extremity of the Perijá Mts. (1, *beebei*). The western slope of the Eastern Andes in Cundinamarca and Tolima (*harterti*).

100. HOODED TANAGER
(Nemosia pileata)

Description. 5¼ - 5½". ♂: Upperparts, wings and tail blue-gray. Lores and entire underparts white. Top and sides of head, sides of neck extending to sides of breast, black. ♀ like ♂, but without black on head and sides of breast, and the breast tinged buff.

Range. Venezuela and the Guianas, northeastern Peru, Brazil, Paraguay, Bolivia, northern Argentina.

Colombia. Open woodland. Tropical zone. The Caribbean coast from the Sinú Valley eastward and southward down the Magdalena Valley to 8°N. (*hypoleuca*).

101. GUIRA TANAGER
(Hemithraupis guira)

Description. 5¼ - 5½". ♂: Above bright olive green, rump ochraceous buff. Forehead, eyebrow adjoining patch on side of neck golden yellow (or eyebrow ochraceous yellow, 1), throat and sides of head black. Upper and under tail-coverts yellow. Breast ochraceous, rest of underparts pale grayish, sulphur yellow to ochraceous in center of belly. ♀: Upperparts bright olive green, yellowish on upper tail-coverts. Underparts greenish yellow, under tail-coverts yellow. Wings and tail brown edged with bright greenish yellow.

Range. Venezuela, the Guianas, Brazil, Ecuador, Peru, Paraguay and Argentina.

Colombia. Forest edge, open woodland. East of the Eastern Andes in Boyacá (*nigrigula);* in Amazonas (*huambina*). Tropical and subtropical zones of the middle and upper Magdalena and Cauca Valleys (1, *guirina*).

102. YELLOW-BACKED TANAGER
(Hemithraupis flavicollis)

Description. 5¼ - 5½". ♂: Top and sides of head and the upper back black,

lower back, rump and the throat golden yellow (or sides of throat golden yellow, middle of throat white, 1). Underparts white somewhat mottled with black, under tail-coverts golden yellow. Wing-coverts black (or middle wing-coverts tipped with yellow, 2). ♀: Upperparts, wings and tail olive. Throat, breast and under tail-coverts bright yellow, abdomen pale yellow (or whitish, 1).

Range. Eastern Panama. Southern Venezuela, the Guianas, Brazil, eastern Ecuador, Peru, northern Bolivia.

Colombia. Forest. Tropical zone. Extreme northwestern Colombia near the Panama border (*ornata*). The upper Sinú, lower Cauca and middle Magdalena Valleys (1, *albigularis*). The eastern base of the Eastern Andes from Meta southward to Putumayo (2, *peruana*). Eastern Vaupés (*aurigularis*).

103. SCARLET-AND-WHITE TANAGER
(Erythrothlypis salmoni) Plate XIX

Description. 5¼ - 5½". ♂: Mostly flame scarlet, sides of body white. Wing feathers dark brown the outer web pinkish orange. Tail dusky the feathers margined rufous red. ♀: Above dull olive brown, dirty white below. Wing feathers dusky, margined dull olive green, tail dusky olive.

Range. Northwestern Ecuador.

Colombia. Forest. Tropical zone. Pacific coast from the Baudó Mts. southward to Nariño. Possibly eastward into the middle Cauca Valley.

104. FULVOUS-HEADED TANAGER
(Thlypopsis fulviceps)

Description. 5½ - 5¾". ♂: Head orange-rufous (or chestnut-rufous, 1). Above gray; breast pale gray, belly white, under tail-coverts pale buff. ♀ generally similar to ♂, but throat whitish and back tinged olive.

Range. Northern Venezuela.

Colombia. Forest. Subtropical zone. The eastern slope of the Eastern Andes in Norte de Santander (*fulviceps*), the western slope in southern Magdalena (1, *intensa*).

105. RUFOUS-CHESTED TANAGER
(Thlypopsis ornata)

Description. 5½ - 5¾″. Head, chest, sides of body and under tail-coverts orange-rufous, center of breast and abdomen white. Upperparts, wings and tail gray.

Range. Ecuador and Peru.

Colombia. Temperate zone. The southern end of the Central Andes *(ornata)*.

106. ORANGE-HEADED TANAGER
(Thlypopsis sordida)

Description. 5½ - 6″. Top and sides of head orange-rufous, throat yellow. Upperparts brownish gray, breast and sides of body pale gray, center of abdomen white.

Range. Southern Venezuela, eastern Ecuador, Brazil, Bolivia, northern Argentina.

Colombia. Open woodland. Tropical zone of eastern Nariño *(chrysopis)*.

107. WHITE-CAPPED TANAGER
(Sericossypha albo-cristata)
Plate XIX

Description. 10¾ - 11½″. ♂ : Mostly black. Crown and region before eye white. Throat and breast carmine red becoming purplish on lower border. Wings and tail glossy blue-black. ♀ like ♂ , but throat and breast dusky red.

Range. Western Venezuela, eastern Ecuador and eastern Peru.

Colombia. Flocks of 6 to 20 in very tall forest trees. Subtropical and lower temperate zone of the east slope to the Eastern Andes from Meta southward to Nariño and the west slope of the Central Andes at their southern end.

108. COMMON BUSH-TANAGER
(Chlorospingus ophthalmicus)
Plate XVIII

Description. 5 - 5½″. Above bright olive green. Top and sides of head brownish black to black (or gray with a dusky line below eye, 1) ; eye-ring white. Throat white speckled with black (or entirely white, 1.) Broad band across breast greenish yellow, sides of body and under tail-coverts yellowish olive, center of underparts white.

Range. Mexico southward through Central America to western Panama. Northern Venezuela to Bolivia and northwest Argentina.

Colombia. Forest, thickets and underbrush. Upper tropical and subtropical zones. East slope of the Eastern Andes in Norte de Santander and Boyacá *(eminens)*. West slope of the Eastern Andes in Magdalena and Santander *(jacqueti)*. The west slope of the Eastern Andes from southern Santander to the Bogotá region (1, *flavo-pectus*). The Macarena Mts. *(macarenae)*. Subtropical to lower temperate zones of the east slope of the Western Andes at the northern end. Both slopes of the Central Andes and the head of the Magdalena Valley *(nigriceps)*. The east slope of Mt. Tacarcuna in northern Chocó *(tacarcunae)*.

109. YELLOW-THROATED BUSH-TANAGER
(Chlorospingus flavigularis)

Description. 6 - 6½″. Above yellowish olive green. Lores gray; throat yellow (or yellow at sides only, 1), rest of underparts white, flanks and under tail-coverts olive.

Range. Panama, western Ecuador. Eastern Ecuador, Peru, and western Bolivia.

Colombia. Forest. Tropical zone. The east slope of the Eastern Andes in Meta and the west slope of the Central Andes in Antioquia *(flavigularis)*. West slope of the Western Andes from southern Cauca southward to Nariño (1, *marginatus)*.

110. SHORT-BILLED BUSH-TANAGER
(Chlorospingus parvirostris)

Description. 6 - 6½″. Very similar to No. 109, distinguishable only by darker gray underparts, yellow of throat more orange and shorter bill.

Range. Eastern Ecuador. Peru and Bolivia.

Colombia. Forest. Subtropical zone. East slope of Eastern Andes in Cundinamarca and Meta southward to the mountains of Nariño. The head of the Magdalena Valley. Usually above the range of No. 109 *(huallagae)*.

111. ASHY-THROATED BUSH-TANAGER
(Chlorospingus canigularis)

Description. 6 - 6¼". Above olive. Top and sides of head gray, ear-coverts darker. Band across chest and under tail-coverts yellow. Throat and rest of underparts grayish white.

Range. Costa Rica. Northwestern Venezuela. Ecuador, northwestern Peru.

Colombia. Forest edge. Subtropical zone. Western slope of Eastern Andes in Cundinamarca *(canigularis)*. Both slopes of the Central and Western Andes in Huila, Caldas, Valle and Cauca *(conspicillatus)*.

112. DUSKY-BELLIED BUSH-TANAGER
(Chlorospingus semifuscus)

Description. 6 - 6¼". Above olive green. Top and sides of head brownish gray. Underparts dark gray (or brownish gray, 1); sides of body olive.

Range. Western Ecuador. Central Peru.

Colombia. Upper tropical and subtropical zones. West slope of the Western Andes from the upper río San Juan to southwestern Cauca *(livingstoni)*. Pacific slope of Nariño (1, *semifuscus)*.

113. GOLDEN-BELLIED HEMISPINGUS
(Cnemoscopus rubrirostris)

Description. 6¾ - 7¼". Above yellowish olive. Top of head dark gray, throat and breast pale gray. Underparts bright yellow. Bill and feet light reddish brown.

Range. Extreme western Venezuela; eastern Ecuador; central Peru.

Colombia. Forest. Subtropical to temperate zones throughout the country with the exception of the Santa Marta Mts. *(rubrirostris)*.

114. BLACK-CAPPED HEMISPINGUS
(Hemispingus atro-pileus)

Description. 6½ - 6¾". Above olive; below yellowish olive, tinged ochraceous on throat and breast. Top and sides of head black, long eyebrow buffy white.

Range. Western Venezuela, eastern Ecuador, Peru, Bolivia.

Colombia. Forest. Subtropical to temperate zones throughout with the exception of the Santa Marta Mts. *(atro-pileus)*. Southeastern Nariño *(subsp ?)*.

115. WHITE-BROWED HEMISPINGUS
(Hemispingus superciliaris)

Description. 5¾ - 6". Above olive green; bright yellow below. Forecrown and sides of head gray (or black, 1); eyebrow white.

Range. Northern Venezuela. Ecuador, Peru and Bolivia.

Colombia. Forest. Subtropical to temperate zone. The Eastern Andes in Cundinamarca *(superciliaris)*. The Central Andes from Caldas southward to the mountains of Nariño (1, *nigrifrons)*.

116. OLEAGINOUS HEMISPINGUS
(Hemispingus frontalis)

Description. 5¾ - 6¼". Upperparts, wings and tail dull olive green; underparts oily yellowish olive.

Range. Northern Venezuela. Ecuador, Peru.

Colombia. Forest. Subtropical zone throughout excluding the Santa Marta Mts. and Nariño *(frontalis)*.

117. BLACK-EARED HEMISPINGUS
(Hemispingus melanotis)

Description. 5¾ - 6¼". Crown and upper back gray, shading to olivaceous on lower back and brown on upper tail-coverts; wings and tail grayish olive. Narrow eyebrow grayish white, sides of head black (or sides of head dusky, no eyebrows, 1). Underparts tawny (or dull brownish, tawny on under tail-coverts, 1).

Range. Northwestern Venezuela. Ecuador, Peru, Bolivia.

Colombia. Forest. Subtropical zone. The Central Andes in Antioquia, Caldas and Tolima; the Eastern Andes in Cundinamarca, the east slope in Nariño *(melanotis)*. Pacific slope of the Andes of Nariño (1, *ochraceus)*.

118. BLACK-HEADED HEMISPINGUS
(Hemispingus verticalis)

Description. 5¾ - 6". Head black, a broad stripe down center of crown pale grayish brown; rest of plumage gray, paler below with center of abdomen white.

Range. Western Venezuela to eastern Ecuador.

Colombia. Forest. Temperate and lower páramo zones of Eastern Andes in Cundinamarca, the Central Andes in Caldas southward to the mountains of Nariño.

119. BLACK-BACKED BUSH-TANAGER
(Urothraupis stolzmanni)

Description. 7¼ - 7½". Above black. Throat white, breast and center of abdomen mixed gray and white; flanks grayish brown. Wings and tail black.

Range. Eastern Ecuador.

Colombia. Forest. Temperate zone. The Central Andes from Caldas southward to Cauca.

120. GRASS-GREEN TANAGER
(Chlorornis riefferii) Plate XIX

Description. 8¼ -8 ½". Bright grass green, mask and crissum chestnut, wing-coverts shiny bluish green. Bill and legs red.

Range. Ecuador, Peru, Bolivia.

Colombia. Forest. Upper tropical to temperate zones of the Andes from Cundinamarca and Antioquia southward to Nariño *(riefferii)*.

121. FINCH-LIKE TANAGER
(Oreothraupis arremonops) Plate XX

Description. 8½ - 9". Forehead, sides of head, chin and broad stripe at sides of crown black, eyebrows and broad stripe down center of crown, prolonged backwards onto nape, ashy gray. Back and wings reddish brown. Lower throat and breast orange-rufous, center of abdomen gray; sides of body and under tail-coverts reddish brown. Tail blackish brown. Probably better placed with the finches.

Range. Northwestern Ecuador.

Colombia. Thick forest. Terrestrial. Upper subtropical zone of the Western Andes from Antioquia southward to Cauca and probably Nariño.

122. MAGPIE TANAGER
(Cissopis leveriana)

Description. 10¼ - 11". White. Head, breast, wings and tail black. Tail long, much graduated, feathers broadly tipped white. Feathers of breast lanceolate and extending in a point to center of abdomen.

Range. Venezuela, the Guianas, Ecuador, Peru, Brazil, Paraguay, Bolivia, Argentina.

Colombia. Forest. Tropical zone east of the Eastern Andes from Norte de Santander southward to Amazonas *(leveriana)*.

123. BLACK-FACED TANAGER
(Schistochlamys melanopis)
Plate XVIII

Description. 7¼ - 7¾". Bill thick, short and curved. Mostly gray. Forecrown, sides of head, throat and upper breast black. *Immature*: Olive above, yellowish below, greenish on breast.

Range. Venezuela, the Guianas, Peru, and Bolivia.

Colombia. Scrub, open woodland. Tropical and lower subtropical zones of northern Colombia from the lower Cauca Valley eastward to the Santa Marta region and Vichada and southward to Caquetá and Vaupés *(aterrima)*.

AMERICAN ORIOLES AND BLACKBIRDS (Icteridae)

Fig. 85. Chestnut-headed Oropendola
(Zarhynchus wagleri) p. 377

American orioles are not related to the well-known European oriole, and are called orioles only because in many species their colors are black and yellow as in the European bird.

The bills are rather long and sharply pointed. The birds vary in size from that of a starling to a crow. In the genera *Zarhynchus* and *Gymnostinops* the maxilla is expanded and swollen over the forehead into a flat casque. In many species, although the color of the sexes is similar, females are notably smaller than males. Inhabitants of forest, marsh, and meadowland, living on fruits and insects, some icterids are gregarious and many species nest in colonies. Their nests are beautifully made. Sometimes they are very long, purse-shaped structures, woven from grass suspended from the ends of branches of tall trees high above the ground. The cowbirds, however, are parasitic, laying their eggs in other birds' nests. Active and conspicuous, some species are excellent songsters. (35 Col.; 58 S.A.; 94 N.&S.A.; 94 wld.)

AID TO IDENTIFICATION

All black or chestnut and black, or black and white (outer tail-feathers yellow) 1, 2, 3, 5, 7, (tail all black) 24E, 35.
All or partly olive, outer tail-feathers yellow 4E, 6E, 7.
Black and yellow 8, 22, 24, 25, 26, 27, 28, 29, 30E, 31, 32.
Olive above, yellow below 22, 23.
Red and black 9E, 10, 18, 33.
All black, or glossy purplish or brownish (bill pale) 11, 12E, 13, 14 (imm.) ; (bill black) 14, 15E, 16, 17, 19, 20, 21E.
Streaked above 32, 33, 34, 35.
Sandy to dusky brown above, sometimes streaked below 15, 16, 19, 20.

1. CHESTNUT-HEADED OROPENDOLA
(*Zarhynchus wagleri*) Fig. 85

Description. ♂ 13 - 14″, ♀ 10 - 11″. Bill yellowish green, tip bluish gray. Whole head, hair-like crest feathers, upper back, upper breast, flanks, lower back, rump, upper and under tail-coverts, bay. Center of back, lower breast, center of abdomen, wings and central tail-feathers shiny greenish black; rest of tail-feathers yellow, outer web of outer tail-feather black.

Range. Southern Mexico to western Ecuador.

Colombia. Forest. Tropical zone. The Pacific coast and eastward in northern Colombia to the middle Magdalena Valley in Antioquia and Santander (*ridgwayi*).

2. CHESTNUT-MANTLED OROPENDOLA
(*Gymnostinops cassini*)

Description. ♂ 17 - 18″, ♀ 14 - 15″. Bill black, tip red or orange: large bare cheek patch flesh color. Head and hair-like crest feathers, upper back, throat, breast, line down center of abdomen, thighs and central tail-feathers glossy black. Most of back, rump and wings chestnut, flanks bay. Tail-feathers except central pair yellow.

Range. Colombia.

Colombia. Forest. Tropical zone. The Pacific coast south to the Baudó Mts.

3. BLACK OROPENDOLA
(*Gymnostinops guatimozinus*)

Description. ♂ 18 - 20″, ♀ 15 - 16″. Bill black, tip red; bare cheek patch dusky flesh color. Head and hair-like crest, mantle, underparts, remiges and short central rectrices glossy black. Wing-coverts, back, upper and under tail-coverts maroon. All but central tail-feathers yellow.

Range. Eastern Panama.

Colombia. Forest. Lower Atrato Valley eastward to the upper Sinú and middle Magdalena Valleys, from Antioquia to Cundinamarca.

4. OLIVE OROPENDOLA
(*Gymnostinops yuracares*)

Description. ♂ 18 - 21″, ♀ 17 - 18″. Bill black, tip red; bare cheek patch flesh color. Head, hair-like crest, neck and breast chartreuse green. Back, wings, and rest of underparts chestnut. Central tail-feathers olive, rest bright yellow.

Range. Southern Venezuela, Brazil, Ecuador, Peru and Bolivia.

Colombia. Tall forest. Tropical zone east of the Eastern Andes from Meta southward to Putumayo, Vaupés and undoubtedly Amazonas (*yuracares*).

5. CRESTED OROPENDOLA
(*Psarocolius decumanus*)

Description. ♂ 17 - 19″, ♀ 15 - 16″. Bill greenish white, no bare cheek patch. General color glossy greenish black (or tinged with maroon on back and underparts, 1). Lower back, rump and upper and under tail-coverts chestnut. Central tail-feathers black, rest bright yellow.

Range. Panama, Venezuela, the Guianas, Brazil, Argentina, Ecuador, Peru and Bolivia. Trinidad and Tobago.

Colombia. Forest and clearings. Tropical zone, occasionally subtropical. West of the Eastern Andes rather generally but not recorded from Nariño or the south part of the west coast (*melanterus*). East of the Andes from eastern Cundinamarca to Putumayo, Vichada and Vaupés (1, *decumanus*).

6. GREEN OROPENDOLA
(*Psarocolius viridis*)

Description. ♂ 17 - 18″, ♀ 14 - 15″. Bill greenish ivory, no bare cheek patch. Head, hair-like crest, upper back, throat, breast and belly and wing-coverts olive green; upper tail-coverts chestnut. Remiges black, central rectrices black, remainder yellow.

Range. The Guianas and southern Venezuela southward to the Amazon Valley and westward to northeastern Peru and eastern Ecuador.

Colombia. Forest. Eastern Vaupés and undoubtedly Amazonas.

7. RUSSET OROPENDOLA
(Psarocolius angustifrons)

Description. ♂ 15 - 17½ ", ♀ 13 - 14". The only large green oropendola without a basally expanded maxilla. Bill yellow (or black, 1). Forehead bright yellow (or with no yellow on forehead, 1), whole crown and crest or hindcrown olive (or hindcrown blackish, 1). Mantle olive brown (or chestnut, 2), lower back and upper tail-coverts cinnamon brown; wings and central rectrices blackish (or olive, 1). Underparts olive, tinged with brown on belly and under tail-coverts (or throat whitish rest of underparts very dark olive brown, under tail-coverts cinnamon, 3). Outer tail-feathers olive, next pair olive on the outer webs, remainder except central pair yellow (or all except central pair yellow, tipped olive, 1).

Range. Venezuela southward in western South America to Bolivia.

Colombia. Forest. Tropical and subtropical zones. Both slopes of the Western Andes from Antioquia southward to Nariño (3, *salmoni*). Western slope of the Eastern Andes in Santander, Cundinamarca and the east slope of the Central Andes in Huila (2, *sincipitalis*). Upper tropical and subtropical zones on the eastern slope of the Eastern Andes in Meta (*neglectus*). Tropical zone from Villavicencio southward to Putumayo and Amazonas (1, *angustifrons*).

8. YELLOW-RUMPED CACIQUE
(Cacicus cela)

Description. ♂ 11 - 11½ ", ♀ 9½ - 10". ♂: Bill greenish or yellowish white. General plumage glossy black. Large (or small, 1) patch on inner wing-coverts, lower back, rump, upper and under tail-coverts and basal half of tail bright golden yellow (or only extreme base of tail yellow, 1). ♀ duller below than ♂, lower breast and abdomen dusky olivaceous.

Range. Eastern Panama, Venezuela, the Guianas, Brazil, Ecuador, Peru and Bolivia. Trinidad.

Colombia. Treetops in forest and clearings. Tropical zone. Western coastal district of the Santa Marta region and the lower and middle Magdalena Valley westward to the Pacific coast in northern Chocó (1, *vitellinus*). Eastern coastal district of the Santa Marta region southward east of the Eastern Andes to Amazonas (*cela*).

9. RED-RUMPED CACIQUE
(Cacicus haemorrhous)

Description. ♂ 10½ - 11", ♀ 8½ - 9". Bill pale yellowish green. ♂: Shiny blue-black, lower back and rump scarlet. ♀ like ♂ but underparts dull black.

Range. Southern Venezuela, the Guianas, Brazil, Ecuador, Paraguay and northern Argentina.

Colombia. Forest. Tropical zone east of the Eastern Andes from Meta southward to Caquetá (*haemorrhous*).

10. SCARLET-RUMPED CACIQUE
(Cacicus uropygialis)

Description. ♂ 11 - 12", ♀ 9 - 9½ " (or ♂ 10", ♀ 8", 1). Bill pale yellow basally, tipped pea green. ♂: Glossy blue-black; rump orange-scarlet; ♀ similar to ♂ but duller, rump more orange.

Range. Nicaragua to northern Peru.

Colombia. Forest. Rarely upper tropical zone; mostly subtropical zone of the west slope of the Eastern Andes from Huila northward; east slope in Norte de Santander. The middle Magdalena Valley, Cauca Valley, and the subtropical zone of the west slope of Western Andes (*uropygialis*). Tropical to upper tropical zone of the Pacific slope of the Western Andes south to Nariño. The lower Atrato, upper Sinú and lower Cauca Valleys (1, *pacificus*).

11. GOLDEN-SHOULDERED CACIQUE
(Archiplanus leucoramphus)

Description. ♂ 11½ - 12", ♀ 10 - 10½ ". Bill bluish white; black with white tip in young birds. Plumage black; inner wing-coverts, lower back and rump bright yellow. Differs chiefly from the Yellow-rumped Cacique by having no yellow on the underparts or in the tail.

Range. Western Venezuela. Eastern Ecuador, Peru.

Colombia. Forest. Subtropical to temperate zones, rarely tropical zone of the three Andean ranges. Not Santa Marta (*leucoramphus*).

12. BLACK CACIQUE
(Archiplanus solitarius) Plate XVIII

Description. ♂ 10½ - 11", ♀ 9½ - 10". Bill white, tinged yellowish green. Plumage entirely black, head with a short crest. Iris hazel.

Range. Northern Venezuela. Western South America south to Bolivia and eastward south of the Amazon to Paraguay, Uruguay and Argentina.

Colombia. Forest. Tropical zone east of the Eastern Andes from Arauca southward to Caquetá.

13. YELLOW-BILLED CACIQUE
(Amblycercus holosericeus)

Description. ♂ 9½ - 10", ♀ 7½ - 8". Bill light yellow to greenish yellow (or dark yellow to orange yellow, 1). Plumage entirely black. Iris pale yellow or white.

Range. Southern Mexico, southward through Central America to Venezuela, Ecuador, Peru and Bolivia

Colombia. Thickets. Tropical zone. From northern Chocó eastward along the Caribbean coast to Cartagena (*holosericeus*). Subtropical, occasionally temperate zone in the Santa Marta Mts. Both slopes of the Eastern Andes from Norte de Santander to Cundinamarca and the northern portion of the Central Andes in Tolima and Caldas (*australis*). The Pacific slope south of the range of *holosericeus* southward to Nariño (1, *flavirostris*).

14. GIANT COWBIRD
(Scaphidura oryzivora)

Description. ♂ 13½ - 14½", ♀ 11 - 12". Bill black, yellow in immature birds. ♂ : Entirely black, the body plumage glossed with shiny purple, the wings and tail blue-black. The feathers of the sides of neck expanded forming a ruff. Iris yellowish white. ♀ : Black, slightly glossed with blue and ruff much reduced.

Range. Southern Mexico southward through Central America to Venezuela, the Guianas, Brazil, Ecuador, Peru, eastern Bolivia and Paraguay. Trinidad.

Colombia. Scrub and pastureland. Tropical and lower subtropical zones throughout (*oryzivora*).

15. BRONZED COWBIRD
(Tangavius aeneus)

Description. 8 - 9". Lustrous, bronzy brown. Immature birds are dull dusky brown.

Range. Southern Texas to western Panama.

Colombia. Range little known. Recorded with certainty only from Leticia on the north bank of the Amazon. Records from Cartagena etc. are probably erroneous for the bird has not been found there by any recent collector. (*armenti*).

16. SHINY COWBIRD
(Molothrus bonariensis)

Description. ♂ 9 - 11", ♀ 8 - 9". ♂ : Shining purple-blue; wings and tail black with a strong green gloss. Iris brown. ♀ : Above grayish brown, (or earthy brown, 1) the feathers with dark centers. Throat and eyebrow pale sandy, underparts brownish gray; wings and tail brown. Young birds have the underparts somewhat streaked.

Range. Eastern Panama, Venezuela, the Guianas, Ecuador, Peru, Brazil, Bolivia, Paraguay, Uruguay and Argentina. Lesser Antilles, Trinidad and Tobago.

Colombia. Pasturelands, often accompanying cattle. Tropical zone. Virtually throughout west of the Eastern Andes excepting Nariño (*cabanisii*). The Pacific slope of Nariño (*aequatorialis*). East of the Eastern Andes from the Zulia Valley southward to Meta and Vichada (1, *venezuelensis*). From Caquetá southward to Amazonas (*subsp.?*).

17. MOUNTAIN GRACKLE
(Macroagelaius subalaris)

Description. ♂ 11¼ - 12½", ♀ 10½ - 11". Bill black. Glossy black; inner wing-coverts and axillaries chestnut. Tail rather long, 6", fan-shaped.

Range. Colombia.

Colombia. Forest. Subtropical and temperate zones of the west slope of the Eastern Andes from Santander to Cundinamarca.

18. RED-BELLIED GRACKLE
(Hypopyrrhus pyrohypogaster)
Plate XIX

Description. ♂ 12½ - 13″, ♀ 11 - 12″. Tuft at sides of breast, the belly and under tail-coverts scarlet, rest of plumage black. Feathers of crown, nape, sides of head and throat narrow, stiff, with shiny, enamel-like shafts.

Range. Colombia.

Colombia. Forest and moist scrubland. Locally distributed throughout the subtropical zone; east of the Andes in northern Caquetá and west of them in Cundinamarca, Tolima, Antioquia, Caldas, and the west slope of the Western Andes in Caldas.

19. CARIB GRACKLE
(Quiscalus lugubris)

Description. ♂ 10½ - 11″, ♀ 8 - 8½″. Bill 1.1″ curved and slender. ♂: Shiny purple-black, wings and tail shiny greenish black. Tail fan-shaped. Iris pale to bright yellow. ♀: Dull purplish black. Iris yellow. *Immature:* Much paler and browner, especially below. Throat palest. Iris straw white.

Range. Northern Venezuela, British Guiana, northern Brazil. The Lesser Antilles; islands off the coast of Venezuela. Trinidad and Tobago.

Colombia. Open country often near villages. East of the Andes in Arauca and Meta *(lugubris)*.

20. GREAT-TAILED GRACKLE
(Quiscalus mexicanus)

Description. ♂ 15 - 17″, ♀ 12 - 13″. Bill long, slender. ♂: Black shot with shining purple-blue to greenish blue. Wings and tail black glossed with green. Tail long, 8-9″, much graduated, wedge-shaped. ♀: Crown and upper mantle dull brown becoming progressively darker on back until it becomes blackish brown on upper tail-coverts, mantle somewhat glossed with green. Eyebrow and throat buffy, sides of head dusky brown. Underparts buffy brown becoming dusky on flanks and under tail-coverts. Tail fan-shaped of normal length.

Range. Southwestern United States, Mex-

ico, southward through Central America to northwestern Venezuela, western Ecuador and northwestern Peru. The Pearl Islands.

Colombia. Open country, either humid or arid. The Caribbean coast and the Pacific coast south to Buenaventura Bay in Valle, not ranging far inland *(peruvianus)*.

21. VELVETY-FRONTED GRACKLE
(Lampropsar tanagrinus) Plate XVIII

Description. ♂ 10½ - 11″, ♀ 8 - 8½″. Bill short, 6″. Black, glossed with blue. Feathers of forehead and lores black, dense and plush-like. Tail fan-shaped.

Range. British Guiana, Venezuela and the Amazon Valley from the rio Negro westward to Ecuador, Peru and Bolivia.

Colombia. Open woodland, often near water. East of the Andes from Caquetá southward undoubtedly to Amazonas *(tanagrinus)*; further east, in Vichada, a much smaller form, *L. t. guianensis*, undoubtedly occurs.

22. BALTIMORE ORIOLE
(Icterus galbula)

Description. 7 - 8″. ♂: Whole head, throat, mantle, wings, central tail-feathers black, wing-feathers margined with white; outer tail-feathers yellow, basally black. Underparts, wing-coverts, lower back, rump and upper tail orange yellow. ♀: Above grayish olive. Crown and rump tinged yellow. Throat, breast and under tail-coverts yellow, belly whitish; wings blackish with two white wing-bars. Tail dull yellowish brown. Occasionally females are strongly shaded orange and have a certain amount of black around the head.

Range. Breeds in southern Canada southward to Texas and Mexico. Winters from Mexico to western Venezuela.

Colombia. Forest and woodland. Winter resident from October to May in northern Colombia. Recorded once from the eastern llanos *(galbula)*.

23. ORCHARD ORIOLE
(Icterus spurius)

Description. 6 - 6½″. ♂: Head, mantle, wings and tail black. Greater wing-coverts and inner remiges margined with white. Lesser wing-coverts, lower back, rump and upper tail-coverts, breast and abdomen chestnut. ♀: Upperparts and tail yellowish olive, center of back shaded with gray. Wings with double white wing band. Underparts greenish yellow. The young ♂ resembles the ♀ but has a black throat.

Range. Breeds from southern Canada southward through the central and eastern United States to Texas and Mexico. Winters from Mexico southward to western Venezuela.

Colombia. Forest and woodland. Winter resident. Recorded from August 5 to the beginning of March. Northern Colombia and east of the Andes southward to Meta (*spurius*).

24. MORICHE ORIOLE
(*Icterus chrysocephalus*)

Description. 9 - 9½". Black, center of crown, nape, shoulders, rump and thighs yellow.

Range. The Guianas and Venezuela southward to northern Brazil, eastern Ecuador and Peru.

Colombia. Scrub and woodland. Tropical zone east of the Eastern Andes from Meta east to Vichada and south to Vaupés and Putumayo.

25. YELLOW-TAILED ORIOLE
(*Icterus mesomelas*)

Description. 9¼ - 9¾". Pale golden yellow. Ocular region, throat, sides of neck, upper breast, mantle, wings and central tail-feathers black, wing-coverts and outer tail-feathers golden yellow.

Range. Mexico southward through Central America to northwestern Venezuela, Ecuador and western Peru.

Colombia. Abandoned plantations, moist brushlands. Tropical zone. The lower Atrato Valley and the Pacific coast south to the río San Juan and eastward through northern and central Colombia to Norte de Santander and Cundinamarca (*carrikeri*). The race in Nariño is probably *taczanowskii*.

26. ORANGE-CROWNED ORIOLE
(*Icterus auricapillus*)

Description. 8½ - 9". Yellow, crown orange. Ocular region, forehead, throat, sides of neck, upper breast, mantle, wings and tail black.

Range. Eastern Panama. Northern Venezuela.

Colombia. Tropical zone. Caribbean coast from the east shore of the Gulf of Urabá eastward to the Catatumbo lowlands and Arauca.

27. YELLOW-BACKED ORIOLE
(*Icterus chrysater*) Plate XIX

Description. 8 - 9" (or 9 - 10", 1). Rich yellow (or sometimes orange, 2), occasionally tinged with brownish on upper breast. Forehead, ocular region, throat, sides of neck, upper breast, wings and tail black.

Range. Mexico southward to northern Venezuela.

Colombia. Tropical occasionally lower subtropical zone of the Pacific slope southward to the Cauca-Nariño border and eastward to the middle and the upper Magdalena Valley. The eastern base of the Andes in Meta and eastern Cundinamarca (2, *hondae*). Upper tropical to lower temperate zone of the Andes virtually throughout above the range of *hondae*, absent in the Santa Marta region (1, *giraudii*).

28. YELLOW ORIOLE
(*Icterus nigrogularis*)

Description. 8 - 8¾". Golden yellow brightest on sides of neck and upper breast. Lores, throat, wings and tail black, wing-coverts and wing-feathers broadly margined with white, tail narrowly tipped with white.

Range. Northern Venezuela, British Guiana and adjacent Brazil. Trinidad, the islands in the southern Caribbean.

Colombia. Tropical zone of the Caribbean coast from the Sinú Valley to the Guajira Peninsula and southward to the lower and middle Magdalena Valley. The llanos east of the Andes from Meta to Vichada (*nigrogularis*).

29. TROUPIAL
(Icterus icterus)

Description. 9½ - 10½". Entire head, upper breast, mantle, wings and tail black. Lesser wing-coverts yellow, middle wing-coverts and margins to inner remiges conspicuously white. Broad collar on hindneck, lower back and rump and underparts orange yellow, the black feathers of throat and breast narrow and pointed, giving a ragged look where they meet the yellow on the upper breast. Skin about eyes light blue, base of mandible blue-gray.

Range. Northern Venezuela. Margarita Island and the Dutch West Indies.

Colombia. Open woods. Arid coastal region of northeastern Colombia (*ridgwayi*). East of the Andes in Arauca (*icterus*).

30. ORANGE-BACKED ORIOLE
(Icterus croconotus)

Description. 9 - 10¼". Orange yellow. Forehead, facial area, throat, sides of head, neck and upper breast, wings and tail black. Wing-coverts yellow, patch on secondaries white.

Range. British Guiana southward through the Amazon Valley to eastern Ecuador, Peru, northern Bolivia and Paraguay.

Colombia. Putumayo to Amazonas (*croconotus*).

31. ORIOLE BLACKBIRD
(Gymnomystax mexicanus)

Description. 11 - 12". Space about eye and moustacial region bare, black. Head, underparts and wing-coverts bright yellow. Back, wings and tail glossy black. *Immature*: Similar but with crown black.

Range. The Guianas and Venezuela southward to the Amazon, eastern Ecuador and eastern Peru.

Colombia. Gardens, fields and open woodland. Gregarious. Tropical zone east of the Eastern Andes from Meta south to Amazonas.

32. YELLOW-HOODED BLACKBIRD
(Agelaius icterocephalus)

Description. 7¼ - 7¾" (or 8 - 8¼", 1). ♂: Head, neck and upper breast bright yellow, rest of plumage glossy black. ♀: Eyebrow, throat and upper breast dull yellow; crown, sides of head, nape olive. Back, wings and tail brown, the back streaked with dusky, the wing margined with olive. Underparts grayish brown, more or less shaded with dull olive yellow.

Range. The Guianas, Venezuela and northern Brazil westward to northeastern Peru. Trinidad.

Colombia. Marshland. Tropical zone of the Caribbean coast from the lower Atrato Valley eastward through the middle and lower Cauca and Magdalena Valleys to the Santa Marta region. East of the Andes from the Zulia Valley southward to Amazonas (*icterocephalus*). Temperate zone of the Eastern Andes in the marshes around Bogotá northward to Boyacá (1, *bogotensis*).

33. RED-BREASTED BLACKBIRD
(Leistes militaris) Plate XIX

Description. 7 - 7½". ♂: Throat, breast, upper belly, inner wing-coverts crimson, rest of plumage black, the feathers broadly edged with sandy brown; these edgings gradually wear off and the bird becomes black above. ♀: Crown dark brown, central streak and eyebrow buff. Upperparts streaked sandy brown and blackish, wings brown, tail barred black and brown. Underparts buffy more or less stained with crimson on breast and narrowly streaked with dusky on breast, broadly so on sides of body. (See No. 35).

Range. From Panama and Venezuela southward to Brazil, eastern Peru, Argentina and Bolivia. Trinidad.

Colombia. Grassy plains and marshes. Tropical zone of the Caribbean coast, southward into the middle Magdalena Valley and westward to the Gulf of Urabá and recently to the upper Cauca Valley. Llanos east of the Andes in Meta and Vichada (*militaris*).

34. EASTERN MEADOWLARK
(Sturnella magna)

Description. 9¼ - 10¼ ". Tail short, outer feathers mostly white. Crown and streak behind eye dark brown. Lores yellow, eyebrow streak and streak on center of crown buffy white. Mantle mottled reddish brown and blackish brown, the feathers pale-margined giving a streaked appearance. Outer remiges brown, inner remiges and central tail-feathers barred brown and black. Throat, breast and center of abdomen bright yellow, crescentic band across breast black. Sides of body and under tail-coverts sandy buff, streaked with blackish.

Range. Southern Canada and United States east of the Rocky Mts. Cuba. Mexico southward to western Panama. Venezuela, British Guiana and northeastern Brazil. Surinam.

Colombia. Open, grassy lands; terrestrial. Tropical and subtropical zones of the southern side of the Santa Marta Mts. southward to the western base of the Eastern Andes in the vicinity of Aguachica, Magdalena [8°N.] (paralios). Subtropical to temperate zone of the Eastern Andes from Norte de Santander southward, with the cutting of the forests, to the head of the Magdalena Valley, formerly only to Cundinamarca (meridionalis). Tropical zone of the eastern llanos in Meta and Vichada (praticola).

35. BOBOLINK
(Dolichonyx oryzivorus)

Description. 6½ - 8". ♂ : Head and lower parts, wings and tail black. Mantle black feathers edged with sandy brown, becoming black with wear. Broad collar on nape and hindneck buff, lower back gray, scapulars and rump white. ♀ : Above dark brown, the feathers pale edged, broad coronal streak and eyebrows buff. Below buffy, streaked on flanks with dusky. Looks very much like the ♀ of No. 33 when there is no crimson shading on breast, but is readily distinguishable by the pointed, uniform instead of barred tail-feathers. The ♂ in winter resembles the ♀.

Range. Breeds in Canada and United States. Winters in western Brazil, Bolivia, Paraguay and northern Argentina.

Colombia. Transient. Recorded from September to end of November and from March to May.

PLATE XX

RED-CAPPED
CARDINAL
(*Coccopis g. gularis*)
Page 388

BLUE-BLACK GROSBEAK
(*Cyanocompsa c. cyanoides*)
Page 389

YELLOW GROSBEAK
(*Pheucticus chryso-
peplus chrysogaster*)
Page 389

CHESTNUT-BELLIED
SEEDEATER
(*Sporophila
c. castaneiventris*)
Page 392

CINNAMON-HEADED
BRUSH-FINCH
(*Atlapetes semi-
rufus zimmeri*)
Page 398

BUFF-THROATED
SALTATOR
(*Saltator maximus iungens*)
Page 387

BAND-TAILED
SEEDEATER
(*Catamenia analis
schistaceifrons*)
Page 393

WEDGE-TAILED
GROUND-FINCH
(*Emberizoides herbi-
cola apurensis*)
Page 401

OLIVE FINCH
(*Lysurus castaneiceps*)
Page 399

SAFFRON FINCH
(*Sicalis f. flaveola*)
Page 395

FINCH-LIKE
TANAGER
(*Oreothraupis arremonops*)
Page 375

ORANGE-BILLED
SPARROW
(*Arremon aurantii-
rostris erythrorhynchus*)
Page 399

E.L. Poole

PLUSH-CAPPED FINCHES (Catamblyrhynchidae)

Fig. 86. Plush-capped Finch
(*Catamblyrhynchus diadema*)

Plush-capped finches inhabit the subtropical and temperate zones of the Andes from Venezuela southward to central Bolivia. Virtually nothing is known of their habits. They are said to be found in pairs or in mixed flocks of birds in open woodland and shrubbery. In Ecuador they have been observed singly in the higher forest trees. In Venezuela they have been found in sparsely wooded country. Their bills are short, thick and stubby, the maxilla strongly curved.

Some would place them with the finches, others among the tanagers. Until more is known of them it seems best to leave them as a family of their own. (1 Col.; 1 S. A.; 1 N. & S. A.; 1 wld.)

PLUSH-CAPPED FINCH
(*Catamblyrhynchus diadema*)

Description. 5½ - 5¾ ″. Above gray; below chestnut. Front half of crown golden yellow, the feathers stiff and plush-like, hindcrown and lores black. Tail strongly graduated, fan-shaped. *Immature:* Olive brown above, forehead dusky gray; under surface tawny buff, browner on throat and breast.

Range. The Andes from Venezuela to Bolivia.

Colombia. Upper subtropical to temperate zones throughout Colombia from the Santa Marta Mts. southward (*diadema*).

FINCHES, SEEDEATERS, GROSBEAKS, ETC.
(Fringillidae)

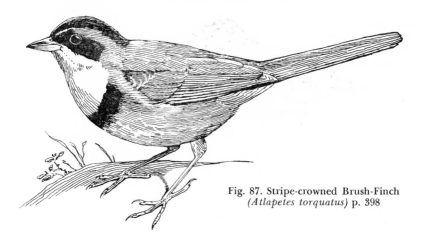

Fig. 87. Stripe-crowned Brush-Finch
(Atlapetes torquatus) p. 398

Finches comprise a very large number of species of small birds found through-out the world with the exception of Madagascar, Australia and Oceania. Some northern species are migratory, and a very few North American species reach Colombia in winter.

In contrast to tanagers, finches are for the most part soberly colored, but a few species do exhibit brilliant plumage. Their short, conical bills are adapted to cracking seeds on which they live, a diet supplemented to a certain degree by fruit and insects. Some species are terrestrial and most live in scrub, fields and open woodland, while a few others inhabit thick forest. They occur from the hot tropical lands to cold and snow-capped mountain peaks.

Many are excellent songsters. Their usually cup-shaped nest is situated in shrubs or trees, and sometimes on the ground; a number of neotropical species build domed nests. (77 Col.; 159 S.A.; 281 N.&S.A.; 374 wld.)

The classification of the *Fringillidae* is as yet not final, different ornithologists taking different views of its limits. The birds gathered under *Fringillidae* in this book are placed in three distinct families by some authors.

The cardueline finches conventionally regarded as forming a subfamily of the finches *(Carduelinae)* and containing among others the goldfinches, siskins, seedeaters, purple finches, Evening Grosbeak, crossbills and grass finches are transferred to the family of Weaverbirds *(Ploceidae)* to which the House Sparrow and a large number of African and tropical Asiatic "finches" belong. The subfamily of Buntings *(Emberizinae)* are raised by some to family rank *(Emberizidae)*. In it are the many Old World buntings, the juncos, the American "sparrows", longspurs and others. Many are inhabitants of open or scrub country and live on or near the ground. Left in the true finches *(Fringillidae)* is the American subfamily *Richmondininae* containing such well-known groups as the cardinals, saltators, blue grosbeaks, the Rose-breasted Grosbeak and relatives, American "buntings", grassquits, brush-finches and others.

As these changes are still unaccepted by all, the conventional arrangement used in current guidebooks is adhered to in this book.

AID TO IDENTIFICATION

Streaked above
  Streaked below also 13, 32, 33, 39, 45, 47, 49, 50.
  Not streaked below 19, 31, 33, 34, 35, 40, 45, 48, 73, 74ᴱ, 75, 76, 77.
Not streaked above
  Upperparts olive or yellowish olive
        Head conspicuously striped or with contrasting cap 26, 40, 42, 46ᴱ, 55, 57,
          59, 61, 64, 65, 66, 67, 68ᴱ, 69, 70, 71, 72.
        Head not striped, no contrasting cap 1, 2, 5, 6ᴱ, 7ᴱ, 17, 18, 40, 43, 44,
          46ᴱ, 47, 58, 62, 63.
  Upperparts gray or grayish 3, 4, 8, 20, 21, 22, 28ᴱ, 29, 30, 32, 35, 49, 50, 51, 52,
      53, 54, 56, 57, 60.
  Upperparts brown 14, 15, 16, 20, 21, 22, 23, 24, 25, 26, 27, 28, 29, 36, 37, 38, 41.
  Upperparts black, or black combined with another color (all black) 25, 37, 38,
      39, 44, 55, 60, (combined with yellow) 11, 12, 43, 61, (combined with
      white) 24, 27.
  Upperparts blue 14, 15, 16, 36.
With red in plumage 9ᴱ, 10, 13, 41ᴱ, 51.

---

1. BUFF-THROATED SALTATOR
(Saltator maximus) Plate XX

Description. 8 - 9″. Entire upperparts, wings and tail yellowish olive. Forehead and short eyebrow white, forecrown and sides of head gray, moustacial streak black. Upper throat white, lower throat cinnamon-buff, center of underparts buff, sides of breast and sides of body gray; under tail-coverts cinnamon-buff.

Range. Southeast Mexico, southward through Central America to Venezuela, the Guianas, Ecuador, Peru, Brazil, Paraguay and Bolivia.

Colombia. Open woodland and scrub. Tropical, occasionally subtropical zones. Santa Marta region and the middle Magdalena Valley southward east of the Eastern Andes from the southern slopes of the Perijá Mts. to Amazonas *(maximus)*. The entire Pacific coast eastward to the Sinú and lower Cauca Valleys *(iungens)*.

2. BLACK-WINGED SALTATOR
(Saltator atripennis)

Description. 7¾ - 8½″. Top and sides of head and neck black, crown grayish or mixed gray and black. Upperparts yellowish olive. Throat and center of abdomen white, undertail-coverts cinnamon, rest of underparts gray. Wings and tail black.

Range. Western Ecuador.

Colombia. Open woodland, pastures and thickets. Upper tropical and subtropical zones. Western slope of the Eastern Andes in Cundinamarca *(caniceps)*. Western slope of the Central and both slopes of the Western Andes from Antioquia southward to western Nariño *(atripennis)*.

3. GRAYISH SALTATOR
(Saltator coerulescens)

Description. 8½-9½″. Upperparts, wings and tail light grayish brown, (or plumbeous gray, 1). Short, narrow eyebrow and throat white, moustacial streak black; breast pale brownish gray becoming pale buff on sides of body and under tail-coverts (or breast gray becoming dark grayish brown on sides of body and cinnamon on under tail-coverts, 1).

Range. Southern Mexico southward to Venezuela and the Guianas, Argentina and Bolivia. Trinidad.

Colombia. Open woodland. Tropical zone. The Caribbean coast from the río Sinú eastward to the lower Magdalena Valley *(plumbeus)*. East of the Eastern Andes in Norte de Santander and Arauca *(brewsteri)*. The eastern base of the Andes from Meta southward undoubtedly to Amazonas (1, *azarae)*.

4. ORINOCAN SALTATOR
(Saltator orenocensis)

Description. 7½ - 8″. Upperparts and wings leaden gray. Long, broad eyebrow, spot at base of mandible, throat and center of abdomen white; sides of head and neck black; breast, sides of body and under tail-coverts pale buff. Tail blackish.

Range. Northern Venezuela.

Colombia. Scrub. The Guajira Peninsula *(rufescens).*

5. STREAKED SALTATOR
(Saltator albicollis)

Description. 6½ - 7½″. Top of head grayish olive, short, narrow eyebrow white. Back and wings dull olive green becoming ashy on rump and upper tail-coverts (or upperparts gray tinged olive on mantle, 1). Underparts white streaked with olive or grayish olive on breast and sides of body. Tail ashy gray. Bill black. *Immature:* Heavily streaked below. Tip of bill yellow.

Range. Costa Rica southward to Peru. Eastward along the coast of Venezuela. The Lesser Antilles, Trinidad and the Pearl Islands.

Colombia. Dry scrub. Tropical and lower subtropical zones. Northeastern Colombia in Magdalena, northeastern Bolívar and Norte de Santander *(perstriatus).* Pacific slope of southwest Colombia from the Patía valley southward to Nariño (1, *flavidicollis).* The rest of Colombia west of the Andes *(striatipectus).*

6. GREEN GROSBEAK
(Caryothraustes canadensis)

Description. 7½ - 8″. Mask and upper throat black. Upperparts, wings and tail bright olive yellow; underparts bright yellow, tinged olive at sides of breast.

Range. Eastern Panama, southern Venezuela and the Guianas to northern and eastern Brazil.

Colombia. Forest. Tropical zone. Southeast Colombia in Vaupés *(canadensis).* A related form *C. c. simulans* is found near the Colombian border in Panama and probably occurs west of the Gulf of Urabá.

7. YELLOW-SHOULDERED GROSBEAK
(Caryothraustes humeralis)

Description. 7½ - 8″. Top of head leaden gray, lores and ear-coverts black, throat and moustacial streak checkered black and white. Upperparts, wings and tail bright olive yellow, underparts pale gray. Lesser wing-coverts and under tail-coverts bright yellow.

Range. Upper Amazonia to eastern Ecuador and northeast Peru.

Colombia. Known in Colombia only from "Bogotá" but undoubtedly occurs in the tropical zone of the southeast.

8. SLATE-COLORED GROSBEAK
(Pitylus grossus)

Description. 8¼ - 8¾″. Bill crimson to bright scarlet. ♂: Dark blue-gray. Center of throat white, sides of neck black continuing across breast to form a broad band. Tail black. ♀ similar to ♂ but without black at sides of neck and across breast.

Range. Nicaragua southward to western Ecuador. Venezuela, the Guianas, Brazil, eastern Peru, and northern Bolivia.

Colombia. Scrub, clearings, open woodland. Tropical zone east of the Eastern Andes from Meta to Amazonas *(grossus).* The whole Pacific coast eastward in northern Colombia to the middle Magdalena Valley *(saturatus).*

9. RED-CAPPED CARDINAL
(Coccopis gularis) Plate XX

Description. 6¾ - 7¼″. Top and sides of head and upper throat scarlet, lores, lower throat extending into point on breast black (or top of head, throat extending into point on breast scarlet, broad stripe through eye black, 1). Upperparts, wings and tail glossy blue-black; below white.

Range. Southern Venezuela, the Guianas southward to Brazil, Peru, and eastern Bolivia.

Colombia. Scrub, clearings, open woodland. Tropical zone. From southern Meta south to Amazonas *(gularis).* East of the Andes in northern Meta, Arauca and Vichada (1, *nigro-genis).*

10. VERMILION CARDINAL
(Pyrrhuloxia phoenicea)

Description. 7½ - 8". ♂: Head including long crest and underparts vermilion; back, wings and tail rose red. Narrow line surrounding bill black. ♀: Long crest vermilion, dark red toward tip. Sides of crown and head gray. Upperparts sandy gray; throat white, breast grayish rest of underparts cinnamon-buff; lores white, narrow line surrounding bill black. Wings brown, outer margins tinged red; tail dull rose. Bill in both sexes bluish flesh.

Range. Northern Venezuela, Margarita Island.

Colombia. Scrub. Arid tropical zone. The Guajira Peninsula to the eastern base of the Santa Marta Mts.

11. YELLOW GROSBEAK
(Pheucticus chrysopeplus) Plate XX

Description. 8 - 8½ ". ♂: Whole head and underparts bright golden yellow, under tail-coverts white. Center of back mixed black and yellow, lower back and rump greenish yellow. Wings black, base of primaries, inner greater wing-coverts and large spots on inner remiges white; upper tail-coverts black, tipped white. Tail black, all but central pair of feathers broadly tipped white on inner web only. ♀: Generally similar to ♂. Top of head streaked dusky, rump yellow spotted with black, wings and tail blackish brown, outer tail feathers with conspicuous white tips on inner web, rest with small indistinct white tips.

Range. Mexico southward to western Panama. Northern Venezuela, Ecuador and Peru.

Colombia. Forest. Subtropical zone of the Santa Marta Mts. (laubmanni). The mountains of Nariño (chrysogaster).

12. BLACK-BACKED GROSBEAK
(Pheucticus aureo-ventris)

Description. 8½ - 9¼ ". ♂: Head, throat, breast and back black, lower back and rump spotted with yellow, upper tail-coverts tipped white. Wings black, inner wing-coverts and base of primaries white, lesser wing-coverts yellow. Lower breast and abdomen bright yellow spotted on sides with black (or similar, but center of throat and breast yellow like rest of underparts, 1). Tail black, outer feathers tipped white. ♀ generally similar to ♂ but throat spotted black and white and breast spotted black and yellow (or like ♂ but with yellow eyebrow, 1).

Range. Northern Venezuela southward through the Andes to Ecuador, Peru, Bolivia, western Mato Grosso and northwestern Argentina.

Colombia. Forest. Subtropical to temperate zones of the Eastern Andes from Norte de Santander to Cundinamarca and the temperate zone of the Central Andes in Cauca and Huila (uropygialis). The mountains of Nariño in the subtropical zone (1, crissalis).

13. ROSE-BREASTED GROSBEAK
(Pheucticus ludovicianus)

Description. 7 - 8". ♂: Entire head, upper back and upper breast black, lower back and rump white, under wing-coverts and lower breast rose-colored continued downward in a point to upper belly. Wings and tail black, base of primaries, inner wing-coverts and patch on inner web of outer tail-feathers white. ♀: Crown and sides of head dark brown, coronal streak, eyebrow continued backwards forming collar on hindneck white. Back streaked grayish brown and dusky brown; underparts white to buffy white, streaked on breast and sides with brown. Upper wing-coverts tipped with white, under wing-coverts orange. ♂ in winter resembles ♀ but breast is tinged with rose.

Range. Breeds in North America east of the Rocky Mts. from southern Canada southward to Kansas and Georgia. Winters from Mexico southward to western Venezuela and Ecuador.

Colombia. Winter resident of tropical to temperate zone from the middle of October to April.

14. BLUE-BLACK GROSBEAK
(Cyanocompsa cyanoides) Plate XX

Description. 6 - 6½ ". ♂: General color dark blue, blackish on chin, slightly brighter (or much brighter, 1) on forecrown, eyebrow and at base of mandible. Wings and tail blackish. ♀: Uniform reddish brown. Tail blackish.

Range. Southern Mexico southward to western Ecuador. Venezuela, the Guianas, Brazil, Peru and Bolivia.

Colombia. Scrub. Tropical zone west of the Eastern Andes including Santa Marta (*cyanoides*). East of the Eastern Andes in Meta and probably south to Amazonas (1, *rothschildii*).

15. ULTRAMARINE GROSBEAK
(Cyanocompsa cyanea)

Description. 6¾ - 7¼". ♂: Very similar to No. 14 (1), but brighter and smaller. ♀: Rather similar to the ♀ of No. 14 but paler, especially below.

Range. Northern Venezuela. Brazil, Bolivia, Paraguay and Argentina.

Colombia. Scrub. Upper tropical zone in the upper Cauca, Dagua and upper Patía Valleys (*caucae*).

16. INDIGO BUNTING
(Passerina cyanea)

Description. 5 - 5¼". ♂: General plumage indigo blue when seen against light; turquoise blue with head indigo blue when seen away from light. Readily distinguishable from the blue grosbeaks by its small, conical bill. ♀: Upperparts reddish brown, wing and tail darker, tail faintly edged with pale blue, wing-coverts pale edged. Underparts whitish, lightly streaked on breast and sides with brown.

Range. Breeds in eastern North America. Winters from Mexico south to Panama; casually to Venezuela. The Greater Antilles.

Colombia. Casual. Recorded in January and February in northern Chocó and Magdalena.

17. YELLOW-FACED GRASSQUIT
(Tiaris olivacea)

Description. 4¼ - 4½". ♂: Lores, short eyebrow and upper throat orange yellow. Forecrown, cheeks, sides of neck and the breast black, rest of underparts grayish

olive. Upperparts, wings and tail olive. ♀: General color dull olive, wing-feathers edged brighter, center of abdomen and under tail-coverts buffy.

Range. Mexico southward through Central America to western Venezuela. The Greater Antilles.

Colombia. Grassy pastures and brush. Upper tropical and subtropical zones west of the Andes except Santa Marta (*dissita*).

18. BLACK-FACED GRASSQUIT
(Tiaris bicolor)

Description. 4¼ - 4½". ♂: Very like No. 17, but without orange on head. Crown, sides of head, throat and breast sooty black, belly grayish white. Upperparts, wings and tail dull olive. ♀: Very like No. 17 but paler and grayer, particularly below.

Range. The Bahamas, West Indies, southern Caribbean islands and coastal Venezuela.

Colombia. Pastures and open fields. The Guajira Peninsula and western Santander (*omissa*). The upper Magdalena Valley (*huilae*).

19. DICKCISSEL
(Spiza americana)

Description. 6 - 7". ♂: Crown yellowish olive, sides of head and hindneck gray, eyebrow and spot at base of mandible yellow. Upper throat white, lower throat extending downward to upper breast black, breast yellow. Mantle brown, streaked black; lower back and rump gray. Wings and tail brown, wing-coverts chestnut. ♀: Sparrow-like. Crown brown narrowly streaked dusky, eyebrow, spot at base of mandible and breast pale yellow. Line of dark spots at side of throat, breast with a few dusky shaft streaks. Back, wings and tail as in ♂.

Range. Breeds from Ontario and Wyoming southward to Texas and northern Georgia. Winters from Guatemala southward to Venezuela and the Guianas.

Colombia. Grasslands. Winter resident from mid-September to May.

Sporophila

The seedeaters are a large group of small finches occuring in flocks in grasslands, marsh and forest clearings. The males have quite distinctive plumage but the females all look very much alike, are impossible to distinguish in the field and even hard to tell apart in museum collections. Most of them are light brown above, paler below and will not be described in the text.

20. SLATE-COLORED SEEDEATER
(Sporophila schistacea)

Description. 4¾ - 5". ♂: Upperparts, sides of head, center of throat, breast and sides of body gray, a white patch at sides of throat. Lower breast, center of abdomen and under tail-coverts white. Wings and tail gray, wing with a small white speculum. Bill yellow.

Range. Southern Mexico. Costa Rica south to western Ecuador. Venezuela, the Guianas, northern Brazil, Bolivia. Trinidad.

Colombia. Arboreal. Low trees and clearings. Tropical zone. Southwestern Córdoba eastward to western slope of Eastern Andes in Norte de Santander (schistacea). Western slope of the Western Andes from the headwaters of the río San Juan southward to Nariño (incerta). East of the Andes at the base of the Macarena Mts. in Meta (longipennis).

21. GRAY SEEDEATER
(Sporophila intermedia)

Description. 4½ - 4¾". ♂: Very similar to No. 20 and difficult to distinguish, (or very much darker mostly blackish gray, 1) but bill is smaller, tarsus slightly longer and nails dark instead of light. Bill yellow.

Range. Venezuela, British Guiana, Trinidad.

Colombia. Clearings and weedy pastures. Tropical and subtropical zones. Caribbean coastal region, the lower Magdalena Valley and the llanos east of the Andes (intermedia). The Magdalena Valley from Honda southward (agustini). Western slope of the Western Andes in the San Juan and Dagua Valleys eastward to the Cauca

Valley (bogotensis). The valley of the rio Anchicayá in Valle (1, anchicayae).

22. PLUMBEOUS SEEDEATER
(Sporophila plumbea)

Description. 4½ - 4¾". ♂: Above gray; upper throat white, breast pale gray, abdomen and under tail-coverts white. Wings and tail black, wing speculum white. Bill black.

Range. Southern Venezuela, the Guianas and northeastern Brazil. Southern Brazil, Paraguay, eastern Bolivia and northeastern Argentina.

Colombia. The llanos east of the Andes (whiteleyana); west of the Andes in Bolívar; possibly Santa Marta (colombiana).

23. DULL-COLORED SEEDEATER
(Sporophila obscura)

Description. 4¼ - 4½". ♂: Upperparts, wings and tail dull brown; (or dull reddish brown, 1); throat, breast and sides of body, grayish (or brownish, 1); center of abdomen and under tail-coverts whitish (or buffy, 1).

In this species the sexes are similar. If a flock of small brown seedeaters is seen composed of birds without contrasting plumages it will probably be this species.

Range. Western Venezuela. Peru, Bolivia and northwestern Argentina. Western Ecuador.

Colombia. Cultivated lands near forest. Tropical zone. Lower Cauca Valley and the Pacific coast from the río Dagua southward (obscura). The Santa Marta region (1, haplochroma).

24. VARIABLE SEEDEATER
(Sporophila americana)

Description. 4¼ - 4½". ♂: Head and back glossy black, ear-coverts bordered posteriorly with white. Rump white or white mottled with black. Below white with a broad black pectoral band (or without it, or with a band interrupted in the center of the breast, 1), chin and throat sometimes black (or with a narrow black pectoral band, chin and throat white, never black, 2). Wings and tail black, wing speculum white, wing-coverts sometimes fringed white.

Range. Southern Mexico southward through Central America to western Ecuador, Venezuela, the Guianas and the lower and middle Amazon. Trinidad, Tobago.

Colombia. Cultivated land and clearings. Tropical zone. The Atrato Valley and southward on the Pacific coast to the río Dagua (*chocoana*). The Pacific slope of Nariño (2, *ophthalmica*). East of the Andes in Caquetá (1, *murallae*).

25. BLACK-AND-WHITE SEEDEATER
(Sporophila luctuosa)

Description. 4¼ - 4½". ♂ : Glossy black; center of abdomen and wing speculum white. Bill pale bluish gray.

Range. Western Venezuela; eastern Ecuador, Peru and northwestern Bolivia.

Colombia. Open fields. Tropical and subtropical zones. Throughout the country with the exception of Nariño.

26. YELLOW-BELLIED SEEDEATER
(Sporophila nigricollis)

Description. 4 - 4¼". ♂ : In pattern very similar to No. 25. Crown, sides of head, throat and breast black; lower breast and belly pale sulphur yellow. Back, wings and tail dull olive. No wing speculum. Bill pale bluish gray.

Range. Costa Rica, Panama Canal Zone. Western Ecuador. Venezuela, British Guiana. Eastern and southern Brazil. Eastern Peru. Trinidad and Tobago, Grenada.

Colombia. Brushy pastures. Tropical and subtropical zones of western Nariño, Gorgona Island? (*vivida*); the rest of Colombia (*nigricollis*).

27. LINED SEEDEATER
(Sporophila lineola)

Description. 4 - 4¼". ♂ : Glossy blue-black. Cheeks, sides of neck, wing speculum, rump and underparts white; white coronal streak or spot sometimes present.

Range. Venezuela, the Guianas, Brazil, Argentina, eastern Bolivia, Peru, eastern Ecuador. Trinidad, Tobago.

Colombia. Scrub and savanna. Tropical zone of the lower Magdalena Valley (*restricta*). East of the Andes from Meta southward to Amazonas (*lineola*).

28. CHESTNUT-BELLIED SEEDEATER
(Sporophila castaneiventris) Plate XX

Description. 4¼ - 4½". ♂ : Blue-gray; throat, breast, line down center of belly and under tail-coverts chestnut.

Range. Southern Venezuela and the Guianas. The middle Amazon westward to Ecuador, Peru and Bolivia.

Colombia. Pastures, clearings and forest glades. Tropical zone in Caquetá and Vaupés (*castaneiventris*).

29. RUDDY-BREASTED SEEDEATER
(Sporophila minuta)

Description. 3¾ - 4". ♂ : Top and sides of head, upper back and upper tail-coverts brown, feathers sometimes pale centered; upperparts sometimes brown tinged gray, very rarely pure blue-gray. Rump and under surface orange-chestnut. Wings and tail dark brown, pale edged, wing speculum and, very rarely, base of tail white.

Range. Mexico southward through Central America to northeastern Ecuador. Venezuela and the Guianas southward through the lower Amazon Valley to southern Brazil, Argentina, Paraguay, Uruguay and eastern Bolivia. Trinidad.

Colombia. Open fields. Tropical and subtropical zone virtually throughout the country except the southeast (*minuta*).

30. TUMACO SEEDEATER
(Sporophila insulata)

Description. 3¾ - 4". ♂ : Upperparts mouse gray, narrow band on rump rufous-chestnut. Wings and tail black, wing and tail-feathers basally white. Underparts rufous-chestnut.

Range. Colombia.

Colombia. Known only from Tumaco Island off the coast of Nariño.

31. CHESTNUT-THROATED SEEDEATER
(Sporophila telasco)

Description. 3¾ - 4". ♂ : Top and sides of head and back gray, the mantle streaked dusky; band across rump white, upper tail-coverts gray. Wings and tail dark brown edged gray, wing speculum and base of tail white. Throat chestnut, rest of underparts white. ♀: Differs from all other species by having upperparts grayish brown streaked with dusky. Lower parts buffy white. Base of tail white, tail-feathers with pale tips.

Range. Northwestern Ecuador southward through western Peru to extreme northern Chile.

Colombia. Recorded only from Gorgona Island.

32. BAND-TAILED SEEDEATER
(Catamenia analis) Plate XX

Description. 5 - 5½″. ♂: General plumage gray, paler below, whitish (or brownish gray, 1) on belly; under tail-coverts chestnut. Inner webs of all but central tail-feathers with large white patch forming a band across the central part of the feathers. ♀: Above reddish brown broadly streaked with black; below fulvous-white streaked with dark brown. Tail as in ♂ but white patches smaller.

Range. The Andes from Ecuador southward to northern Chile and western Argentina.

Colombia. Bushes. Temperate and páramo zone. The Santa Marta Mts. up to about 14,000 ft. (1, *alpica*). The Eastern Andes in the vicinity of Bogotá *(schistaceifrons).*

33. PLAIN-COLORED SEEDEATER
(Catamenia inornata)

Description. 5 - 5¼″. ♂: Upperparts grayish tinged brown on mantle and streaked with black. Throat and breast grayish becoming buffy on abdomen; under tail-coverts chestnut. Wings and tail blackish. ♀ like ♂ but browner and more heavily streaked on the back. *Immature:* Brown, paler below, streaked both on back and breast.

Range. Western Venezuela southward through the Andes to Bolivia and western Argentina.

Colombia. Upper subtropical to páramo zone of the Eastern and Central Andes and the mountains of Nariño *(minor).*

34. SANTA MARTA SEEDEATER
(Catamenia oreophila)

Description. 5 - 5¼″. The ♀ resembles the ♀ of No. 33 but is less distinctly

streaked above and has a much smaller bill. The adult ♂ of this species is not known; it is perhaps but a subspecies of No. 35 which *oreophila* resembles in general proportions. The only ♂ known is immature and is said to resemble the ♀ of No. 33 in color.

Range. Colombia.

Colombia. Upper subtropical and temperate zones of the Santa Marta Mts. between 6,700 and 10,000 ft.

35. PARAMO SEEDEATER
(Catamenia homochroa)

Description. 5½-5¾″. ♂: Dark gray, blackish on forecrown and ocular region; under tail-coverts chestnut. Wings and tail dark gray. ♀: Upperparts, wings and tail olive brown streaked with black above. Below fulvous-brown; under tail-coverts chestnut.

Range. Venezuela southward through the Andes to Bolivia.

Colombia. Scrubby mountainside. Temperate and lower páramo zone of all three Andean ranges and Nariño *(homochroa).*

36. BLUE SEEDEATER
(Amaurospiza concolor)

Description. 5 - 5½″. ♂: Dark, dull blue; ocular region blackish; under wing-coverts white. ♀: Uniform cinnamon brown, cinnamon buff on center of abdomen. Wings and tail dark brown.

Range. Honduras to the Panama Canal Zone. Northwestern Ecuador.

Colombia. Upper tropical zone of the Pacific slope of Nariño *(aequatorialis).*

37. LARGE-BILLED SEED-FINCH
(Oryzoborus crassirostris) Plate XVIII

Description. 6 - 6¼″. ♂: Bill very thick, yellowish white. Glossy blue-black; base of primaries, wing speculum and under wing-coverts white. ♀: Bill thick, dark brown. Upperparts, wings and tail brown; lower parts pale rufescent brown.

Range. Nicaragua. Western Ecuador. Venezuela, the Guianas south to southeast Brazil, Peru and Bolivia. Trinidad.

Colombia. Rice fields, clearings near rivers. Tropical zone east of the Eastern Andes *(crassirostris)*. Tropical to lower subtropical zone in the middle Magdalena, lower Atrato and middle and upper Cauca Valleys *(occidentalis)*.

38. LESSER SEED-FINCH
(Oryzoborus angolensis)

Description. 5 - 5¼". ♂ : Bill black. Black; wing speculum, under wing-coverts and axillaries white (or lower breast, belly and under tail-coverts maroon chestnut, 1). ♀ : Bill dark brown. Above drab brown, below dull cinnamon brown.

Range. Mexico southward through Central America to western Ecuador. Venezuela and the Guianas southward to Brazil, eastern Ecuador, Peru, Bolivia and Argentina. Trinidad.

Colombia. Pastures, scrub and forest edge. Tropical and lower subtropical zones. Across northern Colombia from the Panama border to Santa Marta and down the Pacific coast to Nariño. Birds from the Santa Marta region often have chestnut mixed with the black of the lower breast and belly *(funereus)*. East of Eastern Andes from Arauca southward to Vaupés (1, *torridus*).

39. BLUE-BLACK GRASSQUIT
(Volatinia jacarina) Plate XVIII

Description. 4¼ - 4¾". ♂ : Shiny blue-black, a concealed white patch at sides of breast. ♀ : Upperparts, wings and tail dull grayish brown, below buffy white streaked on breast and sides with brown.

Range. Mexico southward through Central America to Venezuela, the Guianas, Brazil, Ecuador, Peru, Bolivia, Paraguay, northern Argentina. Trinidad, Tobago, Granada.

Colombia. Thickets and clearings near cultivations. Tropical and subtropical zone throughout *(splendens)*.

40. ANDEAN SISKIN
(Spinus spinescens)

Description. 4¾ - 5". ♂ : Cap black. Back dusky green; rump, upper tail-coverts and underparts olive yellow. Wings black with a large patch of yellow at base of primaries and secondaries. Tail black, all but central tail-feathers with yellow bases (or without yellow at base, 1). ♀ : Grayish olive above becoming olive yellow on rump and upper tail-coverts. Underparts grayish, tinged olive on throat and breast, white on center of abdomen and under tail-coverts. Wings and tail as in ♂ .

Range. Western Venezuela.

Colombia. Open scrub. Upper subtropical to temperate zone. The Santa Marta Mts. *(capitaneus)*. The northern portion of the Central and Western Andes (1, *nigricauda*). Eastern Andes and the southern end of the Central Andes *(spinescens)*.

41. RED SISKIN
(Spinus cucullatus)

Description. 4¼ - 4½". ♂ : Mostly crimson red. Head, wings and tail black. Bases of primaries and secondaries edged crimson red forming a wing patch. Inner remiges tipped white. ♀ : Reddish brown above, pinkish brown below. Wing speculum and base of secondaries orange. Tail dark brown.

Range. Northern Venezuela. Monos Island, Trinidad.

Colombia. Open scrub and pastureland. Tropical zone in Norte de Santander.

42. SOUTHERN SISKIN
(Spinus magellanicus) Plate XVIII

Description. 4½ - 5". ♂ : Head black. Back olive green, the feathers with dark centers giving a faintly streaked appearance; below olive yellow. Wings and tail black. Wing speculum and bases of secondaries bright yellow, inner remiges edged white. Tail black, basally yellow. ♀ : Crown and sides of head olive, rest of upperparts, wings and tail like ♂ . Throat and breast olive green, rest of underparts grayish, or entirely grayish below.

Range. The Andes southward from Ecuador to Chile and western Argentina. Eastern Venezuela, British Guiana, and from Bahía, Brazil southward to eastern Argentina and Uruguay.

Colombia. Scrubby pastures. Upper tropical to lower temperate zone. Central Andes in Caldas and Nariño *(capitalis)*.

43. YELLOW-BELLIED SISKIN
(Spinus xanthogaster)

Description. 4½ - 5". ♂: Mostly glossy black. Lower breast and belly, patch on wing and base of tail bright yellow. ♀: Above dark olive green, feathers of crown with dark centers. Wings and tail as in ♂. Throat, breast and sides of body olive, center of abdomen and under tail-coverts yellow.

Range. Costa Rica, western Panama. Ecuador and western Venezuela. Northern Bolivia.

Colombia. Pastureland. Subtropical and temperate zones of the three Andean ranges. Not recorded from Nariño *(xanthogaster)*.

44. DARK-BACKED GOLDFINCH
(Spinus psaltria)

Description. 4¼ - 4½". ♂: Entire upperparts, wings and tail glossy blue-black. Wing speculum, tips of inner remiges and basal portion of outer tail-feathers white, the amount of white in the tail is variable, sometimes even absent. Entire under surface bright golden yellow. ♀: Dull olive to pale olive brown above, yellowish below. Wings and tail dark brown, inner remiges and wing-coverts pale tipped.

Range. Western United States from Oregon and Utah southward to Mexico, Central America and western South America to northern Peru. Northern Venezuela.

Colombia. Pastureland. Upper tropical and subtropical zones virtually throughout the country *(colombianus)*.

45. CITRINE GRASS-FINCH
(Sicalis citrina)

Description. 4¼-4½". ♂: Crown, nape, sides of head, rump and upper tail-coverts yellow olive. Back grayish olive to yellowish olive, broadly streaked dusky. Entire underparts bright yellow, sides of breast tinged olive. Wings dark brown, outer pair of tail-feathers with a large white patch on inner web. ♀: Upperparts sparrow-like, brown streaked dark brown, rump olivaceous. Underparts buffy yellow streaked on breast and side with dusky, center of abdomen and under tail-coverts pale yellow. Wings dark brown, the

feathers pale edged. Tail dark brown, outer feathers with white patch smaller than in ♂.

Range. British Guiana and Venezuela. Southern and eastern Brazil and western Argentina.

Colombia. Open country. Tropical and subtropical zones. Santa Marta Mts., Eastern and Central Andes *(browni)*.

46. ORANGE-FRONTED GRASS-FINCH
(Sicalis columbiana)

Description. 4¾ - 5". ♂: Forecrown orange, back, wings and tail bright olive yellow; entire underparts bright yellow. Wings and tail dusky, the feathers edged olive yellow. ♀: Entire upperparts grayish brown, tinged olive, very slightly streaked, wings and tail brown, the feathers edged bright olive yellow. Below dingy white.

Range. Lower and middle Orinoco Valley, eastern Brazil and the Amazon Valley eastward to Peru. Trinidad.

Colombia. Grassy river banks. Known only from the banks of the Orinoco in Vichada *(columbiana)*.

47. SAFFRON FINCH
(Sicalis flaveola) Plate XX

Description. 5¼ - 5¾". ♂: Rather like No. 46 but much larger, the back and underparts brighter. ♀: Upperparts streaked dusky brown and sandy brown. Underparts buffy white, whitest on throat and center of abdomen, streaked on breast and sides with dusky. Under wing-coverts and axillaries bright yellow. *Immature male:* Above much like ♀. Below dingy white with a broad pale yellow pectoral band and yellow under tail-coverts.

Range. Virtually all of tropical South America from Venezuela southward to Uruguay and Argentina. West of the Andes in southwestern Ecuador and northwestern Peru. Trinidad. Panama. Jamaica (introduced).

Colombia. Yards, gardens. Tropical zone of the Caribbean coast, the lower Magdalena Valley and the eastern base of the Andes in Meta *(flaveola)*.

48. YELLOW GRASS-FINCH
(Sicalis luteola)

Description. 5¼ - 5¾ ". ♂ : Lores and eyebrow yellow, forecrown yellowish streaked dusky, cheeks grayish olive. Upperparts streaked reddish brown or olive brown and blackish, rump unstreaked, yellow olive. Wings dark brown, wing-coverts and inner remiges pale edged. Tail blackish, pale edged. Entire underparts bright yellow, tinged olive at sides of breast and body. ♀ like ♂ but duller yellow below, the breast and sides tinged brownish.

Range. Southern Mexico south to Panama. Tropical South America east of the Andes from Venezuela south to Argentina. West of the Andes in Peru and Chile.

Colombia. Open country. Tropical zone of the Magdalena Valley; upper tropical zone of the upper Cauca Valley and subtropical zone of the Western Andes *(luteola)*. Subtropical and temperate zones of the Eastern Andes from Norte de Santander to the Bogotá region and the temperate zone in Nariño *(bogotensis)*.

49. PLUMBEOUS FINCH
(Phrygilus unicolor) Plate XVIII

Description. 6¼ - 6¾ " (or 5¾ - 6¼ ", 1). ♂ : Entirely plumbeous gray, paler on lower parts, upperparts obscurely streaked blackish. Wings and tail black, edged gray. ♀ : Upperparts streaked brown and blackish, lower parts grayish white broadly streaked with dark brown. Wings and tail dark brown, the feathers pale edged.

Range. Venezuela southward through the Andes to Tierra del Fuego.

Colombia. Open country. Upper temperate and páramo zone of the Santa Marta Mts. between 8,000 and 15,000 ft. (1, *nivarius*). Páramo zone of the Eastern and Central Andes and Nariño *(geospizopsis)*.

50. SLATY FINCH
(Haplospiza rustica) Plate XVIII

Description. 5¼ - 5½ ". ♂ : Uniform dark slaty gray. Rather like No. 49, but smaller, much darker and the tail relatively shorter. ♀ : Dark olive brown above; underparts paler olive brown, palest on throat, somewhat streaked dusky on lower throat and breast, center of abdomen pale buffy.

Range. Southern Mexico. Honduras. Costa Rica and western Panama. Western South America from northern Venezuela southward through the Andes to Ecuador, Peru and northern Bolivia.

Colombia. Forest borders, bushes. Partially terrestrial. Upper tropical and subtropical zone of the three Andean ranges and Nariño *(rustica)*.

51. PILEATED FINCH
(Coryphospingus pileatus)

Description. 5¼ - 5½ ". ♂ : Mostly gray. Forehead and lengthened feathers at sides of crown black, center of crown crimson, feathers forming a flat crest. Lores, throat, belly and under tail-coverts dull white, band across breast pale gray. Tail blackish. ♀ : Sandy gray above. Lores and underparts white lightly streaked on breast with pale gray. Tail blackish brown.

Range. Northern Venezuela south to the Orinoco. Eastern and southern Brazil. Margarita Island.

Colombia. Scrub. Arid tropical zone. The northeastern and southern side of the Santa Marta Mts. *(brevicaudus)*. The upper Magdalena Valley *(rostratus)*.

52. WHITE-NAPED BRUSH-FINCH
(Atlapetes albinucha)

Description. 7½ - 8". Top and sides of head black, stripe down center of crown from between eyes to nape white. Upperparts, wings and tail dark slaty gray. Underparts bright yellow; sides of body and under tail-coverts olivaceous.

Range. Southern Mexico.

Colombia. Thickets and scrub. Exact range not known. Specimens recorded from "Cartagena" and "Bogotá" perhaps do not come from Colombia at all.

53. YELLOW-THROATED BRUSH-FINCH
(Atlapetes gutturalis)

Description. 7½ - 8". Above like No. 52. Throat yellow, rest of underparts white tinged with gray at sides of breast, brownish on belly and under tail-coverts.

Range. Southern Mexico southward through Central America to Colombia.

Colombia. Thickets and scrub. Subtropical zone of the Eastern, Central and Western Andes *(gutturalis)*.

54. SANTA MARTA BRUSH-FINCH
(Atlapetes melanocephalus)

Description. 6¾ - 7″. Crown, nape, chin and sides of throat black, ear-coverts silvery gray. Back, wings and tail ashy gray. Underparts bright yellow, sides of body olive.

Range. Colombia.

Colombia. Forest and scrub. Confined to upper tropical and subtropical zone of the Santa Marta Mts. between 1,200 and 8,000 ft.

55. WHITE-RIMMED BRUSH-FINCH
(Atlapetes leucopis)

Description. 7¼ - 7½″. Cap chestnut, sides of head and neck black; eye-ring white prolonged into a short streak behind eye. Back black tinged olivaceous on rump and upper tail-coverts. Throat grayish olive, rest of underparts olive green. Wings and tail black.

Range. Eastern Ecuador.

Colombia. Subtropical zone. The head of the Magdalena Valley and the east slope of the Eastern Andes in Nariño.

56. PALE-NAPED BRUSH-FINCH
(Atlapetes pallidinucha)

Description. 7 - 7½″. Forecrown cinnamon-buff, tinged yellow on forehead, center of hindcrown prolonged in a band to nape, dirty white; sides of crown and head and faint moustacial streak black. Back gray with a very slight olivaceous tinge (or dark gray, 1). Throat bright yellow, rest of underparts yellow tinged olive, becoming olive on flanks and under tail-coverts. Wings and tail blackish.

Range. Western Venezuela and western Ecuador.

Colombia. Forest and scrub. Upper tropical to temperate zone. The Eastern Andes *(pallidinucha)*. The Central Andes southward to Nariño *(1, papallactae)*.

57. RUFOUS-NAPED BRUSH-FINCH
(Atlapetes rufinucha)

Description. 6¾ - 7¼″. Crown and nape rufous, sides of head black. Back slaty gray (or back gray, tinged olive, 1). Wings

gray with a small white speculum (or with a large white speculum, 1, 2). Underparts bright yellow, flanks and under tail-coverts olive. Tail black.

Range. Western Venezuela southward through the Andes to Ecuador, Peru and Bolivia.

Colombia. Forest and scrub. Subtropical and temperate zones. The Perijá Mts. *(nigrifrons)*. The Eastern Andes in Boyacá and probably Cundinamarca *(simplex)*. Northern portion of the Central Andes *(1, elaeoprorus)*. The eastern slope of the Western Andes and the western slope of the Central Andes at their southern end *(2, caucae)*. Upper subtropical to temperate zone of the Andes of Nariño *(spodionotus)*.

58. DUSKY-HEADED BRUSH-FINCH
(Atlapetes fusco-olivaceus)

Description. 6¾ - 7¼″. Forecrown, ear-coverts and moustacial streak sooty black. Hindcrown, back, wings and flanks dark olive green. Underparts bright yellow. Tail rounded, blackish.

Range. Colombia.

Colombia. Forest and scrub. Subtropical zone at the head of the Magdalena Valley.

59. MOUSTACHED BRUSH-FINCH
(Atlapetes albo-frenatus)

Description. 6¾ - 7¼″. Forehead and sides of head and neck black, ear-coverts tinged gray. Moustacial streak (not always present) white. Back, wings and tail olive green. Throat white, rest of underparts bright yellow, flanks and under tail-coverts olive.

Range. Western Venezuela.

Colombia. Forest. Upper tropical and subtropical zone on both slopes of the Eastern Andes from Norte de Santander to Cundinamarca *(albo-frenatus)*.

60. SLATY BRUSH-FINCH
(Atlapetes schistaceus)

Description. 7 - 7½″. Crown and nape rufous-chestnut (or dark chestnut, 1). Sides of head black, moustacial streak white. Back, wings and tail black (or back gray, wings with a conspicuous white

speculum, 1). Underparts gray, throat pale gray (or throat and center of abdomen white, breast and sides of body gray, 1). **Range.** Western Venezuela southward through the mountains to Ecuador and Peru.
Colombia. Forest. Upper subtropical and temperate zone. The Perijá Mts. *(fumidus)*. Both slopes at the northern end of the Eastern Andes in Santander, Boyacá and Norte de Santander *(tamae)*. The mountains of the rest of Colombia (1, *schistaceus*) .

61. TRICOLORED BRUSH-FINCH
(Atlapetes tricolor)

Description. 7 - 7½ ". Crown and nape old gold (or brownish yellow, 1), sides of head black. Back, wings and tail glossy black (or dusky olive, 2). Throat, center of breast and abdomen bright yellow, sides of body and under tail-coverts dark olive.
Range. Ecuador and Peru.
Colombia. Mossy forest. Tropical and subtropical zones. The eastern slope of the Western Andes (1, 2, *crassus*). The western slope of the Western Andes at the headwaters of the río San Juan *(subsp.?)* and the Pacific slope of Nariño (2, *subsp.?*).

62. OLIVE-HEADED BRUSH-FINCH
(Atlapetes flaviceps)

Description. 6¾ - 7". Crown olive; lores, sides of head, indistinct collar on hindneck olive yellow. Back dark olive; wings and tail dusky, edged dark olive. Throat, breast and center of abdomen bright yellow.
Range. Colombia.
Colombia. Forest. Subtropical zone. Known only from the upper río Toche on the eastern slope of the Central Andes.

63. CINNAMON-HEADED
BRUSH-FINCH
(Atlapetes semirufus) Plate XX

Description. 7 - 7½ ". Whole head, extreme upper back, throat and breast cinnamon. Lower breast and belly yellow, flanks and under tail-coverts olive. Back, wings and tail olive green (or dark olive with a gray tinge, 1).

Range. The mountains of northern and western Venezuela.
Colombia. Forest and scrub. Subtropical to temperate zone. The eastern slope of the Eastern Andes in Boyacá and Norte de Santander (1, *zimmeri*). The western slope of the Eastern Andes in Boyacá *(majusculus)*. The eastern slope of the Eastern Andes in Cundinamarca *(semirufus)*.

64. CHESTNUT-CAPPED
BRUSH-FINCH
(Atlapetes brunnei-nucha)

Description. 7¼ - 7¾ ". Crown and nape chestnut bordered laterally by cinnamon, forecrown and sides of head black; spot in front of eye and streak in center of forehead white. Back and wings olive green, bend of wing yellow. Throat and center of underparts white, sides of breast and body gray mixed with olive; band across breast black. Tail dusky, feathers edged olive.
Range. Southern Mexico southward through Central America to Venezuela, Ecuador and Peru.
Colombia. Forest. Upper tropical and subtropical zone of all three Andean ranges southward to Nariño *(frontalis)*.

65. STRIPE-CROWNED
BRUSH-FINCH
(Atlapetes torquatus) Fig. 87

Description. 7½ - 8¼ ". Crown and nape gray, with two broad black stripes on side of crown, eyebrow gray; lores, cheeks and ear-coverts black. Upperparts yellowish olive (or bronzy olive, 1). Underparts white with a black band across breast (or no black band, 2). Sides of body gray mixed with olive (or brown, 1). Wings and tail dusky, edged olive (or bronzy olive, 1), bend of wing yellow.
Range. Mexico southward through Central America to Venezuela, and through the Andes from Ecuador to Bolivia.
Colombia. Forest and scrub. Upper tropical to temperate zone. The Santa Marta Mts. (1, *basilicus*). The eastern slope of the Eastern Andes *(perijanus)*. The three Andean ranges except the western slope of the Western Andes (2, *assimilis*).

66. BLACK-HEADED BRUSH-FINCH
(Atlapetes atricapillus)

Description. 8½ - 9". Top and sides of head black. Upper surface and wings bright olive green, bend of wing yellow. Entire under surface white; sides of body and under tail-coverts gray mixed with olive. Tail black.

Range. Eastern Panama.

Colombia. Little known. Recorded from the western slope of the Eastern Andes in Santander and both slopes of the Central Andes in Tolima and Antioquia in the upper tropical zone *(atricapillus)*.

67. OLIVE FINCH
(Lysurus castaneiceps) Plate XX

Description. 7 - 7¼". Olive green. Cap chestnut sides of head and the throat sooty gray. Tail blackish.

Range. Ecuador. Southeastern Peru.

Colombia. Forest, terrestrial. Upper tropical and subtropical zone. Western slope of the Western Andes from Antioquia southward to southwestern Cauca and probably western Nariño and the eastern slope of the Andes in Caquetá and Nariño.

68. PECTORAL SPARROW
(Arremon taciturnus)

Description. 6 - 6¾". ♂: Coronal stripe gray; eyebrow white; forehead, sides of crown, sides of head and chin black. Back yellowish olive. Wings and tail dusky; shoulder patch bright yellow. Underparts white, band across chest black (or no breast-band, but black patch at each side of upper breast, shoulders more extensively yellow, 1). Bill all black (or lower mandible yellow, 1). ♀: Differs from ♂ by having coronal stripe buffy, the underparts buff and the breast-band or patches barely indicated.

Range. Most of tropical South America east of the Andes from Venezuela and the Guianas southward to southeastern Brazil and northern Bolivia.

Colombia. Forest and scrub. Tropical zone. Extreme eastern Colombia along the Orinoco *(taciturnus)*. East of the Andes in Arauca, eastern Boyacá and Meta (1, *axillaris*) .

69. GOLDEN-WINGED SPARROW
(Arremon schlegeli)

Description. 6½ - 7". ♂: Tops and sides of head, chin and patches at base of neck black. Upper mantle gray; rest of back and wing-coverts olive yellow (or entire back gray slightly tinged with olive on lower back; wing-coverts golden olive, 1). Underparts white, sides of body pale gray. Wings and tail dark blue-gray. Bill yellow (or yellow, ridge of culmen black, 1). ♀ like ♂ but underparts slightly tinged buff.

Range. Northern Venezuela.

Colombia. Woods and scrub. The Caribbean coast west to northern Bolívar *(schlegeli)*. Macuira Mts. above 1400 ft. *(fratruelis)*. Western slope of the Eastern Andes in Santander (1, *canidorsum*).

70. ORANGE-BILLED SPARROW
(Arremon aurantiirostris) Plate XX

Description. 6¼ - 6¾". Coronal stripe gray (or olive, 2); eyebrow white; sides of crown, neck, chin and rather narrow (or broad, 1) band across upper breast black. Upperparts olive green; bend of wing yellow (or orange, 2). Throat and center of underparts white, sides of body grayish olive. Bill orange.

Range. Southern Mexico southward through Central America and western South America to northeastern Peru.

Colombia. Forest, woodland. Terrestrial. Tropical zone. Middle and upper Atrato Valley and the entire Pacific coast, usually up to 3000 ft., rarely as high as 5500 ft. *(occidentalis)*. The extreme lower Atrato Valley (1, *strictocollaris*). The upper Sinú Valley eastward through the lower Cauca to the middle Magdalena Valley *(erythrorhynchus)*. Eastern base of the Andes in Putumayo. (2, *spectabilis*).

71. TOCUYO SPARROW
(Arremon tocuyensis)

Description. 5½ - 6". Similar to the next species but much smaller; back pale grayish brown and bend of wing paler yellow.

Range. Northwestern Venezuela.

Colombia. Scrub. Arid tropical zone of the Guajira Peninsula and the region around Riohacha.

72. BLACK-STRIPED SPARROW
(Arremon conirostris)

Description. 7¼ - 8". Top and sides of head gray with two broad black stripes at sides of crown and another narrow one through the eye. Back, wings and tail dull grayish olive (or bright olive green 1; or dark brownish olive, 2). Below mostly white, breast tinged gray (or throat white, breast gray, flanks and under tail-coverts dark grayish brown, 2). Bend of wing yellow.

Range. Honduras south to Venezuela and western Ecuador.

Colombia. Clearings and woodland glades. Tropical zone from the lower Atrato Valley southward down the Pacific coast (1, *striaticeps*). The Caribbean coast from the upper Sinú Valley eastward to the eastern foothills of the Santa Marta Mts. in the upper Ranchería Valley. The Magdalena Valley south to about 4°N. and east of the Eastern Andes from Arauca to Meta (*conirostris*). East of the Andes in Norte de Santander (2, *umbrinus*). The arid tropical zone in the upper Magdalena Valley (*inexpectatus*).

73. GRASSLAND SPARROW
(Myospiza humeralis)

Description. 4½ - 4¾". Upperparts streaked gray, black and chestnut. Supraloral streak and lesser wing-coverts yellow; inconspicuous eye-ring white. Breast and sides of body buffy gray, throat, abdomen white. Wings brown, inner remiges edged chestnut. Tail brown. Lower mandible flesh color.

Range. Venezuela, the Guianas southward through tropical South America to southeastern Brazil, Argentina and Bolivia.

Colombia. Thickets and grasslands. Tropical, occasionally subtropical zone in the Cauca Valley, the Santa Marta region, the Magdalena Valley south to Villavieja. The Eastern Andes and the plains east of the Andes to the Orinoco (*humeralis*). The Guajira Peninsula (*pallidula*).

74. YELLOW-FRONTED SPARROW
(Myospiza aurifrons) Plate XVIII

Description. 4¾ - 5¼". Differs principally from No. 73 by being less sharply streaked above and by having a large yellow spot in front of the eye and at base of mandible, the eyebrow dull yellowish; no chestnut on outer web of inner remiges; size somewhat larger and lower mandible blue-gray instead of flesh color.

Range. Western Venezuela southward. The Amazon Valley, eastward to Ecuador, Peru and northern Bolivia.

Colombia. Pastures, gardens and scrub. Tropical zone. East of the Andes in Norte de Santander, Arauca and Boyacá (*apurensis*). Llanos del Meta (*cherriei*). The Caquetá region (*aurifrons*); eastern Vaupés (*tenebrosa*).

75. GRASSHOPPER SPARROW
(Ammodramus savannarum)

Description. 4¾ - 5". Very like No. 73 but with feathers of the mantle black, edged gray and chestnut, giving a spotted rather than streaked appearance; inner remiges mottled with black, tail-feathers pointed. The sides of the head buffy rather than gray with no trace of yellow. The throat and breast buff not grayish.

Range. Southern Canada, the United States east of the Rocky Mts. and locally in Mexico and Central America southward to western Ecuador.

Colombia. Tropical zone. Grassy areas in the upper Cauca Valley (*caucae*).

76. RUFOUS-COLLARED SPARROW
(Zonotrichia capensis)

Description. 5¾ - 6¼". Coronal stripe gray with two broad black bands on sides of crown and a narrow one through the eye. Collar around hindneck continued on sides of neck and forming a patch on sides of breast orange-rufous. Upper mantle brown, lower back streaked with black, rump and upper tail-coverts grayish brown. Wings and tail dark brown pale edged, wing-coverts tipped with white. Throat white, broken collar across foreneck black; breast grayish, rest of underparts whitish. *Immature*: Differs from adult by having underparts buffy white thickly spotted with dusky, throat white, and the crown and back reddish brown streaked with black.

Range. Southern Mexico southward through Central America and most of South America from Venezuela and the Guianas to Tierra del Fuego. Hispaniola. Curaçao, Aruba.

Colombia. Scrub and pastureland. Upper tropical to temperate zone of the Santa Marta Mts., the Eastern, Central and Western Andes, and the mountains of Nariño (costaricensis). The Macarena Mts. (roraimae).

77. WEDGE-TAILED GROUND-FINCH
(Emberizoides herbicola) Plate XX

Description. 7¾ - 8¾". Tail long and pointed, much graduated (4-4½"). Entire upperparts streaked reddish brown and black (or sandy gray and black, 1).

Bend of wing yellow, wing-coverts and outer margin of remiges bright olive. Eye-ring white. Lower parts white tinged with buff on breast, sides and under tail-coverts. Tail dark brown near shaft with pale margins. *Immature*: Differs from adult by being strongly tinged yellow below.

Range. Costa Rica southward to Venezuela, the Guianas, Brazil and eastern Bolivia, Paraguay and Argentina.

Colombia. Tropical and subtropical zone in grassy and bushy places. West of the Andes, with the exception of Nariño, and east of the Andes in southern Meta (sphenurus). East of the Andes in northern Meta and Cundinamarca (1, apurensis).

ENGLISH-SPANISH GLOSSARY

A

abdomen   abdomen
above   por encima
absent   ausente
across   a través
adult   adulto
alar speculum   espécula alar
all   todo
almost   casi
also   también
always   siempre
amethyst   amatista
ant   hormiga
appearance   aspecto
around   alrededor
as far as   hasta
ashy   ceniciento
attenuated   atenuado
autumn   otoño

B

back   dorso, lomo
backward   hacia atrás
band   banda
bar   barra
bare   desnudo
barred   con estrías horizontales
base   base
bay (color)   bayo
beak   pico
becoming   haciéndose
before   antes
behind   atrás
belly   vientre
below   por debajo
bent   angulado
bigger   mayor
bill   pico
bird   ave, pájaro
black   negro
blue   azul
bluish   azulado
body   cuerpo
bordered   bordeado
both   ambos
breast   pecho
breeding   nidadores
bright   vivo
brilliant   brillante

broad   ancho
broken   interrumpido
bronze   bronce
brown   pardo
buff   color vicuña
bush   arbusto

C

cap   capucho
center   centro
central   central
changing   cambiando
character   carácter
checkered   formando cuadros, en daniero
cheek   mejilla
chest   pecho
chestnut   castaño
chin   mentón
chocolate   chocolate
cinereous   cinéreo
cinnamon   canela
claw   uña
clear   claro
clothed   vestido
clouded   nublado
coarse   grueso
coast   costa
collar   collar
color   color
comparatively   comparativamente
concealed   escondido
conspicuous   conspicuo
in contrast   en contraste
copper   cobre
coverts   cubierteras
creamy   crema
crest   copete, cresta
crimson   carmesí
crimped   encrespado
crissum   abdomen
crossed   cruzado
crown   corona
curved   curvado

D

dark   obscuro
deep   profundo
defined   definido
dense   denso

diagonal   diagonal
differ   se diferencia
diffused   difuso
dirty   sucio
disk   disco
distinguishable   distinguible
dot   puntilla, manchita
double   doble
drab   uniforme, poco vistoso
dry   árido
dull   apagado
dusky   obscuro, negrusco

E

ear   oreja
easily   fácilmente
east   este
edged   marginado, bordeado
emerald   esmeralda
enamel   esmalte
encircle   encerrar
entirely   completamente
erect   erguida
except   excepto
extend   extender
extreme   extremo
eye   ojo
eyebrow   ceja

F

face   cara
fade   atenuando, aclarando
faint   apenas coloreado
fan shaped   en abanico
fawn color   color de vicuña
feather   pluma
feet   patas
female   hembra
few   poco
filament   filamento
finely   finamente
flank   flanco, costado
flat   chato
flesh color   rosado
fly   volar
follow   continuado, seguido
foot   pata
forecrown   parte anterior de la corona
forehead   frente
forest   selva
form   forma
forked   furcado, horquillado
forward   anterior
freckled   pecoso
frequently   frecuentemente
fringe   franja
front   frente
fulvous   fulvo

G

generally   generalmente

glistening   centellante
glittering   resplandescente, brillante
glossy   lustroso
golden   dorado
gradually   gradualmente
graduated   graduado
grass green   verde hierba
grassland   pastizal
gray   gris
grayish   grisáceo
greater   mayor
green   verde
greenish   verdoso

H

hair   pelo
half   mitad
hardly   apenas
head   cabeza
heavily   densamente
hidden   escondido
hind   posterior
hollow   hueco
hood   capuchón
hooked   ganchudo

I

immaculate   inmaculado
immature   inmaduro
inch   25.4 mm.
including   incluyendo
indefinite   indefinido
inner   interior
instead   en vez de
inwardly   interiormente
iridescent   iridiscente
iris   iris
iron gray   gris acerado
isabelline   blanco sucio
island   isla
ivory   marfil

J

jet   azabache
join   juntar

K

knob   protuberancia

L

lack   falta
large   grande
lavender   lavanda
lead-colored   plomizo
leg   pierna
lemon   limón
length   largo
lengthened   alargado
less   menos
lesser   menor

404

light   claro
light blue   celeste
like   como
line   línea
little   pequeño
locality   localidad
long   largo
longitudinal   longitudinal
lores   region entre el pico y el ojo
lower back   lomo
lower parts   parte ventral
lustrous   lustroso

M

malar   malar
male   macho
mantle   manto
marbled   jaspeado
margined   marginado, bordeado
marked   marcado
maroon   pardo rojizo
marsh   pantano
mask   máscara
median   medio
medium   mediano
metallic   metálico
middle   centro
migrant   migratorio
missing   falta
mixed   mezclado
more   más
mostly   principalmente
mottled   moteado
mountain   montaña
mouse   ratón
moustacial streak   raya en forma
   de bigote
much   mucho

N

nail   uña
nape   nuca
narrow   angosto, estrecho
neck   cuello
never   nunca
north   norte
notched   muescado

O

occasionally   ocasionalmente
ochraceous   ocráceo
ocular   ocular
often   frecuentemente
oily   aceitoso
olive   oliváceo
one   uno
only   solamente
open country   campo
orange   anaranjado
outer   exterior

P

pale   pálido
palm   palmera
part   parte
pasture   pasto
patch   mancha
pink   rosado
plum color   morado
plume   pluma
plumage   plumaje
pointed   puntiagudo
pond   estanque
portion   parte
primaries   plumas primarias
prolonged   prolongado
prominent   prominente
protrude   sobresalir
puff   bullón, pompon
purple   púrpura
purplish   purpúreo

R

race   raza
range   cordillera
rarely   raramente
rather   bastante
reaching   de. . . hasta. . .
recognizable   reconocible
rectrix   rectriz
red   rojo
reddish   rojizo
reduced   disminuido
reflections   reflejos
regularly   regularmente
remainder   resto
remiges   remiges
replace   reemplazar
resemble   asemejár
rest   resto
restricted   restringido
rich   rico
ring   anillo
river   río
round   redondo
rufous   rufo
rump   rabadilla, lomo
rusty   rojizo

S

salmon   salmón
same   mismo
sandy   arenoso
scale   escama
scapulars   escapular
scarlet   escarlata
scrubby   arbustivo
secondaries   secundarias
separate   separado
sepia   sepia
shade   tonalidad
shaft   astil, cañón

shape forma
sharp agudo
sheen brillo
shining luciente
short corto
shoulder espalda
side flanco
silver plata
similar parecido
single unica
size tamaño
skin piel
slate-color apizarrado
slaty pizarreño
slightly apenas
slope vertiente
small pequeño,
smoke humo
soiled sucio
sometimes a veces
somewhat algo
solid sólido
sooty holliniento
south sur
speckled moteado
speculum espejo alar
spine espina
spot mancha
spot (small) pinta
spotted manchado
square cuadrado
stain tinta
steel acero
stiff rigido
stomach estómago
straight recto
straw color color de paja
streak raya, estría
stream arroyo
stripe raya, lista
strong fuerte
subterminal subterminal
sulphur azufre
summer verano
superciliary stripe linea superciliar
surface superficie
surround circundar
swamp pantano

T

tail cola
tarsus tarso
tawny leonado
terminal terminal
tertials terciales
throat garganta
thick grueso, denso
thigh pierna
thin delgado
three tres
tinged tinto
tip punta

toes dedos del pie
tone tono
top ápice
town pueblo
transient pasajero
transverse transversal
tree árbol
tuft penacho
turning to haciéndose
two dos
typical típico

U

ultramarine ultramarino
umber ocre obscuro
under debajo
underparts parte ventral
uniform uniforme
unknown desconocido
upper superior
upperparts parte dorsal
upward ascendente
usually usualmente

V

varied variado
variegated jaspeado
vermiculated vermiculado
verditer azulado
very muy
vinaceous vinoso
violet violeta
virtually virtualmente
visitor visitante

W

washed lavado
water agua
wavy ondeado
waxy ceroso
web barba, membrana
west oeste
white blanco
whitish blanquecino
whole entero
wide ancho
wing ala
wing bar barra alar
winter invierno
with con
without sin
wood brown color de madera
wood bosque

Y

yellow amarillo
young jóven

♂ macho
♀ hembra

406

REFERENCES

The present book deals with birds of continental Colombia. The birds from the insular possessions are not included. However, the following papers give an account of the avifauna of the islands.

1938   J. Bond and R. Meyer de Schauensee: "The Birds of the Island of Malpelo" (Proc. Acad. Nat. Sci. Phila., vol. 90).

1944   J. Bond and R. Meyer de Schauensee: "Results of the 5th George Vanderbilt Expedition. The Birds of Old Providence and St. Andrews, and the Keys in the Southwest Caribbean outside the 100 Fathom Line" (Acad. Nat. Sci. Phila., Monograph No. 6, pp. 10-21).

1950   J. Bond: "Birds of Cayo Largo (Cuba), San Andres and Providencia" (Proc. Acad. Nat. Sci. Phila., vol. 102).

Systematic books and papers which have been used in the preparation of "The Birds of Colombia" are the following:

1917   F. M. Chapman: "The Distribution of Bird-Life in Colombia" (Bull. Amer. Mus. Nat. Hist., vol. 36).

1922   W. E. Clyde Todd & M. A. Carriker, Jr.: "Birds of the Santa Marta Region, a Study in Altitudinal Variation" (Ann. Carnegie Mus., vol. 14).

1924-29   C. E. Hellmayr, et al.: "Catalogue of Birds of the Americas" (Field Mus. Nat. Hist., Zool. Ser., 13, pts. 1-11).

1926   F. M. Chapman: "The Distribution of Bird-Life in Ecuador" (Bull. Amer. Mus. Nat. Hist., vol. 51).

1931-53   J. T. Zimmer: "Studies of Peruvian Birds" (Amer. Mus. Novitates).

1931-62   J. L. Peters, et al.: "Check-List of Birds of the World" Vols. 1-7, 9, 15.

1938-44   O. M. de O. Pinto: "Catálogo de Aves do Brasil" (Rev. Mus. Paulista, vol. 22, pts. 1, 2).

1942-43   J. Bond and R. Meyer de Schauensee: "The Birds of Bolivia" (Proc. Acad. Nat. Sci. Phila., pt. 1, vol. 94; pt. 2, vol. 95).

1948-52   R. Meyer de Schauensee: "The Birds of the Republic of Colombia" (Caldasia, vol. 5, nos. 22-26).

1950-63   W. H. Phelps & W. H. Phelps, Jr.: "Lista de las Aves de Venezuela" (Boll. Soc. Venez. Cienc. Nat., 12, no. 75; 19, no. 90; 24, nos. 104-105).

1955   E. Eisenmann: "The Species of Middle American Birds" (Trans. Linnaean Soc., N.Y., vol. 7).

1957   "Check-List of North American Birds". Fifth Edition. (American Ornithologists' Union).

Many excellent, short articles on Colombian birds have appeared in Colombian scientific journals such as *Caldasia* and *Lozania,* published by the Universidád Nacionál de Bogotá, and Novedades Colombianas, the organ of the Universidád del Cauca at Popayán. Among the authors of the studies are Ignacio Borrero, M. A. Carriker, Jr., Armando Dugand, Jurgen Heffer, F. Carlos Lehmann, Brother Nicéforo-María, Brother Antonio Olivares and Kjell von Sneidern. Unfortunately these are usually available only in scientific libraries.

An interesting paper, "Seasonal Activity and Ecology of the Avifauna of an American Equatorial Cloud Forest" by Alden H. Miller, is to be found in the University of California *Publications in Zoology, 66,* 1963. It deals with mountain forests in Colombia.

Except for the present volume the only current guide books to South American birds are:

"Las Aves de Chile" by Goodall, Johnson & Philippi, Buenos Aires, 1951.

"Las Aves Argentinas" by C. C. Olrog, Tucumán, 1959.

Among books which will be of interest to the student of tropical American birds, and would be useful for northern Colombia are:

"Birds of the West Indies" by James Bond.

"Birds of Mexico" by Emmet R. Blake.

"Life Histories of Central American Birds" by Alexander F. Skutch (Cooper Orn. Soc., Berkeley Calif., no. 31 1954, no. 34 1960).

"Aves Venezoelanas, Cien de las mas Conocidas" by Kathleen D. Phelps (Creole Petroleum Corp., Caracas, 1954); one hundred birds reproduced in color, most of which are found in Colombia.

"The Birds of Trinidad and Tobago" by G. A. C. Herklots, London, 1961. The avifauna of these islands is South American rather than West Indian. Therefore this book is very useful as a guide to birds of northeastern South America.

For marine birds W. B. Alexander's "Birds of the Ocean", New York, 1961, will prove indispensable.

Colored figures of all North American migrants to Colombia can be found in Roger Tory Peterson's field guides.

SPECIES ADDED SINCE FIRST PRINTING

The quick acceptance of THE BIRDS OF COLOMBIA has made necessary a new printing much sooner than had been anticipated. This affords an opportunity to make a number of minor corrections to the text, to add an index to families, to furnish full scientific names in the legends for the paintings and to add a number of species, new to Colombia, of which two are treated in the body of the book: *Cathartes melambrotos* (P. 46) and *Neopelma chrysocephalum* (P. 254). Descriptions of the others appear below.

MACAWS, PARROTS AND PARAKEETS (Psittacidae)

23a. YELLOW-WINGED PARAKEET
(Brotogeris versicolurus) (see p. 106)

Description. 9 - 9½". Green, primaries bluish green, secondaries white, tertials canary yellow.

Range. French Guiana. Most of Brazil southward to northern Bolivia, northwestern Argentina and Paraguay.

Colombia. Southern Amazonas (Leticia).

OWLS (Strigidae)

8a. BARRED SPECTACLED OWL
(Pulsatrix melanota) (see p. 117)

Description. 15 - 17". Back, wings and tail dark chocolate brown, the wings inconspicuously barred with broken bars of fulvous, the tail with a few narrow white bands. Area in front of eye, white, continued over eye forming an eyebrow. Sides of head and the throat blackish brown, patch on upper breast white, lower breast chocolate brown barred with white, rest of underparts white barred with brown. Tarsal feathers buff. Iris brown.

Range. Eastern Ecuador, through eastern Peru to Bolivia.

Colombia. Presumably southeastern portion.

HUMMINGBIRDS (Trochilidae)

53a. VIOLET-CAPPED HUMMINGBIRD
(Goldmania violiceps) (see p. 143)

Description. 3.3 - 3.5" (.75"). ♂: Crown shining purple. Back emerald green, bluer on upper tail-coverts. Entire underparts shining grass green, under tail-coverts short, shining grass green, the three center ones comparatively long, silky white, curved and very stiff. Tail somewhat forked, chestnut, edged and broadly tipped with bronze. ♀: Above uniform dull emerald green, underparts white, sides of neck and body with green discs. Under tail-coverts as in ♂. Middle tail feathers bronze green with a narrow rufous shaft streak basally, rest like ♀ but duller, all except central pair with a small white spot on tip.

Range. Upper tropical and subtropical zone of eastern Panama.

Colombia. The east slope of Mt. Tacarcuna in the northern tip of Chocó on the Panama boundary.

WOODCREEPERS (Dendrocolaptidae)

2a. WHITE-CHINNED WOODCREEPER
(Dendrocincla merula) (see p. 198)

Description. 7¾ - 8¼". Uniform wood

brown; wings and tail rufous chestnut. Chin and upper throat whitish.

Range. The Guianas, southern Venezuela, Amazonian Brazil, eastern Peru, northeastern Bolivia.

Colombia. Known only from Vaupés.

ANTBIRDS (Formicariidae)

93a. CRESTED ANTCATCHER
(Rhegmatorhina cristata)
(see p. 238)

Description. 6¼ - 6½″. Head somewhat crested. Crown, nape, sides of neck and the breast chestnut, sides of head and throat sooty black; lower breast dull chestnut becoming rufescent olive brown on the belly. Back and tail dull olive brown. Wing-coverts and wings rufous-brown. ♀ differs from ♂ chiefly by lacking the crest, the head blackish chestnut and the more russet brown back marked with blackish spots.

Range. Northwestern Brazil.

Colombia. Known only from Vaupés.

TYRANT FLYCATCHERS (Tyrannidae)

68a. RORAIMA FLYCATCHER
(Myiophobus roraimae) (see p. 282)

Description. 5 - 5¼″. Above olive brown, crown with a concealed orange-rufous crest; below pale yellowish. Wings blackish with two broad rufous bars. Tail brown. ♀ similar but without crest.

Range. Eastern British Guiana, southern Venezuela.

Colombia. Known only from Vaupés.

71a. WHITE-CRESTED SPADEBILL
(Platyrinchus platyrhynchos)
(see p. 282)

Description. 4¼ - 4½″. Top of head smoky gray with a broad, semi-concealed white patch in center. Upper surface and tail olive brown; throat whitish, rest of underparts ochraceous. Wings dark brown, feathers narrowly edged olive brown.

Range. British and Dutch Guiana, southern Venezuela, eastern Ecuador, eastern Peru, northwestern Bolivia, Amazonian Brazil.

Colombia. Known only from Vaupés *(griseiceps)* .

72a. CINNAMON-CRESTED FLATBILL
(Platyrinchus saturatus) (see p. 282)

Description. 4¼ - 4½″. Above olive brown, crown darker with broad median orange-cinnamon patch. Throat and center of abdomen white, breast and sides of body tinged brown. Wings and tail brown, the feathers edged with dull rufous-brown.

Range.. The Guianas, southern Venezuela, northern Brazil to the south bank of the Amazon.

Colombia. Known only from Vaupés.

121a. NOISY ELAENIA
(Elaenia strepera) (see p. 293)

Description. 6¼ - 6¾″. ♂ : Upperparts, sides of head, throat and breast and sides of body slate gray. Concealed crest, eye-ring and center of belly, white. Wing-coverts tipped with dull gray forming two inconspicuous wing-bars. Bill short, wide, mandible tawny flesh. ♀ and *imm*: Tinged olive especially on upper wing-coverts. Wing-bars cinnamon buff, center of abdomen yellowish white to pale yellow.

Range. Breeds in northwestern Argentina, eastern Bolivia and Peru. Migrant to eastern Venezuela (May-September) .

Colombia. Recorded once from the Macarena Mts. (March) .

LIST OF FAMILIES

411

INDEX

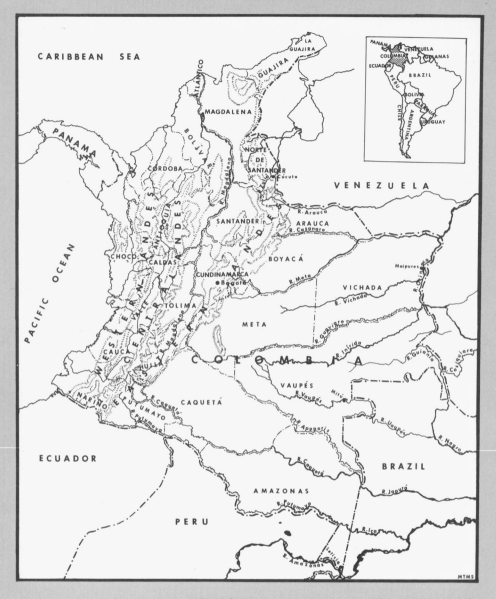

The above map shows the Republic of Colombia and bordering countries. The location of Colombia on the South American continent is shown on the inset map. The detailed map (right) shows that part of western Colombia embracing the three Andes ranges and the Santa Marta Mountains.